A GEOGRAPHY OF MAN

SECOND EDITION

by Preston E. James, *Syracuse University,*
with the collaboration of Hibberd V. B. Kline, Jr.,
University of Pittsburgh

GINN AND COMPANY

**Boston · New York · Chicago · Atlanta · Dallas
Palo Alto · Toronto · London**

PREFACE

GEOGRAPHY IS THAT FIELD of learning in which the characteristics of particular places on the earth's surface are examined. It is concerned with the arrangement of things and with the associations of things that distinguish one area from another. It is concerned with the connections and movements between areas. The face of the earth is made up of many different kinds of features, each the momentary result of an on-going process. A process is a sequence of changes, systematically related as in a chain of cause and effect. There are physical and chemical processes developing forms of the land surface, the shapes of the ocean basins, the different characteristics of water and climate. There are biotic processes by which plants and animals spread over the earth in complex areal relation to the physical features and to each other. And there are economic, social, and political processes by which mankind occupies the world's lands.

As a result of all these processes the face of the earth is marked off into distinctive areas: geography seeks to interpret the significance of likenesses and differences among places in terms of causes and consequences.

Since the early nineteenth century, scholars have given more and more attention to systematic studies; that is, to the study of those features that are systematically related to each other because they are the result of a single process. Geography has sometimes been called the mother of sciences, since many fields of learning that started with observations of the actual face of the earth turned to the study of specific processes wherever they might be located. These new disciplines are defined by the subjects they investigate. Some of the processes at work on the surface of the earth, notably the physical and chemical ones, have been reproduced under laboratory conditions where they can be examined in isolation from the environments of particular places. From these studies there has been a great increase in the understanding of cause and effect relations, and numerous fundamental principles have been formulated to describe the ideal or theoretical sequences of change. In a similar way the biotic processes have been examined under controlled conditions, and such important concepts have been developed as those of evolution and natural selection. The social sciences, too, have sought to understand the theoretical sequences of economic, social, and political change as these sequences are presumed to go on when isolated from the disturbing circumstances of actual places. Since the so-called cultural processes cannot be isolated in laboratories, they are isolated symbolically by such a phrase as "other things being equal."

Modern geography starts with the understandings provided by the systematic sciences. Unlike these other fields, geography cannot be defined by its subject matter, for anything that is unevenly distributed over the surface of the earth can be examined profitably by geographic methods. Rather, geography is a point of view, a system of procedures. It makes three kinds of contributions to understanding: (1) it extends the findings of the systematic sciences by observing the differences between the theoretical operation of a process and the actual operation as modified by the conditions of the total environment of a particular place; (2) it provides a method for testing the validity of concepts developed by the systematic sciences; and (3) it provides a realistic analysis of the conditions of particular places and so aids in the clarification of the issues involved in all kinds of policy decisions.[1]

A Geography of Man deals specifically with those aspects of geography that are concerned with man and his works. It asks such questions as: Where are people located on the earth, and in what densities? What caused these differences in population density to develop as they have? What are the effects of differences of population density, habitat, way of living, and political organization on the conditions of poverty, hunger, insecurity, and conflict? How has man formed connections with the physical land and with the cover of plants and animals that

[1] Quoted from the author's chapter on "Geography" in the *Encyclopaedia Britannica,* edition of 1956.

constitute the habitat? What is it that determines the significance to man of the features of the habitat?

The book presents geographic concepts or principles, and illustrates the methods of geographic analysis. It contains an adequate factual content to permit the application of geographic ideas, but the ideas are presumed to be more important than completeness of content. The first two chapters are introductory. First there is a discussion of the meaning of race and culture, and a summary of culture history as a background for an understanding of man on the earth today. Second there is a survey of the major physical characteristics of the earth—its continents, its oceans, and its climates, and an outline of the major groups of natural regions defined in terms of surface features and vegetation cover. The main part of the book is organized around the eight groups of natural regions which constitute the habitats of man. In each group of regions, after a characterization of the physical and biotic features, the experience of man in occupying this kind of habitat is treated with historical perspective. Certain countries are discussed in some detail to illustrate the nature of the problems of man-land relations with which they are faced. The concluding chapter re-examines the population pattern of the earth from three new viewpoints: from that of culture areas, from that of political sovereignty, and from that of the process of population growth itself.

A Geography of Man is written for a variety of uses. The main body of the text requires a minimum of specialized background knowledge. The ideas, and the supporting factual material, constitute the kind of knowledge of world geography that should be at the command of every educated man and woman. The breadth of treatment suggests the use of this book as a basis for a course in general education. It is fundamental for anyone specializing in the social sciences.

Technical material necessary as an introduction to the study of geography is placed in the appendixes. Appendix A, by Hibberd V. B. Kline, Jr., presents a general, elementary picture of the nature and use of maps. Appendixes B, C, and D give in outline form the principal facts and processes of climatology, geomorphology, and hydrography. By making use of the up-to-date lists of references to major works in these fields, the material in this book can be greatly amplified. At the end of the appendixes there is a new list of bibliographic references, including a discussion of bibliographic sources. Throughout the book several methods of expository writing and geographic analysis are demonstrated.

A Geography of Man is the successor to the author's *An Outline of Geography* (Ginn and Company, Boston, 1935). The original work was recast around the central theme of population distribution and was published in 1949. This volume is a new and revised edition, incorporating the latest factual information and the newest formulation of geographic ideas. The central theme is an examination of differences of population density from place to place set against the background of eight groups of natural regions defined in terms of surface configuration and original cover of vegetation.

P. E. J.
Syracuse, 1958

CONTENTS

REFERENCE MAPS

A GEOGRAPHY OF MAN

No man can reveal to you aught but that which already lies half asleep
  in the dawning of your knowledge.
For the vision of one man lends not its wings to another man.

And even as each one of you stands alone in God's knowledge,
  so must each one of you be alone in his knowledge
  of God and in his understanding of the earth.

KAHLIL GIBRAN

INTRODUCTION

Part One

POPULATION AND CULTURE

MOST PARTS OF THE EARTH'S SURFACE are empty of human inhabitants. Vast areas are only very thinly peopled, with small communities separated by many miles of empty land. In southeastern Asia, on the other hand, about half of all the people in the world are crowded into less than a tenth of the world's habitable area. In Europe a little less than a fifth of mankind is occupying an area which amounts to less than one twentieth of the habitable world.

Yet to draw the conclusion that a great movement to the empty lands of the world is about to take place would be quite wrong. People are concentrated in certain parts of the world because these parts offer greater opportunities for the support of human life than other places. These opportunities are in part the result of the resources of the earth itself, and in part they are man-made. But the tendency today, as always, is for people to move from areas of lesser to areas of greater economic opportunity. The population in areas of concentrated settlement is becoming more concentrated; the population of thinly peopled areas is becoming thinner.

The fact of uneven population distribution is basic to the study of human societies and human institutions. Population density and arrangement are involved directly or indirectly in every economic, social, political, or strategic problem. Underlying all the great domestic and international issues of our time are the facts of man's relation to the earth. In every occupied square mile of the earth's surface man encounters a unique set of physical conditions, and, in order to survive, he must establish some workable connection between the human society and the resources of the earth. Man is intimately bound to the earth: from it he derives all the materials for his food, clothing, and shelter; from earth materials he fashions the tools which give him economic power and the weapons which give him military power. Man's civilizations have always been, and always will be, constructed on the foundations of a particular set of relations to the land. As

John Dewey has written: "Human nature exists and operates in an environment. And it is not 'in' that environment as coins are in a box, but as a plant is in the sunlight and soil."

The influence of the natural environment on human life is chiefly one of limitation and hindrance. The stimulus to such action as will overcome obstacles or take advantage of opportunities is provided by man himself. Man alone, among all the forms of life on the earth, possesses the capacity to raise his head and look about him, to observe his surroundings and himself, to simplify the confused complexity of the things he sees by arranging and classifying them, to imagine explanations, and to make use of his knowledge, little as it may be, in altering and transforming at least the more plastic parts of his habitat. Yet most of the basic conditions of life are beyond his control: he is still a product of the earth and dependent on it.

Nature itself is quite indifferent to human aspirations. A land is neither friendly nor unfriendly, except as man has always personified the natural forces about him and given them human attributes. Repeatedly history offers examples of the changing habitability of specific regions. The same countries which to one people seem to be inhospitable and lacking in resources, to another people may seem to offer great advantages for the development of human society; and the same countries which once provided support for a flourishing civilization, may now appear as difficult places in which to make a living. What is the difference? In some cases, perhaps, there have been climatic changes, or shifts in the courses of rivers, or other natural phenomena that do actually change the physical character of the land; but in many other instances there is no evidence of such change. The difference is in the human group. For a people without steel plows, railroads, or great urban markets, the world's grasslands, for example, were rated as lands of low productivity; but for a people armed with the mechanical equipment and possessing the economic institutions of the industrial era, these same lands became major sources of wheat and meat. The story does not always run in the direction of progress, however. There are many regions in which a human society, armed with primitive tools, was once able to form a workable connection with the resources of the land, but in which men with machines have been unable to survive because of the rapid destruction of the resources. What degree of slope is too steep for agriculture? The answer to this question depends on the technique of farming, for slopes which can be cultivated with hoes may be much too steep for plows. In other words, the significance of the physical conditions of the land depends on the attitudes, objectives, and technical abilities of the inhabitants.

These attitudes, objectives, and technical abilities of a people are traits which form a part of the traditional way of living. In the long course of human history various human groups have appeared, each having its own peculiar set of beliefs, its own institutions, its customs, its familiar foods, its consecrated system of moral values. The tendency is strong to resist change. The aggregate of all these customary forms of thought and action which characterize a people is what the anthropologists describe as a *culture*.

RACE AND CULTURE

A clear distinction must be made between race and culture. Race is a biological matter. Racial characteristics are hereditary, passed on from parents to their children. Culture, however, is learned. Young people learn from contact with parents and other children to adopt the accepted ways of behavior of the social group. By a process of education such things as language, religious beliefs, or technical skills are passed on from generation to generation. An individual is born into a race; but he learns to live in accordance with the ways of a culture. In nonscientific writings race and culture are not always clearly distinguished.

To define a race is not a simple matter. The popular distinction of races on the basis of skin color is not accepted by the anthropologists. Skin color is only one of a number of hereditary physical traits. There are also such traits as stature; head form; hair color, texture, and form; eye color and shape; and nose shape. These are not necessarily associated with skin color. There are actually no "pure" races.

Nevertheless, the anthropologists recognize three broad and very general subdivisions of mankind, three racial types. These are *Caucasoid, Mongoloid,* and *Negroid.* The anthropologist Melville Herskovits summarizes the major racial types of mankind as follows.[1]

[1] Melville J. Herskovits, *Man and His Works: The Science of Cultural Anthropology,* New York, 1948.

Caucasoids have a skin color ranging from pink to olive brown, are medium to tall in stature, and have straight or wavy hair ranging from light blonde to dark brown, eyes ranging from blue to dark brown, and noses usually with a high bridge and with narrow to medium-broad form. *Mongoloids* have a skin color ranging from saffron to yellow-brown or reddish-brown, are medium tall to medium short, and have straight brown to brown-black hair, brown to dark-brown eyes, and noses with low bridges and medium broad form. *Negroids* have a skin color ranging from brown to brown-black, include some groups that are very tall, some that are very short, and many that are in between, and have curly to kinky brown-black hair, brown to brown-black eyes, and noses usually with low bridges and with forms medium broad to very broad.

The world is full of misinformation about racial inheritance. History records many examples of the attempt by self-conscious human groups or societies to explain assumed pre-eminence on the basis of racial superiority. The great Christian principle that all men are brothers has never been widely accepted, even among Christians. The fact that this principle expresses what scientists are step by step proving to be a fundamental truth does not alter the fact that belief in racial purity and superiority is a very common cultural attitude.

Culture is not hereditary. The individual learns to behave as he is taught by those around him. He learns the technical skills of his group; he learns how to make use of the familiar tools; he learns to accept the framework of the social, political, and economic institutions; he learns to think in terms of the religious beliefs of the group, and to express himself through the accepted art forms. And, above all, he learns to communicate, even to think, in terms of a particular language. These are all parts of a culture, or a way of living. Because a culture is passed on by a learning process, its traits tend to be preserved with little change. Cultural stability and uniformity are much more common than revolutionary change.

PREHISTORIC CULTURAL DEVELOPMENT

Mankind has existed on the earth for something like a million years. The earliest men appeared in a zone extending from southeast Asia to Central Africa. But apparently this zone was broken in the middle, perhaps by climatic changes. Early man in the southeastern area probably became extinct. The modern races of man seem to have eventually emerged from Central Africa, gradually again occupying the tropical and subtropical zone of southern Asia. For many hundreds of thousands of years primitive man continued to occupy this same habitat. His way of living was simple. Although he knew how to use fire, he could not always rekindle it easily. His tools were few and made of stone. For food he depended on hunting and fishing, and on collecting the fruits and seeds of wild plants. Very early in his career he had been joined by the dog, but he had no other domestic animals. Still these primitive men had certain essentially human attributes: they had the capacity to communicate with one another by language, and because they had language the memory of past events could be made concrete in terms of words. They could learn from experience, and pass on to others what they had learned. This long period of human prehistory is known as the *Paleolithic*.

Revolutionary changes of culture are few, but when they do take place they modify the way of living fundamentally. It was only some thirty or forty thousand years ago that such a revolutionary change first occurred. Measured against the long period of time since man first appeared, this change has come quite recently. The *Neolithic* period began with the discovery of the methods of planting and cultivating crops, and of domesticating animals. Suddenly man was able very greatly to increase and stabilize his food supply. The first such revolution took place in southeast Asia. It involved the cultivation of rice, bananas, sweet potatoes or yams, sugar cane, and certain tropical fruits. It also involved the domestication of the pig and the chicken. In India the domestication of cattle took place. Whether because of this new capacity to produce food, or for other reasons, man started suddenly to spread from his original tropical and subtropical habitat. People still Paleolithic in culture were pushed on by more complex cultures, until, within only some ten thousand years, all the continents except Antarctica had been inhabited. Some people pushed southward in Africa, some northwestward into Europe, some southeastward into Australia, and some across Bering Strait into the Americas. Farthest out along the land routes from man's original habitat are found today the most primitive cultures: the Hottentots of southern Africa, the Bushmen of Australia, and the Fuegians of southernmost South America.

In the process of spreading, the world's cultures were diversified. Not only did human groups come upon quite diverse habitats but also they remained isolated from each other. The Mongoloid peoples who migrated into America brought with them no domestic animals and no knowledge of the cultivation of crops. These cultural developments were made independently in America. In tropical America the cultivation of the maize plant was started, and also several other distinctive American crops, such as tobacco, tomato, squash, and cacao. The Indians of Peru learned how to cultivate the potato and to domesticate the llama. But none of the American natives ever discovered the principle of the wheel, and most of them never had any domesticated beasts of burden.

The cultivation of wheat and barley began in southwest Asia, somewhere near the eastern side of the Mediterranean, less than ten thousand years ago. It seems likely that the grains rye and oats grew as weeds along with wheat; but as people spread northwestward into Europe they found that the weeds did better than the original crop.

A large number of domestic animals originated in southwest and central Asia. These include the horse, the camel, the sheep, and the goat. Men learned how to ride and to fight on horseback, and how to hitch horses to vehicles with wheels. Knowledge of these domestic animals spread rapidly over Africa, Europe, and Asia, but not to America or Australia.

This cultural revolution brought with it conflict and turmoil. Those who had adopted the new way of living could easily defeat the simpler peoples in war, pushing them out of their hunting grounds. Many more people could be supported per square mile in those areas physically suited to the cultivation of crops or the pasture of animals.

CULTURAL DEVELOPMENT IN HISTORIC TIMES

The next great revolution in human living took place at the dawn of written history. At six widely separated parts of the earth, groups of men established the first "civilizations" based on law and government.

The first two of these appeared about 4000 B.C.: one was Babylonia, in the valley of the Tigris-Euphrates; the other was Egypt, in the valley of the Nile. Along both these valleys there were small village communities of farming people, each self-sufficient. Each family worked to provide its own food, or the food of the village community. There was no surplus, but only annual variations between what was barely enough and what was not enough to prevent famine. In these valleys farmers had to irrigate their crops; but since there was no common control of water, the villages downstream were at the mercy of those higher up. The formulation of codes of water laws and the organization of a government to administer the law were a revolutionary step forward. For the first time the villages could raise more food than could be consumed locally. The surplus could be sold or exchanged for the products of another place. And for the first time a new class of city people could be supported—people who did not have to spend all their time just providing their own food. These city people could become merchants, or priests, or government administrators. For the first time part of mankind, even if a small part, was free to devote its attention to the study of the stars and the observation of the earth, and to speculate about the meaning of what it saw.

Early civilizations based on law and government appeared in four other parts of the world. The great Hindu civilization developed in the valley of the Indus River in India. Chinese civilization had its beginnings in the valley of the Wei River, a tributary of the Hwang (Yellow River). In Yucatán and Guatemala the Maya civilization appeared. And in the Andes of Peru the Inca civilization developed.

Again, this revolutionary change in the way of living made possible a very great increase in the population. The poorer, more primitive people outside the civilized areas were attracted by the new luxury. Their prosperous, well-fed neighbors seemed fat and lazy to the hungry nomadic warriors. Repeatedly there were conquests; but always the conquerors were absorbed by the conquered, adopting their ways and discarding their own. Such is the story of the conquests of Babylonia by the Assyrians, of the conquests of China by the people from Manchuria and Mongolia, of the conquests of the Maya by the Toltecs, and of the conquests of the Toltecs by the Aztecs. Even Egypt, surrounded by deserts, was subject to invasion. Only the Empire of the Incas was so isolated that no outsiders ever could challenge its armies until the arrival of the Spaniards.

For thousands of years after the rise of these early civilizations the world saw no fundamental change in culture. There were the same methods of transporting things from place to place, the same dependence for power on human or animal muscles, on wind, or on falling water. There were the same agricultural methods, the same basic skills used in manufacturing things by hand. There was the same division of mankind into the well-to-do minority of city people, and the great majority of farm workers on whose incessant labor the whole system was based. Most of the people had no time to lift their eyes from the land. Only a minority had the leisure to enjoy luxury, or to devote themselves to scholarship, or religion, or art.

For most of this time the various cultures of the world remained distinct. If a Marco Polo traveled to China and came back to Europe with reports of the burning of black rocks, the people at home refused to believe him. In terms of economy, or the way of making a living, the Oriental cultures from India to China were built around the cultivation of rice, and the American cultures were built around maize. The Mediterranean cultures of Greece and Rome were based on wheat and barley, and these grains, along with rye and oats, became the basis of living north of the Alps. Cattle and domestic animals were used throughout Europe, Africa, and Asia. Not until the great age of exploration that started in the fifteenth century did the Europeans make contact with all the other peoples of the earth. Often the contact meant destruction for the simpler peoples. But it also meant that such American crops as maize, potatoes, and manioc were spread over the parts of the world suitable for them; and that to America were brought wheat, barley, rye, oats, rice, coffee, sugar cane, citrus fruits, grapes, and many other things. To America also came the Old World's domestic animals.

The culture of the people of Europe, at that time, was developed largely from Greek and Roman sources. What we may call Occidental, or Western, culture, as it had developed by the end of the sixteenth century, was essentially an "illiterate agriculturism." With the traditional farm techniques widely in use, yields per acre were small (wheat, for instance, gave only from six to ten bushels to the acre); and each community was entirely dependent on the food products of its immediate vicinity. It was a system of local self-sufficiency, of economic independence for small areas. Because transportation overland was slow and costly, only luxury goods of high value could be brought from distant places, and such goods were of interest only to a small minority of well-to-do people. Local crop failure meant famine, even if supplies were abundant in some neighboring area perhaps less than a hundred miles away. Only where sailing ships could bring bulky products to seaports could commerce reach out to the foods and raw materials of many distant places. Especially in England, and around the continental shores of the North Sea, commercial towns made their appearance early, and to these places came not only the goods but also the ideas of many people all around the world's oceans. Basically it was a society dominated by the land-owning aristocracy. Associated with the aristocracy were the officers of the army, the priests of the church, the higher civilian officers of the government, perhaps a few of the more lucky artists and scholars. But the majority were illiterate, ill-fed, ill-clad, and without rights or powers with respect to decisions of political policy. The land was divided into vast private estates. The many, whose endless toil supported the whole system, were clustered about the great castles, or within the walled towns where soldiers could give protection.

All of this is now in process of change. Another of the great revolutions of culture history is taking place, and we live in the midst of the turmoil, confusion, and conflict which inevitably accompany such change. Actually there are two revolutions in human living which are going on at about the same time, but not always in the same areas. These are the *Industrial Revolution* and the *Democratic Revolution*.

THE INDUSTRIAL REVOLUTION

January 5, 1769, is a date of profound importance, for on that day James Watt patented his first successful steam engine. This was the first important use of controlled inanimate power. In 1785 a steam engine was first used to run the machinery of a textile mill at Popplewick, near Nottingham in England. Early in the nineteenth century a steam engine was used to pull cars on a railroad; but it was not until 1825 that the first passenger railroad began operation—between Stockton and Darlington in England. The first steamship crossed the Atlantic in 1819.

This was just the beginning. The change from human and animal muscles, wind, and falling water to controlled inanimate power appeared first in Great Britain. It spread then to the countries of Western Europe, and rapidly to the English-speaking countries of other continents. Once the basic techniques of experimental science and engineering had been mastered, new control over the forces of the physical earth came at a faster and faster rate, until now we have taken the first steps toward the use of controlled nuclear power. All the mechanical aspects of life have been changed, and where these changes have occurred man is no longer a lifter and mover. Inanimate power applied to manufacturing industry has so immeasurably increased man's capacity to produce useful things from earth resources that it has now become mechanically possible for all people to live in greater material comfort than was possible for kings in centuries past. Inanimate power applied to agriculture has rendered time-honored farm techniques obsolete, and has transformed lands which were once rated as poor into lands of high potential productivity. Transportation has been so completely changed that now, for the first time in human history, it is possible to transport vast quantities of foods and other materials from one part of the earth to another. The capacity of man to produce and to move his products about has been increasing at a more and more rapid rate for about a century and a half.

The Industrial Revolution has brought with it numerous changes in the relation of people to the land. For the first time in history the presence of coal underground became a significant factor in the location of people. With power furnished by steam engines, large industrial establishments could produce not only the essentials of life but also what were once the luxuries in much greater quantities and at much lower cost per unit than had ever been possible before. Quickly the luxuries came into such common use that these new items became necessities. The traditional prestige of the owners of the land was challenged by the new economic and political power of the owners of capital; that is, of the tools or machines with which people worked.

The new system raised the general level and security of living. Not that everyone could be free from wants. In fact, one of the peculiar traits of the new way of living is the continued expenditure of effort to increase the wants, and so the frustrations, of the people. But, compared with the way of living in the pre-industrial society, the variety and certainty of the foods, the quality of the clothing, and the adequacy of shelter were all raised to an unprecedented level while the hours of labor were decreased.

The unprecedented scale on which goods were exchanged in the new system gave significance to locations where natural routes of travel converge. Here cities grew. Great cities—that is, cities of more than a million inhabitants—made their appearance for the first time in history. London passed a million in 1802; Paris about 1850; New York about 1870; Vienna in 1878; Berlin in 1880; Tokyo, Chicago, and Philadelphia about 1890; Calcutta in 1900; Buenos Aires about 1906. In 1959 there were well over eighty great cities in the world.

The use of controlled inanimate power made these cities possible. Previous to the use of such power so many people in such a small area could not have been supplied with food. But with the development of railroads and ocean ships, an urban population was able to devote itself to commerce, manufacturing, and arts and sciences, or to serving other people in these professions; and such non-food-producing people could be supplied with food from distant sources of supply so scattered that local crop failure had little effect. The urban people can produce so much beyond their own needs that they have plenty to exchange with those who supply them with things they lack. But never before the present time has there been such a demand for the raw materials of the earth. The mining of ores and fuels, the cutting of forests, and the exploitation of all resources have proceeded on a scale never before imagined.

The new industrial society by its essential nature was global in its scope, international in its needs. Local self-sufficiency had to be abandoned for world-wide economic interdependence. Society had the possibility of building with all the varied resources of the earth; but in so doing, society became vulnerable to any natural or human disturbance of the steady flow of traffic along the new lines of transportation. The old economic, social, political, or military forms became insufficient because the new society could accept no limitations but the globe itself.

The industrial society had its origins around the shore of the North

Sea in Europe. In Britain, northern France, and parts of neighboring countries, the Industrial Revolution introduced the new way of living more than a century and a half ago. This change can now be studied only in the history books. But the transformation did not stop there. Like ripples on the water, the industrial way of living spread from this center. It came quickly to the United States, Canada, Australia, and New Zealand. It moved more slowly eastward into parts of Germany and Austria, and southward into northern Italy. At present it is making its appearance in the great cities of Latin America—in São Paulo, Buenos Aires, Santiago, and Mexico City. Elsewhere in the Occidental world the older way of living still exists, only slightly modified by contacts with the centers of industry. In such places great resistance has developed to the profound changes which follow industrialization. The Fascists attempted to select certain aspects of the industrial way of living and to reject the others. Along very different lines the people of the Soviet Union are attempting to do the same.

THE DEMOCRATIC REVOLUTION

Meanwhile another revolutionary change in human living has been going on. The Democratic Revolution consists of a revolt against special privilege. Leaders, selected by those who follow the leadership, there must be; but the revolt is directed against inherited power, against power or privilege granted on the basis of social status, race, or creed. The beginnings of the Democratic Revolution are also to be found in Great Britain, and in the countries around the North Sea. But these beginnings first appear in the seventeenth century. The Plymouth Compact of 1620—written by the Pilgrims coming to America from Great Britain and Holland—is the first written document setting forth the principle of government by consent of the governed.

There are at least five basic principles involved in the Democratic Revolution. First is the right of the individual to equal treatment before the law. Second is the right of the individual to protection from the arbitrary acts of those in authority. Third is the right to be represented where taxes are levied or laws made. Fourth is the right to choose representatives and to record opinion on questions of public policy by secret ballot. And fifth is the right to free access to knowledge and to the free discussion of public issues. Government is not something forcibly imposed by a minority; rather it is to be based on majority opinion—the 51 per cent principle, as opposed to the veto principle. In the long history of mankind there has been no more profound change in the status of the individual. This is the most revolutionary idea to appear in many thousands of years.

THE INDUSTRIAL SOCIETY, THE PRE-INDUSTRIAL SOCIETY, AND THE SOVIET SOCIETY

As a result of the twin revolutions now going on, Occidental culture has been sharply divided, and all the other cultures of the world have been modified in one way or another.

Where the Industrial Revolution and the Democratic Revolution have both gone on rapidly, the culture has been most profoundly affected. In Great Britain, after bitter civil warfare, the new principles became firmly established, even though set in the traditional framework of a titled aristocracy. In France, the French Revolution eliminated the landed aristocracy. Both revolutions have gone forward rapidly in the Scandinavian countries, and in Belgium and the Netherlands. But the revolutionary changes touched only western Germany, only northern Italy, only the northeastern corner of Spain, only the Bohemian part of Czechoslovakia. Elsewhere both revolutions moved rapidly in the English-speaking world. At the present time both are moving into Latin America. The ideas of the Democratic Revolution are sweeping Africa and Asia.

Naturally these changes are resisted by those who benefit from the old order. It is difficult to resist the tremendous economic productivity and military power brought by the Industrial Revolution; and, in fact, the new technology is being eagerly learned throughout the world. But the Democratic Revolution meets strong reaction in those places where the power of the ruling groups was great. Fascism can be described as an attempt to adopt the new technology but at the same time to deny the principles of democracy. Communism starts with an attack on privilege, even to the forceful liquidation of the landowning class. But it proceeds to set up a new and equally rigid class structure, with power and privilege going to members of one political party. In these terms the communist countries represent a reaction against the most profound revolutionary movement of our time.

Occidental culture, therefore, has been divided into three chief parts. The *industrial society* is that part in which the twin revolutions have gone forward most rapidly—today incomparably the most prosperous and powerful part of the world, and the part in which the individual has the greatest freedom. The *pre-industrial society* is that part in which the traditional forms of economy and privilege remain. And the *soviet society* is that part currently dominated by the Communist Party.

These changes have had a tremendous impact on the other cultures of the world—the non-Occidental cultures. The world's simpler cultures have been all but wiped out during the past few centuries as a result of contacts with Occidentals. Consider the case of a hunting people, where the number of hunters is in delicate balance with the supply of game animals. Into such a community the Occidental trader comes to establish a trading post. He sells firearms, among other items, in exchange for furs. But firearms quickly upset the balance of hunters and game, and very soon the hunters are forced to abandon the land they once occupied because of lack of food. The new technology has resulted in an exhaustion of the resource base. Around the trading post, or around a mission station, the poverty-stricken remnants of the hunting people are clustered, an easy prey to the white man's diseases against which they had developed no previous immunity.

Contact of the Occidentals with the more complex cultures of the Orient has also brought changes of enormous significance. All the countries from India and Indonesia to China and Japan are in various ways attempting to make use of the new industrial productivity. They have accepted enough democracy, also, so that they demand equality of treatment in international affairs, and an end to their former status as colonies, subservient to European powers. Today communism and democracy, in this densely populated area, are locked in a struggle for the control of men's minds.

THE INDUSTRIAL SOCIETY AND POPULATION

One of the far-reaching results of the growth of the industrial society has been the increase of population. Before the beginning of the nineteenth century the population of Europe, for example, was increasing slowly from about 100,000,000 in 1650 to about 140,000,000 in 1750, to about 187,000,000 in 1800. Birth rates were high, but so were death rates. Deaths, especially of children, were due to lack of hygiene, to poor nutrition, and to poverty. Famines and epidemics prevented any very rapid increase of the population. But during the eighteenth and nineteenth centuries population suddenly expanded: cities burst from inside the ancient walls that had long protected them; forests were cleared and new farms established farther and farther from the market centers. By 1900 there were 400,000,000 people in Europe, and by the middle of the century there were nearly 600,000,000 people.

Not only did population grow in Europe, but from that continent came one of the greatest migrations of history. More than 50,000,000 people left Europe in the century after 1846. Most of them poured into the United States, but large numbers also went to Argentina and Brazil in South America, to Canada, Australia, and New Zealand, and to many other places. Between 1775 and 1950 the population of the United States increased from 2,500,000 to over 150,000,000—a growth which has no equal in all history.

The growth of population with industrialization is a common phenomenon. The industrial way of living brings better food supplies, less danger of local famines, larger economic opportunity, an increase of literacy and education, and better hygiene and sanitation. The result is a drop in the mortality rate, especially among children—a drop which began slowly in the early nineteenth century, but which continues at an increasingly rapid rate. Birth rates at first remain high, but after a lag they too begin to decline at a more and more rapid rate. The net result is a period of very rapid population increase, followed by a decline in the rate of growth, and finally the achievement of a nearly static population again. The whole cycle has been passed through in parts of Western Europe. It is just beginning in the Soviet Union, however; and what will happen following the industrialization of China, India, and Java remains a major issue not only in the economic problems of the world but also in the problems of political reorganization.

The period of expanding population was an extraordinarily prosperous one in the Western world, especially in those oversea countries where Europeans were able to move out into new first-class lands, as in the United States. As cities grew and markets for food products were constantly increasing, pioneer settlers moved onto new land from which the very scanty native population had been all but completely removed. Railroads were extended to provide cheap access to markets. As new settlements appeared, as new railroads were built, as new towns were established, and as population as a whole continued to grow, there was a steadily increasing market for the manufactured products of the cities. Steady expansion—interrupted, to be sure, by panics and depressions, but nevertheless always going on to new heights—this was the basic characteristic of the nineteenth century capitalist society. And in both country and city the increase of population and the spread of settlement brought about a great increase in land values—the so-called "unearned increment" of the economists. This increase of land value is the basis not only of many large fortunes but also of a vast number of small ones.

Between the two world wars, especially in the period of the depression, people were forced to take a new look at the industrial society. With no new empty pioneer land suitable for farm colonization, and in the face of rapid population increase, questions were raised about the capacity of the earth to support many more people. But while the economic institutions were shaken, the scientists and engineers continued their research studies and proceeded to the development of new machines and new techniques.

Since World War II the revolution in agriculture in the United States has been spectacular. A farm worker in the years from 1935 to 1939 could produce enough food to feed himself and ten others. In 1955, however, he could feed himself and nineteen others. The great problem of the future is to apply the new technology, and especially to spread its use to areas now economically underdeveloped. This involves readjustments in many other aspects of our culture.

Under all the confusion and uncertainty of this extraordinary period of human history in which we are privileged to live there is the fundamental fact that no human society can long survive which fails to establish workable connections with the resources of the land. Even our highly productive technical skills will not insure survival if we squander the essential raw materials of the earth without thought of replacement. Many of the simpler cultures have been more successful than we in the establishment of permanently workable connections with the land they occupy. In the United States we have used forests, minerals, and soils at rates which, if continued, cannot fail to bring us to disaster. Even the much publicized "substitutes" developed during World War II by the chemical industries require the use of raw materials from the earth.

Whether the resources of the earth are sufficient to maintain a permanent industrial society in which all the world's people might participate is a question. There are some who insist that if earth resources are used in accordance with the best techniques, there is "enough and to spare"[1]; and that only the wasteful methods dictated by the division of the earth into sovereign states, each desiring self-sufficiency, or by the nineteenth-century system of exploitation for private gain, or by the wars on the scale of those in the modern era, can destroy resources so fast that man may again be faced by basic lacks. On the other hand, there are others who quote the enormous figures of production which would be necessary if all the world's people were raised to what is commonly described as a minimum standard. To provide all the world's people with such a standard would, according to a United Nations committee, require increases of production of the following order: cereals, 50 per cent; meat, 90 per cent; milk and other dairy products, 125 per cent; vegetable oils, 125 per cent; and fruits and vegetables, 300 per cent.[2] The question is whether our capitalist economy or any other system could manage to develop and maintain such vast increases in food production at sufficiently low cost. The answer is not clear.

Before these problems of social science can be studied profitably, it is essential to examine the present distribution of people in the world and their relations with the resources of the land. For what befalls mankind in the centuries ahead will, in part, flow from the present; and, similarly, to understand the present it is necessary to go back to origins and trace developments. The present pattern of people is obviously not a static thing; it is a stage in a process of which the two basic elements are the human culture and the land.

---

[1] Kirtley F. Mather, *Enough and to Spare,* New York, 1944.
[2] Quoted in Guy Irving Burch and Elmer Pendell, *Population Roads to Peace or War,* Washington, D. C., 1945, p. 30.

INTRODUCTION

Part Two

THE LAND

IN HUMAN PROBLEMS, as we have said, the land plays a neutral role. It has often been likened to the stage setting on which a drama is taking place. But the stage is a very complex thing, and it contains many items of no significance to the action of the play, and many other things which come temporarily into importance during a particular act or scene. The physical patterns of the earth should be considered as something entirely separate from the human patterns, although, to be sure, in each region, district, or locality there is the constant need to adjust human activities to the conditions of the land. To the human drama, however, the land remains neutral—neither favorable nor unfavorable in itself, but only as the play gives it these qualities. Furthermore, in terms of the human time scale, the land is relatively permanent and enduring. Man with his comings and goings, his wars, even his ideals and aspirations, seems small indeed when measured against the earth, the surface of which he inhabits.

THE MAJOR LINEAMENTS

The face of the earth itself is an extraordinary place. In spite of the wide range of possible temperatures that exist in nature, from the tremendous heat of the hottest star to the appalling cold of the outer reaches of space, here at the earth's surface are found air temperatures at which water will neither freeze nor boil. All the organic forms we know, including man, are dependent on the fact that life is only possible in the presence of water which is a liquid. The distribution of water on the earth is a basic fact of existence.

Among the major lineaments which make up the face of the earth are the continents and ocean basins. The continents are composed of relatively upstanding masses of the earth's crust between relatively down-sinking portions, which make up the ocean basins. The difference in elevation, or relief, above the center of the earth of these contrasted parts of its surface averages only about three miles, or less than

1/1300 of the radius. The maximum difference in elevation is about 12 miles (between Mount Everest, about 29,000 feet above sea level, and the ocean deep off the Mariana Islands, more than 35,000 feet below sea level). But even this is only about 1/330 of the earth's radius. Small as are these differences of elevation compared with the size of the planet, they nevertheless measure the major relief features of its surface.

Only about 28 per cent of this surface, however, stands above the sea. Water fills the ocean basins and, overflowing these, inundates also the margins of the continental masses. As a result the continents are for the most part isolated, while the oceans are relatively continuous. There is more than twice as much land north of the equator as south of it. Except for Antarctica all the continents are broadest in the north, even those in the Southern Hemisphere. There is an almost complete ring of land around the basin of the Arctic Ocean, while, in contrast, the tapering of the continents toward the south leaves an almost uninterrupted sea in the higher middle latitudes of the Southern Hemisphere.

All these various continental masses are tied together by more or less

The arrangement of mountains and continents

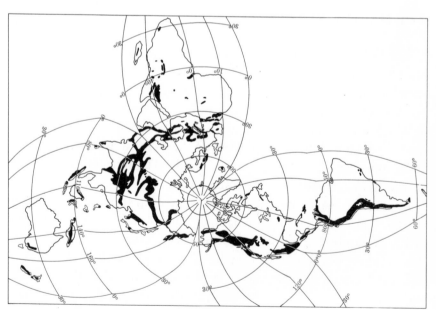

continuous chains of high mountains. These mountain ranges, passing from continent to continent or festooned around the oceans in strings of islands, form a framework to which are joined the other major lineaments of the earth's face. Without regard to the complexity of detail at this time, the general distribution pattern of high mountains is one of relative simplicity but profound significance. In a sense the central and southeastern part of Asia is the core of the world's lands, and in the present-day world it is composed of a complex knot of towering mountain ranges. From this core mountain axes extend in three directions: one westward through southern Asia, southern Europe, and northern Africa to the edge of the Atlantic Ocean basin; and one northward and one southward to form, through the American continents and the Pacific margins of the Antarctic Continent, a broken ring of mountains around the basin of the Pacific Ocean. The manner in which the several continental masses are joined to this framework gives to each its own peculiar shape. Yet these various lands, when plotted on a polar projection, appear as three peninsulas radiating from the Asian core (map, p. 26): Europe and Africa, depending from the western limb of the mountain system; the East Indies, Australia, and New Zealand, depending from the southern limb; and the American continents, attached to the limb which starts northeastward through eastern Asia and crosses into the Western Hemisphere through Alaska. The land masses of the world, therefore, are not symmetrically arranged with reference to the poles and the divisions of latitude and longitude.

THE PATTERN OF CLIMATES

These major lineaments of the face of the earth are produced by the characteristics of the lithosphere, the rock crust of the earth, and the hydrosphere, the earth's water. Overlying these two spheres is a third one, the atmosphere. This is a thin film of gases clinging to the earth's surface. It is made up of nitrogen (about 78 per cent), oxygen (about 21 per cent), and small amounts of water vapor, carbon dioxide, and other gases. Artificial satellites lifted a few hundred miles above the earth are beyond this film of gases, into which man himself has penetrated only about twenty miles. It is important to keep in mind that if a circle were printed on this page to represent the earth, the whole atmosphere would lie within the width of the black line. Yet it is the average condition of this thin film of gases that produces the earth's pattern of climates.

The climatic features, unlike the land masses, are symmetrically arranged with reference to the poles and the divisions of latitude and longitude. If you know the latitude of a place and its longitudinal position (eastern or western side of an ocean; eastern, interior, or western part of a continent), you can describe in a general way the nature of its climate. This symmetry of the climatic pattern is explained by the nature of the physical controls of climate.

Latitude. The first of the controls of climate is latitude; that is, distance north or south of the equator. Because of the fact that the earth's axis is tilted $23\frac{1}{2}°$ from the plane of the earth's orbit around the sun, all the latitudes from $23\frac{1}{2}°$ N. (the Tropic of Cancer) to $23\frac{1}{2}°$ S. (the Tropic of Capricorn) receive the sun's rays vertically twice during a year. As one proceeds northward from the Tropic of Cancer or southward from the Tropic of Capricorn, the sun's rays reach the surface of the earth at larger and larger angles from the vertical or zenith. Much more heat is received at the earth's surface when the sun's rays are vertical than when they reach the earth at an angle. Very little heat is received when the sun rises only a little above the horizon even at noon.

The atmosphere receives most of its heat from the surface of the earth. The sun's radiation passes through the gases of the atmosphere, affecting their temperature only to a small degree. But direct contact with the earth or radiation from the earth does affect the air temperature. Therefore the air has a higher temperature close to the earth, and temperature decreases with altitude. And since the earth is heated more in the low latitudes (within 30° of the equator) than in the high latitudes (60° to the poles), the average annual air temperatures are generally higher at the earth's surface the lower the latitude. If the earth were all land or all water, temperature would correspond quite closely to latitude.

Land and Water. The surface of the earth, however, is anything but uniform. The simple arrangement of temperature by latitude, therefore, is modified by the effect of land and water; so much so that in some places the direction of greatest temperature contrast is east and west instead of north and south (see Plate 24). For a variety of reasons (which are outlined in Appendix B), land heats up by day and in summer much more rapidly than does water; and at night and in winter the land cools off much more rapidly than does water. The air over the water, therefore, has a more equable temperature than does the air over the land. At any given latitude the summers are hotter and the winters colder over the land than over the water. Ranges of temperature between coldest and warmest months increase with increasing latitude and distance from the sea. A distinction is recognized between *marine* climates and *continental* climates (see Appendix B, Section 19).

Land and water also have an important effect on the distribution of rainfall. Rain is produced in nature through the cooling of moist air; that is, air in which there is a relatively large amount of water vapor. Air picks up water vapor by evaporation. Because evaporation is very much more rapid from warm water than from cold water, the one major source of atmospheric moisture in the world is warm ocean water. Plate 23 shows that the oceans are symmetrically marked off into regions of warm and cold water, as well as water of intermediate temperature. By comparing the map of rainfall (Plate 7) with the map of ocean water (Plate 23), it is clear that rainfall is generally greater over the warm water, and over the margins of the continents bathed by warm water. Rainfall is small over cold water or over the continental margins bordered by cold water. Rainfall also is low in the continental interiors distant from warm ocean water.

Prevailing Winds. There are two basic physical principles to keep in mind regarding the movement of air. In the first place, air with a low temperature is dense and heavy compared with air with a high temperature. Relatively cold air is therefore pulled by gravity toward places where air is relatively warm and light. The warm light air is pushed up by the heavier cool air. Air tends to move over the surface of the earth from cooler places to warmer places. This would suggest a general movement from high latitudes to low latitudes; and also a movement from water to land by day and in summer, and from land to water by night and in winter.

The second physical principle introduces a complication, however. All these air movements take place over the surface of a rotating sphere. Excepting air in motion within a few degrees on either side of the equator, all moving air is deflected to the right in the Northern Hemisphere and to the left in the Southern Hemisphere. Outside of the equatorial regions, therefore, air movements tend to become whirls. Instead of moving from an area of high air pressure directly toward an area of low air pressure (pressure is the weight of the atmosphere above a given point), the air in the Northern Hemisphere swings to the right until it moves along with high pressure to its right and low pressure to its left. Only when friction with the earth's surface or other things interfere, can air actually move into an area of low pressure.

Based on these principles, a general pattern of prevailing winds at the surface of the earth can be recognized. There are three elements in this general pattern. First is the *oceanic whirl.* These whirls (Plate 26) are centered over the cold ocean water on the eastern sides of the five ocean basins (North Atlantic, South Atlantic, North Pacific, South Pacific, South Indian) at about latitude 30°. The air circulates in a clockwise direction in the Northern Hemisphere and in a counterclockwise direction in the Southern Hemisphere. The whirls are so large that they cover most of the ocean basins and the bordering margins of the continents. Air circulating around the North Atlantic whirl, for example, moves through the low latitudes from northeast and east. Approaching eastern North America, it comes from the southeast and south. In the middle latitudes, on the northern side of the whirl the air crosses the North Atlantic from southwest, west, and northwest. Over the western side of Europe and North Africa the wind is from the north. Only near the equator can the air move in a straight line. In South America air from the North Atlantic oceanic whirl passes all the way across Brazil to the eastern side of the Andes. But in the middle latitudes air circulating in these whirls cannot reach the continental interiors, which are consequently dry.

The second element of the general pattern of winds is the *polar outburst.* Over the permanent icecaps of Greenland and Antarctica, and over the very cold snow-covered surfaces of northern North America and northern Eurasia in winter, the air over the land is greatly chilled. It becomes very cold and heavy. Cold air accumulates until it becomes so heavy in relation to warmer and lighter air that it slides off, moving toward the nearest warm place where air is light and pressure low. These cold air masses move like drops of water on a windowpane—with a steep, rolling front and a streamlined top. Because the air is heavy, it stays close to the earth and the deflective force of the earth's rotation has little effect. The cold air masses burrow into the poleward parts of the oceanic whirls, creating rotating eddies known as cyclonic storms. The cold air moves under the relatively warm and light oceanic air and pushes it up. The oceanic air is thereby cooled and, if it contains enough water vapor, it drops this moisture in the form of rain or snow. It is the interaction of these polar outbursts with the oceanic whirls that brings the variable weather of the middle latitudes. Especially stormy are the higher middle latitudes of the Southern Hemisphere around Antarctica. But also very stormy are the North Atlantic and the North Pacific.

The third element of the world's prevailing winds either re-enforces or interrupts the first two elements along certain of the continental coasts. Where a continental margin faces toward the equator within 30° of the equator, there is a seasonal shift of wind direction which is known as a *monsoon*. In a true monsoon the air moves in summer from the relatively cool low latitude ocean onto the relatively hot bordering land; and in winter it moves from the relatively cool land onto the relatively warm ocean. In each case the deflective force of the earth's rotation makes the air swing to the right in the Northern Hemisphere and to the left in the Southern Hemisphere. These winds blow with little interruption for six months in one direction and for six months in the opposite direction. The greatest monsoon region of the world is along the southern margin of Asia (Plate 26). The northern margin of Australia is another monsoon region. Monsoon winds also develop along the Guinea coast of West Africa, and over the south-facing Pacific coast of Central America.

As one travels away from the low latitudes along the eastern margins of the continents in the Northern Hemisphere, monsoons of a somewhat different character are found. Here also, as in the southeastern part of North America and the southeastern part of Asia, the prevailing winds of winter are from the northwest, and those of summer are from the south and southeast. These winds, however, are interrupted both in summer and winter by winds from other directions; they are statistical monsoons, in that it is only the prevailing wind that shows the monsoon character. Actually, along these mid-latitude coasts the oceanic whirl is dominant in summer, only occasionally interrupted by a polar outburst; and the polar outbursts are dominant in winter, only occasionally interrupted by winds circulating about the oceanic whirls.

Climatic Regions. The patterns of temperature, rainfall, and wind direction, together with other climatic elements, combine to form the climatic regions of the world. It should be noted that the traditional division of the world into temperate, torrid, and frigid zones is unacceptable to geographers; for, in spite of its simplicity, it obscures more important climatic relationships than it reveals. The world's highest and the world's lowest temperatures at the earth's surface occur in the so-called temperate zone; the only truly temperate climates in the world occur over the tropical oceans in the so-called torrid zone. Because of these, and of other facts to be noted later, the use of these terms has been dropped.

The system of climatic regions presented in this book is one which was devised by a German geographer, Wladimir Köppen. It is a system based on quantitative definitions, and as such can be applied to any part of the earth where climatic data are available. The definitions and the methods of using the classification are presented in Appendix B; the map of the world's climatic regions is on Plate 8; representative climatic data on which the map is partly based are in Appendix E.

For those who do not wish to make use of the Köppen system as a quantitative classification of climate, the following description of the characteristics of each of the major climates shown on Plate 8 is presented.

Af-Afi Am-Ami	Tropical rainy climate with no cool season, with little range of temperature, and with no dry season or only a short dry season
Aw-Awi	Tropical climate with no cool season, with little range of temperature, and with a distinct rainy season and a distinct dry season
BSh	Hot, semiarid climate
BSk-BSk′	Cool, semiarid climate
BWh	Hot, arid climate
BWk-BWk′	Cool, arid climate
Cwbi-Cfbi	High altitude, low latitude climate
Cwa-Cwb	Mid-latitude climate with mild, dry winters and rainy summers
Csa	Mid-latitude climate with mild, rainy winters, and hot, dry summers

Csb	Mid-latitude climate with mild, rainy winters, and cool, dry summers
Cfa	Mid-latitude continental and east coast climate with mild winters and hot summers, and with no dry season
Cfb	Mid-latitude marine climate with mild winters and cool summers, and with no dry season
Cfc	Mid-latitude marine climate with mild winters and short, cool summers, and with no dry season
Dfa	Mid-latitude continental climate with severe winters and hot summers, and with no dry season
Dfb	Mid-latitude continental climate with severe winters and cool summers, and with no dry season
Dfc	Mid-latitude continental climate with severe winters and short, cool summers, and with no dry season
Dwa, Dwb, Dwc	Same as Dfa, Dfb, and Dfc, but with very dry winters
Dfd, Dwd	Same as above, but with extreme low winter temperatures
E	High latitude or high altitude climate with no summers

THE PATTERN OF VEGETATION

All the features of the face of the earth that are in any way related to the climate are, like the pattern of climates, symmetrically arranged. Climate itself is not directly observable. Climate is the average state of the atmosphere. In practice this is determined by systematic observations of temperature and rainfall continued over many years. The climatic lines are interpolated between the known conditions at the points where there are climatic stations. In many ways more useful than climatic lines for the definition of major natural regions of the earth are the lines bounding different categories of vegetation—lines which are observable in the field. The earth's cover of plants and animals—the biosphere—is in its broader patterns a reflection of the underlying pattern of climates.

The chief difficulty with the use of vegetation as the basis for a definition of major natural regions is the extent to which vegetation has been changed by human action during the million years of man's presence on the earth. There are some places, as in eastern China (Plate 18), where the original arrangement of the vegetation can no longer be reconstructed. Furthermore, prehistoric man, although few in total numbers, was able to make profound changes in the character of the plants and animals through the use of fire. It is thought that the mid-latitude grasslands that occur in humid climates were created by pre-historic burning, and that even in semiarid climates the original grass-lands were probably covered with brush. In other words, it is probably correct to say that in very few places, if any, does the original natural vegetation remain unmodified.

Nevertheless, the major categories of vegetation, whether in part man-made or not, do in fact occupy characteristic positions within the climatic framework. In certain kinds of climatic conditions man's fires, raging out of control, created grasslands where open stands of forests may once have existed. These partially man-made types of vegetation had been on the land long enough, when Europeans first came upon them in the sixteenth century, so that under them was a distinctive kind of soil, found under no other conditions. In many of these places, too, there was a distinctive animal population. For the purposes of this survey of the geography of man it is permissible to treat the major types of plant cover as "natural" vegetation, without raising the more or less philosophical question of whether or not man is a natural agent.[1] The major vegetation regions of the world, as they are believed to have existed when historic man first came upon them, are shown on the plates at the back of the book. They are defined and described in the chapters which follow.

The general correspondence between the pattern of climate and that of the vegetation is clear. The areas of arid climate in the world are scantily covered with drought-resistant plants, with bare ground between the plants. The semiarid climates are usually sufficiently moist so that there is a complete cover of plants over the earth, al-though they are plants which are adapted to survival under dry condi-tions. In many cases the semiarid areas are covered with a scrubby woodland; but where man has intervened with fire, the woodland has gone and there is a cover of grass, which can survive fire. The humid parts of the world are covered with different kinds of forests. The

[1] See William L. Thomas, Jr., and Others (editors), *Man's Role in Changing the Face of the Earth,* Chicago, 1956.

tropical forests are made up of species of trees that cannot stand low temperatures. In the middle latitudes, broadleaf trees and conifers (needleleaf trees) are variously arranged. Here, also, there is evidence that certain pure stands of pine are the result of man-made fires under particular conditions of soil, water, and climate. In the very severe winter climates of the northern continents, the forests are made up of hardy conifers, such as spruce, fir, and larch. Corresponding in general to the climates with no summers are the open tundras beyond the limits of the forest.

THE GROUPS OF REGIONS

The face of the earth, which is the habitat of man, is made up of many different kinds of features, resulting from different kinds of processes of change. There are physical and chemical processes, operating in accordance with the laws or principles established by students of physics and chemistry. There are biological processes, described by the students of biology. There are various cultural processes, examined by the several social sciences. In modern times each group of processes has become the subject matter of a systematic field of scholarship. Great advances in the understanding of these processes has come from the method of isolating them under laboratory conditions to see how they work when no unrelated, outside conditions interfere. In the social sciences, where laboratory experiment is usually impossible, processes are isolated symbolically by use of such a phrase as "other things being equal." It is the responsibility of geographic scholarship to see how these processes operate, not in isolation, but in the actual context of total environments in particular places.

In this book the focus of attention is on the significance of the differences of population density from place to place. Significance is to be sought in terms of causes and consequences. The systematic field which studies the process of population growth or decline is called *demography*. A geography of man must make use of the understandings provided by demography, but must then examine specific groups of people in particular places, and must seek the areal relationships of population with other elements of the total environment. The basic question is: How is mankind distributed on the earth in relation to the features of the physical, biotic, and cultural environment, and how did this pattern of population develop? The answers are basic to all the economic, social, and political problems of our time.

To provide a basis for the study of the areal relations of population to the underlying qualities of the land, the face of the earth is divided into eight groups of regions. Each group includes regions in different parts of the world that are broadly similar with respect to surface features and the cover of vegetation. The first seven groups of regions are not mountainous, and are separated from one another on the basis of the cover of vegetation. Each of these groups of regions can be subdivided into subregions on the basis of the surface configuration. The eighth group, on the other hand, includes all those parts of the world that are mountainous. The order, as presented in the following list, is a matter of expediency.

GROUP I
    The Dry Lands
GROUP II
    The Tropical Forest Lands
GROUP III
    The Mediterranean Scrub Forest Lands
GROUP IV
    The Mid-Latitude Mixed Forest Lands
GROUP V
    The Grasslands
GROUP VI
    The Boreal Forest Lands
GROUP VII
    The Polar Lands
GROUP VIII
    The Mountain Lands

The importance of the map in geographic study must be emphasized. Appendix A is devoted to a discussion of maps. The plates at the back of the book, however, show in concrete form the areal spread of the various things discussed in the text. Plates 1 to 6 show the patterns of population density. Plates 9 to 20 show, for the same continental areas, the surface configuration and the natural vegetation. On the vegetation maps the actual spread of each of the groups of regions can be seen; and on the surface configuration maps the subdivisions of the first seven groups can be read.

In the chapters which follow we shall discuss the nature of the habitat and the story of man's experience in occupying the habitat in each of the groups of regions. Because so large a proportion of mankind is concentrated in the regions of Group IV, we shall treat these areas in three chapters: one devoted to the physical and biotic character of the group; one to the areas of Oriental culture; and one to the areas of Occidental culture. In the concluding chapter we shall return to a world view of some of the major problems of population, and of cultural and political geography.

THE DRY LANDS

Dry Lands

WATER AND SUNLIGHT are the basic needs of life. In the dry lands of the earth there is abundant sunlight, but the supply of water is small. Over vast areas life forms can gain a foothold only by persistent struggle against drought, or through ability to endure long periods without water and to carry on the life processes hurriedly and vigorously during those rare periods when water is available. However, in those spots in the dry lands where water is present a most amazing exuberance of life exists.

Man too concentrates his activities on these wet spots. His problem is constantly to maintain or enlarge his supplies of water. Yet for all his efforts an almost negligible proportion of the deserts has proved permanently habitable. The rich green of the oasis vegetation and the teeming activity of the numerous inhabitants are set in striking contrast against a background of barren solitudes. Beyond the sharp line which separates the land of life from the land of death one enters another world, a strange and unnatural one for those who are familiar with the abundance of growing things where rainfall is adequate. Here the land needs only water to make it bloom, but, lacking only water, it has remained a wilderness.

The Land

DESERT CLIMATE AND DESERT VEGETATION

The basic fact concerning the dry lands is that they are deficient in moisture. Much more water would evaporate during the average year than is supplied by the rainfall. In most deserts rains come only at infrequent and irregular intervals, many years elapsing between showers. When rain does fall, it comes in the form of cloudbursts, tremendously heavy downpours sometimes accompanied by hail and lasting several hours or even several days. Damage by floods, strange as it may seem, is a characteristic occurrence in deserts; for the heavy

Desert vegetation in Death Valley

rains are all the more destructive because of the lack of well-defined stream channels, the sparsity of vegetation, the hard-packed soil, and the character of the buildings and other human works which are not made to withstand much water.

Very few parts of the world are truly rainless, although portions of the Libyan Desert and of the Atacama Desert approach this condition. In all deserts the hills and mountains receive more rain than the flatter lands. Over some of the higher ranges clouds may hang most of the time, supporting a little green pasturage in the cloud zone throughout the year; but even here the rule of desert rainfall is irregularity and uncertainty.

Temperatures in the dry lands vary considerably according to the latitude. In the poleward portions of the deserts, especially in the Northern Hemisphere, the winters are very cold. At lower latitudes, however, are found the highest air temperatures ever recorded at the face of the earth. Death Valley, in California, formerly held the record with a temperature of 134.1° [1]; but not long ago this was exceeded by Azizia, located about twenty-five miles south of Tripoli, where the temperature reached 136.4°. Temperatures well over 100° occur regularly during the summers in all but the poleward areas or in areas close to the oceans. Such heat, together with the glaring reflection from the bare desert surfaces, aggravated by the clouds of dust which the desert winds pick up, makes traveling in the afternoon hours uncomfortable or even difficult.

The desert night, on the other hand, generally brings a rapid drop of the temperature. Especially on elevated plateaus the surface of the earth cools rapidly under the clear night sky, and great diurnal ranges of temperature are the result. In fact, the desert holds the world's record for this also; in the Saharan oasis of In-Salah the temperature ranged from 26° to 126° within twenty-four hours.

Desert Vegetation. These climatic conditions are reflected in the landscape by a characteristic type of vegetation cover. Contrary to popular impression very few parts of the deserts are entirely barren. Such bare places do occur, but they are rare. Even the great sandy deserts have a scattering of drought-resistant shrubs in the hollows between the dunes, and where water seepage brings moisture near the surface the result is a profusion of plants. The typical desert scene includes a cover of low shrubs and grasses, which, at least after a rain, gives the landscape a distinctly greenish tinge.

The vegetation which can exist under these extreme conditions of drought and high evaporation must be especially adapted to them. This is accomplished in various ways. There are annuals which evade the drought by lying dormant during the long dry period, springing into bloom and rapidly completing the life cycle during the rare intervals when water is available. Then there are the perennials which

---

[1] Climatic data throughout this book are given in Fahrenheit degrees and in inches, unless otherwise specifically stated. Official air temperatures are always taken in a shelter which provides shade but does not shut out the wind.

endure the drought, quickly sending forth leaves and stems during the periods of rain, but remaining brown and apparently dead as long as no moisture reaches them. There are also the succulent plants, such as the cacti, which resist the drought by storing water inside their roots and stems and by protecting themselves from evaporation by thick bark, by narrow, hairy, or waxy leaves, or by a complete absence of leaves. Such plants are protected also from the attacks of thirsty animals by an armament of thorns.

Desert plants usually grow some distance apart, and have a remarkable development of the root system—both laterally, to catch the infrequent rains, and vertically, to tap the deep-lying supply of water. The lack of a complete mat of vegetation over the surface is one of the distinguishing features of the dry lands. Because of the short growing season those plants which are especially attractive to insects, the carriers of the fertilizing pollen, have an advantage of survival. Hence among the most striking peculiarities of desert vegetation are the brilliant coloring and penetrating odor of the flowers (picture, p. 42).

Plants which are adapted in these various ways to dry conditions are called *xerophytes,* or xerophytic plants. A scattered cover of xerophytic shrubs with bare ground between the plants is the characteristic natural vegetation of the regions of Group I. In fact, the lack of a complete cover of vegetation is the feature which distinguishes the regions of this group from those of neighboring groups.

Vegetation and Rainfall Effectiveness. The various plant associations included in the general term "desert" occur in areas which are deficient in moisture. But moisture deficiency is not solely a matter of low rainfall. Deserts cannot be defined as having less than, say, 10 inches of rain a year, because there are a number of things which combine to determine the effectiveness of rainfall in terms of plants.

When rain falls on the ground, part of it is evaporated again, part runs off over the surface, and part sinks into the soil. Only the part which sinks into the soil can be effective in the support of vegetation. The presence of only scattered xerophytic shrubs, therefore, may be the result of low rainfall, rapid evaporation, rapid drainage, or a combination of these. The rate of evaporation is much greater at high temperatures than at lower ones, and it increases also with lower humidity and with higher wind velocities. And there are still other elements affecting evaporation. The amount of water which remains on the surface to be evaporated after a rain depends on the degree of slope, on the nature of the soil, and, to a certain extent, on the nature of the cover of vegetation. It also depends on the rate at which the rain falls, for much more water is soaked up by the soil in a long-continued drizzle than in one of those violent cloudbursts which are so typical of the deserts.

Desert vegetation, a visible result of moisture deficiency, is the product of all these numerous factors, some *climatic* (resulting from the average state of the atmosphere), and some *edaphic* (resulting from the character of the soil and surface). In general, the broad outlines of the desert regions are the result of climatic conditions, whereas the details observed in particular localities are the result of edaphic conditions.

Two examples from the United States will make clearer the effect of differences of temperature and rainfall in determining moisture effectiveness. Denver, Colorado, is located east of the Rocky Mountains in an area once covered by short grass. It is outside the dry-land region, with a climate which is described as semiarid rather than arid. Denver's average annual rainfall is 14 inches, which comes chiefly in summer and is therefore less effective than if it came when temperatures were lower. Denver's average temperature is about 50°. Under these circumstances the amount of rain necessary to support a continuous grass cover is about 10 inches.

El Paso, Texas, is located in a part of North America where the climate is arid, and where typical dry-land vegetation is to be found with bare ground between the plants. El Paso's average annual rainfall is just under 10 inches, and, like the rainfall at Denver, it comes chiefly in summer. The average annual temperature is about 63°. Experience indicates that at such temperatures more than 12 inches of rain are necessary for the support of grass vegetation.

The World Distribution of the Dry Lands. An examination of the maps (Plates 9–20) shows that the regions of Group I are more or less systematically arranged on the earth. They occupy a similar position on all the continents. They occur on the west coasts, roughly between 20° and 30° both north and south of the equator. In South America, to be sure, the desert extends much farther toward the equator than on any other continent, although in Africa, also, it crosses latitude 20° S. Allowing for the individual peculiarities of each continent, we can nevertheless find a desert on the west coast somewhere between these latitudes in all parts of the earth. The deserts also extend inland from the west coast, and as we follow them toward the continental interiors we note that they reach farther and farther poleward. In Somaliland and in southern South America the dry lands reach the east coasts, but elsewhere these parts of the continents have no moisture deficiency.

There are five great areas of desert in the world. These are listed in the following table, together with the regional names of the various parts:

1. NORTH AFRICA-ASIA
   Sahara, including Libya; Somaliland; Arabia; Iran; Thar; Turkestan; Tarim; Gobi
2. NORTH AMERICA
   Mexican Plateau, Lower California, Sonora, Colorado Plateau, Mojave, Great Basin, Wyoming Basin, Columbia Plateau
3. SOUTH AMERICA
   Coastal desert of Peru, Atacama, Western Argentina, Patagonia
4. SOUTH AFRICA
   Kalahari, Namib
5. AUSTRALIA
   Great Sandy Desert, Great Victoria Desert

The general world distribution of deserts is a result of the symmetrical arrangement of certain basic climatic features on the earth. Plate 23 shows that the west coasts of all the continents are bathed in part by cold ocean water, and that where the cold currents extend farthest toward the equator, as off western South America and western South Africa (Peru Current and Benguela Current), the deserts also extend farthest in this direction. The presence of a wide area of cold water off Patagonia (Falkland Current) also corresponds to the east-coast desert of southern Argentina. The Somaliland desert, however, is bordered by warm water.

The low rainfall, which is a major factor in moisture deficiency and so in the development of deserts, is a result of the failure of moisture-bearing air to reach these sections of the continents. The only important sources of moisture in the world are the warm parts of the oceans. From cold water there is relatively little evaporation, but the air over warm water picks up large amounts of moisture. When warm, moisture-laden air moves onto the land, the areas it reaches are supplied with copious rain. The world's deserts extend to the coasts only where the water offshore for a long distance is cold, or where the air blows parallel to the coast (as in Somaliland). The continental interiors, especially where they are protected by high ranges of mountains, remain dry because the moisture-bearing air cannot get into them. The world's wind systems which bring moisture to other parts of the continents will be discussed in later chapters.[1]

SURFACE FEATURES AND DRAINAGE

These great desert areas, however, are by no means uniform in character. The concept of a desert as a vast expanse of shifting sand is incorrect, for actually only a relatively small proportion of the dry-land area is of this sort. A much larger proportion is composed of rocky plateaus channeled by dry watercourses, or of basins surrounded by barren mountains.

Desert Landforms.[2] To a person used to the forms of hills and valleys in rainy regions the deserts are strikingly different. In the first place, because of the scanty covering of vegetation, even the minor irregularities of form are revealed—especially, late in the day, when the shadows make the relief stand out boldly. One notices, too, the prevailing absence of permanent streams, although in some deserts the surface is scored by numerous dry watercourses. Perhaps the most striking peculiarity, however, is the accumulation of rock waste, the flood of debris which masks the base of every hill and cliff and which fills the valleys and basins. In the rainy lands, with permanently flowing streams, the waste material is gradually carried away; but in the deserts, outside of the immediate valleys of the few streams which do flow through to the sea, the only agent which can carry off the loosened

[1] The principles of meteorology and the methods of classifying climates are discussed in Appendix B.

[2] For a discussion of the forms and origins of the various kinds of surface features, see Appendix C.

rock waste is the wind. Only the finer particles can be picked up in this way. In the rainy lands on the lee sides of the great deserts, accumulations of fine dust, known as *loess,* tell something of the extent of wind erosion.

Mountain and Bolson [1] **Deserts.** From the point of view of the larger surface features two chief kinds of deserts may be recognized. The first of these is hilly or mountainous; the second is of much lower relief and is composed of rocky plateaus and sand-filled basins.

The first desert type, known as the *mountain and bolson* desert, is characterized by scattered ranges of barren hills or low mountains separated by more or less extensive basins or bolsons. In this kind of country most of the rain falls on the highlands. Because of the steep slopes and the violent nature of the showers, a very large part of the rainfall runs off over the surface, rapidly eroding deep V-shaped ravines and gullies. Although the desert rains may be infrequent, and many years may elapse between showers, most of the work of sculpturing the mountain ranges is accomplished by the violent rains and resulting floods. When the flood waters emerge from the mountains and enter the bolson, however, their rate of flow is suddenly checked. Much of the load of sand and gravel picked up in the mountains is deposited in the form of alluvial fans which spread out in front of each valley mouth along the margins of the bolson. During a cloudburst, and for a short time after, water may actually cross the alluvial fans and reach the center of the bolson, there forming a temporary shallow lake. But the rapid evaporation speedily removes the water from such a lake, leaving in its bed an accumulation of dazzling white salt. In some of the larger bolsons enough water may enter to support a shallow salt lake permanently, like Great Salt Lake in Utah; but more commonly the lakes in the bolsons are temporary, known technically as *playa* lakes, their beds marked most of the time by salt accumulations left over from the repeated evaporation of water.

There are, then, three chief divisions of the surface of mountain and bolson deserts. There are the mountain ranges with their steep, rocky slopes; there are the alluvial fans smoothing the angles between bordering mountains and bolson bottoms; and, in the lowest part of the

[1] From the Spanish word *bolson,* meaning "pocket."

basin, there is the playa, either a shallow salt lake with fluctuating shores or simply a flat salt plain over which at rare intervals the flood waters may form a lake. It is the alluvial fans of such regions which offer the best sites for human settlement; for by irrigating the fans with water from the mountain streams and permitting it to drain off easily to the playa, rich oases may be formed.

Hamada and Erg Deserts. The second type of desert is composed of rocky plateaus of relatively slight relief, in some places interspersed with extensive sand-filled basins. The Saharan terms are adopted in Anglicized form to describe these features: for the rocky plateaus, the term *hamada;* for the sandy areas, the term *erg* (picture, p. 50).

Although the surface of the hamada is covered with a regolith of angular rock fragments, this mantle is not very thick and does not obscure the underlying rock. The character and position of the geologic formations are therefore of primary importance in determining the landforms of the hamada. Especially varied are the forms which appear in areas of stratified rocks where the strata are of varying degrees of resistance to weathering and erosion. The weaker formations are quickly excavated, leaving the stronger rocks standing out in bold relief as *mesas* or *cuestas.*

Many hamadas are shaped as broad, flattish domes. Erosion by streams or wind may strip off the layers of sedimentary strata from the higher parts of the dome, leaving a core of massive crystalline rocks exposed in the center. In desert areas many of the crystalline rocks disintegrate more easily than sedimentary strata, so that the rocks in the center of the structural dome may be worn away to form a surface basin. A few types of crystalline rocks, however, especially recent igneous rocks, may stand out boldly. Around the crystalline center a series of infacing cuestas correspond to the outcrops of resistant strata. This is a common geologic structure not only in the dry lands but also in many other parts of the world.[1]

There are many other kinds of hamadas, however, besides those formed of simple horizontal layers of stratified rock or those produced by a broad doming. Some hamadas possibly represent the final product in the erosion of mountain ranges, and the neighboring ergs may

[1] See the illustrations in Appendix C, especially those on pages 547–556.

An erg landscape in the Sahara

be the filled bolsons of earlier geologic periods. It is not uncommon to find the monotonous surfaces of such hamadas surmounted by a few mountain remnants. Steep-sided pinnacles of crumbling rock rise so abruptly from the rocky platforms on which they stand that, viewed from a distance, they resemble islands rising from a sea. Because of this the Germans have given them the descriptive name *inselberge,* or "island mountains." All stages of transition, from the well-defined mountain and bolson desert to the subdued surfaces of the hamada and erg type, may be observed in the various parts of the world's dry lands.

The dry desert valley, cut, perhaps deeply, into the surface of the hamada, is a characteristic and striking element of the desert landscape. Excavated in the course of long periods of time by the recurring floods, these steep-sided ravines remain most of the time quite dry.

When rain does fall, torrents fill the ravines from wall to wall; but as the waters subside, the load of alluvium which is being swept along by the floods is deposited in the channels. The ravine bottoms, therefore, are flat and are composed of a fill of coarse sand or gravel (picture below). To designate these dry desert valleys, the Arabic term *wadi* has been adopted (they are known as *arroyos* in the western United States).

Of all the desert surfaces, however, the one which is most familiar to people who have never visited the dry lands is the erg, or sandy desert. The ergs are extensive basins, or depressions, filled with sand which the wind forms into great dune ridges. Here we find the standard desert scene of the "movies," although actually this kind of surface is less extensive than any of the other types. Unlike the bolsons, the ergs do not usually have playa lakes, for the water which drains into them through the wadis of the neighboring hamadas is rapidly absorbed by the porous sands.

Water in the Deserts. The most important physical condition in the desert from the point of view of life is the occurrence of water. Knowledge of the places where fresh water may be found is of vital concern

Rio Puerco, New Mexico, northwest of Albuquerque

Photo by J. G. Widdison

Sunkist Photo

Irrigated orange orchards on an alluvial fan near Los Angeles

to desert dwellers, and habitability is in almost direct proportion to the amount of water which can be made available. There is a supply of ground water in most deserts, just as in humid lands, but the water table [1] lies at a much greater depth below the surface. Therefore the places where the water table can be reached by ordinary surface wells are few and far between.

In the mountain and bolson deserts, even where no permanent surface stream reaches the bolson from the neighboring ranges, water is

[1] For a discussion of the occurrence of water and the meaning of hydrographic terms, see Appendix D.

52   *The Dry Lands*

usually to be found in the gravel fill of each mountain valley. As soon as the water reaches the alluvial fan it sinks deep into the porous material and is difficult to reach with wells. The playa is of no value as a source of water; for even where moisture is abundant enough to support a more or less permanent playa lake, the evaporation renders the lake salty. Fresh water is usually not available even on the lower fan slopes. The best place to dig a well in such deserts is at the apex of an alluvial fan, near the mouth of a mountain ravine.

Water in the hamadas is most commonly to be found in the gravel fill of the dry valleys. Ordinary wells in the wadi bottoms are usually able to reach a fairly dependable supply, and if floods are not too frequent an almost continuous string of oases may become established along these dry stream-courses. Hamadas which are crossed by numerous wadis, such as the plateaus lying south of the Atlas Mountains in the western Sahara, may support a relatively large population. On the other hand, hamadas which are cut by few wadis, such as the Libyan hamada, west of the Nile, are among the least habitable portions of the deserts.

The water supply in an erg depends on the number of wadis draining into it. Where these are numerous, as on the southern slopes of the Atlas Mountains in western Sahara, the erg basins act as huge reservoirs, and the porous sands protect the water from evaporation and so from becoming salty. The hollows between the dune ridges are closest to the water table, and here a considerable growth of desert shrubs may reveal the presence of moisture not far below the surface.[1] But where the ergs are poorly supplied with water, generally because few wadis drain into them, the zone of saturation may lie so far below the surface that it cannot be reached even in the deepest depressions. Very dry areas, whether in ergs or hamadas, in which no forms of life can gain a foothold are known in the Sahara as *tanezroufts*.

In addition to the ordinary surface well, there is another important method of reaching water in the deserts. This is by means of an artesian well tapping a deep-lying source of water. Artesian springs may

[1] See the classic description of two Saharan oases, one occupying the hollows between the dune ridges of an erg, the other occupying the wadis of a hamada, in *Human Geography*, by J. Brunhes, Abridged Edition by M. Jean-Brunhes Delamarre and Pierre Deffontaines (translation by E. F. Row), pp. 177–186. London, 1952.

occur naturally, in some cases as the result of a crack, or fissure, in the bedrock. Not a few of the oases of the Sahara are dependent on such a natural source of water. During the last century many artesian wells have been made artificially, either creating an entirely new wet spot in the desert or supplementing the ground water of an earlier oasis. Artesian wells are dependent on the existence of a certain geologic structure, and they may occur, where this structure is found, in hamadas or ergs or even, in some cases, in mountain and bolson deserts (see pages 578–579).

Another important source of water in the dry lands is provided by the so-called *exotic* streams. The deserts as a whole are characterized by a lack of native surface streams rising within the areas of arid climate. There are numerous cases, however, where streams rise in rainy areas elsewhere and maintain a flow across the dry lands. Such streams may be illustrated by the Nile in Egypt, the Colorado in the western United States, the Indus in Pakistan, the Loa in Chile, and many others. These exotic rivers have the peculiar character of decreasing in volume downstream and of lacking tributaries. Owing to the progressive loss of volume, they are constantly dropping a part of their load of mud, silt, and sand, which they are no longer able to carry, so that the river is split by sand bars into a number of distributaries, or separate channels. Such rivers are said to have *braided channels*. On entering a dry-land region, rivers tend to spread out in broad areas of shallow lakes or marshes and in some cases fail to continue across the desert, the water being evaporated so rapidly that the surface flow cannot be maintained. A comparison of the Niger, the Shari, and the Nile shows how these streams have spread out on reaching the desert margin.

Surface and Drainage Features in the Deserts. These various surface and drainage features are elements which give variety to the different desert areas. The actual distribution of these basic conditions is shown on the accompanying maps (Plates 9–20). These maps show that the Sahara and Arabia are mostly composed of hamada and erg surfaces, with only a few isolated mountain ranges. The deserts of Iran, on the other hand, are of the mountain and bolson type. The Thar Desert of India is composed of hamada and erg. The various deserts in inner Asia are built on a huge scale. They might well be considered as bolsons of continental proportions, with the Aral Sea or the Lob Nor as playas; but in addition to the usual features of bolsons, there are extensive areas of rocky plateau and erg. The Australian desert is composed of hamada and erg, whereas the desert of southern Africa is mostly hamada. The deserts of North and South America are mostly mountain and bolson, but with a few rocky plateaus, such as the Colorado Plateau in the United States or the Patagonian Plateau in southern Argentina.

All the desert areas except Australia are crossed by exotic rivers. Not all of them, however, are like the Nile, the Niger, the Tigris-Euphrates, or the Indus. The Colorado, except in its lower course, is deeply trenched in a canyon, as are also the Loa and the Orange. Although the Amu Darya and the Syr Darya do not flow out to the sea, along their courses they are much like exotic streams.

The Occupance [1]

Only a small proportion of the world's population is found in the dry-land regions. Although deserts, as defined in this book, occupy about 18 per cent of the land surface of the earth, only about 4 per cent of mankind live in them. Water and sunlight, we have said, are the basic needs of life: in the hot deserts there is an abundance of sunlight, but a lack of water. This lack of water imposes a general limitation on the numbers of people who can be supported permanently in such regions; and although different cultures have from period to period of human history approached the problems of desert living in different ways, no culture has ever overcome the limitation on habitability imposed by scarcity of water. In the world's deserts we have a relatively simple relationship between man and the land because the basic problems are related to the scarcity of just one element—water.

[1] The term *occupance* is an obsolete word revived and adopted in geography to indicate the process of occupying or living in an area and the transformations of the original landscape which result. A distinction is made between *occupance* and *occupation*. *Occupation* refers specifically to the economic activities of a people, that is, to their mode of gaining a living from an area or in an area. *Occupance* refers not only to these economic activities but also to other activities only indirectly or not at all related to the economic life, such as the construction of buildings, roads, etc. The term *occupance* (occupancy) was first suggested by R. S. Platt and D. S. Whittlesey.

Although the regions of Group I as a whole are occupied by only a small proportion of mankind, the places where water is available are among the most densely populated spots on earth. The Nile Valley, for example, is occupied by more than 1700 people per square mile. At the dawn of history the wet spots in the deserts were already populated more or less in proportion to the amount of water regularly available. The succession of ways of living in the desert as practiced by different people has brought great changes in the techniques of using water, and many of these changes have resulted in an increase or a decrease in the density of population. But, with certain exceptions, the pattern of population—which bears a simple relation to the pattern of water—has remained the same.

Can the deserts be occupied by larger numbers of people than at present? Does the nature of the land forever restrict the habitability of these regions as compared with the wetter parts of the earth? It is generally true that the number of people dependent on agriculture that can be supported in an area is greatest in humid regions and in regions which are not too cold. Low rainfall and low temperature in the dry lands and in the polar lands create conditions which make widespread human settlement difficult or impossible. But to say that this would always and inevitably be true would be to go beyond the limits of our knowledge. Theoretically, at least, the way is still open for the kind of discovery or invention which will radically change the habitability of these regions.

So far as it is possible to predict, however, changes in the number of people that can be supported in the dry lands can only be small. In order to appreciate how small, it is necessary to examine the actual story of human settlement in certain of the world's desert regions. We need to know about man's experience in dealing with the problems of desert living.

THE WESTERN SAHARA

Nowhere is the record of man's experience with the desert longer or more varied than in the Sahara. The word itself means "The Great Desert." The popular impression of the Sahara as one vast sea of shifting sand is far from the truth, for actually the surface is mostly rocky

The western Sahara

hamada, surmounted in a few places by mountain ranges, and with scattered depressions occupied by sandy ergs (Plate 13). Something of the complexity of the Sahara is apparent on the map above, which shows the western part of the desert between the Mediterranean and the Sudan.

The Western Sahara 57

Not all the area shown on this map is desert. In the south the country around Lake Chad and south of Timbuktu on the Niger is a grassy savanna. In the north, similarly, there are grasslands along the Mediterranean and in the Atlas Mountains. The Sahara begins along the southern margin of the Atlas and a short distance south of the Mediterranean.

The Earliest Period of Human Settlement. The long record of human settlement in this area can be divided into three periods. The earliest period, which lasted in the western Sahara until near the end of the Roman Empire, was marked by the gradual invasion of the desert from the south by a Negroid people from the Sudan. The process had gone on for some time before the dawn of history, for the earliest written records describe the wet spots of the desert as densely populated. These were the black people whom the Greek and Roman geographers interpreted as having been burned by living in lands which were too hot for white men. Neither the Greeks nor the Romans did much more than touch the northern fringe of the desert. For the most part the people who lived in the oases were isolated from the outside world; they were farmers, raising millet under irrigation for their own local food supply. Considering the tools at their disposal, it is evident that they did a remarkable job of tapping the water supply and applying it to the thirsty land.

In the western Sahara the wet spots where these people lived are not very different from the wet spots of today. The oases were mostly in wadi bottoms where wells could reach water seeping through the gravel. There were oases along the wadis radiating from the central part of the Ahaggar (east-central part of map on page 57). Oases were strung out along the wadis descending toward the south from the southern range of the Atlas Mountains. In-Salah, located near the center of the map, was then, as it is now, an important oasis. So also were Ghadames and Ghat toward the east, where artesian water rises through a natural fissure to the surface. But the very dry area known as "The Tanezrouft," lying west of the Ahaggar, was entirely unoccupied. The ergs, except for a few spots where water entered them from the bordering hamadas, were also unpopulated.

The Moslem Period. The second stage in the human experience with the western Sahara began with the invasion and conquest carried out by the Moslem peoples, chiefly the Berbers and Arabs. This period began when two new things were brought into the Sahara from Arabia. These were the date palm and the single-humped camel, or dromedary. The Berbers, a pastoral people living to the west of the Nile along the Mediterranean shore, quickly adopted the date and the camel and, pushed on by the Arabs behind them, moved rapidly westward and then southward. Soon the wave of Moslem conquest brought the whole Sahara under control. The conquerors went far beyond: southward into central Africa, and northward across the Strait of Gibraltar into Europe.

The Berbers and Arabs brought fundamental changes to the process of living in the Sahara. Because of their great mobility with the camel they were able to travel swiftly from one oasis to another. They could practice pastoral nomadism on the marginal grasslands to the north and south of the Sahara, or on the pastures high in the mountains. But they also established their ownership of the oases. They were not interested in farming, and consequently they left the Negroid oases dwellers to tend the crops, returning only at harvest time to collect a share. But now the oases were made much more productive by the introduction of the date palm. New oases appeared in a few places—for example, in the Erg Oriental east of Touggourt, where the roots of the date palm could tap the ground-water supply in the hollows between the dune ridges, places which had previously been uninhabitable. Otherwise the pattern remained unchanged, but the number of people who were supported in each oasis was considerably increased.

Another major change was the organization of a caravan trade across the Sahara. From the Sudan the Moslem traders brought such high-value goods to the shores of the Mediterranean as ivory, ostrich feathers, or Negro slaves. From whatever part of the western Sudan these caravans originated, from Lake Chad to Timbuktu, they had to cross the Ahaggar, where oases provided food and shelter. The Berbers who lived in the Ahaggar grew rich on tolls levied on each caravan.

The European Period. The third and present period of human settlement started in the nineteenth century when the Europeans extended their conquest across the Sahara. In the western part of the desert the conquest was chiefly French. There was a long period of warfare with the desert tribesmen, but in the end came the recent but inevitable victory of the better-equipped Europeans. In other parts of the dry lands there are groups of people who remain semi-independent politically, but it is doubtful if any desert people could be found today whose way of living has not been changed, at least in its material aspects, by contacts with Occidentals. In the western Sahara the once warlike Ahaggar tribes have been almost wiped out. Only a few hundred remain of a once powerful people who collected tribute on every caravan that crossed the Sahara. Those who survive have adjusted their lives to the Europeans—they are garage mechanics, hotelkeepers, perhaps chauffeurs on the motor-stage route from Algiers to Gao on the Niger River. A few still tend herds of sheep, goats, and camels in the pastures of the central Ahaggar.

The first result of the European conquest was the destruction of the old way of living and, with it, of the individuals who could not adapt themselves to new things. But thereafter the Europeans built a new way of living. The date palm, used during the second stage for the production of food for both farmers and herders, has been developed as an export crop by the Europeans. With Occidental machines, large engineering works have been built to increase and regularize the supply of water in the oases. For example, there is now an almost continuous ribbon of date palms along the course of the Wadi Saura for some 750 miles from the base of the Atlas Mountains to In-Salah. Date culture has been extended, too, along the wadis radiating from the Ahaggar, such as the Igharghar, which leads northward, the Tamanrasset, which leads westward, the Tafasaset, which leads eastward, and the Tesselaman, which leads southward. These changes represent an extension of the wet spots, but no radical change in their pattern; they also mean a considerable increase in the density of population that can be supported. In addition, the use of well-drilling machinery creates entirely new oases by tapping the deep-lying artesian water. Whereas the sedentary oasis farmers of the first period were able to dig wells as much as 150 feet deep at Ghardaia, for example, in the hamada west of Touggourt, the Europeans can bore wells the depths of which are measured in thousands of feet. To be sure, the increased use of the underground sources of water has resulted in a decrease of the supply, and this decrease now threatens the whole pattern of settlement in this region. For a time, however, more area could be irrigated and more people could be supported in the desert. The Europeans have also substituted a commercial economy, based on the export of a surplus product and the import of goods from outside the region, for a subsistence economy, in which the people were entirely dependent on the products of their own locality. Can such a commercial economy be maintained permanently? Will the discovery of oil in the area near In-Salah usher in a new kind of occupance?

The geographers have a term which they use in referring to such a succession of different ways of living as we have just described. The sequence of different processes of settlement—of different modes of occupance—is called *sequent occupance*.

THE NILE VALLEY

The eastern Sahara differs in a number of important ways from the part we have just discussed. The extensive rocky hamadas of the Libyan Desert (west of the Nile Valley) are not surmounted by any ranges of mountains like the central part of the Ahaggar or the Tibesti Mountains north of Lake Chad (Plates 13–14 and map, p. 62). Consequently there are no extensive wadi systems such as those in the west. The Libyan hamada is a monotonous rock-covered or gravel-covered surface unbroken by wadis. In only a few spots are there breaks in the rocky surface which permit the deep-lying artesian waters to rise to the surface and form little natural lakes in the bottoms of small wind-blown depressions. Such are the oases of Kufra, Dakhla, and Kharga. But because of the absence of wadis, the hamadas outside these tiny wet spots offer no opportunities for permanent settlement. Libya is also one of the driest places on earth. The lack of pasture, as well as the small number of wet spots, in this eastern Sahara provided so little opportunity for the conquering Berbers and Arabs that this part of the desert remained very empty. No small part of the security which permitted the early flourishing of civilization in Egypt was due to the protection from outside conquest afforded by the very dry Libyan Desert on the one hand and the Red Sea on the other.

Through this desert flows an exotic river, the Nile, the waters of which provide the essential basis for the support of the Egyptian people.

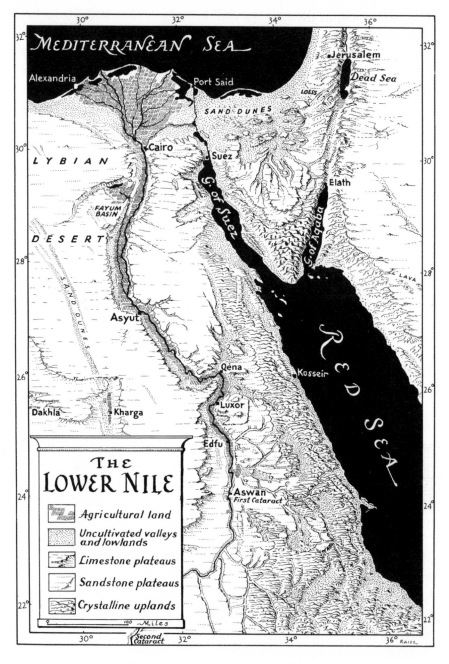

The lower Nile and adjacent territory

62

The Nile, rising in the mountains of equatorial Africa and emerging from Lake Victoria (Plate 13), and again reinforced by the torrential waters of the rivers descending from Ethiopia, has enough volume to continue all the way across the desert to the Mediterranean. Under natural conditions (that is, before the building of the Aswan Dam and other irrigation works) the river rose and fell in accordance with the floods poured in by the tributaries from Ethiopia. In the summer there are heavy rains which descend in torrents through the rivers which drain this mountain country. The Nile, receiving this water, begins to rise sharply in May and reaches flood stage in September. During this time of the year about two thirds of the water in the Nile comes from Ethiopia. But thereafter, each year, the floods subside, reaching the lowest stage in April and early May. At low-water stage about 85 per cent of the volume comes from the main course of the Nile.

For thousands of years the Egyptians irrigated their lands by the natural floods of the Nile. The silt-laden water was permitted to enter diked fields and settle there, dropping the rich load of silt to form new soil. When floods were higher than normal there was plenty to eat; when floods were unusually low there was famine. The Egyptians attempted important engineering works to hold back the flood waters and increase the flow onto the land, but they were nevertheless subject to the changes in productivity brought about by the differences in the rainfall in Ethiopia from year to year. This type of irrigation is known as *basin irrigation*. It supported several million people in the irrigable area between Aswan at the first cataract and the Mediterranean. According to the census of 1882 (the first modern census), this system supported at that date about 7,600,000 people, or about 562 people per square mile of irrigable land.

The European Period. The British control of Egypt resulted in developments similar to those recorded for the western Sahara. The distressing effects of adopting European ways in Egypt are to a certain extent typical of similar effects elsewhere throughout the Moslem world. The problem of the relation of people to the land in Egypt lies in the background of the political and strategic questions which focus on this area today.

British engineers completed the construction of the great dam at

Aswan in 1902. This dam held back the flood waters from Ethiopia so that irrigation was possible in the valley below Aswan at any time of the year, and with much greater regularity and certainty than ever before. Canals carried the water from the reservoir to the fields on either side of the river, and even into the Fayum Basin just west of the Nile. The Egyptian farmers were no longer dependent on basin irrigation; they could practice *perennial irrigation.*

But the British traders wanted a commercial crop. No longer could the Egyptian farmers grow only the foods and fibers for their own immediate use, or for the use of the rulers and wealthy people who lived in Cairo and Alexandria. They were paid for the surplus production of long-staple Egyptian cotton, and with the money thus earned they could purchase imported manufactured goods or foods. There was a better and more certain food supply, and there was better attention to hygiene. As a result of these things, the Egyptian population began to increase at a rapid rate. In 1910 there were some 10,000,000 people in the country; by 1937 the number had reached 16,000,000; today there are well over 24,000,000. Measured in relation to the irrigable area of some 13,000 square miles, the density of population is now more than 1700 per square mile, one of the greatest densities in the world for a people essentially dependent on agriculture.

There are a number of reasons why the average Egyptian farmer is poorer than he was before the European period began. Because Moslem law requires that an estate be divided equally among the heirs after the death of the owner, the farms have been divided and sub-divided far below the limits of economic efficiency. In 1938 some 70 per cent of the owners of land had less than an acre each. Meanwhile, however, foreign capitalists or wealthy Egyptians had gained control of over two thirds of all the irrigable land. Only 7 per cent of the landowners controlled 68 per cent of the land. For these large landowners, a money crop was more important than a food crop.

And in addition, the yield of crops per acre was threatened. Since basin irrigation was no longer practiced, the Nile silt could no longer provide an annual enrichment of the soil. Meanwhile two crops a year were seriously depleting the soil fertility. It was increasingly necessary to apply fertilizer: either pigeon excrement, gathered in pigeon towers, which are now a common feature of the Egyptian landscape, or phosphate from local sources, or imported nitrate from Chile. All this has added to the cost of farming.

The independence of Egypt and the departure of the British have raised new problems. As population pressure continues to mount, the new Egyptian government has undertaken programs of land reform and urban industrialization. But Egypt needs capital. The seizure of the Suez Canal by the Egyptian Government in 1956 was prompted by the hope that this action would provide a new source of income.

THE MOSLEM WORLD

The conditions in Egypt and in the western Sahara illustrate a situation that exists throughout the Moslem world (map below). Most of this area was until recently under the colonial rule of one or another of the European powers. Now most of the countries are ruled by small minorities of wealthy chieftains or by army officers. Most of the people are miserably poor and illiterate.

The Moslem world (after Bowman) and the arid boundary (after Köppen)

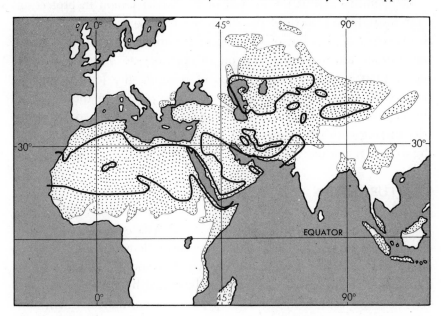

Today the Moslem world is in turmoil. Underlying this turmoil is the impact of the Democratic Revolution itself. In all the countries there is an increasing number of educated city people, and among these there is a burning demand for equality of treatment and an end to the ancient system of privilege. The first step was to throw off foreign control. Now impatient people are attracted by communist promises of quick action against privileged classes.

The problem is enormously complicated, however, by four conflicting interests. First, Great Britain and other countries of Western Europe regard Suez as a critical transit route to the Orient and Australia. Even the airlines pass through Cairo and Karachi in order to avoid the mountains to the north and the Indian Ocean to the south.

Second, the countries of Western Europe depend on the vast oil reserves of the area around the Persian Gulf, which has the largest proved oil reserve of the world. The rulers of Saudi Arabia and Iran, as well as a few other independent chieftains, have become incredibly wealthy as a result of oil royalties. But other Moslem countries control the movement of oil to Europe. More than three quarters of the tonnage passing through Egypt's Suez Canal consists of oil. Pipelines carry oil to the Mediterranean across Jordan, Syria, and Lebanon.

Then, third, there is the interest of the Soviet Union in protecting its industrial cities north of the Black Sea from air attack by pushing the Western powers out of the area to the south, and also the traditional desire for an ice-free port on an open ocean. Finally, to complicate matters almost beyond hope of solution, the Jewish state of Israel has been carved out of Moslem territory right in the midst of this explosive region. All these divergent interests, focused on countries stirring with the intoxicating ideas of equality, combine to create the world's major danger spot.

THE TURKESTAN

The desert heart of the great continent of Asia is occupied by scattered groups of people. The distribution of settlement in the Turkestan, the dry country east of the Caspian Sea and west of the great mountains on the border of China, is illustrated by the map on page 67. This vast depression is made up partly of uninhabitable erg and

66 *The Dry Lands*

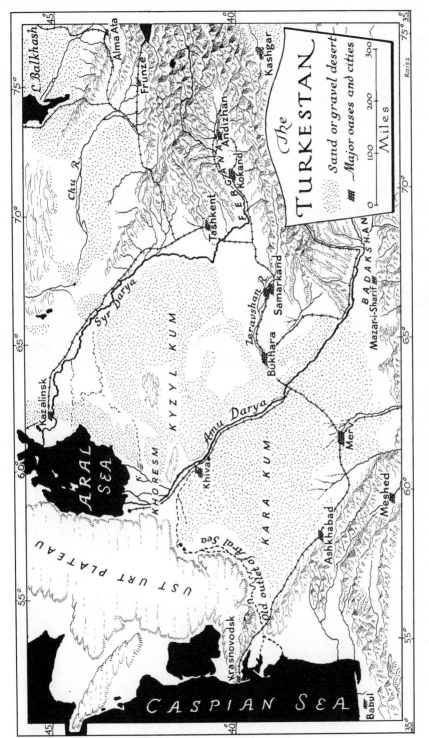

The following text labels appear within the map image:

45° · 40° · 75° · 35°

L. Balkhash

75° · 70° · 65° · 60° · 55°

Alma Ata

Frunze

Chu R.

Kashgar

Andizhan

F E R G A N A

Kokand

Tashkent

The TURKESTAN

Sand or gravel desert

Major oases and cities

300

200

100

Miles

0

Raisz

BADAKSHAN

Zeravshan R.

Samarkand

Bukhara

Mazar-i-Sharif

Syr-Darya

KYZYL KUM

Kazalinsk

10° · 60°

ARAL SEA

KHORESM

Amu Darya

Merv

KARA KUM

Khiva

Meshed

old outlet of Aral Sea

UST URT PLATEAU

Ashkhabad

Krasnovodsk

55° · 60° · 65°

CASPIAN SEA

Babul

45° · 40° · 35°

The southern portion of the Aral depression

hamada, and partly of alluvial fans built where the rivers descend from the bordering mountains (Plates 17–18). The Amu Darya and the Syr Darya support ribbons of irrigated lands as far as the shores of the Aral Sea, and lesser rivers provide the support for smaller oases. Along the mountain front are such famous old trading towns as Bukhara, Samarkand, Tashkent, and Kokand. The caravan routes connecting Mediterranean Europe with China and India which used to pass through these places are no longer of such importance as they were before the invention of steamships, railroads, and airplanes. In modern times the Soviet Union has greatly increased the irrigable area along the mountain front, and has created here a major area of cotton production.

THE TARIM BASIN

Another remote desert region of inner Asia is the Tarim Basin, which lies to the east across the mountains from the much lower and warmer Turkestan. Here is a vast depression many hundreds of miles across, its center occupied by an erg (the great Taklamakan), which is

The Tarim Basin

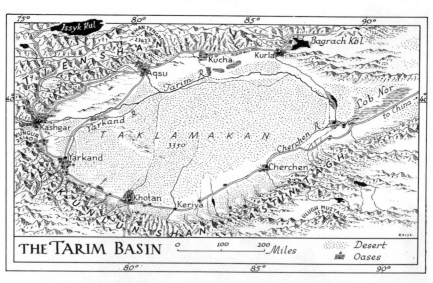

68   *The Dry Lands*

uninhabitable and scarcely even explored. Just as the waters of the rivers which flow into Turkestan are eventually brought together in the salty Aral Sea, so those of the Tarim Basin flow into the Lob Nor. The Lob Nor is composed of salt-encrusted flats, with here and there some salty marshes and seldom any open water. But where the rivers emerge from the mountains, near the apexes of the alluvial fans, an abundant supply of water is available, and here the oases are located. From Kashgar and Yarkand the old caravan routes run eastward either along the northern edge of the basin or along the southern edge, passing from oasis to oasis. Along these routes, which eventually reach the populous eastern part of China, two-humped camels are still used to carry a small current of trade in highly valuable products. People are permanently settled only at the isolated wet spots, and in this remote region there is little likelihood that any serious attempt will be made to provide irrigation works to increase even slightly the productivity of the desert (map, p. 68).

THE ATACAMA

There are many other deserts of the world. The great Gobi of Mongolia, like the Tarim, is cold and wind-swept as well as arid. There are hot deserts, such as those of Australia, where isolated settlements are scattered a many days' overland journey apart and where the few isolated settlers raise sheep for a meager living.

In Northern Chile there is the Atacama Desert, important because of the lesson it offers in the permanency of desert settlement. This desert (map, p. 70) lies between the Pacific Ocean and the very high western cordillera of the Andes on the border of Chile and Bolivia. The land rises abruptly from the sea to an elevation of more than 3000 feet. But inland from this abrupt rise there is a long structural valley of gentle slopes extending parallel to the mountain front. Along the west-facing front of the Andes very small valleys emerge onto alluvial fans that stretch out westward as much as forty miles into the desert. But since the mountains are also dry, only those streams that rise in the snow fields above 20,000 feet in altitude carry water all the year round. The others offer only enough water to support small oasis communities— some of only a few hundred people. The only exotic river is the Río

Loa, which emerges from the mountains near Calama, but shortly thereafter enters a deep gorge cut through the coast range and into the floor of the structural valley (Plates 11–12).

The Atacama

The Early Period. Human settlement in this region goes back thousands of years before the Inca rulers who lived in the mountains to the north established a route of communications through the Atacama to Middle Chile. The communications were maintained by runners who went from oasis to oasis along the mountain front. Each little oasis was built at the very apex of an alluvial fan, sheltered even within the mountain valleys. With water supplies very small, the best place to dig a well is exactly where the fan begins to emerge from the mouth of the valley. Farther out on the fan slope, the water is too far below the surface. Only where the rivers carry much water, as in the Turkestan, can the oases extend well down the fan slopes.

The European Period. When the Spaniards came to the Atacama the north-south line of communications was abandoned and east-west roads were built to the coastal ports. As a result Calama, a relatively large oasis supported by the water of the exotic Loa, became an important Spanish settlement.

An open-pit copper mine at Chuquicamata, Chile

During the nineteenth century two important minerals were found in the Atacama. These were copper and nitrate. Big mining establishments were built, railroads were built to connect them with ports along the coast, and thousands of workers were brought into the region. In such a desert all the fuel, all the building materials, even all the food had to be brought in from outside to supply the mining camps and the ports. In some cases pipelines, such as the one from Pica to Iquique, were built into the mountains to bring water to the mines. But in many cases water was actually brought in by steamer and distributed to the mining towns by tank car. Only such valuable products as copper or nitrate could pay the high cost of such expensive settlement (picture above).

And then the mines had to curtail their production or shut down entirely. Copper was too abundant on the world markets, and nitrate was being produced from the air by a manufacturing process. Workers by the thousands had to leave the Atacama since they could no longer be supported there. Today production of both copper and nitrate continues at a reduced rate; but the time will come, and in the not distant future, when the supplies of these minerals are exhausted, and what then? The ports will be abandoned, since there will be no commerce to pay to keep the aqueducts in order or to import supplies. Only Calama and the ports that serve it will remain active. But the Indian farmers along the western front of the Andes, long forgotten by the busy world of industry and commerce, will continue to occupy their little oases. They alone have formed a permanently workable connection with the land.

THE ORANGE RIVER

European settlement in the dry lands is not necessarily temporary, although the unregulated exploitation of resources for quick profit, which is an Occidental trait, makes continued settlement impossible in many places. In the Orange River region of South Africa (map, p. 73) we have an example of apparently successful settlement by European farmers based on irrigation. Much of South Africa is arid or semiarid, and the Orange River, like the Nile, rises in a rainy mountain region and flows as a dwindling exotic stream across country which becomes drier and drier.

In the larger sense, most of South Africa is a plateau standing 4000 to 6000 feet above the sea. The watershed between the Atlantic and Indian oceans is in a high and mountainous escarpment edge known as the Drakensbergen, which overlooks the coastal region around Durban. Many short swift rivers run to the Indian Ocean, whereas the Orange and its principal tributary, the Vaal, take the westward drainage from the Drakensbergen to the Atlantic over a course of 1640 miles. The eastern two thirds of this distance is through areas that receive an annual rainfall of from two to fifteen inches, with temperatures that permit a growing season throughout the year. Here the natural vegetation changes toward the west from a semiarid grassland to a true desert with only scattered desert succulents and almost no grass. Upstream, above the junction of the Orange and the Vaal, rainfall is more adequate, and cultivation of the land is possible without irrigation or with supplementary irrigation. Even in this humid area

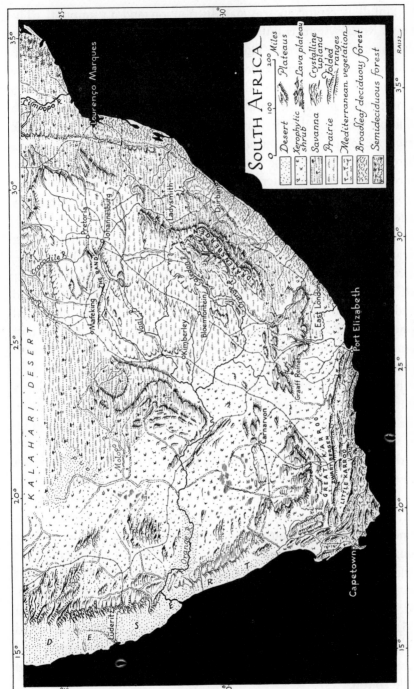

SOUTH AFRICA

0   100   200 Miles

Desert
Xerophytic shrub
Savanna
Prairie
Mediterranean vegetation
Broadleaf deciduous forest
Semideciduous forest

Plateaus
Lava plateau
Crystalline upland
Folded ranges

RAISZ

South Africa

the rainfall is erratic in seasonal distribution and in amount. The Orange River system is unlike the Nile in that its waters come from only one catchment area. Thus the irregular rainfall at the source is translated into non-periodic occurrences of high and low water in the valley lower down. In the dry-land section, the Orange may be a raging torrent at one time and a series of stagnant pools at another, a condition which makes irrigation difficult. Another difficulty is the narrow trench-like character of the valley. There are only a few places where alluvial land can be reached by canals and feeders and also be protected against floodwaters. And, finally, the dams and canals used to control the waters are quickly filled with silt because of the heavy burden of sediment carried by the Orange River.

Because of these difficulties only particular places are suitable for irrigation projects. One such area is the middle course of the Orange, where the valley is open and broad, with alluvial terraces, and the river itself is a braid of several channels enclosing low-lying silt and sand islands. Occasional narrows where hard rock structures are intersected by the stream provide sites for storage and diversion dams. Only a half century ago this middle course, where the rainfall is less than 10 inches a year, was occupied almost solely by pastoral Hottentot peoples who had been driven to the water by prolonged droughts. They made only primitive attempts to divert water to their gardens. The first farming project by white men in this desert was undertaken in 1894 at Upington, which is located where the northwest-southeast railroad crosses the river. At that place Boers (South Africans of Dutch-Huguenot ancestry) settled and developed the land under the auspices of the Dutch Reformed Church. The church and individuals sponsored other small but independent irrigation projects until, in 1929, the federal government of the Union built the Buchuberg Dam, some 100 miles above Upington, to act as a reservoir for all the improved land as far as the Aughrabies Falls, about 75 miles below Upington. Thus in the short span of one generation an oasis has been created where formerly mankind had no permanent habitation. Today the oasis has a population of 35,000, including the town of Upington (10,200), which is supported by the intensive cultivation of some 70 square miles of irrigated land producing raisin grapes (sultanas), alfalfa, wheat, oranges, maize, and a little cotton.

The fight to win the land along this part of the Orange River has been successful; the fight to maintain the victory continues. The Buchuberg dam is silting rapidly, so that eventually other reservoirs (such as the Vaaldam, north of Kimberley, 700 miles away) must be used. There is always the danger of extreme drought, and the even greater risk of combined heavy floods on both the Orange and the Vaal, which might severely damage any irrigation works below their confluence.

THE GREAT BASIN

There are deserts also in the United States and Mexico. The characteristics of the large area of inland drainage between the Sierra Nevada on the west and the Wasatch Mountains on the east are illustrated by Plates 9–10 and the map on page 76. This is a portion of the Great Basin—a mountain and bolson desert where flat-floored bolsons separate irregularly-placed desert ranges. Water from the high Sierra Nevada or the Wasatch Mountains is abundant and provides support for large oases; but from the desert ranges comes only a small supply of water, and here the oases are small and placed high on the fans. The Humboldt River, however, rises in the high ranges in the central part of the basin and provides water for irrigation at several places along its course. Carson City and Reno are surrounded by extensive irrigated lands. On the eastern side there is an almost continuous fringe of irrigated land on the alluvial fans of the Wasatch Mountains. The important cities are Salt Lake City and Ogden, in Utah. The rivers from the Wasatch drain into Great Salt Lake, the fluctuating shores of which reflect the varying quantity of water supplied to it.

The sequence of settlement in the Great Basin is much simpler than that of the Sahara, or even the Atacama. The Indians of this part of America were a hunting people. The few who inhabited the Great Basin itself sought the wild game of the mountains and formed no permanent settlements in the bolsons. The first people of European origin to settle in the region were the Mormons, who, at Salt Lake City, established a farming community in a spot they hoped would be so remote that their persecutors would never reach them. In this hope they were disappointed, for the discovery of gold in California soon brought many travelers plodding westward across deserts and

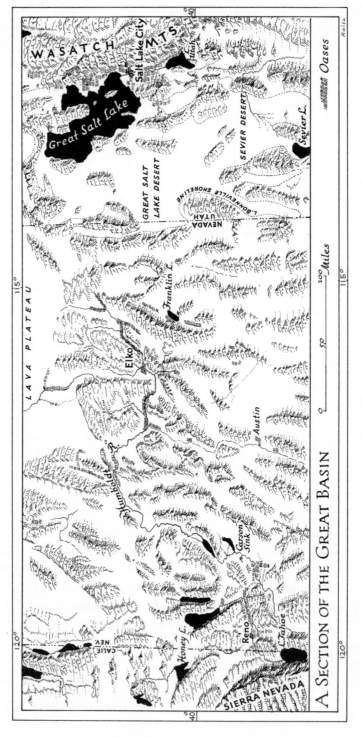

A Section of the Great Basin

A portion of the Great Basin of the United States

WASATCH MTS

Salt Lake City

Utah

Great Salt Lake

GREAT SALT LAKE DESERT

SEVIER DESERT

Sevier L.

BONNEVILLE SHORELINE

NEVADA
UTAH

Oases

LAVA PLATEAU

115°

115°

40

40

120°

120°

Franklin L.

Elko

Humboldt R.

Austin

Carson Sink

Honey L.

Reno

L. Tahoe

CALIF
NEV.

SIERRA NEVADA

0   50   100 Miles

Raisz

difficult mountain passes. The Mormons were caught up in the fabric of American settlement in the course of time and made a part of it. The isolated oases of the Great Basin were reached by railroads. From a purely subsistence economy, the oasis communities adopted commercial crops which could be exchanged for the much-desired manufactured products of the eastern cities. Since these oases are too far north to permit such hot-desert specialties as cotton (which can be grown at Phoenix) and dates (which can be grown along the lower Colorado), the greater part of the irrigated lands in Utah and Nevada are used for growing summer feed crops to be fed to animals during the winter, and for such high-value but hardy crops as sugar beets and potatoes.

AGRICULTURE AND COMMERCE IN THE DRY LANDS

Looking at all the world's desert regions, we find certain general similarities and certain differences. In every desert there are the same problems of securing water, and there is the same lack of permanence where occupance is not closely adjusted to available supplies of water. But, on the other hand, every desert region is unique in many of its most important aspects. Especially is this true with regard to the significance of its location in the world. Some deserts, like those of Iraq and Iran, are of great strategic importance in the conflict of modern great powers outside the desert; some, like the Tarim Basin, are so remote that the modern currents of life pass them by; some, like the Great Basin, were originally sought because of remoteness, yet inevitably came into the direct line of new settlers. All these things must be analyzed individually for each desert region, and all affect the answer to our question as to the number of people the deserts can support.

Agriculture in all the world's oases has certain marked peculiarities. As might be expected in the very small spots in the deserts where life is concentrated, all the processes of occupance take on an intensive character. Within the oasis no land can be wasted. Whatever the culture may be, an intensive economy is the rule.[1] The results, however, justify

[1] The economist recognizes land, labor, and capital as the elements of production in our Western culture. Where large amounts of capital or of labor are expended per unit of land, the economy is said to be *intensive;* where the expenditure of labor and capital per unit of land is relatively small, the economy is said to be *extensive.*

the expenditure of much effort. Probably few agricultural sites in the world bring greater returns per acre for a given amount of labor or capital than do the irrigated lands of the deserts. The abundant sunshine; the ability to apply water to the growing crops when it is needed and in the desired amounts; the richness of the desert soil, especially of the alluvial soils of exotic valleys; the freedom from insect pests and weeds which, in rainy lands, come from uncultivated areas close by—these and other elements contribute to the very large crop yields of the irrigated lands.

While a concentration of activities in the oases is the rule in all cultures, the entry of the Occidental peoples into the deserts has brought one notable change in the agricultural practices. Most of the earlier oasis peoples cultivated chiefly *subsistence* crops; that is, crops which are consumed within the region. One of the distinguishing features of the Occidental culture, however, is the widespread development of commerce, not only in luxury goods, as formerly, but even in the basic necessities of life. The effect of this on desert agriculture is to emphasize the *commercial,* or *money,* crops; that is, the products which are exported from the region. While in many places the same crops have been retained on a greatly expanded basis, in other places an entirely new assortment of crops has been introduced. This new regime means greater material prosperity for some of the desert dwellers; but it also means less economic security, since commercial ventures are in a very important way dependent on events in distant places over which the producer has no control.

The crops which are raised in the oases of the world's deserts do not make up a long list. In the warmer parts of the dry lands, especially in the Sahara and southern Asia, the date is at the present time of chief importance, primarily as a subsistence crop but also, in some of the oases, as a commercial crop. The date palm is limited to the hot deserts because it is very sensitive to cold. Its requirement of very dry air for the ripening and drying of its fruit (both of which processes take place on the tree), together with its need for abundant water, limits this tree to the desert oases. The feathery fronds of the date palm, which stands "with its head in the sun and its feet in the water," make up a characteristic part of the oasis scene. Originally a native, probably, of Arabia, and first cultivated on a large scale in the exotic valleys of the Tigris and the Euphrates, this tree is now grown from India across Iran and Arabia to the western Sahara. In the other deserts of the world it is not so common, although its introduction into the Imperial Valley of California during World War I, as a purely commercial crop, has been successful (picture, p. 80).

Other subsistence crops are raised along with the date palm in the warmer deserts of the Old World or form the chief support of the oasis dwellers in other lands. Figs, pomegranates, apricots, peaches, and grapes are found in certain more or less specialized areas, especially on the borders of the Mediterranean lands. But the most common and widespread crops include wheat, barley, rice, millet, maize, and beans. Small quantities of cotton, too, should be included in the list of subsistence crops. In some of the cooler deserts alfalfa and other hays are raised during the summer to be fed to domestic animals during the winter season, a type of economy which will be discussed at greater length in a later chapter.

Many of these same crops may be raised for commerce. Dates, for instance, are grown for export in some of the more accessible oases. But by far the most important commercial crops are cotton and sugar. Not that the deserts produce more than a very small proportion of the world's supply of either of these commodities, but in the oases they are the products which furnish the financial returns demanded by the economics of the Occidental peoples. In many oases, but not all, the long-staple varieties of cotton are raised. Since these varieties cannot be grown so successfully in the rainy lands, they command a higher price than the much larger quantities of cotton with shorter fibers. Sugar cane is also raised in many oases, although it cannot be grown in the colder sections, since it requires a year-round freedom from frost. In the United States north of the Colorado River and north of southern California, sugar beets have brought the necessary financial support for the irrigated tracts, protected, however, by tariff barriers against sugars which might be produced more cheaply elsewhere.

Oasis Towns. The oasis towns of the deserts are the focal points of a highly concentrated life. The arrival in an oasis town is to the desert traveler what the arrival in port is to a sailor. For the desert nomad the oasis furnishes not only a place to exchange his products for other things that he needs but also a place to meet and talk with other people,

A grove of date palms in southern California

a place offering many amusements and distractions. From the writings of early Persia we have Omar Khayyám's vivid pictures of the colorful and sophisticated life of the oasis towns, forming the most complete contrast with the loneliness of the vast stretches of desert, in which life is full of difficulties and dangers and yields few distractions. "Every oasis is a Babylon in miniature."

The buildings of the oasis towns differ in detail of architecture from place to place in accordance with the various human cultures, but throughout the world's deserts there are certain general items which are repeated. A very common building material is baked mud brick, held together with straw. In some few places where stone is available this more substantial material has been used, but wooden houses are very rare. The desert architecture, in places very ornate, seems quite out of keeping with the prevailing building material. The flat roof, in the warmer deserts not uncommonly used for sleeping, is a very widespread form. In the oases of the Moslem world the tall minarets of a mosque usually rise prominently above the general house-level of the town, whereas in the Latin American deserts the square towers of a Roman Catholic church are the dominating structures.

Ruins. In contrast to the intense life of the present oases are the numerous ruins of once thriving settlements now abandoned. Throughout the world's deserts such ruins have been found, marking the spots where cities once flourished in places now barren and deserted. Some students have explained these signs of decline in population by a gradually increasing aridity which forces the abandonment of settlements because of decreasing water supply. It is a well-established fact that during the glacial period, while ice sheets were formed in cooler and rainier lands, the present desert areas received more rain than they do now. It is supposed that many of the wadi systems, such as those in the western Sahara, are relict forms produced during this period of heavier and more frequent rains. The nitrate salts of the Atacama are thought to have been deposited in the beds of ancient lakes, now long since dried up. The shores of formerly more extensive lakes are clearly visible around the basin of Great Salt Lake in Utah. The body of water which occupied this area in the glacial period is known as Lake Bonneville (map, p. 76). Over long periods of time—much longer than the brief span of written history—it is certain that the climates of the world

Salt Lake City, at the base of the Wasatch Mountains, in Utah

have varied. However, to show conclusively from statistical data that the climate has changed during historic times is very difficult. There are cycles of wetter years and drier years, but progressive desiccation has been shown beyond reasonable doubt in very few places.

On the other hand, the maintenance of a large oasis is dependent on a strong political authority which enforces co-operation in the use of water and the maintenance of the irrigation works. Weak governments collapse, and with them go the material works of the people, especially in a land where the price of survival is a high degree of fitness. The ruins of the desert, then, may possibly be explained by the decline of social organization or by wars and conquests. However, it is quite plausible that a cycle of dry years extended over a long enough period of time might result in the crumbling of a government, which, in turn, would make the contest against the desert no longer possible.

The Nomadic Mode of Occupance. In addition to the sedentary modes of desert occupance, with the close attachment of people to the sources of water, the nomadic mode of occupance is found in some dry-land regions. Nomadism in the desert, however, is essentially linked with fleet-footed domestic animals, such as camels and horses. No culture has developed a nomadic occupance of arid lands without these animals. Because no domestic animals of this sort were included in the native cultures of North and South America before the coming of the Europeans, nomadism was not found in the dry lands of the Western Hemisphere. The same is true of Australia and South Africa. Even in the Sahara the Arabs and Berbers did not adopt the nomadic life until the introduction of the dromedary, or single-humped camel, during the eleventh century after Christ. Before that time Negroid oasis dwellers raised their subsistence crops of grains in blissful isolation. The introduction of the camel and the date palm at about the same time inaugurated a new period in the sequent occupance of the Sahara, which was terminated only by the European conquest eight centuries later.

Nomadism achieves its freest development on the grassy steppes bordering the dry lands—regions which will be described in a later chapter (Group V). Here is found relatively abundant pasturage for the flocks and herds of domestic animals. Those nomads who remain in the dry-land regions are to a certain extent tied to the oases. While they may spend a part of the time wandering in search of pasturage for their animals, they must return to an oasis every now and then as a ship must put in to port. The exchange of animal products (leather, wool, meat, or milk) for the agricultural products of the oases, especially dates, is a characteristic feature of the desert economy.

The latest period in the sequent occupance of the deserts is not aiding the nomadic life. The Europeans have eliminated the caravan trade and have flooded the oasis markets with European-made goods. The nomad finds his mode of existence no longer possible. He is forced to adjust himself to radically different ways of living or to perish.

THE TROPICAL FOREST LANDS

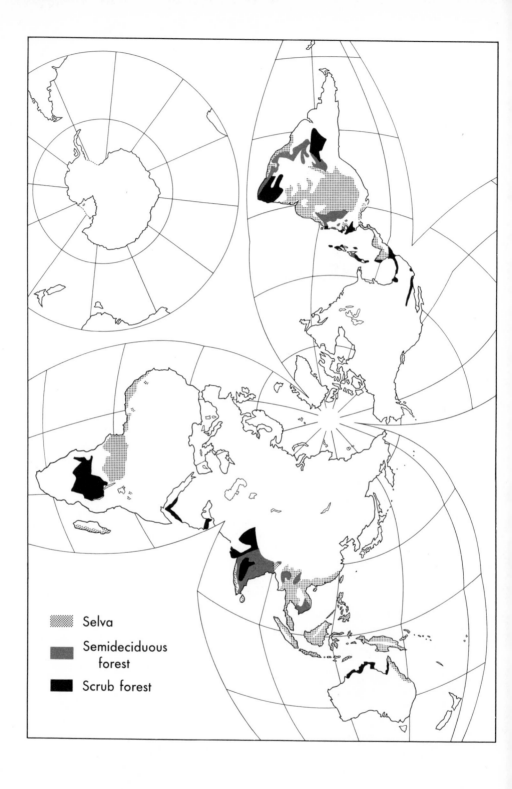

	Selva
	Semideciduous forest
	Scrub forest

THERE IS NO ONE PHYSICAL FACTOR which limits settlement in the tropical forest regions as scarcity of water does in the dry lands. The problem of making a living in the deserts is basically a question of maintaining or increasing the supply of water. But in the tropical forest lands the physical conditions which affect human settlement depend to a much larger extent on the attitudes, objectives, and technical abilities of the people themselves. For simple hoe cultivators, tropical living is one thing; for Oriental rice farmers the connections that are built with the resources of the land are quite different. Europeans and Americans, moreover, have to overcome a strong prejudice against these regions, inherited from the writers of antiquity, and this prejudice still colors the attitudes of Occidental people toward settlement in the low latitudes.

The regions of Group II differ from one another with respect to the density and pattern of population. The great area of tropical forest in the Amazon Basin is one of the world's largest areas of very scanty settlement. In contrast, Java is one of the more densely populated parts of the world, and smaller areas of very dense settlement are to be found in parts of the American tropics and in parts of India. The densely populated areas have so many people in them that the regions of Group II as a whole, which include about 15 per cent of the world's land area, are occupied by some 28 per cent of the world's population.

The Land

VEGETATION AND CLIMATE

The regions of Group II are identified by the presence of forest vegetation in which the species of trees are mostly those which cannot withstand low temperatures. In the very wet regions, where there is a superabundance of moisture, the forest is luxuriant; here is found the world's heaviest growth of vegetation, the *tropical rain forest*. At the other extreme, where the climate is subhumid, near the dry margin of forest growth, the characteristic cover is a *tropical scrub forest* mixed with open grasslands. In between, where the climate is humid, is found the *tropical semideciduous forest.*

The Tropical Rain Forest. The tropical rain forest, or *selva,* is the world's most vigorous vegetation growth. Unlike most of the forests which are familiar to mid-latitude people, the selva is composed of an extraordinary variety of species. In one square mile of the island of Trinidad, where a special study of the forest composition was made, nearly three thousand distinct species of trees and plants were identified. It is not unusual to find as many as eighty to a hundred different kinds of trees on a single acre. For the botanist such conditions offer a fascinating and almost inexhaustible field of study; but for the person who wishes to make commercial use of any one kind of tree, this profuse variety is a major handicap, for the individual trees of any one species are usually widely scattered throughout the forest.

The tropical rain forest is an impressive sight for persons brought up in other parts of the world. The monotonous variety of vegetation forms defies detailed description. Within the selva one feels shut in, as in the crypt of a cathedral, for little light is able to reach the forest floor. The individual trees are tall and straight-stemmed, with only a plume of branches and foliage at the top. From the ground one sees only the massive perpendicular trunks which support the thick canopy of leaves overhead where the branches are interlaced in the relentless struggle for sunlight and life. In the gloom below there is little color and little underbrush; but the space between the tree trunks is laced with a network of lianas, some as fine as hairs and others like great knotted ropes.

The remarkable rapidity of vegetation growth is best revealed when a clearing is made. Perhaps the clearing is an abandoned garden plot; perhaps it is the result of the fall of some giant tree which has crushed in its descent all the lesser trees within reach. Through the hole in the leafy covering the sunlight is able to reach the ground. In a very brief time an impenetrable tangle of plants fills the opening. There is a period of fierce struggle to grow upward to the light, which is ended only when another forest giant has replaced the fallen one, and the fabric of the foliage is whole once more.

The rhythm of life in the selva is confused. Each individual plant goes through the life processes, producing leaves, flowers, fruits, and seeds in its own period. At all times of the year there are individual trees losing their leaves, or budding new leaves and flowers, or covered with ripened fruit, which, for a short time, attracts a multitude of birds. The forest is evergreen.[1]

The Tropical Semideciduous Forest. Such a vegetation growth as the selva can be supported only by excessive amounts of moisture: where the moisture supply is less abundant, or where a dry season imposes at least a partial rhythm, a lighter forest which is semideciduous in character is the result.

The semideciduous forest is characterized by a more open stand of trees than the selva. Instead of being shut out by an almost unbroken canopy of foliage, as in the selva, here the sunlight penetrates to the

[1] An evergreen tree is one which does not drop its leaves and stand with bare branches during any season of the year. It may drop one leaf at a time, or even all its leaves at one time, but each leaf is immediately replaced with a new sprout. A forest composed mostly of trees of this sort is described as evergreen. A deciduous tree is one which does lose all its leaves and which stands with bare branches during a season of the year. A forest composed partly of evergreen and partly of deciduous species is described as a semideciduous forest.

Preparing to saw a fallen mahogany "stick" in the tropical rain forest of Sierra Leone, West Africa

Photo by H. V. B. Kline, Jr.

ground and supports a dense undergrowth, or *jungle*. Between the rather widely spaced larger trees there is a tangle of smaller plants woven together with vines and creepers, with here and there a thicket of bamboo. Passage through a virgin stand of this forest may actually be more difficult than through a selva on account of the tangle of undergrowth; but because the trees themselves are smaller and spaced farther apart, the clearing of the semideciduous forest is a much easier task than the removal of the rain forest.

Another great difference between this and the rain forest is the existence of a seasonal rhythm. The dry season, which is more pronounced in these regions of lighter forest, imposes a period of rest on the vegetation, just as the winter season imposes a similar period on the forests of the middle latitudes. Many, although not all, of the trees lose their leaves, and the landscape takes on a brownish or grayish tinge. The beginning of the rainy season brings back the dark green of vigorous and thriving vegetation. The sprouting of new leaves, the budding, the flowering, and the ripening of fruit are synchronized.

The Wet Margin. Where both the tropical rain forest and the tropical semideciduous forest border the ocean along low, shelving coasts, there has developed a peculiar vegetation type which has a number of unique characteristics. This is the mangrove forest—not distinguished from the other kinds of tropical forest on the plates because it occurs only in a fringe along the coast which is usually too narrow to show on the maps. True mangrove consists of only one kind of tree of the genus *Rhizophora*. On the shores of tidal swamps where the water is brackish there is a dense tangle of evergreen trees which grow some 15 or 20 feet in height, with spreading bushy branches and numerous aerial roots. The bark is reddish in color and useful as an astringent; the leaves are oblong and glossy; the pale yellow flowers and conical berrylike fruit appear at all times of the year with no seasonal rhythm. New trees develop from seeds which germinate in the air and which are attached to the root system of the parent trees. The result is a tangle of bushy forest which is all but impenetrable. The mangrove fringe actually makes long stretches of most tropical coasts unapproachable; many established ports owe their location to natural breaks in the mangrove large enough to permit the entrance of ships and the construction of roads to the higher country behind the coast.

The Tropical Scrub Forest. Rainfall effectiveness in the tropical lands is relatively low, for the high temperatures result in a very rapid evaporation. Even with fairly high annual rainfalls there are many parts of the tropical forest lands which support only a scrub forest. In some places the low trees are protected by thorns—a vegetation type known as the *thorn forest* (or *caatinga,* to use the Brazilian term). The trees are small in diameter and spaced far enough apart so that the ground is little shaded. The forest floor is usually grass-covered, giving the landscape the appearance of a poorly kept orchard. All such scrub forests have a definite seasonal rhythm in harmony with the rains. During the growing season the trees are a mass of foliage and flowers of brilliant coloring, but during the dry season the leaves fall to the ground and the branches are bare. See picture on page 102.

The scrub forest does not have so great a variety of species as either the selva or the semideciduous forest. The kinds of trees which compose it are remarkably similar in the different continents. In both Africa and South America, for instance, the trees belong to the family *Mimosaceae;* in Africa they are of the genus *Acacia;* and in South America, of the genus *Mimosa.* It would be difficult for a person not trained in botany to distinguish between the African scrub forests and those of South America.

The Dry Margin of the Tropical Forests. The dry margin of the tropical forests is not a sharp one. Excepting where man has intervened, the scrub forest extends all the way to the margins of the regions of Group I. The individual scrubby trees become smaller and more widely spaced and the cover of grass becomes sparser until bare ground appears between the plants. Scrub forests border the dry lands in several parts of the world: for example, in the Chaco of northern Argentina; in northeastern Mexico south of the Rio Grande; in Yemen; and around the edge of the Thar Desert in Pakistan (Plates 10, 12, and 18).

In many parts of the world, however, man has intervened. The very earliest remains of prehistoric man show that he had learned how to make use of fire, if only to aid in the hunting of animals. In the wetter areas of Group II such fires could not easily spread out of control; but in the areas with a long dry season the repeated annual burning resulted in the destruction of young trees. In the course of many thousands of years the activities of primitive man appear to have had the

A waterbuck at the margin of a stream in the tropical scrub forest in Uganda

effect of changing certain parts of the scrub forests into savanna. There are vast areas of the interior of Brazil, and of Africa and Australia, which, when man first came upon them in historic times, were covered with a mixture of coarse savanna grasses and scattered fire-resistant trees or scrubby thickets. In almost all these savannas the floodplains of the rivers are followed by ribbons of tall semideciduous forest. These river-bank forests are called *galerias* (from the Italian word for tunnel) because the smaller streams, at least, may flow under a complete arch of foliage. The savannas are included in the regions of Group V.

Human Population. To judge by the present distribution of people in the tropical forest lands, there is a marked preference for the regions of moderate humidity covered by the semideciduous forests. The tropical rain forests, with some important exceptions, are thinly populated. The exceptions are mostly in the Asian low latitudes where a rice-growing people have established themselves with great density on the floodplains of the rivers, and on the terraced lower slopes of hills or mountains where rainfall is heavy. The scrub forests and savannas seem to offer the poorest conditions for settlement, for only in a few places have these subhumid regions been occupied by farmers. Irrigation must usually be practiced; yet in these regions, where there is commonly a season of heavy rains, provision must also be made for drainage. Most of the areas of major settlement in the regions of Group II are in the semideciduous forests.

Native Animals of the Tropical Forests. The native wild animals of the tropical forests differ considerably on the different continents. In the South American forests there is a notable paucity of large ground animals, although there are many different kinds of birds, monkeys, and snakes which inhabit the dense foliage far above the ground. Underneath, in the deep shadows, close observation reveals a multitude of insects, such as ants and spiders. The termites, or white ants, are particularly destructive of any organic matter which chances to fall on the ground. Whole villages have been abandoned in the face of an invasion of ants.

These various kinds of animals are also represented in the tropical forests of the other continents, but in these other regions they are a part of a larger and more abundant fauna. Africa, especially, is famous for its animal population. While most of the African animals really belong to the savannas, they penetrate the relatively small areas of forest in central Africa and so must be included in a discussion of Group II. A great many different kinds of herbivora feed on the savanna grasses during the rainy season or cluster about the water holes during the dry season (picture, p. 92). This fauna includes such fleet-footed types as the antelope, the zebra, and the giraffe. In the Congo Basin are found the elephant, the okapi, the buffalo, and the wart hog, and, in the rivers, the hippopotamus and the crocodile. The actual distribution of some of these animals is related to the particular types of vegetation which furnish them food. In southern Africa, for instance, the giraffes are found only in areas where the acacia trees grow. Most of these plant-eating animals are preyed upon by carnivora, and the distribution of the latter usually agrees closely with the distribution of the species they pursue. The lions, for example, in parts of Africa are very largely confined to regions inhabited by the gazelles.[1] In the semideciduous

[1] E. L. Trouessart, *La Distribution géographique des animaux*, Paris, 1922, p. 79.

forests of southeastern Asia the fauna includes the elephant, the buffalo, and the tiger.

The insect life of the tropical forests on all the continents is abundant, especially in the transitional areas between the forests and the grasslands. Because many of the insects are carriers of disease they form a serious obstacle to human occupance or to the introduction of domestic animals not immune to these diseases. The mosquito is the most common and dangerous; but there are many others, such as the famous tsetse fly of Africa, which carries the dreaded sleeping sickness.

Weather and Climate in the Tropical Forests. One of the parts of the world where weather and climate come close to meaning the same thing is in the wetter parts of the tropical forest regions. As these terms are properly defined, weather is the state of the atmosphere at any given time, whereas climate is the average of weather at a particular place and for a particular period. But in the tropical rain forest, at least, the day-to-day and month-to-month weather is so remarkably uniform that the two words seem to have almost the same meaning. The weather is so similar from day to day that the common small talk of mid-latitude peoples is difficult to carry on, and appointments are made in terms of the showers and alternating periods of sunshine.

These regions are characterized by monotonously high temperatures. The common belief that the equatorial regions are unbearably hot is quite incorrect. The highest temperatures in the world have been observed, as we have seen, in the deserts. Temperatures in summer in the lower middle latitudes (in the Mississippi Valley, or the Ganges Valley, or the Argentine Chaco) are much higher than any which are ever experienced in the low latitudes near the equator. Belém, near the mouth of the Amazon, for example, rarely, if ever, has a temperature over 100°. The highest temperature recorded at a place farther up the Amazon was 96.3°. Yet between the average of the coldest and warmest months there is a range of only about 3°. It often has been said that "night is the winter of the tropics," for the diurnal range is actually greater than the annual range. At Belém the temperatures at night drop some 15° below those of the hottest part of the day. In such a climate the terms *summer* and *winter* are misleading, for there is really nothing which corresponds to our mid-latitude concept of winter. The average annual temperatures are between 70° and 80°—few are higher than that. Only rarely are very high temperatures experienced, and rarely do the temperatures drop below 60°. At Belém the average highest and lowest temperatures of the year are 91.4° and 68.0° respectively.

The *heat equator* is the line connecting the places of the world which have the highest average annual temperatures. It passes along the northern coast of South America and along the Guinea Coast of Africa—lying some five to ten degrees north of the geographic equator in these continents. It runs south of the geographic equator only in northern Australia.

Temperatures such as are recorded in the rainy tropics would be quite comfortable were it not for the rains and the humidity. In the tropical rain forests the humidity is especially high. Even though the year in all but a few parts of the tropics is divided into a rainy season and a dry season (instead of summer and winter), the dry season in the selva is actually only a season of less rain. On a characteristic day the sun rises in a clear sky. Fog is sometimes hanging in the low valleys, but this speedily rises in curling wisps of vapor as the land is heated by the sun's rays. Soon puffy cumulus clouds appear, before long covering a large part of the sky. A light shower may occur, often as early as eight or nine o'clock in the morning. This is followed by a period of brilliant sunshine and then by another shower. Showers and sunshine alternate in this way throughout the day, the former becoming more severe and of longer duration as the day progresses. About four in the afternoon a very heavy shower occurs—a deluge of rain accompanied by little wind. The storm, at first torrential, later settles down to a steady rain which continues into the evening. It is a characteristic remembrance of the rainy tropics: the beat of rain on an iron roof, the monotonous splash as the water runs off onto the ground, and the sticky wetness that penetrates everything and leaves one soaked with perspiration. Well into the night the rain gradually ceases and is succeeded by a deep silence, relieved only by the dripping of water from the soaking foliage and by the hum of the dreaded mosquito. Without the cooling winds of an exposed coast the tropical rainy lands may become quite uncomfortable.

But there are many parts of the tropical forest lands where the climate is not at all like this. Especially on the east coasts of the continents and islands, strong easterly winds increase the evaporation and in part compensate for high humidity. Where the graceful coconut palms toss their heads in the steady, strong breeze from the water and where the buildings are open to the moving air, life can be untroubled by the stimulating effect of variable weather such as is experienced in the middle latitudes. Here, in a veritable paradise, men may relax if they know how to do so.

The paradise is a dangerous one, however. It is a fact that where the human body is not subject to the necessity for making adjustments to frequent changes in temperature and humidity, it eventually loses the capacity for such adjustment. The "chills" which are described as dangerous for health in almost all handbooks on tropical living can result from a drop of only a few degrees in temperature. Long residence in the extremely monotonous climates of parts of the low latitudes can, apparently, produce bad physiological effects on the human system. It is the monotony, rather than the high temperature, which is bad; and it is equally bad for the people of all races.

Wartime studies of the effect of high temperature and high humidity on the human system have demonstrated that there are certain maximum combinations of heat and humidity beyond which the human body cannot survive. Heatstroke and death can result where the air is saturated with moisture and where the temperature reaches 85°. Where the air contains 70 per cent of all the moisture it can carry (in other words, where the relative humidity is 70 per cent) the danger point is reached when the temperature is 95°. These combinations of heat and humidity are actually experienced occasionally in nature, but no place on earth has average conditions of this sort. The fact is, too, that the places where high heat and high humidity occur together most often are generally not in the rainy tropics. The part of the world in which human life is most difficult in terms of these weather elements is along the shores of the Red Sea, in a region which receives very scanty rainfall.

Distribution of the Tropical Forest Lands. The general arrangement of the tropical forest lands in the world can be described quite simply. They occupy a belt somewhat less than 20° wide on either side of the equator and extend poleward along the eastern sides of the continents to the margins of the low latitudes. Even more than in the case of the dry lands, this general position is modified in detail on each of the continents. As a result of the disposition of the land masses, however, there are three chief areas of occurrence: in the Americas, in Africa, and in Asia-Australia.

The largest single area of selva in the world is in the Amazon Basin and parts of the Guianas (Plate 12). The westward extension of this forest is limited by the Andes, and only a narrow fringe of selva is found along the Pacific Ocean in Ecuador and Colombia. On the east coast of South America the selva is found as far south as latitude 25° S.; and a semideciduous forest extends somewhat farther south in the Paraná Valley of eastern Paraguay. Most of the eastern margin of the Brazilian Highlands has a semideciduous forest. In the northeastern part of Brazil, however, both the selva and the semideciduous forests are interrupted by a tropical scrub forest—a caatinga (picture, p. 102); and between the scrub forest and the Amazon selva there is a narrow belt of savanna. A considerable area of scrub forest also occupies the Gran Chaco, in the upper Paraná Valley. North of the equator the tropical forests are found throughout the Antilles as far north as southern Florida, and they occupy the lowlands on the eastern side of Central America and Mexico almost as far north as the mouth of the Rio Grande, and on the western side to about 20° N.

In Africa selvas and semideciduous forests occupy parts of the Congo Basin and parts of the south-facing Guinea Coast. The Congo forests, in part because of the higher altitude of this region, are probably not so luxuriant as the analogous forests of South America. In southern Africa, separated from the Congo forest by a belt of savanna, there is a large area of scrub forest. The east coast of Africa has only a narrow fringe of tropical forest.

Selvas and semideciduous forests occupy the lowland areas of the East Indies and many of the small scattered islands of the southern Pacific. Scrub forests and semideciduous forests fringe northern and northeastern Australia. Semideciduous forests are extensive on the eastern coast of Indochina and in the great river valleys of southeastern Asia—the Mekong, the Chao Phraya (Menam), the Salween, the Irrawaddy, and the lower Ganges-Brahmaputra. The lowlands of Ceylon and the Malabar Coast of India are occupied by selvas. The Deccan Plateau and most of the upper Ganges and Indus valleys are covered by scrub forest, which in the northwest extends beyond latitude 30° N.

Winds and Rainfall of the Low Latitudes. This distribution of the various types of tropical forests is related to the basic facts of rainfall effectiveness. As we have seen in the previous discussion of the world's dry lands, it is important to know not only the total amount of rainfall each year, but also the balance of other factors that determine how much of the rainfall is effective. Where temperatures are always high, evaporation is rapid. As a result, a low effective rainfall is revealed in the natural cover of vegetation at places where the average annual rainfall is still high—high, that is, as measured by middle-latitude experience. In the central part of the United States, for example, average annual rainfall between 30 and 40 inches can be considered as moderate—certainly adequate for unirrigated crops or for a continuous forest cover. But in the low latitudes, where temperatures throughout the year are high, an annual rainfall below 40 inches, even if well distributed through the year, can support only a scrub forest or a poor semideciduous forest.

The occurrence of generally heavy rainfall on low-latitude east coasts is related to the world's wind systems and the world's ocean currents. In the low latitudes, over the oceans, the winds are moving generally from east to west—from the northeast in the Northern Hemisphere and from the southeast in the Southern Hemisphere. These low-latitude winds are known as the *trade winds*. As the oceanic whirls approach the eastern margins of the continents in higher low latitudes, the air follows a curving path to the right in the Northern Hemisphere and to the left in the Southern Hemisphere. Along the equator, where the two whirls converge, there is between them a belt of shifting winds and calms which is known as the *doldrum belt*.

The ocean currents move in harmony with the prevailing winds. In the Northern Hemisphere ocean basins the water circulates generally in a clockwise direction, and in the Southern Hemisphere ocean basins it circulates in a counterclockwise direction. Where the two currents converge near the equator there is an equatorial countercurrent which moves back from west to east.[1] These ocean currents are shown

---

[1] It is customary to name a wind by the direction from which it comes, but to name an ocean current by the direction toward which it flows. Thus an east wind is one which moves from east to west; and an easterly ocean current is one which moves from west to east.

on Plate 23, which also distinguishes warm and cold water. From this map it can be seen that the continental east coasts are bathed by warm water, and, similarly, the west coasts for some ten degrees on either side of the equator are warm. But the continental west coasts between about 15° and 35° N. and S. are bathed by cold water.

Rain is produced only where air which has picked up a large amount of water vapor is forced to rise and cool. The major source of water vapor is warm ocean water, for here evaporation from the water surface is rapid—very much more so than over cold water. Air is forced to rise when air masses converge, as in the doldrum belt along the equator, on the margins of continents where the wind is onshore, or on the windward slopes of mountains. For this reason the eastern coasts of low-latitude continents where air is moving strongly onshore from across warm ocean water are especially rainy (Plate 7).

The Monsoons. In regions dominated by the monsoons there are heavy rains when the winds are onshore, and very little rain when the wind is offshore. But in many places the rains of the rainy season are so heavy that a forest vegetation—usually a semideciduous forest—can survive the dry season. Throughout the low latitudes between southern Asia and northern Australia the prevailing winds shift seasonally, bringing strongly marked rainy and dry seasons which depend on the orientation of the land with reference to the seasonal winds (compare Plate 7 and Plates 25, 26, and 27). Thus northwestern Java gets its heaviest rain when the winds are moving out of Asia and toward Australia, in the Southern Hemisphere summer; and southern Java gets its maximum rain at the opposite time of the year, in the Northern Hemisphere summer.

The two weather stations in the world which bid for the distinction of receiving the highest average annual rainfall are both located on windward mountain slopes where strong onshore winds come heavily laden with moisture picked up from warm water. The present high record is held by a station on the northeastern slopes of the mountainous island of Kauai, the northernmost of the Hawaiian group, where an average of 476 inches a year is reported, fairly evenly distributed throughout the year. The second rainiest place on earth is Cherrapunji, located in the hills of Assam, a little north of Calcutta, where an average of 457 inches a year is reported. This place, however, receives most of its rain during the onshore monsoon of summer. July averages 109 inches of rain; but December averages only 0.2 inch (see the climatic data for selected stations in Appendix E).

SURFACE FEATURES

The surface features of the humid lands of the world are quite different from those of the dry lands. There are, to be sure, the same kinds of geologic structures and rocks in both; but the manner in which the rock structures have been sculptured by the processes of erosion in the rainy lands is very different from that in the dry lands. Under rainy tropical conditions, where there is a dense cover of forest vegetation, the rock surfaces are usually decomposed to great depths by chemical action. The mantle of loose earth which covers the solid rock is molded into rounded forms quite different from the angular forms of the deserts. Rivers find their ways to the ocean and carry with them large quantities of alluvium. Where structural basins occur, which in the dry lands might form bolsons, they are filled with water. The rift depressions of East Africa (Plate 13), which are filled with fresh-water lakes, are very similar in geologic structure to such dryland rifts as Death Valley in California or the Dead Sea depression of Palestine.

Surface Configuration. The larger surface features which stand out when we examine continental maps—and which are comparable to such features as hamadas, ergs, or mountains and bolsons in the dry lands—are four in number: plains, plateaus, hilly uplands, and low mountains. The high mountains, which in some places closely border the regions of this group, are included in Group VIII.

The words used to describe these four major surface features are all common in non-technical language. The words used by geographers to describe the surface features of the dry lands are strange to most people who speak English, but every such person thinks he knows what is meant by the words plain, plateau, hill, or mountain. Yet the actual use of these words in naming the features of the land suggests that in the popular vocabulary there is no very careful definition of them. The Turtle Mountains of North Dakota, for example, are only a few hundred feet high above the plain upon which they stand; they are really a part of the plain, but the local people call them mountains. If they are to be called mountains, then the Berkshire Hills of Massachusetts would certainly have to be renamed. To use these words in a more exact sense in geography, we must define them more carefully than does the dictionary; but in so doing we must be prepared to find that features which are popularly called mountains are really plains, that features called plateaus are really hills, or that features called hills are really plateaus. We must be ready to distinguish between proper names and the more or less technical geographic terms which describe them.

These four categories of surface features may be given somewhat more accurate definition as follows. A *plain* is an area of low relief,[1] generally less than five hundred feet. It is low-lying with reference to bordering areas, and is usually, but not in every case, low in altitude. A *plateau* stands distinctly above bordering areas, at least on one side; and it has a large part of its total surface at or near the summit level. Its local relief may be very great in cases where it is cut by canyons; or it may have as small a local relief as a plain, from which it differs in such a case only because of its position with reference to bordering areas. A *hilly upland* has more than five hundred feet of local relief and has a relatively small proportion of its surface at or near the summit level (picture, p. 102). *Low mountains* have more than a thousand feet of local relief, and, like hilly lands, have a relatively small proportion of the surface near the summit level. High mountains, which are given further definition in the chapter dealing with Group VIII, generally have a local relief in excess of three thousand feet.

These distinctions between the major surface features of rainy lands are, of course, arbitrary, and in many places are difficult to apply. An area which fulfills the definition of a plateau on one side may resemble a plain on the other side; or a hilly upland may seem conspicuous

[1] The relief of an area is the difference in elevation between the highest and lowest points. Relief is different from altitude, which is usually measured from mean sea level. There may be surfaces of very slight local relief standing at very high altitudes—for example, the Plateau of Tibet; or there may be very steep slopes and great differences of local relief within an area which lies below sea level—as on the slopes of Death Valley. Local relief may be defined as difference of elevation within any selected area of restricted size. See V. C. Finch, G. T. Trewartha, A. H. Robinson, and E. H. Hammond, *Elements of Geography, Physical and Cultural,* New York, 1957, pp. 213–216, 265–355.

A hilly upland with tropical scrub forest in the rainy season—Northeast Brazil

enough to be called a mountain from one viewpoint. The name actually applied is more or less a matter of custom. For example, the Congo Basin might be classified as a plateau because it drops steeply toward the sea; or as a plain because it is almost entirely surrounded by higher land and because its local relief is less than five hundred feet. As a matter of fact, it is generally described as a plain.

Distribution of Surface Features. The surface configuration of the several areas of Group II is presented on Plates 9–19. The two great plains regions in this group are found in the Amazon Basin of South America and in the Congo Basin of Africa (maps, pp. 103 and 104). However, although these two regions resemble each other in their relatively low relief, they are otherwise quite different. The Amazon drains a region of low altitude. The main stream is navigable for ocean ships for 2000 miles inland, almost to the base of the Andes.

The Congo, on the other hand, drains a plain which lies over a thousand feet above sea level. The whole continent of Africa, in fact, may be thought of as a huge plateau with steeply scarped sides. The Congo descends over this escarpment in a series of falls and rapids. It is navigable for river steamers above the falls, but ocean ships can do no more than enter its mouth. Elsewhere throughout the regions of Group II small coastal or river lowlands exist, but none are on the scale of the Amazon and the Congo.

The plateaus, hilly uplands, and low mountains of this group are most extensive in Africa and South America. The East African Plateau follows the eastern coast of Africa southward from Ethiopia, leaving only narrow patches of coastal lowlands along the water. In a few places the plateau is surmounted by mountains or broken by great rift valleys. The highlands of Guiana and Brazil are somewhat more complicated. They are composed of a mixture of hilly upland, plateau, and low mountains. From northeastern Brazil far to the south the highland faces the coast with a steep escarpment which rises between two and three thousand feet above sea level. The peninsular part

A part of the lower Amazon Basin. (Vegetation after Denis)

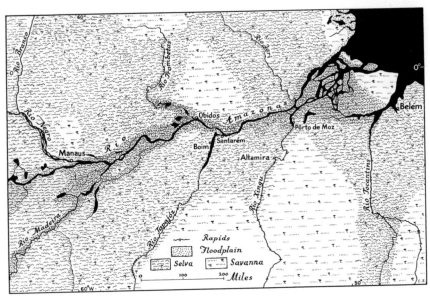

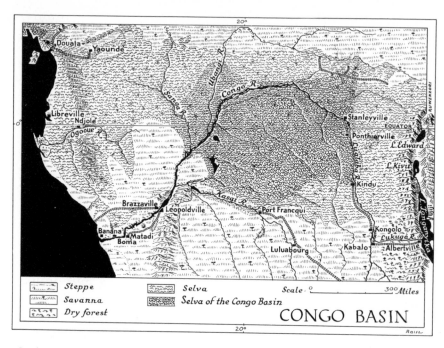

Surface configuration and vegetation cover of the Congo Basin and adjoining areas.
(Vegetation after Schantz and Marbut)

of India is also composed of a mixture of plateaus, hilly uplands, and low mountains, and there is even a small area of high mountains along the southwest side (map, p. 120). South of Bombay the narrow fringe of coastal plain is known as the Malabar Coast. Northern Australia and parts of New Guinea and Borneo are also hilly.

Most parts of the Asian tropics, however, are made up of great river lowlands set in the midst of ranges of high or low mountains. There are extensive plains formed by the alluvial deposits along the lower courses of the Ganges-Brahmaputra, the Irrawaddy, the Chao Phraya, and the Mekong (map, p. 112). There are relatively wide plains along the northern sides of Sumatra and Java and in southern Borneo. But elsewhere there are only narrow delta plains that have formed where the rivers come down from the mountains. Similar conditions exist in Central America, in the Antilles, and in the islands of the southwest Pacific.

LANDFORMS, DRAINAGE, AND SOILS

The detailed surface features, or landforms, of Group II, which are the surface forms visible when studied on large-scale topographic maps, are those which are developed under a forest cover where rainfall is abundant. Wherever there is land standing above sea level the rivers are doing the work of wearing it down, carrying its loose rock particles downhill and eventually to the lowlands or into the sea. Under a dense forest cover, however, fairly steep slopes can remain protected from rapid erosion by the tangle of roots. When such slopes are cleared by man the results are often disastrous, for, with the protection of the forest removed, deep gullies speedily develop unless special measures, such as terracing, are taken to guard against this kind of destruction. When the streams descending from mountains or uplands reach the plains they begin to deposit silt and gravel, building alluvial plains and deltas. The rivers usually wind back and forth, or meander, across the plains, only in time of high water spilling out of their channels and inundating large areas. The land across which a river meanders and which is subject to flooding at high water is called the *floodplain*. It is sharply set off from the rest of the plain, which is not subject to flooding, by steep valley bluffs. Along the lower Amazon (map, p. 103) the floodplain is some fifty or sixty miles wide, and the valley bluffs which border it stand some two hundred feet above the river (see Appendix C, section 10). Only on the floodplains or in lagoons along low coasts are there extensive swampy areas. The evaporation is too rapid to permit the presence of standing water at the surface for any long period of time except when it is actually raining.

In the wet parts of the world a certain proportion of the water which falls on the surface sinks into the ground. We have seen that in the dry lands only a small part of the rainfall actually gets into the soil where it is effective in the support of plants. In regions which are frozen for part of the year, the amount of water sinking into the ground is reduced. But in the rainy tropics the ground is never frozen; water sinks into it whenever rain falls. This percolating water is one of the factors which determines the character of the soil.

Water descending through the loose rock fragments which mantle the surface changes the soil in two ways, physically and chemically. In the first place (the physical change) it carries down with it the smaller soil particles. The upper layer of the soil becomes coarser and coarser; and the fine particles are deposited in a layer at some distance below the surface which eventually becomes a hardpan of clay. This process is called *eluviation*. The longer it goes on the poorer the surface soil becomes for shallow-rooted crops.

The second change produced by percolating water is a chemical one. The minerals which can be dissolved in the water are, little by little, carried away in solution, leaving in the upper soil layers only the relatively insoluble minerals, the ones least valuable for plant food. Like any chemical process, solution goes on more rapidly at higher temperatures than at lower temperatures. This process is called *leaching*, and, as in the case of eluviation, the longer it goes on the poorer the soil becomes. In the rainy tropics the minerals least apt to be dissolved are the iron and aluminum compounds. On level land which is not subject to flooding and so to the deposition of new alluvial material, the soil which develops is a yellowish or reddish sandy material known as a *laterite*. Outside the floodplains, other level lands of these regions normally have soils of low fertility for shallow-rooted crops. That tropical soils are fertile is one of the common misconceptions about the low latitudes which needs to be corrected.

There is a third soil-forming process which contributes also to the characteristic infertility of tropical soils. This is called *humus accumulation*. Organic matter falling on the forest floor is rapidly attacked by bacteria and decomposed. In cooler and less rainy regions bacterial action is slow, and a layer of dark-colored or black humus is found under the fallen leaves. But in the rainy tropics temperatures are high and bacterial action is very rapid. Humus can accumulate only in a very thin layer and in certain spots. When the forest is cleared the humus is quickly destroyed. This is another element of infertility in these soils in terms of the common food plants.

The Occupance

The conquest of these tropical lands by man is far from complete. In a few parts of the world the original landscape has been permanently and radically transformed by human settlement, but in each case this has been accomplished only by large numbers of settlers. Where such settlement has been made the population today is very dense—as in the Oriental rice lands. But the forest does not yield easily to small numbers of pioneers, nor to the more or less temporary activities of Occidental plantation owners. Certain people of simple farming culture have occupied parts of the tropical forest lands with moderate density, but the clearings they make are constantly threatened by the closely crowding cover of vegetation and are usually not permanent. Large areas of Group II are occupied by less than one person per square mile.

The settlement pattern within this group suggests that the regions most favorable for agricultural settlement are those which are covered by semideciduous forests. Apparently the obstacles to settlement found in the grasslands and scrub forests on the one hand or in the selvas on the other have, in most places, discouraged permanent occupance. Not only are the semideciduous forests easier to clear for a people armed only with simple tools, but the soils in these forests are less leached and eluviated than those found under the very rainy conditions which produce a selva. The soils in still drier regions are probably better even than those under the semideciduous forest, but in such regions farming is made difficult by the need for drainage and irrigation.

In these tropical regions, as in the dry lands previously described, the culture determines the way in which people occupy the territory. Besides the Occidental culture, which has in relatively recent times extended its influence into the different parts of this group, there is a considerable variety of "native" cultures. The word "native" is used here to describe non-Occidental cultures, although this use is admittedly somewhat loose, since many of the so-called native cultures were imposed by conquest upon still earlier native peoples, who themselves no doubt entered the region originally from outside. These cultures, which occupied the tropical forest lands before the advent of the Europeans and Americans, range from quite simple, primitive types to the advanced and highly elaborate types of India and Java. Since, unlike the deserts, very few parts of these regions are uninhabitable, the various cultures have a wider freedom to develop patterns of occupance peculiar to themselves. Although in the dry lands all cultures alike are tied to the sources of water, in the tropical forest lands some peoples concentrate permanently on the hot and well-watered alluvial plains, others concentrate on the cooler highlands not too remote from access to the outer world, and still others move about from place to place so that the arrangement of their settlement at any one time is a temporary and fluid one.

OCCUPANCE BY MIGRATORY FARMERS

There are many resources in the tropical forest regions on which a primitive people with few and simple wants can support themselves. Edible fruits and nuts are available for those who know how to find them. The rivers abound in fish and turtles, and many of the primitive tribes make regular seasonal migrations to the fishing places.[1] Sea-fishing is of great importance among those who occupy islands or coastal lands. Many of the rain forests are poor in edible land animals, so that hunting is generally limited to the search for a few kinds of birds and monkeys. The lighter forests, however, especially those of Africa, have a more varied animal life, as we have seen. Some of the primitive tribes of the Congo, such as the Pygmies, are specialized hunters, carrying on no agriculture, but attaching themselves to the outskirts of agricultural settlements and exchanging meat for agricultural products.

In most of these regions the hunting, fishing, and collecting are supplemented by crop cultivation. Imagine, however, the difficulties which stand in the way of a people whose culture includes the use of only a few implements! The removal of the large trees of the forest is a task which requires more effort than the results make worth while. In the Amazon forest the clearings for agriculture are made by removing and burning only the smaller trees. Crops are planted among the charred trunks in the partial shade of the forest giants, which are not touched (picture, p. 109). Such haphazard agriculture is a purely temporary affair; the confusion of weeds which soon springs up among the crops makes it easier to clear a new area elsewhere than to attempt

[1] J. Brunhes, study of the "Fang Tribes" of Africa, in *Human Geography,* Abridged Edition by M. Jean-Brunhes Delamarre and Pierre Deffontaines (translation by E. F. Row), London, 1952, pp. 152–156.

A clearing planted with rice in the semideciduous forest—Central Brazil

a more permanent cultivation. Crops are harvested from a jungle, and the tribe moves on. This is known as *migratory agriculture.*

Other native peoples, however, practice a more elaborate form of migratory agriculture. With the aid of better tools the forest is entirely cleared, except for a few species of trees which bear edible fruits or nuts and are too valuable to be destroyed. In the first year after clearing, these native gardens support an extraordinary wealth of plants. Towering overhead are the fruit or nut trees left over from the forest. Below, the tallest planted crop is the banana. Below this is a haphazard confusion of manioc shrubs,[1] maize, sugar cane, dry-field rice, peanuts, and tobacco. Finally, on the ground are such crops as yams, beans, eggplants, tomatoes, and many others of our common vegetables (picture, p. 110). Although these gardens are inefficient and unsystematic

[1] Manioc is a root crop which continues to yield for a number of years after it is first planted. From it is derived what we know as tapioca. This crop is also called mandioca or cassava.

in appearance, more actual food per acre is probably produced in them than in gardens planted by any other agricultural method.

Such productivity, however, cannot be maintained. In a year or so, after the crops of maize, rice, and vegetables are harvested, the bananas and manioc become so thick that no other crops can survive. The manioc continues productive for as long as four or five years, after which the bushes are cleared away and the bananas and fruit trees alone occupy the land. The banana plants overrun the clearing, intertwined with creepers, vines, and a profusion of other plants. Gradually the former garden takes on the aspect of a jungle. The clearing of new land presents fewer difficulties than the removal of this second growth.

As long as migratory agriculture can be practiced over a wide extent of territory by a relatively small number of people, the essential infertility of the soil may not become important, for only virgin soils are used. In areas of somewhat denser population, on the contrary, the decline of crop yields may become serious. When all the territory in the neighborhood of a village has been worked over and abandoned,

Manioc, maize, and peanuts growing together in an African shamba, *or garden, in Mengo District, Uganda*

Photo by H. V. B. Kline, Jr.

110   *The Tropical Forest Lands*

either the village itself has to be moved to a new site or else previously worked land must be cleared for a second time. The abandonment of the village is a simple matter, for the houses are of light construction and are built of readily available materials. But the repeated use of the land for the production of such heavy crop loads rapidly exhausts the small amount of natural fertility in the soil. Not only are the yields much diminished, but on the abandoned clearings the coarse savanna grasses begin to come in to the exclusion of the other vegetation types which can no longer be supported. For a people armed only with the hoe, the removal of grass is even more difficult than the removal of the forest. Eventually the community is faced with starvation and may break up into several streams of migration, as the Mayas of Yucatan are thought to have done. The abandoned clearings now form open grassy patches in the midst of the forest. To this kind of economy the Germans give the expressive term *raubwirtschaft,* or robber economy, because it makes use of the resources available in nature in such a way as to destroy them.

OCCUPANCE OF THE RICE LANDS

The cultivation of rice is one of the distinguishing traits of several Oriental cultures. The rice plant was first domesticated in the river valleys of Southeast Asia. While at the present time this crop is concentrated chiefly in the mid-latitude regions with mild winters (which we shall describe in a later chapter), it is also found on a large scale in the neighboring parts of the tropical forest lands. The Eastern cultures are in numerous ways built up around rice; for not only does this crop furnish a very large part of the food supply, but the labor of producing it takes up a large part of the working hours of the Oriental peoples, and customs associated with rice are found in the religious ceremonies and in the idiomatic phrases of the language.[1]

The requirements of paddy, or wet-field, rice are quite different from those of any other cereal crop. In the first place, most of the varieties of rice require a hot growing season. Since most of them also require that the fields be inundated during at least a part of the period of

---

[1] In Chinese, for instance, the general word for food (*fan*) is also used specifically for cooked rice.

A part of the East Indies and Southeast Asia

growth, an abundant supply of moisture must be available, either from large rivers or from a very heavy rainfall. Rice is ideally suited, then, to the monsoon type of climate, because of the very heavy rains which come during the summer months. But within the monsoon

112　*The Tropical Forest Lands*

regions not all soils and surfaces are equally suited to this form of cultivation. Some places are too far from a supply of water for flooding the paddies; some soils are too porous. The best places for rice are the floodplains of the larger rivers, where there is a fertile alluvial soil and an abundant supply of water (map, p. 112, and picture, p. 114).

The relatively small amount of first-class rice land, where the most favorable conditions of climate, surface, and soil are combined, leads to the intensive utilization of these places. The land is divided into small field units, generally not more than a quarter of an acre in size. A very great amount of labor is applied to the rice crop; for after the land is plowed and smoothed, in some places with the aid of domesticated buffaloes, the remainder of the planting, cultivation, fertilization of the soil, and harvesting of the crop is done by the energy of human muscles. Dense populations are required for the production of rice by these methods and are in turn supported by its production. In parts of India and Java a population of nearly two thousand people per square mile is reported.

Perhaps under no other agricultural system is the surface of the earth so completely transformed as in the rice lands. No remnant of the original cover of vegetation is left. With certain exceptions the people live in compact villages, almost hidden by a dense growth of planted vegetation. Palms, banana plants, tall, feathery clumps of bamboo, and here and there the towering bulk of a kapok, or silk-cotton tree, or one of the several kinds of tropical fruit trees, such as the mango or the breadfruit,—all these nearly conceal the houses of the villages. Somewhat raised above the general level of the rice paddies, these villages resemble heavily forested islands, especially during the season of the year when the rice fields are brown with bare mud or concealed beneath the flood waters. Roads lead from the villages into the surrounding country, over which the workers pour out in the early morning and return at night, leaving the countryside quite uninhabited.

Outside these nucleated settlements the rice paddies are almost uninterrupted. Here the surface of the earth itself has been remodeled. Each individual field is leveled and surrounded by a dike. In order to insure drainage, each one of the paddies must lie at a different elevation from its neighbor. Whatever may have been the original landforms, man has sculptured the surface for his own needs, neglecting no small bit of this very valuable land. Most spectacular of all is the terracing of hilly areas, where contour-like platforms outline the shape of ridges and valleys. In parts of Java rice terraces have been built on slopes of as much as 45° (picture, p. 116).

Thus a new landscape is created—a landscape which changes its color and its character with the swing of the seasons. While the fields are being plowed the scene is brown and desolate, dotted here and there with the verdant islands, on which lie the hidden villages, or with the few patches of vivid yellow-green where young rice plants have been started and are waiting to be transplanted. Then the paddies are inun-

Rice-field patterns in the plain of the Yellow River

Fritz Henle, from Monkmeyer

dated, and, wading knee-deep in water, the workers set out the young plants. These quickly take root, and in the course of a week or so the pale color of standing water is replaced by the rich green of the growing crop. Myriads of water birds feed on the paddies and on the insects which breed in them, and the nights vibrate with the voices of millions of frogs. As the grain begins to ripen, the color changes again—now to a golden yellow. The water is drained away, and carefully, so as not to lose a bit of the precious crop, the rice is harvested. Again the brownish fields, thick with the stubble of rice straw, await the plowing and the repetition of the cycle. There is nothing left to suggest the tropical forest, over which man with such difficulty establishes his conquest.

Other crops also are grown in the monsoon regions. In some cases a dry-season grain such as wheat or millet, or perhaps sugar cane, is planted on the dry rice paddies. But there are great areas entirely unsuited to rice, either because of low rainfall and consequently inadequate supplies of water or because of porous soil, which allows the irrigation water to seep away too rapidly. Even in Java and India only a relatively small proportion of the country is first-class rice land and supports the dense populations previously mentioned. Of necessity, settlement spreads to the poorer, non-rice-producing areas. Here other subsistence crops form the basis of the occupance: millets of various kinds or a combination of the food crops previously described for the other regions of this group, such as maize, manioc, upland (or dry-field) rice, peanuts, and bananas and other tropical fruits.

The period of European rule in these lands produced problems of population pressure on a vast scale. The Dutch in Java, the British in India, and the French in Indochina introduced two major changes: first, they devoted large areas of the best lands to the cultivation of commercial crops rather than subsistence crops; and second, they reduced the traditionally high death rates through better medical services, better sanitation, and a reduction of local warfare and raiding. The result was a "population explosion" which created such widespread poverty and unrest that, after World War II, European rule was largely ended. Java in 1815 had about 4,500,000 people, concentrated chiefly on the rich soils of the northern alluvial plain around Jakarta. By 1900 the population had increased to about 28,400,000, and in 1945

Rice terraces in the densely populated island of Java

it had reached 50,000,000. Such increases, unless accompanied by numerous cultural changes, raise serious problems of food supply.

India and Pakistan. One of the world's outstanding problem areas is the peninsula now divided between the two self-governing countries, India and Pakistan (map, p. 118). The peninsula as a whole is over a million and a half square miles in area, or almost as large as the continent of Europe excluding the Soviet Union, and it is occupied by almost 450,000,000 people, or about a fifth of the whole human race. Measured in terms of the area suitable for farming, the population density in India and Pakistan, considered together, is 423 per arable square mile. This is not so great as the population density of 769 per arable square mile in Java, or the more than 500 per arable square mile in both the Philippine Islands and Puerto Rico. But in the case of India and Pakistan this density is not a local matter; it involves a very large total number of people.

The peninsula is also an outstanding problem area because the huge

116 The Tropical Forest Lands

population is increasing at a rapid rate. With the very high birth rate of more than 45 per 1000, any decrease of the death rate results in a sudden increase of the total population. At the present time the increase is about six million per year, or fifteen thousand per day. Even when peace and order are maintained by a strong police force, and when some attempt to provide medical service is made in the cities, the death rate remains high owing to famine and disease. Only half the persons born reach the age of twenty-two. If famines and domestic warfare do not wipe out vast numbers of people, and if the level of living is raised by industrialization or better attention to agricultural practices, the decrease in the death rate cannot fail to cause a sudden upturn in the net rate of growth. In a few decades the total number will have reached 700,000,000. To keep such a vast number of people alive, let alone to provide them with what Occidentals would consider to be a minimum standard of diet, the food supply would have to be increased three times.

A major problem in this crowded land is created by the deep-seated religious conflicts. There are approximately 250,000,000 Hindus and 92,000,000 Moslems, whose basic concepts of life are profoundly different. The Moslems are in a majority in Pakistan; the Hindus are in the majority elsewhere. In addition, there are seven other major religious groups. Over two hundred languages are spoken, although Hindi, in India, and Urdu, in Pakistan, are widely understood.

In 1947, when British rule ended, the peninsula was divided into two countries. The republic of Pakistan (map, p. 118) is separated into two parts, one in the northwest and the other in the northeast, with its capital at Karachi. The total number of people in Pakistan is 76,000,000. The remainder of the peninsula is included in the republic of India. But India is far from being in fact a closely-knit unit, for, in addition to the 215,000,000 in the Hindu state, there are at least 100,000,000 in semi-independent princely states. These were 562 in number at the time of partition, and they joined either India or Pakistan.

Of all the people in India and Pakistan, at least two thirds are directly dependent on agriculture. The kinds of crops vary considerably from place to place, however, depending on the physical quality of the land. Only a few places are suitable for the cultivation of rice, but in them a very large part of the arable land is devoted to that

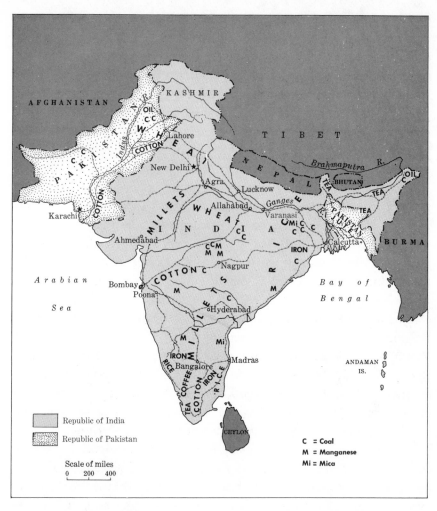

The political divisions and economic areas of India and Pakistan.
(After V. S. Gananathan)

crop. These rice areas are places of great population density. Two of them are in Pakistan: on the Ganges-Brahmaputra Delta, east of Calcutta, and on the alluvial plain farther north, where the two great rivers join through a network of channels. The rest are in India: on the delta of the Mahanadi, on the delta of the Godavari, on the Coromandel Coast around Madras, and on the whole Malabar Coast south of Bombay. But the greater part of the country is too dry for rice. On the drier lands the chief food crops include a grain sorghum (jowar, bajra, or ragi), barley, millet, maize, and a variety of vegetables. A large proportion of the grain must be used for animal feed rather than for human food, however; for India has huge numbers of cattle (about 159,000,000 head, or almost twice the number in the United States). To the Hindu the cow is a sacred animal. Because the Hindu religion does not permit the killing of animals or the eating of meat, all these cattle are useful only as draught animals or for the milk they give. To change this situation in favor of greater use of grain for human food would require a change in the beliefs of one of the world's oldest religions.

Some commercial crops have been raised in different parts of the peninsula. In the northwest, in Pakistan, the borders of the dry lands have been used for wheat. In some years part of the crop was exported through Karachi, but to an increasing extent it has been consumed in the cities, most of them now outside of Pakistan. Commercial crops have been raised in rotation with food or feed grains, including jute in the wet area east of Calcutta and cotton in the drier areas. The chief cotton area is in the Deccan Plateau, in the part indicated on the map (p. 120) as a lava plateau. Here, inland from Bombay, on good quality soils derived from the weathering of the volcanic rocks, a coarse-fibered cotton is grown, the chief use of which is for low-price textiles.

The great majority of the people who are crowded into the territories of India and Pakistan are only barely able to provide themselves with the minimum food required to sustain life. Most of the inhabitants live in the hundreds of thousands of small villages scattered over all but the arid parts of the area. Each village is a self-sufficient community. The food supply comes chiefly from the immediate locality, and since the villages are usually not reached even by a road for wheeled vehicles, local crop failure cannot be relieved by shipment from outside. The map of a portion of the Mahanadi Delta (p. 121) illustrates this pattern of isolated settlements. Each village has its own artisans, its own handicraft specialists. The people are illiterate and until recently have had little to do with the heated discussions of national policy which sound so loud in the cities or in the world outside.

In great contrast are the large commercial and industrial cities. Both Bombay and Calcutta are cities of more than a million inhabitants, and there are several other smaller cities in which both commerce and industry have made an important start. In both Bombay and Calcutta

The peninsula of India

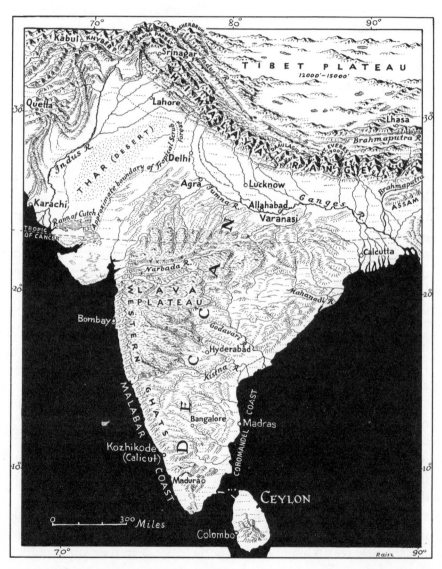

120 *The Tropical Forest Lands*

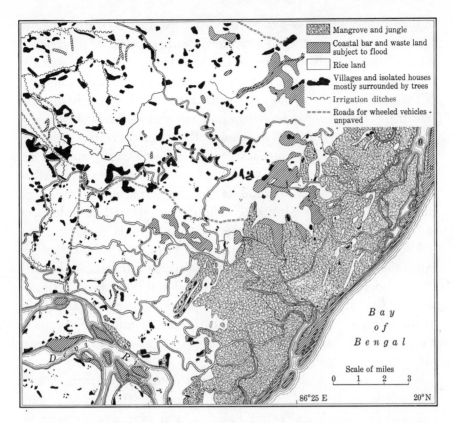

Bay
of
Bengal

Scale of miles
0   1   2   3

86°25 E   20°N

Rice-land topography[1] on the delta of the Mahanadi. The roads for wheeled vehicles lead to the northwest to the city of Cuttack, about thirty miles away. Within this area most of the local communications are by footpath. (From Bihar and Orissa sheets of the British Survey of India, 1928, 1929)

there are big textile mills, and in a town located 155 miles west of Calcutta there is a huge steel plant which makes use of nearby sources of raw materials. This steel plant is the largest single unit of this sort

[1] Unfortunately the general misuse of the word "topography" has caused the loss of its original meaning. In many writings the word is now used to refer only to the landforms or the character of the surface features. In this book, however, its original meaning will be retained. It will refer to the details which comprise the landscape of a small area,—the landforms and also all the other features occurring together on the earth's surface, as on a topographic map. A topographic study refers to the study of a small area. In this sense topography, chorography, and geography form a series of increasing generalization. Chorography refers to studies of larger regions; geography, to a study of the world or of its larger parts.

Occupance of the Rice Lands   121

in the world, and it is said to be the lowest-cost producer in the world. Madras is a center for the manufacture of leather goods. Manufactured goods from India have long been exported to pay for the essential imports of foodstuffs from Burma, Thailand, and the East Indies.

The economy of Pakistan is chiefly agricultural. In this Moslem state there is sometimes a surplus of both rice and wheat. Pakistan also produces most of the jute of the Ganges-Brahmaputra region, although the factories for making jute textiles are all in Calcutta, which is included within India. Cotton, wool, tea, tobacco, furs, hides, and leather are produced in Pakistan beyond its capacity to consume these things. But Pakistan has few industrial establishments. It will be dependent in considerable measure on the urban markets of India.

The part of the peninsula now included in India is the part having much the greater share of the industries and the industrial raw materials, although it is weak in terms of agricultural production. Almost all the coal and iron deposits which supply the big steel plant, all the hydroelectric capacity, and nearly all the textile mills are in India. Exports include manganese, mica, leather products, shellac, oil seeds, cashew nuts, tea, coffee, and textiles.

If the problems of establishing a sound domestic government, and of developing a workable relationship between the two separate countries can be solved, India and Pakistan, and especially India, have the man power and the resources to become important world powers. But if the food supply is not increased rapidly enough to take care of the predictable increase of population during the next few decades, India will be swept by famines of unprecedented severity, and a majority of its people will continue to exist on substandard diets close to the edge of starvation. The emergence of an industrialized state from a mixture of Oriental peoples is a painful process, and one which has great significance for the economic and political patterns of the next century.

OCCUPANCE BY OCCIDENTAL CULTURES

The occupance of the regions of Group II by Occidentals has two quite different phases. One is the establishment of political and commercial control over lands already occupied by native peoples, with the administration carried out by a very small number of white Europeans. The other is the actual settlement of white Europeans on lands that were either empty or very thinly occupied by natives.

Among the colonial powers, Portugal and Spain were the first to establish overseas empires, starting in the sixteenth century. The Portuguese, in Brazil, were the first to build a plantation system based on imported Negro labor. In the twentieth century, however, the chief colonial powers have been Great Britain, France, the Netherlands, and Belgium.

Since World War II the colonial system has been challenged, and to this challenge each of the colonial powers has reacted differently. The British have attempted to bring the colonies to self-government as rapidly as possible. The French have attempted

Photo by H. V. B. Kline, Jr.

A Limba tribesman climbing an oil palm by means of a vine "ladder" in Sierra Leone, West Africa

to make the colonies a part of the French State, and both the French and the Dutch have given up colonial rule only when forced to do so. The Belgians, in the Belgian Congo, still maintain a tight and efficient colonial administration.

Effects on the Native Modes of Occupance. Although the actual settlement of Occidentals is limited to relatively few parts of these regions, the contact of this world culture with the various native cultures has profoundly altered the native way of living. Many radical changes in the distribution of plants, animals, and even people have

Occupance by Occidental Cultures   123

resulted from the development of the Occidental means of circulation. The largest Negro urban groups, for instance, are no longer in Africa, but in industrial North America. Among the crops maize, manioc, rubber, cacao, tobacco, and many others were known only in parts of the American continents before the Europeans carried them to other distant regions. Now the African native agriculture is organized around maize and manioc. Coffee, on the other hand, has been taken from the Orient into South America. Domestic animals, too, have been exchanged, for the American natives had neither cattle nor poultry before these were introduced by Europeans.

The results of the development of world circulation have not been entirely beneficent, however. Many diseases which formerly were localized in rather small areas are now widespread. The introduction of diseases into new regions along lines of travel is not a new phenomenon, but it has never before been exhibited on such a large scale. In recent years medical science has shown the importance of controlling it and the methods of doing so.

Actual commercial contacts have also done much to change or to modify the native way of living. These involve not only the purchase from the natives of certain tropical products but also, in exchange, the sale of manufactured products from the urban industrial establishments. Weapons, agricultural implements, clothing, and liquor are traded even in remote parts of the interior for such valuable items as ivory, tropical cabinet woods, like ebony or mahogany, or other rare products collected in the forests. Where populations are dense and labor is cheap, the native peoples may be led to the production of commercial crops such as wheat, sugar cane, cotton, cacao, palm oil, and many others (picture, p. 123).

Occidental Plantations. There is a long list of agricultural products that cannot be grown in the middle latitudes because of climate, but which have become essential for the needs of an industrial people. Some of these are food crops; others are used in the manufacture of the many kinds of things Occidental people use. Among the food products are sugar cane, which now comes chiefly from Cuba; coffee, which comes from Brazil, Colombia, and Central America; and a long list of lesser items such as cacao, chicle, cinchona, vanilla, spices (such as pepper, cloves, ginger, and cinnamon), and many tropical fruits (such as bananas, coconuts, pineapples, avocados, and mangoes). Rubber is of major importance as an industrial product; although the increasing production and consumption of synthetic rubber make it evident that the rubber industries of the United States are gradually becoming independent of the supplies of natural rubber. About 70 per cent of the world's natural rubber comes from plantations on the Malay Peninsula and on the island of Sumatra (picture below). Other items include Manila hemp, sisal, gums, and insecticides. Even tropical woods are coming into use as their special qualities are appreciated and utilized.

In many cases these products were first brought to the European or North American markets through the collection of the raw material from plants growing wild in the tropical forests. Later, as the demand increased, production costs were greatly lowered per unit by developing plantations. Much of Northeastern Brazil, the Antilles, and some other parts of Latin America were first settled by the plantation system based on Negro slave labor. The crop was sugar cane. As long as the market is good, the necessary number of workers is recruited by whatever system is in use, and the plantation is maintained under the supervision of a small number of resident whites. But such a system is essentially speculative and temporary, for not only may soils be impoverished by repeated cropping, or yields reduced by insect pests, but also other areas with lower costs may capture the market, or the market itself may collapse owing to change in fashion or taste, or to the acceptance of substitutes. The Occidental plantation is a distinct example of *raubwirtschaft,* of the temporary exploitation of a resource and probably of a people.

Occidental Settlement. The actual settlement on tropical

Tapping a rubber tree on a Malayan plantation

United States Rubber Company

lands by Occidental people, doing their own work, is another matter. Three regions of this kind can be used as examples: the hilly uplands and plateaus of eastern Brazil; the hilly upland of Northern Rhodesia and of the southern part of Belgian Congo in Africa; and the plains and hilly uplands of Queensland in northeastern Australia. In all three of these areas Occidental people have established agricultural settlement.

The record of tropical experience is longest in Brazil. During the more than four centuries since the beginning of sugar-cane planting with Negro slaves in the Northeast, the Brazilians have occupied for the most part just one kind of country—the land covered by a tropical semideciduous forest (Tropical Forest in the legend of the map on page 127). The progressive clearing of this kind of forest is shown on the series of four maps on page 128. The year 1700 marks the close of the period of speculative sugar-cane planting in the Northeast; 1800 marks the end of a period of gold mining and diamond mining inland from Rio de Janeiro, during which the forest of that area was used to provide food for the miners; 1930 marks the close of the period of

A railroad swath cut through the "bush" in Southern Rhodesia. The large rectangular clearing is a European farm

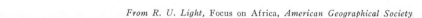

From R. U. Light, Focus on Africa, *American Geographical Society*

The natural vegetation of Brazil. (Reproduced by permission of the American Geographical Society of New York)

speculative coffee-planting in São Paulo; and 1950 shows that forest destruction has continued since 1930 and has now almost reached the limits of this kind of country.

Most of this agricultural settlement was carried on by tenant farmers, not by slaves. On any one piece of land the sequence is as follows. A large landowner comes into possession of an extensive area of forest. The landowner is traditionally interested in cattle, and much less interested in the hard labor of clearing the forest and planting crops. He welcomes the tenant farmer or share cropper, who stakes out a part of the forest and starts clearing it. The farmer cuts all but the

Occupance by Occidental Cultures   127

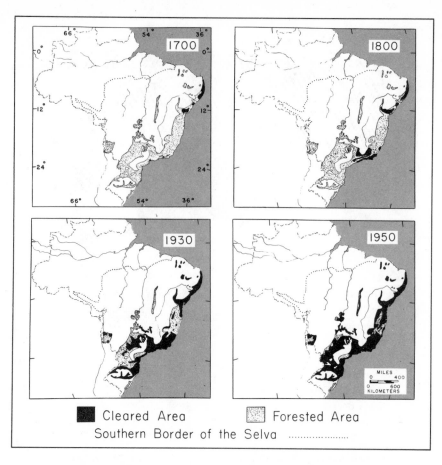

The clearing of the tropical semideciduous forest in Brazil, 1700–1950. (Reproduced by permission of the American Geographical Society of New York)

larger trees and awaits the end of the dry season to burn the tangle of branches and withered foliage. After the burn, he plants crops in between the charred stumps and half-burned trunks. On soil from which the organic matter has not been entirely burned away, and which has been enriched by the wood ashes, he gets good yields of maize, rice, beans, or manioc. After a few years, usually not more than three, his yields begin to decrease and he plants grass in the clearing and moves away. The landowner then has pasture for his cattle. But he takes no care of the pasture, and gradually second-growth vegetation of scrubby trees invades it, the grass is choked out or overgrazed, and the field is again abandoned to the forest. During four centuries, vast areas of Brazil, once covered with semideciduous forest, have been cleared and abandoned again and again. This system of *land rotation* has resulted in spreading the rural population thinly, and in a lack of close attachment of people to place.[1]

European settlers in the Tropical Scrub Forest lands of Africa south of the equator (Plates 3, 13, 14) are less than 2 per cent of the total population of approximately 20,000,000, but they are the dominant economic and political group. Portuguese in Angola, Belgians in the Congo, and British in the Federation of Rhodesia and Nyasaland are concentrated along the railroads, which tend to follow the stream divides. Many of the settlements developed from the exploitation of copper, manganese, tin, uranium, and other ores, particularly in the Katanga Copperbelt deposits lying across the Congo-Northern Rhodesia border. The mining industry has led to urbanization and has provided a market for European farming communities engaged in meeting local needs for meat, dairy products, breadstuffs, and "mealies" (maize) for the native laborers. With improving transportation, European agriculture has been supplying overseas markets with tobacco, tea, cotton, tung oil, and other warm climate crops. European farmers employ the best in machinery and modern practices. The success of their efforts depends not so much on problems of production as upon the vagaries of distant markets, tariffs, and monetary controls. Native African farmers, however, generally raise only mealies and low-grade cattle. Unfortunately, the rapid increase in African numbers is leading to extreme soil depletion and soil erosion, under methods of shifting cultivation, and to resultant poverty. A major problem of these lands is to harmonize the economic activities of the Negro and white peoples in farming, mining, and industry so that peaceful political progress may be assured in the emerging multiracial states.

The spread of white settlement northward in Australia has penetrated lands which were essentially empty of human inhabitants (Plates 6, 19, 20). Pioneers have pushed along the coast north of

[1] This section on Brazil, including the maps on pages 127 and 128, is from Preston E. James, "Trends in Brazilian Agricultural Development," *Geographical Review,* Vol. 43 (1953), pp. 301–328.

Brisbane, chiefly within the narrow band of tropical semideciduous forest. Here sugar cane and cotton are produced entirely with white labor. In northern Queensland and in southern Florida are two areas where workers of European descent have been successful in carrying on farming at sea level in the low latitudes. The Queensland area has been made the subject of much study and may ultimately offer an answer to the problem of white settlement in the tropics.[1]

The spread of settlement along the whole northern coast of Australia will apparently be more difficult than the movement north of Brisbane. To the west the monsoon climate is one of mild, dry winters and hot, rainy summers. The vegetation is mostly savanna with patches of scrub forest along the coast. Today this coastal land is very thinly settled. The problem of holding it against the pressure of Oriental people in the crowded regions of southeastern Asia is one which causes the Australians much concern, for sooner or later the land must be occupied by Australians if the pressure from the north is to be withstood.

Conclusion

The forest still dominates the landscape in most of the areas of this group. The high temperatures and the absence of a winter, the rank vegetation which springs up with such rapidity in every open space, the teeming exuberance of all forms of life, have conspired to create in the minds of middle-latitude visitors the impression of easy living in the midst of an abundance of resources. But this impression is actually far from the truth. The prevailing poverty of the soils is not reflected in the vegetation cover; for the heavy leaching and eluviation and the lack of humus are brought about by those same conditions of the climate which produce the forest, namely, high temperature and humidity. Easy living is possible if wants are few. But the real conquest of the forest for the permanent establishment of human settlement has been accomplished only where great numbers of people have been willing to live lives of unremitting and persistent toil. The way of the pioneer is indeed hard; for those things which can be accom-

[1] A. Grenfell Price, *White Settlers in the Tropics,* American Geographical Society, Special Publication, No. 23, New York, 1939.

plished by great numbers of patient workers do not yield easily to the isolated frontiersman.

People with different cultural heritages face the problems of living in these regions in quite different ways. For the primitive forest dwellers, with simple culture and few wants or ambitions, life is not at all difficult. These people do not attempt the conquest of the forest, but rather are content to accept such living as the untamed selva provides. Until white men came to develop new wants and to spread new diseases, distress or poverty was probably little known. This kind of human occupance, however, develops no fixed patterns of distribution and leaves few traces of its existence on the land.

People with a somewhat more elaborate cultural heritage, on the other hand, have been unwilling to accept the primitive existence afforded by the forest and have sought to establish themselves more permanently on the land. During the course of history a number of such groups of people have actually been able to gain a temporary dominance over the forest. Clearings have been made over a considerable area, and by some variant of the native garden type of occupance a large agricultural productivity has been developed. But this type of conquest is no more permanent than the primitive one. The soils have not withstood continuous agricultural utilization, but have gradually deteriorated until the decreasing food supply could no longer support the increasing population. The ruins of ancient civilizations, such as those of Central America and of Thailand, are now overgrown with a dense jungle cover, all but obliterated by the victorious forest.

The massed human hordes of the rice cultures have succeeded in making their conquest permanent. By completely transforming the original scene they have left no trace of the forest, and by persistent labor they leave no opportunity for its return. The crop around which they have built their way of living yields enough sustenance to support as many as five hundred people per square mile. But only relatively few square miles possess just those qualifications of climate, surface, and soil which permit rice cultivation. On these suitable areas, therefore, the population is concentrated densely, and the use of the land is intensive. The patterns of settlement thus established are fixed and crystallized. Although hitherto this type of occupance has been developed almost exclusively in the Orient, there are many parts of the

African and American tropics which are suitable. The Amazon Basin is physically capable of supporting an enormous number of people—another major nation, but one which will occupy the land in accordance with the Oriental mode.

The Euro-American mode of occupance is quite different. Two chief considerations govern the distribution of settlements. In the first place, the emphasis on commercial relationships with the middle latitudes enforces a close connection of all settlements with the coastal ports. In the second place, white people seek to avoid those hot, humid lowlands so much desired by the rice-growers and concentrate instead on the cooler uplands. The contrast between the patterns of population distribution in Brazil and in southeastern Asia is striking. Yet these two considerations which govern the localization of Occidental settlements are not harmonious: elevation provides relief from the lowland heat and humidity, but at the same time it renders access from the coast much more difficult and brings foremost the problem of transportation.

The Amazon Basin, suitable as it may be for Oriental occupance, is nevertheless politically under the control of a Western nation. Many other parts of the tropical forest lands, notably northeastern Australia and parts of Africa, are in the same situation but on a smaller scale. One of the great problems of the future is the question of whether or not these great empty regions can be occupied by white people and whether white people can establish their hold on these areas in the face of the very effective occupance by people of Oriental culture. The enormous increase of population in southeastern Asia must inevitably lead to expansion, and, but for the political and economic control of the Europeans and Americans, vast new lands await the Oriental colonist. The outcome is not easy to predict.

GROUP III

THE MEDITERRANEAN SCRUB
FOREST LANDS

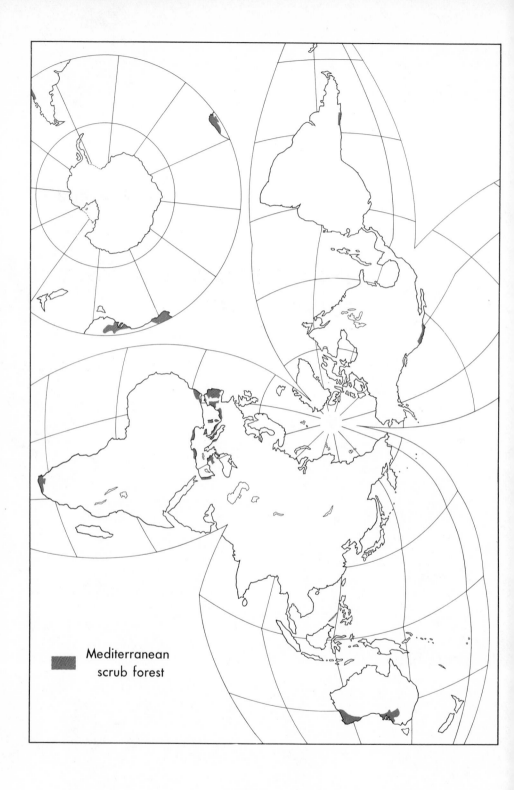

Mediterranean
scrub forest

AT A TIME when little of the world was known, and when Western culture was beginning its development in the Mediterranean [1] countries, Aristotle set forth his famous classification of climates. With the hot, dry Sahara to the south, and with the cool, rainy forest lands of Europe to the north, it is little wonder that the Mediterranean world, with its mild temperatures, its abundant sunshine, and its scanty but sufficient supply of rain, should seem to him the most "temperate" of all lands. His classification of the world he knew included three zones: a torrid zone, too hot to be inhabited by civilized men; a frigid zone, too cold and stormy for any but barbarians; and a temperate zone, the home of the Greek culture, the only habitable part of the world. It is a remarkable evidence of the keenness of Greek thought that on *theoretical grounds alone* the existence of a south temperate zone and a south frigid zone was postulated. This classification is perfectly understandable in view of the knowledge the Greeks possessed, although the application of these zones to the world as a whole has been very misleading. It is to these "temperate" lands of Aristotle and their counterparts in other continents—for some cultures, perhaps, the pleasantest of the world's habitats—that we now turn our attention.

In many ways the classification into zones developed by Aristotle points out the salient peculiarity of the regions of this group. They are essentially transitional; yet in the zone of transition are developed a number of striking characteristics which make them unique among

[1] The borders of the Mediterranean Sea make up the most extensive area of this group. The use of the name "mediterranean" to refer to all the analogous regions throughout the world is in accordance with common practice in other writings on regional geography. In this book Mediterranean will be written with a capital M when it refers to the lands about the Mediterranean Sea, and with a small m when it refers to the group as a whole.

the world's habitats. Transitional in climate, most of the regions of this group lie closely hemmed in between high mountains and the sea. This transitional character is further emphasized by the position of the Mediterranean Basin, on the margins of which are the coasts of three continents—Europe, Asia, and Africa.[1]

The mixture of ideas coming from such widely separated parts of the earth gave to the new cultures developing in the Mediterranean Basin that vitality which arises only as a result of the compounding of diverse elements. During the many centuries of the classical period the Mediterranean peoples were drawing greatly contrasted culture traits from the ends of the known world, and from the clash of these varied ideas and modes of living the fundamentals of what is now broadly called "Western culture" were being worked out and established. History has given abundant proof of the fact that cultural growth takes place not in sheltered spots, but in places where the currents of travel converge,—where all kinds of people come together. Sheltered and isolated places are more commonly regions of survival, where ancient and traditional ways of living are preserved. The evolution of a new culture out of the accumulation and digestion of diverse elements at a focal point in the world lines of circulation is perhaps best illustrated by this "cradle of Western civilization."

The major lines of travel no longer converge on the Mediterranean lands of the Old World. The present larger foci lie elsewhere. Many of the analogous regions in other continents, especially those of the Southern Hemisphere, are notably handicapped by their remote position in the economic world. But all the regions of this group share with the Mediterranean Basin the more permanent qualities of transition: those related to the climate and to the surface features.

For various reasons, then, the significance of the regions of Group III in terms of human affairs, especially in the building of the Occidental culture, is much greater than the total area of these lands would suggest. Of all the world's land masses, only about 1 per cent has this

[1] Our concept of the separateness of Europe, Asia, and Africa is inherited from classical antiquity, when the three sides of the Mediterranean stood out as sharply differentiated, not only physically but also in the very different cultures of the inhabitants. The modern notion of Eurasia—of Europe as a peninsula of Asia—was developed only after the world map had been much more completely filled out.

peculiar type of climate and this unique type of vegetation. Yet on this relatively small area are found today about 4 per cent of the world's population.

The Land

CLIMATE AND VEGETATION

The unique character of the landscapes of this group rests fundamentally on the peculiarities of the climate. In the various parts of the world it is not unusual to find rainfall more or less evenly distributed throughout the year or to find places where there is a summer maximum of rainfall with a winter dry season. The outstanding peculiarity of the mediterranean climate is its winter rains and summer droughts. Lying generally on the west coasts of the continents poleward of the deserts, the regions of this group have a climate that is transitional between the semiarid climates and the cool, rainy climates of the higher middle latitudes, poleward of 40° (Plate 8). As one proceeds away from the deserts the amount of winter rain increases and the length of the summer dry period decreases. The typical mediterranean climate is divided into a hot summer with brilliant sunshine and clear blue skies, and a mild winter with irregular periods of rain.

The mediterranean summers resemble those of the deserts. Near the arid boundary the summer drought may extend over a period of five or six months, as in Israel; but on the poleward margins of the mediterranean lands the drought may be reduced to only one month. Typically the driest month receives no rain at all, but near the poleward margin a little rain may fall even in summer. Day after day the sky remains cloudless. The wind, which becomes quite strong near the water, picks up clouds of dust from the dry earth. Most parts of the mediterranean lands become very hot during these summer months; but near the open oceans, where cool water bathes the coast, the summers are cool and, along the California coast, foggy (map, p. 138).

The mild winters, on the other hand, are quite different from the monotonously clear summers. The winter temperatures generally average between 35° and 50° for the coldest month. If destructive frosts

Climate and Vegetation 137

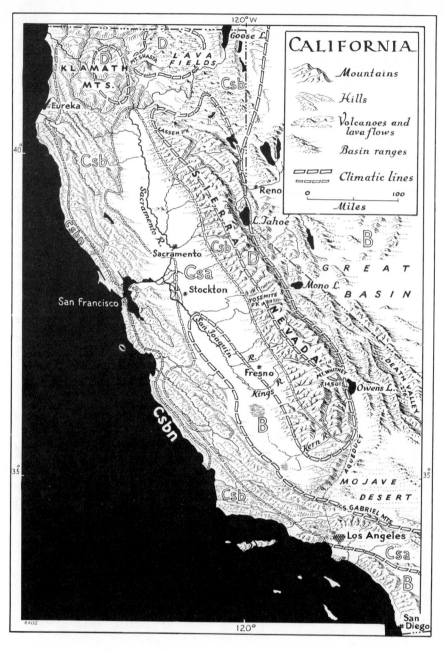

Surface and climates of California. (Climates after R. J. Russell) [1]

and snows occur now and then, they are destructive more because of their rarity than because of their severity. During this season the weather is variable; there are spells of warm, muggy, rainy weather with cloudy skies, followed by cool and brilliantly clear periods.

Cold Air Masses. These varying spells of weather result from the passage of typical middle-latitude storms. We have already noted the characteristic monotony of low-latitude weather. The middle latitudes, in contrast, are variable in weather; so much so that the traditional term "the temperate zone" is highly misleading and has been dropped by many geographers. If we recall the discussion of the major wind systems of the low latitudes, we remember that over the eastern parts of the ocean basins about 30° N. and S. are found the centers of great whirls of air of planetary proportions. The equatorward half of each whirl is marked by air moving from the east, the northeast, or the southeast. The prevailing wind direction in the poleward part of each whirl is from the west, the northwest, or the southwest. The oceanic whirl sweeps over the margin of the neighboring continent, and, unless mountains interfere, penetrates inland as far as is permitted by the deflective force of the earth's rotation. Because of the location of the regions of Group III between 30° and 40° both north and south of the equator on the western sides of the continents, the prevailing wind directions are northwest and north in the Northern Hemisphere, and southwest and south in the Southern Hemisphere (Plate 26). The strong north winds which sweep across Greece, the Aegean Sea, and the eastern Mediterranean were so well known to the ancients that they were given the name *Etesian Winds*.

Another element of the world's climates, however, interrupts the oceanic whirls from time to time. From the snow or ice surfaces of the polar regions come surges of cold air. These cold air masses, being

---

[1] On the map, p. 138, the climates are shown by lines and letter symbols. These are the symbols of the Köppen system, which are explained in Appendix B. Qualitative descriptions for each of the types of climate shown on this map are:

B   = Arid or semiarid climates
Csa = Mediterranean climate with mild, rainy winters and hot, dry summers
Csb = Mediterranean climate with mild, rainy winters and cool, dry summers
Csbn = Mediterranean marine climate with mild, rainy winters and cool, dry summers with frequent fogs
D   = Mountain climates with cold, snowy winters

Climate and Vegetation 139

heavy, lie close to the ground, and when they encounter the relatively warm, light air of the oceanic whirls they push under it and force it to rise. In this way, as the cold air masses move forward, the warm, moist oceanic air is forced to rise and cool, thus forming clouds and bringing rain. The wedge of cold, dense air along which the warm air rises is called a *front*. The cold air masses are known as *polar outbursts*. From both arctic and antarctic regions they move out toward the nearest warm places. Especially strong outbursts have been known to travel all the way to the equator, but usually they are limited to the middle latitudes, and, as they move equatorward, they are picked up in the stream of westerly winds and moved off eastward.

In winter the polar outbursts are especially strong. At this time of the year, therefore, they push farthest toward the equator. On the continental west coasts in winter cold air masses are occasionally strong enough to push beyond latitude 40°, but in summer such air masses rarely cross latitude 40°. Between 30° and 40° on the continental west coasts there is a transitional type of climate which receives rain only in winter, but which shares the dry desert climate with the regions of Group I during the summer.

The winds associated with a passing cold air mass have all been given local names in the Mediterranean countries of Europe. When the cold air pours southward through the Rhône Valley, it is known as the *mistral*. When it pours over the mountainous border between the Danube Basin and the Adriatic Sea (Plate 15), it is known as the *bora*. Because it drops rapidly over the coast of Yugoslavia, it is warmed adiabatically [1]—the bora is a very dry wind that desiccates the crops and picks up clouds of dust.

When a cold air mass pushes into the stream of the oceanic whirl it sets up eddies along its front. In the Northern Hemisphere these secondary whirls rotate in a counterclockwise direction, and in the Southern Hemisphere they rotate clockwise. Meteorologists describe such a whirling storm on the front of a cold air mass as a *cyclone*.[2]

[1] For a discussion of such meteorological processes see Appendix B.

[2] Note that there is a distinction between the popular use of the word "cyclone" to refer to a very violent storm, such as a hurricane or tornado, and the technical use, which includes under the term "cyclone" all whirling storms. When the word "cyclone" is used without modification, it refers to these general storms characteristic of the middle latitudes.

During the passage of one of these secondary whirls in the Mediterranean Basin, the winds come from various directions. Normally, as the cold air mass moves southward, the cyclone advances toward the east. At any one place, the coming of a cold air mass is first heralded by an interruption of the prevailing north or northwest winds. The winds are at first variable, and then come strongly from the south and southeast. The warm, dust-laden air from the Sahara is called the *sirocco*. Crossing the warm Mediterranean Sea, this air picks up large quantities of moisture. North of the Mediterranean, as the cold front approaches, cloudiness increases and usually there is rain. Where the air contains much dust the first showers are apt to contain large amounts of mud. Then, with a sudden shift of the wind to the north or northwest, the skies become clear, and bracing, cool air replaces the depressing air of the cyclone. Such a succession of weather types is experienced several times during the winter. Similar weather types are experienced in all the other regions of mediterranean climate of the world.

Rainfall occurs as the cold front sweeps on toward lower latitudes. It is widespread throughout these regions, but in any case is heavier in mountains and hilly lands than on level lands. Wherever air is forced to rise, it is cooled; and eventually, if it rises far enough, the moisture in the air is condensed to form cloud and rain. In the dry lands, we may recall, rains come frequently to the mountains. In the mediterranean lands the higher mountains are almost always cloud-capped. Because the prevailing winds are from the west, the western slopes of mountains and hilly uplands receive more rain than the eastern slopes. One result is an abundant supply of water for irrigation purposes in all the mediterranean regions of the world where there are bordering mountains.

The Mediterranean Forest and Brush. These climatic conditions support a scrub forest of unique character. The mediterranean vegetation may be described, at somewhat greater length, as a broadleaf evergreen, sclerophyll, scrub forest. Although in the different continents different species and even genera compose the forest, the appearance of the vegetation, resulting from its adaptation to the peculiarities of the climate, is strikingly similar in all the regions of Group III. The broadleaf evergreen forests of southern Europe, for example, are com-

Burton Holmes from Ewing Galloway

Wind-bent scrub pines on the Italian coast north of Livorno

posed mostly of various kinds of oaks (of the family *Fagaceae* and
chiefly of the genus *Quercus*) (picture, p. 143), whereas the similar
forests of Australia belong to the *Myrtle* family, which is of the genus
Eucalyptus.

In all these forests, however, certain common characteristics appear.
The winters are not cold enough, or the summer droughts long enough,
to enforce a period of rest, and as a result there is no season when the
leaves drop from the trees and growth ceases. The sprouting of new
leaves and the accumulation of reserves take place in the fall at the beginning of the rainy season, and the flowering and reproduction take
place in the spring at the end of the rainy season. In this way the mediterranean vegetation differs from the selva, which is also evergreen but

142 *The Mediterranean Scrub Forest Lands*

which has no seasonal rhythm. Furthermore, the seasonal rhythm of the mediterranean forest is of a quite different nature from that of the tropical semideciduous forests, or of the deciduous forests of the middle latitudes.

In numerous ways this mediterranean forest adapts itself to the summer droughts. The individual trees are widely spaced so that each may draw supplies of water from a large area of ground. Between the larger trees there is a heavy growth of underbrush. On all the plants deep taproots and a wide development of the surface root are characteristic. The woody and fibrous parts of the plants are emphasized, and the foliage is relatively light. The evaporation from the plants is diminished by a thick bark (notably in the case of the cork oak, *Quercus suber*) and by the nature of the leaves, which are small, thick, and stiff, with hard, leathery, and shiny surfaces.[1] Very commonly spines and thorns are developed, as in the case of other typically xerophytic vegetation types.

In addition to the scrub forest, many parts of the mediterranean lands are now covered by a low growth of bushes and shrubs, known in Europe as *maquis* and in the western United States as *chaparral*. In some regions this is known to be a second growth which followed the removal of the original forest; but in other regions it is supposed that the maquis itself is a native type growing in places which, for one reason or another, are unsuited to the forest. It is composed mostly of the plants which make up the undergrowth of the scrub

Cutting the bark from a cork oak in Portugal

Casa de Portugal

[1] This characteristic leaf form is described by the botanists as *sclerophyll*.

forest: of dwarf or scrub oak, chestnut, and various kinds of myrtle and laurel. A cover of this sort is almost worthless, for goats are the only animals that can graze on the bark and leaves, and the growth is too thick to permit the existence of grasses.

An outstanding exception is California. Many of the hills and lower mountain slopes of this part of Group III are covered with grasses. During the dry summers this vegetation cover turns a yellowish brown, against which the dark green of the oaks stands out in most striking contrast. These grasses, however, are all of European origin. The original vegetation cover was probably the chaparral or the evergreen forest; but the introduction of foreign grasses into Mexico by the Spaniards was followed by a very rapid spread of these plants—so rapid, in fact, that they were already common in California at the time the first missions were established (picture below).

Bordering Vegetation Types. Most parts of this group are closely hemmed in by high mountains and deserts. Closely associated with

Barley (in foreground) and oats (already harvested) in the Santa Inez Valley of California. On the hills in the background are remnants of the broadleaf evergreen scrub forest

Josef Muench

the mediterranean vegetation, therefore, are types which really belong in the mountain lands or the dry lands. While the broadleaf sclerophyll forest invades the lower slopes of many of the bordering mountains, the higher, or wetter, slopes in many places support dense stands of coniferous forest. The pine and cedar forests of the mountains bordering the Mediterranean Sea were widespread in ancient times (for example, the cedars of Lebanon). There are similar pine forests in the other mediterranean regions; and in the fog belt of the California coast, mostly north of San Francisco, are the stately groves of redwoods.

Grass is found in few parts of these regions outside the United States. Grassy areas of small extent exist in the cloud zone high in the mountains or in the marshy lagoons along the coast. In dry pockets, also, steppe grasses are the characteristic type of vegetation. But although such areas are found in nearly all the mediterranean regions, the grasses are much more widespread in California than elsewhere.

Distribution of the Regions of Group III. The mediterranean forest and the peculiar climate it reflects are found characteristically on the west coasts of the continents between about 30° and 40° N. and S. There are five such locations in the world. The largest area borders the Mediterranean Sea, extending from Portugal and North Africa in the west, eastward to the eastern margin of the Mediterranean, and northward to include parts of the shore of the Black Sea such as the southern side of the Crimean Peninsula, which is known as the "Soviet Riviera" (Plates 10–20). In North America the area included in this group lies between Los Angeles and the southern part of Oregon. In Middle Chile it lies between Coquimbo on the southern margin of the dry lands, and Concepción on the northern margin of the rainy forested region of the south. There is a small area of this group in South Africa around Capetown. The fifth locality is in Australia, where it is divided into a western area around Perth and an eastern area in the neighborhood of Adelaide.

SURFACE FEATURES AND DRAINAGE

Few are the landscapes of this group which do not include either the mountains or the sea as a background. The mediterranean vegetation covers the immediate coast and the lower foothills of mountains

Greece

which, in many places, rise directly from the water. Among the mountains there are numerous small and isolated valley lowlands and delta plains where the rivers empty into the sea. The surface features of

146 *The Mediterranean Scrub Forest Lands*

Greece illustrate this complex pattern of lowlands closely hemmed in by mountains. From the map on page 146 we can understand the background of the growth of the many independent city-states of ancient Hellas, each based chiefly on its own physically distinct area of lowland. Most of the lands around the Mediterranean Basin are of this sort: small, isolated valleys or delta plains bordered by hills and backed by high mountain ranges. No really extensive areas of lowland exist.

Compared with the complex arrangement of plains and mountains around the Mediterranean Sea, the surface features of the other parts of Group III seem relatively simple. In both North and South America (maps, pp. 138 and 148) ranges of high mountains lie parallel to the coast, and the lowlands and hilly belts are longitudinal. In California, west of the Sierra Nevada, lies the broad Central Valley, drained mostly by the San Joaquin and Sacramento rivers. In the southern part of this depression lies the basin of Tulare Lake—a dry-land bolson with its playa. Between the central lowland and the Pacific there are several ranges of hills separated by narrow longitudinal valleys. Because of the trend of hills and lowlands in this region, which differs slightly from the trend of the coast, some of the longitudinal valleys open out to the sea,—for example, the Salinas Valley. The entrance of the sea through the Golden Gate into San Francisco and San Pablo bays partly drowns the lower parts of a number of these valleys. Toward the north the central lowland of California is terminated by the mountains of southern Oregon, which extend westward to join the Klamath Mountains along the coast.

In Chile (map, p. 148) there is a central valley, crossed at right angles by the rivers coming from the east, and separated by projecting ridges of the Andes into more or less distinct basins. Between this longitudinal valley and the ocean is a coastal hilly belt. North of Santiago the longitudinal valley is pinched out by the spurs of the Andes, which reach westward to the coast. The southern part of the central valley, south of the Río Bío-Bío, is heavily forested and is included in Group IV.

Only in South Africa and Australia are the bordering ranges of high mountains lacking (maps, pp. 73 and 170). Even here there are prominent escarpments, as in South Africa, or ranges of hills, as the Flinders Range, north of Adelaide. Only in southwestern Australia is an area of this group developed on a surface which lacks even hills.

Surface Features and Drainage   147

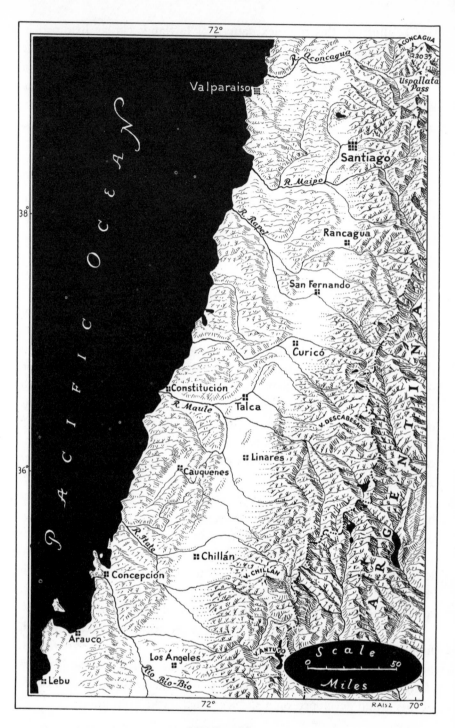

Middle Chile

Relationships with the Mountains. The intimate connections between these plains and the mountains close by are many. In the first place, the relatively heavy rains in the highlands feed numerous torrential streams. Even where the climate is deficient in moisture the mountain piedmonts are supplied with such an abundance of water from the streams that a continuous band of irrigated land can be supported. Then, again, these vigorous, youthful streams in the mountains accomplish a great deal of erosion. The gravels and sands which they bring down with them to the lowlands are piled up in huge alluvial fans along the piedmonts. Where the streams descend directly into the sea extensive delta plains are formed. So great is the amount of load brought down by the rivers that the delta plains grow with remarkable rapidity. In the Mediterranean Basin delta growth is aided by a tideless sea; many towns which are known historically to have been situated on the ocean are now located many miles inland. Owing to the concentration of the rain during the winter season, the regimen of these streams shows a maximum in that season, whereas the summer is a period of low water. However, where the streams rise high enough in the mountains to reach the snow fields, the maximum flow comes during the melting period in the spring and early summer, and considerable water is available in the rivers well on into the dry season.

The removal of the forests from the mountains has in many areas seriously changed this regimen. Forests have the effect of retarding the runoff during a rain and also of delaying the melting of winter snows. The vegetation cover therefore makes the flow of the streams more uniform. The removal of the forests causes severe floods during the winter and spring, and during the summer these floods are followed by droughts, when the streams may become entirely dry. The original forest cover of most of the regions bordering the Mediterranean Sea has been very largely cut off, and this has seriously affected the habitability of the lowlands.

The Karst Lands. The presence of a large amount of soluble limestone in the regions bordering the Mediterranean Sea results in the widespread development of *karst* landforms. The opening of caverns underground and the resulting disappearance of the streams from the surface create a landscape of more arid appearance than the climatic conditions alone would warrant (picture, p. 150). Many of the plateaus

A Karst landscape in Yugoslavia

and hilly uplands are of little value except for poor grazing for sheep and goats. The most habitable spots in such areas are to be found in the bottoms of the larger sinks, or *uvalas,* or on the narrow delta plains along the coast. The prevalence of karst landscapes in the countries of the Mediterranean Basin distinguishes these areas from the analogous regions elsewhere.

Relationships with the Sea; Types of Shores. Since all the various regions of this group are on the continental margins, the character of

150 The Mediterranean Scrub Forest Lands

their shores is a matter of great significance. The northeastern part of the Mediterranean Sea, with its many harbors and its clusters of islands, provided an ideal setting for the early development of the art of navigation. The difficulties of overland connection were more than compensated by the ease of sea travel. Without the contacts by water the spread of the various cultural influences from one shore to another around the Mediterranean Basin would have been very difficult.

Parts of the borders of the Mediterranean Sea are shorelines of submergence; that is, they are embayed by a lowering of the land with reference to the water (diagrams, p. 570). However, the results of submergence are somewhat different when there are mountain chains with axes parallel to the shore and when there are chains with axes at right angles to the shore. In the first case a number of elongated offshore islands are formed, but there are few projecting promontories and few deep embayments. An example of this type is the eastern side of the Adriatic Sea—the Dalmatian coast (maps, pp. 146 and 160). On the other hand, if the mountain axes are at right angles to the shore, long fingerlike ridges project seaward, with strings of partly submerged summits beyond them. Between these ridges there are deep embayments leading well inland and providing fine harbors. The Aegean Sea is bordered by coasts of this sort, of which southern Greece provides an outstanding example.

Most of the shores of the Mediterranean, however, are not indented. In some cases, as on the Rif coast of northwestern Africa or the Riviera of France and Italy, the mountains rise precipitously from the water's edge; but in other cases the shore is low, as in much of western Italy. Most of these various shorelines are shorelines of emergence (diagrams, p. 571). In any case they have been modified by the action of waves and currents.

The borders of the mediterranean regions of other continents are mostly emergent. The western coast of the United States from Puget Sound southward has no large harbors except for the one magnificent example produced by local submergence at San Francisco. The mediterranean coast of Chile is entirely lacking in harbors; even at Valparaiso, the chief port, the shipping must be provided with artificial protection behind a breakwater. Though there are several broad embayments near Adelaide, in Australia, the shores of these embayments are straight and offer only a few harbors. Also because of the large tidal range on the open oceans, these analogous mediterranean regions do not have so many delta plains along their coasts as do the lands bordering the Mediterranean Sea.

The Occupance

The regions which border the Mediterranean Sea have been occupied by relatively advanced and complex cultures for long periods of time. The Mediterranean has been called the "cradle of Western culture," and many of the traditional Western beliefs and practices can only be understood when placed against the background we have just described. But Western culture has been evolved from the fusion of numerous earlier types, with important contributions derived from many very different kinds of people.

Occupance of the Mediterranean Basin. The settlements of the Mediterranean Basin have gone through what appears to be a well-defined succession. The earliest ones were placed back from the coast, usually on defensible highlands. At a later stage, as population increased and as there was increased protection from the raids of pirates, people descended from the hills to form towns near the agricultural lands on the well-watered plains. At this stage some of the town people ceased to interest themselves in primary production, that is, in the production of foods or other materials from agriculture or fishing or from the direct use of natural resources. Instead they made a living by trading, manufacturing, or transporting goods, or in politics or education. These so-called urban activities were carried on by town people who became quite distinct from the people who tilled the soil or watched the herds of domestic animals. The towns grew in proportion to the size and productivity of the territory for which they performed these urban activities. A few of the larger ones, such as Athens and Rome, extended their connections by both economic and military conquest beyond the immediate districts which gave them a start, exchanging commodities with distant parts of the Mediterranean Basin and even with such distant places as Britain and the Orient. Athens came to depend for its wheat supply on shipments from the plains north of the Black Sea. Life in these communities became far more varied and more

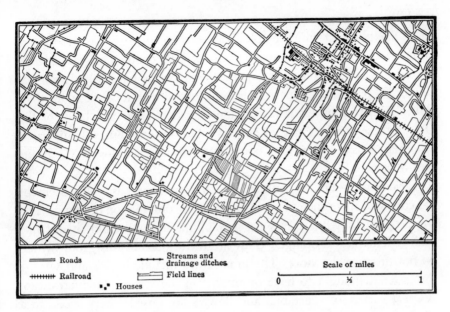

		Streams and	
Roads		drainage ditches	
Railroad		Field lines	
	Houses		

Scale of miles

0   ½   1

Topographic detail of a densely populated agricultural lowland—a portion of the plain of Florence. (Adapted from O. Marinelli, Atlante dei Tipi Geografici, Firenze, 1922)

secure than in the earlier self-sufficient city-states. Thus were formed the seeds of the urban tradition which in modern times has led to the growth of those vast commercial and industrial metropolises which now perform the urban functions for the whole Occidental world.

A visible result of the basic difference between the commercial-minded Occidental society and the self-sufficient Oriental society can be seen by comparing the maps on page 121 and above. In the delta plain of the Mahanadi, in India, the numerous villages are not accessible by road. Only footpaths connect each village with its bordering rice fields. But, in contrast, the plain of Florence, in Italy, is crossed by numerous roads, giving each separate farm access to a market town, which, in turn, is connected by rail and boat line with all the commercial cities of the world.

In the modern period the lands bordering the Mediterranean Basin are, on the whole, densely populated. The distribution of people, however, is very spotty. In Italy, for example, the population is concentrated on the coastal and river plains which are not too marshy, whereas the hilly and mountainous areas have fewer inhabitants (Plates 4 and 15). The plain on which Naples is located has the densest agricultural population in Europe, estimated at about 2000 people per square mile. While this is extreme, many of the delta plains have populations of 200 or 300 people per square mile, and several in Italy have more than 500. Compared with the population densities of the rice lands of the Orient, these densities are not excessive, but for agricultural lands based on other crops than rice such population densities are close to the limits of subsistence.

Agriculture. The agriculture which forms the basis of settlement has consisted since ancient times of a unique combination of crops. The tree crops include figs, olives, peaches, plums, almonds, and citrus fruits such as lemons and oranges. Few are the regions of this group which do not produce the vine. The grain crops include barley and wheat; the latter is thought to have originated in the eastern Mediterranean. A great variety of vegetables and flowers are raised where access to a market can be had. Though many of these crops are produced outside the regions of Group III, the combination is peculiar to this group alone.

Under the prevailing climatic conditions of summer drought, irrigation is a necessity in places where more than a scanty population is to exist. The abundant water supply in the mountain streams makes irrigation much more dependable than in the dry lands. Irrigation systems in the Mediterranean Basin date back to the earliest times. Many of the legendary heroes of Greece and Rome, such as Cadmus and Hercules, were hydraulic engineers whose fame rested on their control of rivers. The drainage of lakes, the damming of streams, and the construction of canals to carry the water great distances were all accomplished by the ancients. Roman aqueducts carrying water hundreds of miles from the mountain sources to the agricultural plains or the urban centers have been continuously in use now for many centuries.

The kind of crops irrigated depends on the rainfall; for near the desert margins the vines, olives, and figs must be watered, whereas in the areas with more abundant rains these crops are placed on the hill slopes, and only the plums, almonds, citrus fruits, and summer-planted crops are irrigated. Wheat commonly occupies the lowlands during the winter season, and is followed during the summer by irrigated alfalfa or by vegetables and flowers. Vegetables and flowers seem to

Hill slopes terraced for orchards near Florence, Italy

have been important in early times; the former made up an important part of the diet of the ancient Greeks and Romans, and flowers were used at all the games and ceremonies and, with olive oil, in the manufacture of perfumes. The year-round productivity of the land thus made possible by irrigation greatly increased the number of people who could be supported in an area, and yielded an agricultural surplus which in turn provided the economic basis for a nonagricultural urban population living by trade and manufacture.

A large part of the Mediterranean area, however, cannot be irrigated;

for example, the slopes of hills, high terraces, or plains too far from the sources of water. In the deserts such lands are lost to cultivation, but in the regions of Group III winter crops or perennial crops can be raised by dry-farming methods. Even in ancient times the unirrigated crops played a very important part in the agricultural scheme, many hill slopes having been terraced for vineyards or covered with orchards of olives and figs (picture, p. 155).

Generally an advance in the methods of living in an area, far from emancipating man from his physical surroundings, makes closer and closer adjustment to those surroundings necessary. For example, the native gardens of the tropical forest lands, with their mixed crops, are located not on any one type of soil nor any one type of surface, but on a variety of areas wherever they can be reached easily from a village. Only a general and rudimentary adjustment can be observed between the patterns of settlement and the gross features of the land. The contrast with the densely populated rice lands is very great, for here population and settlement patterns correspond closely to the areas most suitable for the production of rice.

In the Mediterranean Basin the culture includes the production of a greater variety of crops, and consequently the adjustments are more intricate. Outside the irrigated tracts the areas of superior soil are generally planted to wheat year after year. The rich alluvial lands of the valleys, terraces, and deltas which are not irrigated, or those especially fertile soils produced by the weathering of old lava flows (which here contain minerals to produce an exceptionally fertile soil), are the most favorable sites for wheat. Dry-farming methods have been applied here since ancient times. The crop is planted in the fall after the first rains have moistened the soil, and is harvested the following June during the hot, dry weather, which so favors the best ripening and cutting of wheat. During the summer months the fields lie fallow—not untouched, but plowed and frequently harrowed to keep the surface layer so pulverized that every bit of moisture is preserved.

A very large proportion of the Mediterranean Basin, even of the lowlands, is composed of sandy and gravelly soils which are too porous to support irrigation. These are used for the production of barley and various legumes. The large barley acreage of the Mediterranean countries is evidence of the poor quality of much of the soil.

The vineyards and orchards are generally located on the hill slopes or alluvial fans, the vineyards occupying the best lands. Because of the high yields per acre of the vine, and especially because of the great value of the wine manufactured from this crop, a very intensive form of cultivation can be supported. The vineyards are generally on terraced slopes, and the soil is plowed, harrowed, and manured many times during the year. In the drier and hotter sections the vines are laid on the ground, sometimes in pits about ten inches deep, so that evaporation by the high summer winds is reduced. Only in the cooler, rainier sections are the vines raised on trellises or festooned in the branches of trees. The fox in Aesop's fable, living on the Aegean shores of Asia Minor, was surprised and greatly annoyed to find the grapes hanging beyond his reach, for he was accustomed to finding the luscious bunches lying on the ground (picture below).

The vineyards are also usually placed on the southern sides of the hills, where exposure to the sun produces a superior flavor in the fruit. However, this is not a universal practice, for in some of the drier sections the northern exposure is preferred in order to avoid the very high evaporation during the sunny days in summer. In the regions

One of the many fine vineyards in the Mediterranean Basin

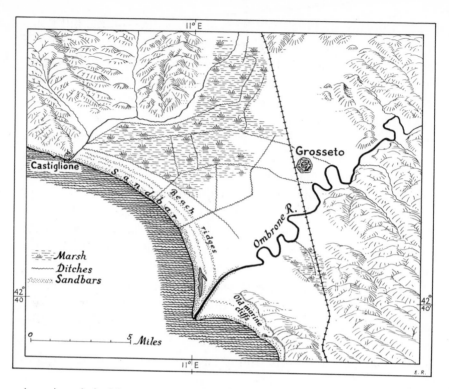

A portion of the Maremma coast of Tuscany—a bar and lagoon coast. (*From O. Marinelli,* Atlante de Tipi Geografici, *Firenze, 1922*)

poleward of this group, where late spring frosts may do great damage to the buds, the placing of vineyards and orchards on the northern slopes or near large water bodies is usual, in order to delay the blossoming until after the danger of frost is passed.

Orchards of olives and figs occupy the less favorable hilly and alluvial sites. Both olive and fig trees are native members of the broadleaf evergreen forest and are well adjusted to existence on the dry, rocky hillsides with only a thin soil mantle.

Pasture Lands. In a region of such intensive agricultural occupance there is little room left for the pasturage of domestic animals. However, two kinds of sites, being unsuited to agriculture, are available for pasture. The first of these is found in the poorly drained, marshy areas of the lowlands,—just the places which peoples of an Oriental culture would have seized most eagerly for rice production. Marshes are found on the lower parts of delta plains or alluvial fans, on the wet spots in the centers of the sink depressions of karst areas, or in the lagoons back of the sand bars along the low coasts. In all such places a rich growth of grasses is available at all times of the year. The very small area of such sites in lands so densely populated leads to an intensive use. Dairy cattle—very uncommon in the regions of this group—are found characteristically in these rare places. An outstanding example of this development is the important modern dairy district which is located on the Maremma coast of Tuscany, near Grosseto (map, p. 158).

Another of these mediterranean pasture sites is found in the neighboring high mountains, where temperatures are too cool for the olives and figs or where the slopes are too steep. Sheep and goats are the animals most commonly found in such places, and these are generally driven up into the mountains during the summer and brought down again to the lowlands for the winter season. This characteristic use of mountain areas will be discussed more fully in the chapter on mountains (Group VIII). In the hilly parts of the Mediterranean region, especially in drier areas, during centuries of human settlement the overgrazing of forested or brush-covered surfaces by sheep and goats has killed off the original vegetation cover and exposed the land to serious erosion. Erosion of this sort not only destroys land which might be used for grazing or even for orchards and vineyards, but also increases the floods and lengthens the periods of low water in the streams draining to the bordering lowlands. Many parts of these regions have been seriously affected by soil erosion so that the number of people that can be supported in them has been considerably decreased since ancient times. The hilly land of Israel is a noteworthy example. Only at great cost can the Jewish and Arab farmers rebuild the land.

The Use of the Sea. For various reasons the inhabitants of these lands turn to the sea. The many harbors and islands of the Aegean formed, as we have said, the cradle of ancient navigation. Then, not only did the growing population on the small plains around the Mediterranean Sea cause a rise of oversea trade, but also the abundance of fish provided a very important supplement to the agricultural products. Since ancient times, therefore, the Mediterranean peoples have made use of the sea as a highway and as a source of food.

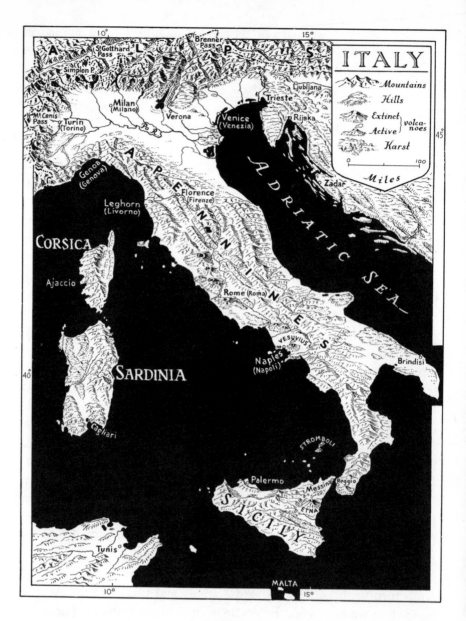

Italy

The Population Problem of Italy. In the census of 1951 Italy had a population of more than 47,000,000. For the country as a whole the density was about 407 people per square mile. The population map of

160   *The Mediterranean Scrub Forest Lands*

Europe (Plate 4) shows that Italy stands out as one of the more densely populated countries of Europe, and it also shows that within Italy people are concentrated in certain areas whereas other areas remain thinly peopled. The largest area of dense population is in the Po Valley. This is one of the regions of Group IV, an area of great cities, of large-scale manufacturing, of well-developed transportation, and of modern agriculture (Plates 15, 16, 21; map, pp. 232–233). But Italy's population problem centers in the southern part of the country—in the part where hilly uplands and small lowland plains in Group III flank the Apennines on either side of the peninsula (map, p. 160).

This southern part of Italy is predominantly agricultural and rural. Most of the workers attempt to make a living from farms that are too small, or as wage workers on large private properties. In this part of Italy the rate of population increase is much higher than in the cities of the Po Valley; but as population continues to increase, economic production remains nearly static. There are very few more jobs than there were in 1871, yet each year there are some 100,000 more potential workers. When there is not enough work to go around, and when income is not sufficient to maintain a level of living that is satisfactory to the inhabitants, a region is said to be "overpopulated." In southern Italy population pressure continues to mount in spite of the continued emigration of people to other parts of Italy or to foreign countries. Poverty and unrest are the results.

Since 1950 the Italian government has been trying to do something about its population problem. Where large private properties are not used to produce all they might produce, the land is expropriated. This has made possible the grant of new farms to selected peasants, although not nearly enough area can be made available in this way. Also, there are ambitious irrigation and drainage projects that will provide some additional new farm land. But an essential part of the program is the creation of new industrial jobs in the small towns and villages.

The only program for Italy which offers much hope is to extend the development of industries into the southern part of the country. Manufacturing industries could provide employment and, at the least, an improvement in living conditions for the large number of rural people now condemned to hopeless poverty. But even the development of manufacturing will be able to bring only temporary relief unless the

The Occupance 161

rate of population increase is lowered, as, indeed, it has already been lowered in the urban centers of the Po Valley.

Israel. Palestine is the name formerly applied to the area between the eastern coast of the Mediterranean and the Jordan River. Back of the coastal plain there is a belt of hilly country, and beyond that is the deep trench drained southward by the Jordan River (map, p. 163). In this trench is the ancient Sea of Galilee (now known as Lake Tiberias), and in the lowest part, 1290 feet below sea level, the salty Dead Sea. Palestine is a region of winter rains, but it is a marginal land where those rains are anything but dependable. Its original scrub forest has long since disappeared as the result of thousands of years of overgrazing by the flocks and herds of a pastoral people. The hill slopes, denuded of their protective cover, have eroded so badly that in places where the Bible tells of green pastures and still waters there is now only bare rock. And in the midst of this land is the city of Jerusalem, the Holy City of three faiths—Christian, Jewish, and Moslem.

For thirteen centuries, from 636 to 1917, Palestine was a Moslem country. Arabic-speaking Moslems farmed the coastal plain and tended sheep and goats in the hilly uplands. Yet Palestine was also the "Promised Land" of the Jews. In addition, after the completion of the Suez Canal, in 1869, Palestine's position took on a new strategic significance.

In 1917 the British army took Palestine away from Turkey, at that time an ally of Germany in World War I. After the war, Palestine was assigned to the protection of Great Britain. It was then decided to name Palestine as the national home of the Jews and to promote Jewish colonization. Farming settlements were laid out where water and soil were suitable. In 1940 the population was still 60 per cent Moslem and only 31 per cent Jewish, but the Jewish colonists had prospered as the Moslems had never been able to do. In part this was due to financial support from Jews all over the world, and in part it was due to the technical skills of the colonists.

In 1947 the United Nations partitioned Palestine between the Jews and the Arabs, and in 1948 the Jewish part became the independent country of Israel. After the partitioning some 650,000 Moslems who had formerly lived in the territory of Israel fled to the neighboring kingdom of Jordan, which had been granted independence by the British in 1946. Jordan annexed Arab Palestine in 1950, but this arid

Israel

country could offer the newcomers no lands as good as those they had abandoned. Meanwhile the population of Israel had been increased by the arrival of great numbers of Jewish refugees from war-torn Europe. By 1956 it was estimated to be 1,850,000. (See map, p. 163.)

To create a prosperous economy in such a land is not easy. First, there is the water problem—the problem of providing irrigation for summer crops. The Jordan River flows in a narrow V-shaped channel. The use of its water for the irrigation of the plains inland from Haifa would require pumping. Wells in the coastal plain and in the area back of Haifa have brought enough water to the surface to irrigate a large new area. But so rapidly has water been taken from these wells that around Tel Aviv and Haifa the surface of the ground water has been lowered below sea level, and salt water has started to seep inland. The use of the Jordan River for irrigation would require co-operation with neighboring countries, and so far this has been impossible.

A modern state cannot be purely agricultural. Israel must develop manufacturing industries, as, indeed, it is doing with the help of outside capital. But factories in Israel must depend on imported raw materials and imported fuels, and the products must be sold abroad. The building of a modern industrial economy would not be impossible with financial assistance, but it becomes most difficult in the face of the hostility of the neighboring Moslem countries which have never accepted the loss of what they still think of as their own national territory.

Occupance of the North American Regions. The analogous regions of Group III in other parts of the world have certain elements of remarkable similarity to these ancient Mediterranean lands, but there are also certain essential differences. The striking resemblance of most of the widely scattered parts of this group as regards physical background has been the subject of much comment, although the bare white limestone surfaces of the Old World karst lands have no counterparts in the other areas of Group III. The greatest differences, perhaps, are in the forms of the occupance. In the first place the North American regions and, especially, the Southern Hemisphere regions are relatively remote and isolated. As a result the settlement is neither so dense nor so intimately adjusted to the land as in the Old World. The Mediterranean countries carry the record of long periods of occupance; in contrast some of the analogous regions exhibit the most modern phases of Occidental occupance, unencumbered by the relict forms of previous settlement. The native inhabitants of these other parts of Group III possessed simple, primitive cultures, with none of what we think of as the characteristic mediterranean crops or techniques. They maintained a poor existence in a land which provided them with only meager resources, and colonization by Europeans or Americans almost entirely eliminated their traces.

The first European penetration of California came in the late eighteenth century. The first pioneers were the missionaries who established mission stations along the route from the centers of Spanish settlement in Mexico northward along the Pacific coast as far as San Francisco (map, p. 138). At the missions the scanty Indian population was gathered together, taught Christianity, and instructed in the methods of agriculture. The crops introduced were those already well known to the Spaniards: wheat, barley, figs, olives, and the vine. Cattle were also introduced, and the Indians were taught to care for domestic

Harvesting spinach in the Salinas Valley of California

Josef Muench

Citrus groves bordering the Los Angeles lowland

animals. With the establishment of Mexico's independence and the removal of the mission system during the first quarter of the nineteenth century, the practice of agriculture in California declined. The land was given in large tracts to colonists from Mexico, but the only use to which it could be put with profit was cattle-ranching; the chief products were hides, tallow, and salt beef. When the gold rush began shortly after the whole area was annexed by the United States, the

166 *The Mediterranean Scrub Forest Lands*

incoming flood of new settlers could not find enough local supplies of food to maintain themselves.

The period since the middle of the last century has been marked by a series of forms of land use, each motivated by the search for speculative profits. Each speculative development was applied to a different part of the land, and, once established, has been continued even after speculative profits could no longer be made. Between 1860 and 1870 wheat farming was started on large areas, chiefly in the Central Valley and mostly unirrigated. Between 1870 and 1880 there was a big development of sheep-herding with wool as the commercial product. Between 1880 and 1890 vast areas were laid out for fruit orchards and vineyards. The decade 1890–1900 saw the beginnings of the use of California's pasture lands for dairy cattle. More recently many small localities have come to specialize in the production of certain vegetables to be sold not only in the cities of the west coast, but also in the east (picture, p. 165).

As these developments appeared one after the other, there was a steady increase in the use of water for summer irrigation. At first the winter runoff was permitted to escape through the rivers to the sea. But now it is widely recognized that a more efficient use of water is needed: that there must be dams and reservoirs to store the winter rain, and a co-ordinated system of canals to spread this water over the lowland farms in the summer. The Central Valley project, now in process of development, will greatly increase the supply of water for use in summer, and will add both new areas of summer crops and a greater volume of production of such crops from older areas.

The present agricultural localizations in California are notably distinct. Where conditions of climate, soil, or water supply are especially favorable for a certain crop, the result—in an economy of relatively unrestricted trade and low-cost transportation—is a concentration of production in the best-suited areas. Today citrus groves cover the irrigated alluvial fans around the border of the Los Angeles lowland (picture, p. 166). Vineyards are found along the alluvial fans of the Sierra Nevada from Fresno northward, and in valleys of the coastal region north of San Francisco. From the Santa Clara Valley, south of San Francisco Bay, comes a large part of the world's supply of prunes. Almost all the lima beans of the United States are grown without

The city of San Francisco, with the Golden Gate in the background

irrigation in the belt of light fogs along the coast (this is to the south of the area noted on the map on page 138 as having almost continuous summer fogs, Csbn). In addition to these localizations, there are areas devoted to barley, which has now greatly surpassed wheat in this region; to rice, chiefly in the lower part of the Central Valley between Sacramento and Stockton; to lettuce in the Salinas Valley; and to sugar beets and cotton.

In California there is no such problem of overpopulation as complicates the process of settlement in parts of the Old World. The rural population of California is densest in the lowland east of Los Angeles. Here the figure is between 75 and 100 per square mile. Over most of the Central Valley, except for the section between Stockton and Sacramento, the density is less than 25 per square mile. In the San Francisco Bay region it is between 25 and 50 per square mile. Los Angeles and San Francisco are among the large commercial and industrial cities of the United States. Especially in the cities around San Francisco Bay there has been a considerable development of manufacturing industry (picture, p. 168).

Occupance of the Southern Hemisphere Regions. In many ways the part of Chile between Valparaiso and Concepción is remarkably similar to California. The arrangement of its surface features (map, p. 148) recalls the essential lineaments of its North American counterpart. But Middle Chile has had a very different kind of occupance. There the land was divided early in the colonial period into vast private estates, and this form of land tenure persists to the present time. Furthermore, Chile has never had access to a large market in which it could dispose of surplus agricultural production in exchange for other things. As a result there are fewer agricultural localizations in Chile than in California. The chief use of the land is for pasture, or for the raising of feed crops such as alfalfa. The chief food grain is wheat. There are also considerable acreages of vineyards, olives, and other mediterranean fruits. But much the same combination of crops is repeated on each estate. The better lands of the valley bottom are used for alfalfa and the poorer lands for wheat—a reflection of the predominant interest of the Chilean landowners in stock-raising; vineyards are on the slopes of the alluvial fans or on wetter hillsides; the bordering hills and mountains are mostly used only for summer pasture. The density of rural population in this part of Middle Chile is generally higher than that of comparable parts of California. In the vicinity of Santiago there are over 400 people per square mile. Poverty among the people who do the agricultural work is widespread.

Typical mediterranean agriculture has made its appearance in only a small area of South Africa and Australia. In the region of Group III around Capetown (Plate 14 and map, p. 73) are found the usual crop combinations. In Australia, settlement is still in an early stage. Around Adelaide, and inland from Perth (Plate 20 and map, p. 170), pioneer colonists are engaged in clearing the broadleaf evergreen forest and maquis and laying out new farms. The chief pioneer crop is wheat.

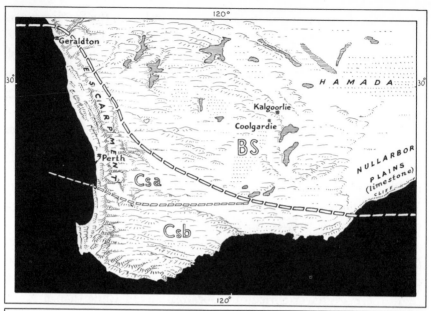

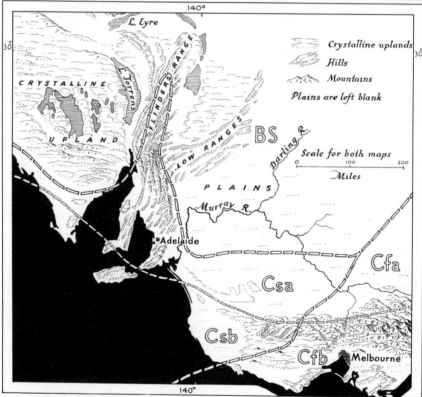

Surface and climates in southwest Australia (top) and in the Adelaide region (bottom)

Conclusion

Stages of Settlement. It is possible, now, to recognize certain rather distinct stages in the settlement of an area by people of Western culture. The *pioneer stage* is characterized by a scattered or patchy distribution of settlements in the midst of undeveloped lands. Usually these first clearings (if they are in a forest) are governed in their location and arrangement by the ease of access to a main artery of travel. The first settlements in Rhodesia, in southeastern Brazil, or in southwestern Australia furnish examples of this pattern of arrangement. As settlement progresses and more people come into an area, the skeleton, so closely articulated to the main lines of travel, is filled in, and numerous branch lines (roads or railroads) link these new settlements with the main arteries. This may be called the *stage of elaboration,* when the outline of settlement is filled in and begins to show a closer and closer relationship to the underlying qualities of the land. Thus, in the pioneer stage, whatever governs the position of the highway also governs the general arrangement of the settlements; but during the stage of elaboration the occupance tends first to adjust itself to the more conspicuous features of the terrain. As settlement continues and transportation is made easier, there is more and more of a tendency toward concentration on the best lands, and, moreover, toward the intimate adjustment of the various forms of land use to the varying qualities of the sites. Adjustment becomes nicer and more detailed; each significant change in the character of the soil, the surface, the drainage, or any other feature of the land is reflected by a change in the way that land is used. This may be called the *climax* of settlement, and is well illustrated by many of the more densely populated regions of the Mediterranean Basin. Here, even in ancient times, each crop had its own peculiar type of site, and even the wet marshes of the coastal lagoons were utilized as intensively as possible.

There is, of course, nothing inevitable about such a sequence of stages. In some cases areas may stagnate almost indefinitely in the stage of elaboration. In others a region may advance rapidly from a pioneer stage to the development of a number of small areas of climax, such as the intimately adjusted Fresno raisin district in the midst of a territory where the settlement pattern is still far back in the process of elaboration. In still others, which have reached a climax, events may cause retrogression. Wars, conquests, epidemics, inventions, political changes, the imposition of tariff barriers, or the development of new currents of trade may cause the decline of an area which had once reached a climax.

There are many examples of decline from an earlier climax in the regions which border the Mediterranean Sea. In the course of the centuries since the flowering of the cultures in this area, the traditions so carefully nurtured were for a time lost to sight, preserved in isolated monasteries or in the writings of Arab scholars. Many hundreds of years later these concepts and techniques were rediscovered and, in the hands of a different people, led with cumulative force to the development of the machine culture as we know it today. The focus of the Occidental world is no longer on the Mediterranean Basin: the nuclear areas of Western culture are now in the mixed forest lands, on the borders of the North Sea in Europe, and on the Atlantic coast of northeastern United States.

THE MID-LATITUDE
MIXED FOREST LANDS

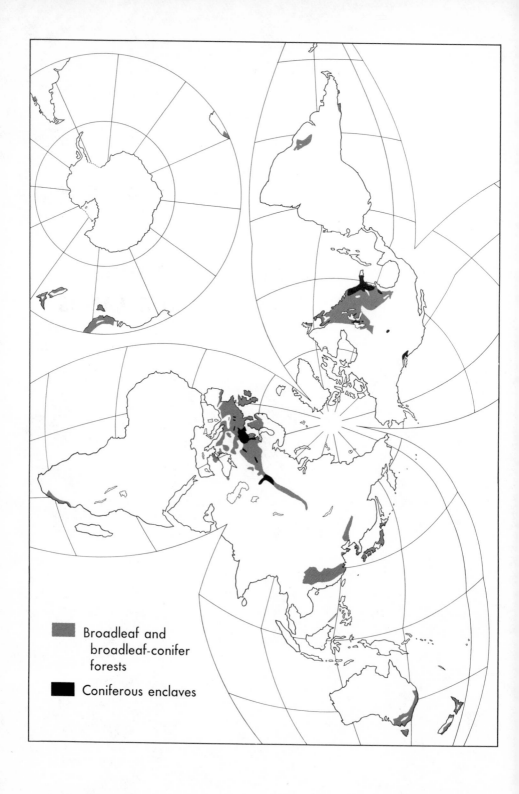

Broadleaf and
broadleaf-conifer
forests

Coniferous enclaves

ONE · PHYSICAL AND BIOTIC CHARACTER

Nearly two fifths of the world's population lives in the mid-latitude mixed forest lands. The concentration of people in the regions of Group IV, which together comprise only 7 per cent of the world's land area, is one of the most striking facts of world geography. Furthermore, within these lands are found the centers of two of the world's chief cultures—the Oriental and the Occidental. The industrial society, one of the major divisions of Occidental culture, had its beginnings around the shores of the North Sea in Europe and its greatest development in eastern North America. The Chinese branch of Oriental culture had its origins in the middle valley of the Hwang (Yellow), and spread into the once forested regions of the Yangtze and southeast China. Today the population of these regions, and of their Southern Hemisphere counterparts, includes 39 per cent of mankind.

The fundamental reasons for the distribution of people have been debated since man first became conscious of his place in the world. The writers of ancient Greece first presented the argument for climatic control: that the torrid lands to the south were too hot and the frigid lands to the north were too cold for civilized men to inhabit. Since that time, however, the centers of Western culture have moved northward into those regions which the ancient Greeks considered fit only for barbarians, and the climatic argument has been suitably revised.

The problem of why so large a proportion of mankind is concentrated in the regions of Group IV is best approached by examining the process of settlement in areas occupied by different cultures. The significance of the physical earth and its resources differs for different groups of people at different periods of time. For rice-growing Orientals the kind of land suited to dense settlement was the kind that was good for this unique crop, with its needs for hot summers with an abundance of water. These qualities of the land had no meaning for

The Mid-Latitude Mixed Forest Lands 175

the European settlers whose chief grain was wheat and who made much use of domestic animals. After the Industrial Revolution a whole new set of land factors became significant in the location of settlement. As is usually the case in geographic study, the problem is best attacked by breaking it down into observable units, each looked at with historic perspective. Otherwise generalization concerning man and the land may become so broad as to be meaningless.

Because of the focus of human interest on these regions, the treatment of Group IV in this book is divided into three parts. First we shall examine the physical and biotic character of the regions of Group IV. Then we shall look at the record of Oriental occupance and, finally, at that of Occidental occupance.

VEGETATION AND CLIMATE

The position of the mid-latitude mixed forest lands in the world pattern is best understood by considering the world as a whole, which we are now ready to do. We find that there are seven major kinds of vegetation: four kinds of forests; grasslands; deserts; and tundras. Between these major kinds lies a variety of transitions. In fact, the major types themselves represent transition, on the one hand from the very dry lands, where only xerophytic vegetation can maintain a precarious existence, to the rainy lands where luxuriant forests cover the surface; and on the other hand from the hot regions of the low latitudes to the cold tundras and ice deserts of the high latitudes or high altitudes.

The pattern of arrangement of these major kinds of vegetation on the earth is a reflection of the underlying pattern of climatic features. As we have seen in the previous discussion of the first three groups, each occupies a characteristic position on each continent. The general distribution of deserts, for example, has been described as follows: they are found on the west coasts of all the continents between 20° and 30° N. and S., and they bend inland and poleward in the continental interiors to about latitude 55°. In specific detail on each continent the arrangement of the dry lands is somewhat different; for the general description of the desert location takes into account only four of the controls of climate, namely latitude, differences of land and water, prevailing winds, and ocean currents. It leaves out the complicating details resulting from specific continental shape and from the arrangement of mountains. These two elements force the generalized pattern of dry-land distribution into the particular pattern to be observed on each continent. But however distorted the particular pattern, it is obviously similar in broad outline to the generalized pattern.

Generalized continent with pattern of natural vegetation

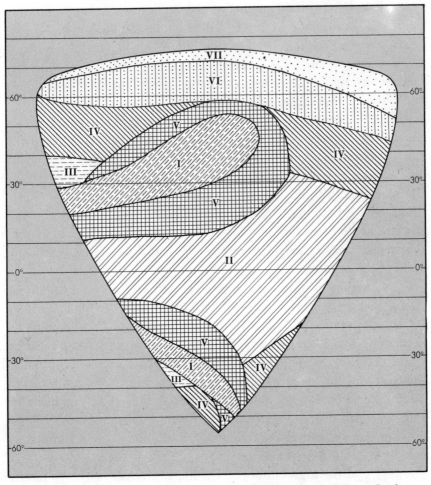

I	The Dry Lands	IV	The Mid-Latitude mixed Forest Lands
II	The Tropical Forest Lands	V	The Grasslands
III	The Mediterranean Lands	VI	The Boreal Forest Lands
	VII	The Polar Lands	

The diagram on page 177 shows a generalized continent, bordered on all sides by ocean. The continental outline is smoothed, but it preserves the general shape of all the land masses in that it is widest in higher middle latitudes of the Northern Hemisphere and tapers toward the south. Except for Antarctica, which is wholly within the south polar desert, the continent which extends farthest south reaches about latitude 55°; therefore the generalized continent is drawn to this latitude. It is assumed that the surface of this generalized continent is a featureless plain, with no mountains to complicate the picture. On this outline the broad patterns of world distribution can be shown.

We can observe the relative position on the continents of the major kinds of vegetation. The position of the dry lands agrees with the general description of desert distribution given above. Surrounding the deserts and conforming to the general pattern of desert distribution lie the grasslands—essentially transitional between places where moisture is abundant and places where it is deficient. The forests of the low latitudes occupy the whole width of the continents for about 10° on either side of the equator, except where highlands, omitted from the generalized continental outline, interrupt. On the continental east coasts, as we have seen, the tropical forests extend poleward to the margins of the low latitudes. Also, in the last chapter we found that the mediterranean forests occupy the continental west coasts just poleward of the deserts.

It is now time to complete this general picture of forest distribution. Along the continental west coasts the forest continues poleward as far as temperature conditions permit tree growth. Where mountains border the sea, as in Norway, British Columbia and Alaska, South Chile, or New Zealand, the forest is limited to a narrow strip along the coast and the lower mountain slopes; but in Europe, south of the Baltic, the forest extends inland and crosses the whole continent of Eurasia, north of the deserts and grasslands, to the east coast. Similarly, in Canada, east of the mountains, the forest lies in a continuous belt between the deserts and grasslands of the continental interior and the tundra of the high latitudes. On the east coasts of the Northern Hemisphere the forest continues into middle latitudes and here also extends as far poleward as tree growth is possible. Thus the middle latitudes are forested on the eastern and western sides of the continents, and where the land masses reach sufficiently high latitudes they are forest-covered from ocean to ocean between, roughly, latitude 50° and the polar boundary. The differences observed on the diagram (p. 177) in the Southern Hemisphere, where, for example, the forest is interrupted on the east coast beyond latitude 40°, are the result of the decreasing width of land area with increasing latitude, and the very wide area of cold ocean water which, under these circumstances, lies off the east coast in higher middle latitudes.

The forests are of various kinds. They may be evergreen or decid-uous, or a combination of these; they may be composed of broadleaf trees or conifers or of a mixture of these types. In general, the tropical forests are composed of broadleaf trees, evergreen except in the regions having a pronounced dry season. The mediterranean forests are also chiefly broadleaf and evergreen. In general, conifers are pushed out by the competition of broadleaf species, and can therefore survive only

An ungrazed oak-hickory forest in the United States

United States Forest Service

where the climate or soil is unfavorable for the latter. The northern, or boreal, forests which cover the whole expanse of the higher middle latitudes of Eurasia and North America, where the winters are long and severe, are mostly coniferous and evergreen.

The mid-latitude mixed forests, composed of both broadleaf and conifer, are transitional between these two extremes. They occupy two distinct positions in the generalized continental pattern in the Northern Hemisphere: east of the dry interior, between, roughly, latitudes 25° and 45°; and west of the dry interior but poleward of the mediterranean forests of Group III, between, roughly, latitudes 40° and 60°. In the Southern Hemisphere, the mid-latitude mixed forest is also separated. It occurs on the eastern side between latitudes 25° and 40°, where it borders the grasslands. On the western side it extends from about latitude 40° to the southernmost point of land.

The Pattern of Climates. These major kinds of natural vegetation reflect the underlying pattern of world climates. In previous chapters we have discussed certain aspects of the climatic pattern. We have described the various factors which determine rainfall effectiveness, and we have shown the relationship between (1) rainfall and temperature, and (2) the four basic controls of climate: latitude, land and water distribution, prevailing winds, and ocean currents. Let us now summarize the effect of these controls on the pattern of climates.

The distribution of air temperature on the earth's surface is determined in general by differences in latitude and by the contrasts between land and water. For reasons which are set forth in the introduction and in Appendix B, the heat received from the sun at the earth's surface is greatest in the low latitudes and decreases toward the high latitudes. If the earth's surface were all land or all water, there would be a simple arrangement of temperature by latitude, with the highest temperatures along the equator. But at any one latitude, land areas heat up much faster when the sun is high, and cool off much more rapidly when the sun is low, than do neighboring water bodies. For this reason, at the same latitude the land becomes warmer than the water in summer and cooler in winter. Continental climates are those which have great temperature differences between summer and winter; marine climates are more moderate throughout the year. The diagram on page 181 shows the generalized position of two lines of equal temperature (isotherms) crossing the same continent shown in the previous figure (diagram, p. 177). The solid line is a winter isotherm—a line connecting places which have a certain average temperature in the coldest month (26.6°). Because the land is colder than the water in winter, this isotherm bends equatorward as it crosses the continent. The dashed line is a summer isotherm, connecting all points which have a

Generalized continent with pattern of summer and winter temperatures

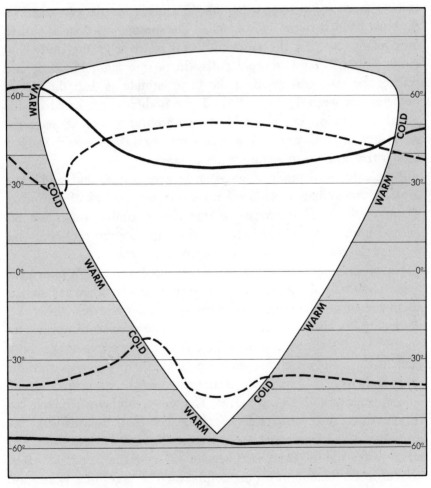

——— Isotherm of 26.6° average temperature for the coldest month

— — — Isotherm of 71.6° average temperature for the warmest month

Vegetation and Climate 181

certain average temperature for the warmest month (71.6°). Because the land is warmer than the water in summer, this isotherm bends poleward in crossing the continent. In the Southern Hemisphere the two isotherms do not cross each other as they do in the Northern Hemisphere. The small land area in higher middle latitudes makes the development of very cold winters impossible. The winter isotherm runs east and west just about as it would do if the world were all water.

The two isotherms in the Northern Hemisphere, however, are not arranged symmetrically on the continents. The winter isotherm reaches the west coast about latitude 60°; it reaches the east coast, on the other hand, between 40° and 45°. The summer isotherm is pushed far equatorward near the west coast, so that it reaches the land about latitude 30°; it bends sharply poleward on the land, however, and reaches the east coast at about the same latitude as does the winter isotherm—between 40° and 45°. These isotherms are based on the actual distribution in the world of two arbitrarily selected temperatures; but any other winter and summer isotherms would show a similar trend in crossing from water to land.

If the only two controls of temperature were latitude and land-water contrast, the isotherms would not show this peculiar lack of symmetry. They are displaced eastward—so that the maximum difference between summer and winter is east of the center of the continent—because of the prevailing winds and ocean currents.

The world's ocean currents are shown on Plate 23. Within each ocean basin and along the shores of each continent there are similar ocean currents. The position of warm and cold water near the shores is roughly the same in each ocean basin. The relation of ocean temperatures to the temperatures on the east and west coasts of the continents is clear. The summer isotherm bends sharply equatorward because of the very cold water along the west coasts between 35° and 15°. This appears in both hemispheres. The winter isotherm is much farther north on the Northern Hemisphere west coasts than it is on the east coasts in part because the west coasts beyond 40° are bathed by warm water and the east coasts beyond 40° are bathed by cold water.

General Circulation of the Atmosphere. The prevailing winds also contribute to this arrangement of the isotherms. As we have seen, there are three major elements to the world's wind systems. There are the oceanic whirls, the monsoons, and the polar outbursts. The oceanic whirls are so geared together that on their equatorward sides, in the low latitudes, the wind comes generally from the east, and on their poleward sides, in the middle latitudes, it comes generally from the west. For this reason the moderating effect of the ocean on summer and winter temperature in the middle latitudes extends farther inland from the west coast than from the east coast. In fact, continental conditions extend eastward to cover all but the offshore islands and peninsulas on that side of the continents. This is brought out strikingly by a comparison of the latitude of the big urban centers of Europe and eastern North America. Due west of London, on the eastern coast of North America, lies sparsely populated Labrador. Such northern European cities as Oslo, Stockholm, Helsingfors (Helsinki), and Leningrad lie in the same latitude as southern Greenland or the northern part of Hudson Bay. In North America, New York and Sitka both have about the same January mean temperature, 30° and 31° respectively; but the warmest month in Sitka is 55°, and in New York it is 73°.

The isotherms, however, tell nothing about rainfall, storminess, and the variability of weather. Rainfall, for reasons described in Appendix B, is caused only when air containing considerable quantities of water vapor is forced to rise and cool. The largest amounts of rising air are found in those places where different air currents converge. Along the equator over the oceans, for example, the air moving equatorward in the oceanic whirls of both hemispheres converges. Because the resulting rise involves air which is filled with water vapor picked up over warm ocean water, the rainfall is heavy (Plates 7 and 26). The convergence of the oceanic whirls is strongest on the western sides of the ocean basins; and because the deflective force of the earth's rotation is not felt at all on the equator and only very slightly for about ten degrees on either side of it, the northeast and southeast winds continue, if terrain permits, far into the continental interiors. Heavy rains on the eastern slopes of the Andes come from the indraft of oceanic air which is especially strong from January to May. On the eastern sides of the ocean basins and on the west coasts of the continents there are wedge-shaped areas of calms in which heavy convectional rains occur during and shortly after the passage of the sun over the equator. These are known as the *doldrums*.

Photo by E. H. Hanlon

Cloud formations along a cold front

Rising air, heavy rains, storminess, and weather variability in the middle latitudes all result from the interaction of the poleward parts of the oceanic whirls with the equatorward-moving polar outbursts. Cold air accumulates over the snow and ice surfaces of the high-latitude regions, especially over Greenland, the Arctic Ocean, the snow-covered continents in winter, and, more than anywhere else on earth, over the ice-covered continent of Antarctica. At intervals the cold air surges out toward the nearest warm spot. It moves close to the ground, for cold air is heavy, and each outburst takes on much the shape of a drop of water rolling over an inclined surface (see maps, p. 532). As the cold air moves into the relatively warm, light air of the oceanic whirl the latter is forced to rise. Eddies are formed around the edges of the cold air masses, and in the centers of these secondary whirls, or cyclones, air is forced to rise vigorously. Along the cold air fronts there are heavy falls of rain, and sometimes violent winds. Those parts of the world over which cold and warm air masses alternate are the areas of greatest storminess and weather variability.

184   The Mid-Latitude Mixed Forest Lands

Actually the world's stormiest areas are found where warm ocean water is relatively close to centers of cold air accumulation. The stormiest part of the world is the higher middle latitudes of the Southern Hemisphere, surrounding the Antarctic Continent. Great storminess is also experienced over the North Atlantic Drift where it passes south and southeast of Greenland; and over the Kuro Siwo where it passes close to the cold Bering Sea and northeast Siberia. Storminess and weather variability, however, extend beyond these maximum zones: the continental coasts both on the west and on the east are very stormy in higher middle latitudes. In winter the cold air masses push equatorward of 40° on the west coasts, and much farther toward the equator on the east coasts, where there are warm ocean currents. The cold air masses that reach western North America come largely from Siberia, the Arctic Ocean, and Alaska; in western Europe, cold air masses come not only from Greenland but also from the continental interior to the northeast. In eastern North America, cold air pours southward from the Arctic Ocean and from Greenland across Canada and the United States. In eastern Asia the very cold area of northeast Siberia is a source of so many polar outbursts that, latitude for latitude, as compared with eastern North America, the winter temperatures of Asia are some ten or twenty degrees lower. The basic cause of the difference is the relative size of Asia and of North America. The temperatures of winter in the continental interior of Asia are much lower than those in the interior of North America.

It is worth noting in passing that the common opinion in the United States concerning the supposed warming effect of the Gulf Stream is erroneous. The fact is that the warmer the water is in the Gulf Stream, the stronger are the cold air masses that move toward it from the higher latitudes. Rising ocean temperatures in the Florida Strait between Florida and Cuba are used by long-range forecasters to predict cold weather and storminess in northeastern United States.

Monsoons and Monsoons. The monsoon is defined as a movement of air from cool places to warm places which for six months goes in one direction and for the other six months goes in the opposite direction. It is produced, as we have seen, by differences in temperature between land and water. The true monsoon is formed where the stream of air continues without interruption. It is found on coasts facing equatorward in the low latitudes—a situation which is not shown on the generalized continental outline, but which is one of the specific departures from the generalized outline which gives each continent its unique pattern. On such coasts there is warm ocean water on the equatorward side which supplies air over it with great quantities of moisture. On the land poleward of the equatorward-facing coast, the temperatures are higher than those over the tropical water in summer, but much lower in winter. Onshore summer winds bring enormous quantities of rain, especially where they rise against mountain fronts.

The true monsoon regions merge with regions along the east coasts of lower middle latitudes in which the alternation of wind direction between summer and winter is statistical rather than permanent. In other words, the average wind direction of winter is north or northwest, both in southeastern United States and in southeastern China, because the polar outbursts come with great frequency at that season. They are occasionally interrupted, however, either by spells of still air between outbursts, or even by warm air masses of the oceanic whirls. In summer, on the other hand, the oceanic whirl is dominant, and winds are mostly from the south and southeast; but even in that season there are occasional interruptions as cold air masses push southward. Actually the monsoon of all of southeastern United States, including that of the margins of the Gulf of Mexico, is an average condition rather than an uninterrupted condition, both in summer and in winter. The monsoon of India, however, protected as it is by high mountains to the north, is almost never interrupted. The two kinds of monsoon in Asia are merged somewhere in the southern part of China.

As a result of all these conditions, the rainfall in the middle latitudes is especially heavy along the whole east coast, and along the west coast poleward of 40°. The continental interiors are dry; but poleward of about 55° in the Northern Hemisphere temperatures average low enough, even in summer, so that the small amount of rain which does fall is highly effective.

Climatic Regions of Group IV. These various climatic features are combined, in the regions of Group IV, to form three major types of climate. They are: the Humid Marine Climate (Cfb, Cfc); the Humid Continental Mild-Winter Climate (Cfa, Cwa); and the Humid Continental Severe-Winter Climate (Dfa, Dfb, Dwa, Dwb).

The Humid Marine Climate occurs chiefly on the continental west coasts, and on islands of the higher middle latitudes. These coasts and islands are bathed by warm ocean water, and the prevailing westerly winds bring an abundance of moisture to the land. The westerlies are frequently interrupted by cyclonic storms. As a result, the winters are mild, cloudy, and rainy, and the summers are cool and a little less rainy. Rain comes in the form of frequent drizzles, rather than torrential storms. On the immediate coast, the average annual rainfall is heavy. Farther back from the coast, however, the annual rainfall decreases, even to less than 30 inches (London 24 inches; Paris 22 inches); but in the absence of any very high temperatures there is so little evaporation that even this relatively small amount is highly effective and supports a luxuriant plant growth. The extreme of this kind of climate is found on oceanic islands or exposed coasts near the poleward limits (as in Iceland, the Aleutian Islands, and South Chile). The climatic type extends across the oceans of higher middle latitudes, and in the Northern Hemisphere touches the east coast in two places: in northern Japan and in Cape Cod.

The Humid Continental Mild-Winter Climate occurs on the eastern sides of the continents in lower middle latitudes, and in a few little spots in southern and eastern Europe west of the grasslands (such as the Po Valley of Italy). It is characterized by mild winters, with occasional freezing weather and falls of snow of short duration. The summers are very hot and humid—considerably hotter than the weather encountered in most parts of the rainy tropics. Compared with the marine climate, there is a much greater range of temperature between summer and winter; there is much less cloudiness, especially in winter; the rainfall maximum comes in summer rather than in winter; and the rain comes in the form of torrential downpours rather than drizzles. On the eastern sides of the continents in the Northern Hemisphere (in China and southeastern United States) the climatic conditions are almost identical latitude for latitude, except that the winters in China are much colder, for the reasons explained above. The average monthly rainfall at Charleston, South Carolina, and at Shanghai, China, is almost exactly the same, with a maximum amount in June and July and a minimum in December and January. At both places the prevailing winds shift from offshore in winter to onshore in summer. Shanghai is 20° colder in January, but in July the temperatures of the two places are almost the same. Clearly, then, to describe the climate of this part of China as a "monsoon" climate is correct only if the climate of eastern United States is also described in this way. Both regions have a Humid Continental Mild-Winter Climate, and both are in the area of the statistical monsoons.

The Humid Continental Severe-Winter Climate occurs on both sides of the dry interior in the Northern Hemisphere, north of the mild-winter climate. The difference between the two is that in the areas of severe winters there is a snow blanket that remains on the ground for weeks at a time. The line between mild winters and severe winters in Köppen's classification of climates (as originally presented by Köppen) is the isotherm of 26.6° average temperature for the coldest month (the distinction between D climates and C climates on Plate 8). This line appears in eastern United States just north of Boston, bends southward in the Appalachians, but returns northward again to pass north of Cleveland, and then runs through the middle of the Corn Belt westward into Kansas. In eastern Asia the line passes through northern Japan, crosses Korea, where it corresponds closely to the line between North Korea and South Korea, and passes to the north of the Yangtze Valley of China. In Europe, on the other hand, this same line runs north and south through Poland, separating the area of mild winters to the west from the area of severe winters to the east. In the southernmost parts of this severe-winter climate summers are hot, as they are in the Corn Belt, in North China and Manchuria, and in a few spots in eastern Europe. Elsewhere, however, summers are cool, as they are in the United States north of the cities of Boston, Detroit, Chicago, and Minneapolis; and as they are in both the eastern and western parts of the Soviet Union.

In the absence of any wide expanses of land in the higher middle latitudes of the Southern Hemisphere, there are no severe-winter climates.

The Vegetation Types and Their Distribution. The mid-latitude mixed forests are composed of a number of different forest associations, some including both broadleaf trees and conifers and some composed wholly of one or the other. Along the continental east coasts, the forests of Group IV are distinguished from those of Group II because of the predominance of species which can endure cold weather in winter. The palm, for example, is a characteristic low-latitude tree, and it does not flourish poleward of 30°, although stunted palms actually are growing poleward of this. The poleward limit of the palm is shown below, together with the coldest-month isotherm of 64.4°, which is commonly used to distinguish climates with mild winters from those with no winters. The same figure shows the distribution in the United States of the black oak (*Quercus velutina*), which is a tree distinctly adapted to mid-latitude conditions. The boundary between the low-latitude and middle-latitude forest types is obviously a zone of transition, and the actual line drawn on the plates (Plates 10–20) is an arbitrary one.

The boundary between broadleaf forests and conifers is even less distinct. Conifers are found far equatorward in the winterless regions of the tropics. The characteristic vegetation of large parts of Florida, Cuba, and the Bahamas is a mixture of pine and palmetto. Throughout the regions of Group IV, on both sides of the continents, there are "islands" or enclaves of pure coniferous forests in the midst of the predominant broadleaf forests. Usually these islands are located on areas of exceptionally poor soil. Pine occurs in pure stands, for example, on

The limits of the palm, the isotherm of 64.4° for the coldest month, and the limits of the black oak in the United States

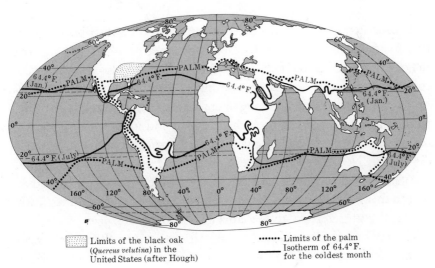

Limits of the black oak (*Quercus velutina*) in the United States (after Hough)

•••••• Limits of the palm
——— Isotherm of 64.4° F. for the coldest month

the sandy coastal-plain soils of southeastern United States. It is found also on the sandy glacial soils of the Lake States and of Europe southeast of the Baltic Sea. On the highlands of southeastern United States, and in a similar position in South Brazil, the original forest was a mixture of pine and broadleaf trees. There are also pine forests on the very rainy mountain slopes of the west coast of the Northern Hemisphere, but only broadleaf trees in a similar position in South Chile. The greater part of the regions of this group, however, were covered originally by various associations of broadleaf trees (picture, p. 179).

On the poleward side in the Northern Hemisphere, where Group IV borders the forests of Group VI, there is a relatively sharp line of demarcation. The forests of the northern lands having severe winters and short summers (Group VI) are made up of pure stands of conifers, chiefly spruce and fir.

Toward the continental interiors, on the dry side of Group IV, the mid-latitude mixed forests are usually bordered by grasslands. As in the case of the tropical savannas, these grasslands seem to have been produced by the fires of prehistoric man. Where fires are controlled in modern times, the forest returns to the prairie lands, and even the semi-arid steppes are covered by scrubby woodland. Fingers of galeria forest extend along the valleys far out into the grassy regions.

SURFACE FEATURES

A discussion of these generalized patterns of forest distribution gives us a basic understanding of the factors or controls which produce the major lineaments of the face of the earth. But it is also true that each continent, each area of mid-latitude mixed forest, can be identified because of its own unique arrangement of surface features. The particular patterns developed on each continent and in each major natural region result from the configuration of the surface and the trend of the coasts. No generalized pattern of surface features can be shown on the generalized continent because, as we pointed out in the introduction to this book, the relief features of the earth are not symmetrically arranged with reference to the equator and the poles.

The regions of Group IV, then, are all different in the arrangement of their surface features. Of all these regions, however, the ones which

A hilly upland in the Appalachian region

are located in Europe are the most intricate in pattern (Plate 15 and map, p. 224). With a much indented coast line, and with many mountain ranges and enclosed basin plains or uplands, this continent is composed of a large number of distinct natural regions more or less isolated from one another. The largest area of low relief is in the east, extending from the Black Sea to the Arctic. Only in its central part is it included in Group IV. Toward the west this plain narrows down like a funnel, constricted on the north by the Baltic Sea and on the south by the mountains and uplands of central Europe. The end of the funnel is on the shore of the North Sea. Here the natural lines of circulation come to a sharp focus; for not only is this the apex of the plain just mentioned, but also it is easily reached from the south through a series of basins and river valleys. Just south of the Plain of Flanders lies the Paris Basin, united by low passes to the Aquitaine Basin and to the Mediterranean through the Saône-Rhône Valley. The Rhine, also, leads to the North Sea. Even in the British Isles the largest lowland area, on which London is situated, faces the North Sea. In this

Surface Features 191

portion of Europe, therefore, is one of the world's greatest foci of natural lines of travel, as guided by the configuration of the surface.

In contrast to Europe, eastern North America is built on a pattern of relative simplicity (Plate 9 and map, p. 261). Its plains are extensive and continuous instead of being broken into numerous isolated units. The various parts of the Appalachian-Ozark system of hilly uplands and low mountains, extending southwestward from New England, are arranged in simple linear fashion, separating the coastal plains of the east and south from the central plains of the interior. The Mississippi Valley, south of the mouth of the Ohio, is one of the world's major river floodplains (map, p. 271). Aside from the several natural foci of routes of travel in the interior of eastern North America, the natural outlets across the barrier of highlands are three in number. Perhaps the most obvious route from the interior plains is down the Mississippi to the Gulf of Mexico. Another natural outlet is provided by the St. Lawrence. For historical reasons, however, a third natural highway has been of greater importance than either of the other two: the Hudson-Mohawk route, by which an easy passage of the Appalachian system is made (with a climb of only four hundred and forty-five feet). This pass contributes an important part of the focus of natural lines of travel on the site of New York City.

Very different from either Europe or eastern North America are the Asian borderlands (Plate 17 and map, p. 199). Here the areas of lowland are relatively small, being restricted by many ranges of hills and mountains to the alluvial valleys of the great rivers. Furthermore, the regions of Group IV are limited to the continental margins by the lofty mountains and desert plateaus of the interior. In China the two mighty rivers, the Yangtze Kiang and the Hwang Ho,[1] have formed the largest areas of lowland, south and north of the Shantung peninsula. Loess, carried by the wind from the deserts of the interior, has been added to the river alluvium to build the Hwang Plain. Smaller valleys, such as the Si Plain of South China, the Chengtu Plain of the interior, or the river plains of southern Manchuria, are found in scattered positions, isolated by the highlands. The southern side of Korea consists of narrow valley lowlands separated by transverse belts of hills

[1] In the language of North China the word *ho* means "river"; in the language of South China *kiang* means "river." It is incorrect to speak of the "Hwang Ho River."

descending from the backbone of high mountains along the east coast. The islands off the coast of Asia, such as western Taiwan (Formosa), and most of Japan are included in Group IV. Japan is crossed by a zone of high mountains, the Japanese Alps, which cut across Honshu from the west coast to the southeast coast between Tokyo and Nagoya (map, p. 353). The rest of Japan is composed of low mountains and ranges of hills, enclosing small interior basins, and with numerous narrow strips of coastal plain or delta plain.

The other parts of the world where regions of Group IV occur are all much smaller. In all of them the lowlands are closely hemmed in by mountains or hilly uplands. In western North America most of the land bordering the Pacific is mountainous (Plate 9). A long, narrow lowland, large enough to be distinguished from the bordering mountains, extends from Eugene, Oregon, to Puget Sound. In Oregon,

Most of Japan is composed of hills and low mountains, with narrow valley lowlands

south of Portland, it is known as the Willamette Valley; in Washington it is called the Puget Sound Lowland. The lowland crosses the border into Canada, where it provides the site for the port of Vancouver in British Columbia. To the north, however, the steep mountain slopes descend directly to the sea, leaving only a few narrow delta plains too small to appear on the maps. In addition to providing for the port of Vancouver, Puget Sound offers fine protected harbors for Seattle and Tacoma.

In the Southern Hemisphere the surface features of the regions of Group IV, like the climates and the types of natural vegetation, show a close similarity to those of western North America. The Central Valley, already described in mediterranean Middle Chile, extends southward, like the Puget Sound Lowland, to the beginning of the embayed section at Puerto Montt. In South Brazil the mid-latitude mixed forest region is found in the states of Paraná, Santa Catarina, and Rio Grande do Sul, and in the eastern part of Paraguay (Plate 11). This whole region consists of hilly upland and plateau, which faces toward the Atlantic with a steep escarpment some 3000 feet in elevation. On the border of Brazil and Paraguay the upland is cut by the deep canyon of the Paraná River, and tributaries to the Paraná which rise near the crest of the escarpment flow westward in valleys which become deeper and deeper. The Iguaçu River descends over great falls into the deep valley of the Paraná. In South Africa there is a small coastal strip which belongs in the regions of Group IV (Plate 13 and map, p. 73). It lies at the base of the escarpment capped by the Drakensbergen and extends from Port Elizabeth to and somewhat beyond Durban. Southeastern Australia is composed of small, isolated coastal lowlands, backed by hills and low mountains,—not unlike the Appalachians in degree of relief (Plate 19 and map, p. 170). Isolated plains are occupied by Brisbane, Sydney, Melbourne, and Hobart. In New Zealand, too, the lowlands are small and isolated, backed by dissected plateaus and rugged mountains.

DRAINAGE AND SOILS

Most of these regions of Group IV are well-watered, but droughts occur as a result of variations of rainfall, just as in the tropical forest

*A flood along the Connecticut River between Vermont and New Hampshire.
Observe the natural levee in the making*

lands. That these droughts result in famines, especially in the densely
crowded agricultural lands of Asia, is a measure of the pressure of the
population on the limits of subsistence rather than of the severity of
the droughts. Similarly, the problem of providing a good water supply
for the modern industrial and commercial great cities is a serious one
and may even limit the size of these cities as it does in the dry lands.
But compared with other parts of the world, the lands in this group
have an abundant water supply.

Floods are perhaps more of a menace than droughts. In the monsoon lands every summer is a period of high water; but every few years more rain falls than usual, and as a result there are disastrous floods along the lower valleys. In the other parts of the group, floods occur during periods of excessive rainfall, especially if the rains come when the ground is frozen so that the water cannot sink into the soil. Spring floods associated with the melting of snow are common in the colder northern portions. The rivers are usually able to take care of the floodwaters, provided the tributaries do not all rise at once. The Mississippi floods of 1927, for example, were caused by the coincidence of several flood crests on the tributary streams.

The removal of forests from the headwaters of tributary streams is an important cause of floods. As in the tropics, the runoff is much increased by the clearing of the land; and in the hilly areas of the middle latitudes, where snow may accumulate to considerable depth in a winter storm, the lack of a forest cover permits rapid melting to take place. The result is that the deforested slopes no longer act as reservoirs to hold back the water and maintain a more even flow, and therefore serious floods alternate with protracted periods of low water. An outstanding example of this is found in China. For more than four thousand years floods and droughts have punctuated its history as a result of the almost complete removal of the forest cover. Similar disasters have accompanied the removal of headwater forests in other parts of the world.

Soils. Many of the same processes of soil development which operate in the tropical forest lands are active also in the middle latitudes, but with certain significant differences. Leaching and eluviation take place wherever rain water is percolating through a soil to the ground-water table. But all chemical processes in the middle latitudes go on more slowly than in the low latitudes, owing to the lower temperatures and less extreme humidity. Humus accumulation, too, is possible in the middle latitudes; for the slower decay of organic litter on the forest floor results in the collection of a black mold, which, mixed with the soil layers, imparts a brownish color.

Three mature soil types are recognized in the regions of Group IV. The red and yellow colored soils of Group II extend poleward into the warmer parts of the mixed forest lands, and are known here as *yellow*

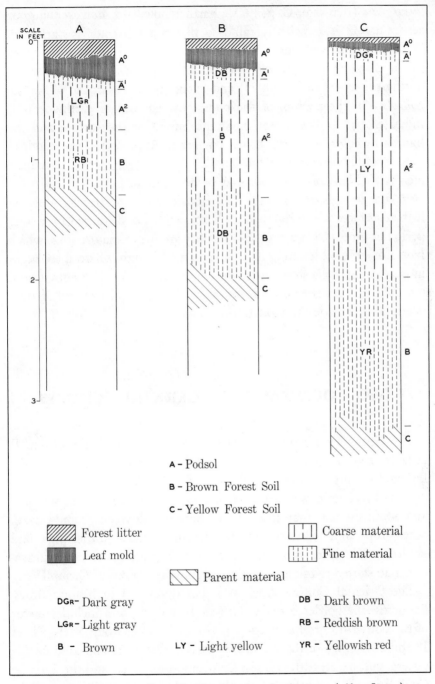

Generalized mature soil profiles developed under forests. (*After Jenny*)

forest soils (diagram, C, p. 197). Farther poleward, however, humus accumulation is sufficiently rapid so that the soil color is darkened. With the aid of earthworms the organic matter is mixed with the upper soil layers to form the *brown forest soils* (diagram, B, p. 197). On the northern borders of Group IV and extending into Group VI lie the *podsols.* In the profiles of the podsol the absence of earthworms is indicated by the concentration of the humus at the surface and the light, ashy color of the soil below (diagram, A, p. 197). The depth of these profiles decreases as the length of the frozen period of winter increases. None of these soils may be described as fertile.

Mature soils, however, with their distinct horizons, develop only on flattish surfaces where the regolith has remained undisturbed for a long period of time. Of much greater fertility are the immature soils, which have not suffered leaching and eluviation, although where these occur in hilly country the steepness of the slopes may make their agricultural use difficult. As elsewhere in the world, the alluvial deposits of river floodplains provide the most fertile lands.

TWO · OCCUPANCE BY ORIENTAL CULTURES

The Group IV regions of eastern Asia together with the Group II regions of southern and southeastern Asia constitute the habitat of the Oriental cultures. The tropical parts of this area were at the eastern end of the zone in which man first appeared on the earth. In India and Southeast Asia man first learned how to cultivate rice and certain other crops, and to make use of domestic animals—cattle, pigs, and poultry. Paleolithic man, even before the beginnings of crop cultivation, had started to migrate northward into the regions of Group IV.

The Oriental Culture Area, as it has developed in historic times, lies across the border between Groups II and IV, and includes pieces of the bordering groups (Group I, Group V, and Group VIII—Plates 18 and 21). Two of the world's six early civilizations appeared in this general culture area: the Hindu Civilization in India; and the Chinese Civilization in the valley of the Hwang Ho (Yellow River) and its

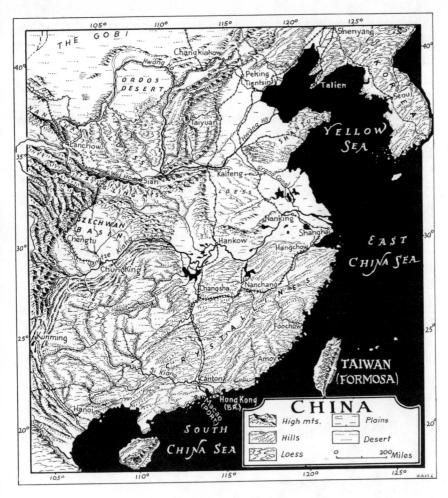

Eastern China

tributary the Wei Ho (map above). India and China have remained the two major culture centers. The countries between India and China have received many traits from both sources. In most of the lands of Southeast Asia the largest minority group is Chinese. Usually the Chinese are concentrated in the cities where they are engaged in commerce. The other two modern countries of the Oriental Culture Area, both in Group IV, are Japan and Korea. Both these countries derived their basic culture traits from Chinese sources.

Occupance by Oriental Cultures   199

In many ways the Oriental cultures differ strongly from those of the Occident. Rice is the basic food, and the material culture is built around this one crop to a remarkable degree. Methods of rice cultivation are intensive and require a vast amount of patient hand labor. In India human muscles are aided by oxen; in China, by water buffaloes and horses. Rice, as we have seen, requires a climate of hot, rainy summers, and alluvial land suitable for the construction of rice paddies. For more than four thousand years the farmers, especially those of China, have been perfecting the methods of intensive rice farming. Although the yield per acre of rice is highest in Japan, China is not far behind. Only where Oriental peoples have had to occupy land unsuited to rice have they adopted other grains, such as wheat or millet.

There are also other distinctive features of Oriental culture. The religious teachings of such masters as Buddha and Confucius have produced attitudes toward the problems of making a living from the land and toward human relations that are very different from those of the Occident. The family plays a role in social organization that makes it,

Transplanting rice seedlings in a Japanese paddy field

Tiers, from Monkmeyer

rather than the community, the basic unit. The family is more important than the individuals who make it up. The worship of ancestors is reflected in the landscape by the considerable areas of good land used for cemeteries. The attachment of the farmer to the land where his ancestors have worked is very strong. Very important, also, is the Oriental attitude toward the passage of time. Often the attitude toward pressing problems of the moment is one of such patience and resignation that the foreigner finds difficulty in understanding it.[1]

CHINA

There are parts of China where the record of continuous human occupance is longer than anywhere else on earth. The forest was cleared from the valleys of the Hwang Ho and of the Yangtze Kiang so long ago that the precise outlines of the area it once occupied can no longer be reconstructed (Plate 18). Even the soils in these areas of dense agricultural settlement have been worked and reworked for so many thousands of years that they are essentially man-made. The Chinese have been so successful in forming a permanently workable connection with the land that the Chinese culture has persisted for a very long period of time. And no country has been invaded and conquered more often than China, and has more often assimilated the conquerors to preserve the traditional culture unchanged.

In the twentieth century, however, the massive, persistent culture of the Chinese is threatened with revolutionary change. The population density and the increasing rate of population growth, resulting in part from contacts with Europeans, had increased the amount of Chinese poverty beyond the point of endurance. The Japanese invasion of World War II tore millions of peasants loose from their ancestral lands. When the communists promised a program of reform they were given wide popular support. The program they undertook was aimed at changing China from an agricultural country to one based on modern manufacturing industry.

[1] The problems of intercultural understanding have been discussed by F. S. C. Northrop in *The Meeting of East and West*, New York, 1946; and in "Man's Relation to the Earth in Its Bearing on His Aesthetic, Ethical, and Legal Values," in W. L. Thomas, Jr., and Others (editors), *Man's Role in Changing the Face of the Earth*, Chicago, 1956, pp. 1052–1067.

A crowded street in Shanghai

202

The Pattern of Population. The pattern of population can be viewed at several different degrees of generalization. On a very small-scale map, such as the map of Eurasia (Plate 5), the concentration of people in the eastern part of China stands out clearly. A large part of the huge national territory has a very thin population. *China proper* is the region with more than 26 people per square mile. This is the area in which most of China's 582 million people (about one fourth of all mankind) are concentrated.

If we look more closely at China on a population map made on a somewhat larger scale, we can see the pattern of population in greater detail (map, p. 204). A comparison of the population map with the map of surface features (p. 199) shows that the delta plains and river valleys of China proper are densely occupied, whereas, even within the general area of concentrated settlement, the hilly areas are only thinly inhabited. Especially high densities can be observed on the delta of the Yangtze Kiang, on the Plain of North China (the alluvial plain of the Hwang Ho), and in the Szechwan Basin of the interior. High densities can also be seen in little patches along the coast south of the Yangtze, and in the narrow valleys of the hilly southeast.

We can look even more closely at China's pattern of population on a map showing topographic detail. On such a map, even within the areas that show a very dense population on the other maps, there are marked differences between places where people actually live and work and places where there are few people. On the plain of the Hwang Ho there are strips of sandy or gravelly alluvium or bits of poorly drained marshland that are almost entirely empty. Settlement is concentrated on the strips of fine-textured alluvium or on the areas covered by wind-blown dust, or loess. On the Yangtze delta, even within the strips of land that are densely occupied, the people are clustered together in compact villages surrounded by the rice paddies which remain empty at night (map, p. 206).

The density of population in the crowded parts of China proper is very high. The world's greatest concentration of rural people is on the Yangtze delta, where there are some 4000 people per square mile. Densities of more than 1000 per square mile are to be found in all the darker patches on the map of China (p. 204). Yet there are such large areas of very little population even in the eastern part of China that

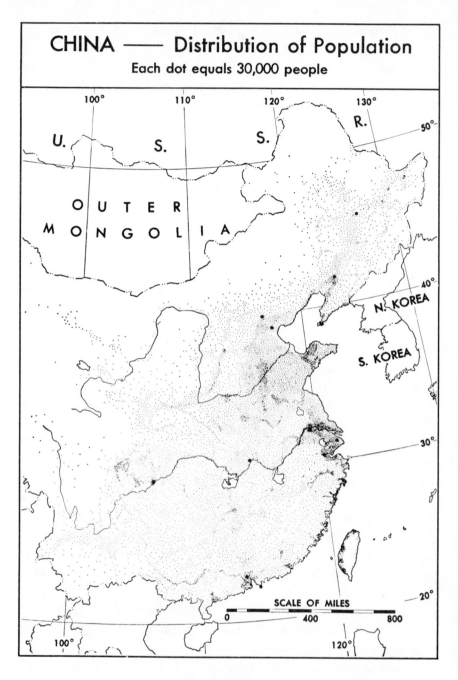

CHINA —— Distribution of Population
Each dot equals 30,000 people

The population of China. (*From George B. Cressey,* Land of the 500 Million, *McGraw-Hill Book Company, Inc., 1955*)

the over-all average of China proper is only 350 people per square mile. The over-all average for the total national territory (205 people per square mile) is a meaningless figure because so large a part of the area has no people at all. Within China proper nearly 90 per cent of the people are squeezed together on only 27 per cent of the area.

Before World War II only a small proportion of the Chinese population lived in cities. Not more than 6 or 7 per cent lived in cities of over 100,000, and only 12 per cent lived in cities of over 10,000. Some 75 per cent of the Chinese people lived in small rural villages or in isolated rural farm homes.

Chinese Agriculture. The reason for the concentration of people on relatively small areas and for the existence of large empty areas even in China proper is to be found in a study of the nature of Chinese agriculture. Since a man with a spade and a hoe cannot take care of much more than an acre of land in the time required by the passage of the seasons, he must concentrate his work only on the most productive places if he is to support his family. On such small farms the yield of crops in hilly areas of thin soil or in semiarid areas would not be enough. In the Occidental world farmers cultivate poorer lands, supporting themselves on larger areas by using machinery; but in China, as population has approached the limits of the food supply, the farmers have worked to produce more per acre. Irrigation is very laborious, requiring a large part of the farmers' time, but it results in very large production per unit of area.

During the thousands of years that the Chinese farmers have faced this problem they have devised one of the world's most productive agricultural systems. The yields of nearly all the crops of China are above world averages. The yield of rice is second only to that produced by the Japanese farmers, and about twice that of the rice farmers of India. There are plenty of people to do the work. The one major objective of the Chinese peasants has been to increase even further the production per acre; not, as in the Occidental world, to increase the production per worker.

The continued increase of population, especially in the last century, has placed a heavy burden on the land. Before World War II the average per capita area of farm land in China proper was about half an acre. Farm sizes, too, were small. In North China, where rainfall

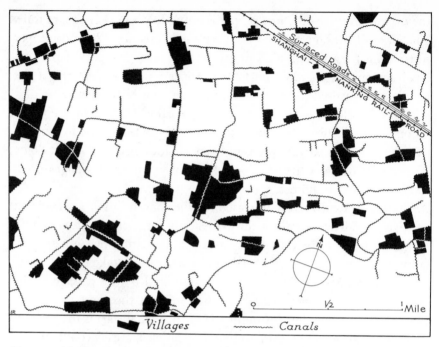

Villages ～～～ Canals

Topographic detail of the Yangtze delta near Shanghai. The railroad, built in 1909, is an Occidental feature superimposed on the ancient settlement forms of the Oriental culture. The space outside the villages is almost exclusively devoted to rice. (From the "Plan of Shanghai," Shanghai, 1928)

is not always plentiful, the average size of farms was five acres; on the crowded Yangtze delta it was only a little more than an acre. In the South, where the hot, humid climate supports a very productive agriculture, the farms averaged less than an acre. But in China proper there are only about 275 million acres of arable land, and this was not enough to provide all the Chinese with farms. There were millions who had no land.

Under these circumstances anything that interrupts the farm work or reduces yields can mean starvation for great numbers of people. Warfare brings starvation; droughts, when the onshore winds of summer fail to bring as much moisture as usual, bring starvation; floods, when there is too much rain or when the Hwang Ho, meandering on its flat alluvial plain, slips out of its channel to seek a new route to the sea—these disasters also bring starvation. For thousands of years the population of China has been held in check by recurring famines when thousands or even millions of people starved to death.

Agricultural Regions. Three different agricultural regions developed within China proper: the South China rice region, the North China wheat region, and the Yangtze Valley rice and wheat region. Rice produces more food per acre than any other grain, and consequently wherever it can be grown well it gets first choice of the land. In China rice does better than wheat as far as the 30-inch average annual rainfall line. This line runs approximately along the Shantung peninsula and toward the projecting fingers of the Tsing Ling Mountains (maps, p. 199 and at right). Where the average annual rainfall is under 30 inches, wheat is more productive than rice.

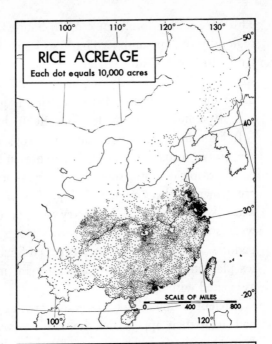

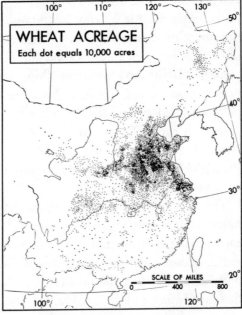

Rice and wheat in China [1]

[1] Adapted, by permission, from William Van Royen, *Atlas of the World's Resources, Vol. I: The Agricultural Resources of the World,* Prentice-Hall, Inc., 1954.

Thus rice is the dominant crop in South China, and in the Group II regions of the far south two harvests yearly can be taken from the same land. In North China, wheat is the dominant crop. It is planted in the spring, and there is only one harvest in late summer or early fall. In the Yangtze Valley, in between, rice is grown during the hot, wet summers, and wheat on the same fields during the mild winters.

In addition to these two dominant crops, certain other farm products are grown, usually on land that is not suited either to rice or wheat. In the tropical south, sugar cane is a minor crop. Cotton and maize are grown in the Yangtze Valley. On the Yangtze delta both cotton and silk are produced. Mulberry trees, on the leaves of which the silk-worms are fed, are planted in rows along the dikes between the rice paddies. In the hilly country between Shanghai and Canton there are tea plantations. In North China a giant millet known as kaoliang is associated with wheat.

Ancient China. These basic patterns of population and agriculture had made their appearance thousands of years ago. By the end of the Han Dynasty (B.C. 206 to A.D. 220) the political area of China was approximately what it is today. Although population was much smaller, the agricultural area was only a little less than that of the present. The distinction between North China and South China had long been recognized. In the long history of China first one and then the other came to dominate the political life. Nanking (which means "southern capital") was used as the capital of China at times. Peking (which means "northern capital") was the capital of China at other periods when North China and Manchuria were dominant. On April 23, 1953, Peking celebrated the eight hundredth anniversary of its first adoption as capital of all China.[1]

The two divisions of China might have wasted their resources in a bitter struggle for supremacy. Instead they became complementary, each making its distinctive contribution to the national economy. Commerce between the two parts was well-developed. It was carried by boats along the rivers and the coast, and along the Grand Canal which tied the Hwang and the Yangtze together. Where there were no rivers, goods were carried by human porters. Chinese economic life faced

[1] The Chinese Nationalist Government on Taiwan (Formosa) denies that Peking is the capital, and so makes use of the name Peiping (map, p. 199).

Looking toward the mainland (Kowloon) from "The Peak" on the island of Hong Kong. The city of Victoria is in the foreground

inland, and the most important cities were places such as Hankow and Chengtu, Nanking and Peking, or Canton.

Nevertheless, long before the arrival of the Europeans, Chinese merchants carried on a considerable amount of trade with distant places. There was an important exchange of goods between China and India, and Chinese merchants were a familiar sight throughout Southeast Asia. Trade was carried on with the great market towns of Turkestan and Persia by means of camel caravans which plodded across the deserts of Inner Asia. Over this route Marco Polo traveled to China in the thirteenth century, returning by sea after many years at the court of the Chinese emperor.

European Contacts. Direct contacts with the countries of Western Europe began in the sixteenth century with the arrival of the Portuguese. The old Portuguese port of Macao, located across the mouth of Canton Bay from Hong Kong, is a relic of that period. The Portuguese name Formosa is still used for the island that the Japanese called Taiwan. After the Portuguese came the Spaniards, the Dutch, the French, the British, and the Germans, all seeking a share in the profitable trade with China.

In the nineteenth century Great Britain gained control of a strategic place just east of the entrance to the Canton River. In 1842 Britain seized Hong Kong Island, and in the war of 1858–1860 took the peninsula of Kowloon on the mainland opposite (picture, p. 209). In 1898 the Chinese government agreed to lease an area of some 390 square miles inland from Hong Kong. This colony and leased territory, which has now an urban population of more than a million, still remains in British hands. It has long served as the main commercial contact between Britain and South China, and, like Singapore, was a major fortress before the days of air power.

Other concessions were granted by the Chinese to the European traders. In Shanghai and other port cities certain districts were set off in which Europeans could reside under their own laws. Because of the importance of the China trade, the port cities grew to be much larger than the old commercial centers of the interior. Shanghai became the largest city of China; Tientsin was established to serve the old capital of Peking. To reach the interior the Europeans built railroads (map, pp. 232–233) and established steamboat lines on the rivers.

The Japanese Invasion. All the commercial and missionary activities of the Europeans only touched the surface of Chinese life. The population, which was about 70 million in 1650, increased to 140 million by 1740, and at a more and more rapid rate thereafter. Population pressure on a land base that was already used to capacity frustrated every effort to do something about poverty and famine.

In the late nineteenth century, Japan began to awaken from its long period of isolation from the rest of the world, and to embark on a program of expansion. In 1894–1895 the Japanese went to war with China and were successful in taking Korea and Formosa (which they called Taiwan). In the war with Russia in 1904–1905 they received certain rights in Manchuria that placed that part of China under Japanese economic domination. In 1931 Japan established Manchukuo as a separate state, and proceeded to build up the heavy industries and to develop the mineral resources of that area. In 1937 the Japanese invaded China proper and in 1941 forced the Chinese government to take refuge in Szechwan. Millions of Chinese peasants were torn loose from the land, either to serve in the army or to avoid the floods along the Hwang Ho when the dikes were broken as a defense against the invaders. When Japan was defeated in 1945 and withdrew from China, the country was in chaos. A bitter civil war developed between the Nationalist Republic of China which had survived the Japanese occupation, and the People's Republic of China which was communist. The communists established their government at Peking in 1949, and in 1950 the Nationalist government fled to the island of Taiwan.

Communist China. The Central People's Government has adopted a program that strikes at the roots of the traditional Chinese culture. The Five-Year Plan of 1953–1957 and the Constitution of 1954 show clearly that the communist objective is to make China once again the major power in the Oriental world by building up a large industrial capacity as quickly as possible. In spite of the fact that 80 per cent of the communist support comes from the peasants, the government has no intention of making the welfare of these rural people its primary concern.[1] Political dominance within China has again been shifted to North China and Manchuria, and away from South China.

[1] See the chapters by Charles A. Fisher in W. G. East and A. E. Moodie (editors), *The Changing World*, New York, 1956.

Nevertheless, one essential of the communist program is agrarian reform. In 1952 the farm population of China was grouped into five classes: landlords, rich peasants, middle peasants, poor peasants, and landless laborers. The land was taken from the first two classes, who probably owned about 60 to 70 per cent of the agricultural area, and was given to the last two classes, who make up a vast majority of the rural population. The liquidation of the landlords and the rich peasants was carried on with popular acclaim and ruthless brutality. Yet the fact remains that there are some 500 million rural people and only 275 million acres of farm land. Eventually the peasants will find that the basic problem of land hunger remains unsolved.

The communists are aware of this problem. Their ultimate aim is to eliminate private property in land, and to organize large collective farms operated with machinery on the Soviet model. But mechanization, wherever it is applied, can only have the effect of increasing the production per worker, not of increasing the production per acre. An attempt is being made to increase the agricultural area through the drainage of marshes and through the cultivation of the semiarid grasslands. Still, it is difficult to see how such a revolutionary change in the agricultural system could possibly produce more food than the traditional Chinese farm practices could do.

The major effort of the communist government is to build manufacturing industries, especially heavy steel industry. In this program China has one great advantage—it is more amply supplied with the basic raw materials for industry than any other Oriental country. China has large deposits of high-grade coal and iron. China is already the world's leading producer of tungsten and antimony, and within the national territory there are large supplies of tin, copper, and salt. With only one exception, the new industrial plants will be located in the north; chiefly in the southern part of Manchuria. Mukden (now called Shenyang), as the urban focus of industrial development, doubled its population between 1949 and 1952.

Partly for the purpose of separating the new China from its former commercial ties with the Occidental world, the communist government is reorienting the economic life, turning it once again to the internal centers and away from the ports. Shanghai is being reduced to about half its former size through the forced removal of millions of its more successful residents. Meanwhile the communists have planned to build new railroads and highways. Eventually a rail line is to be built far to the northwest across the dry interior to connect more directly with the major Soviet centers. Although Chinese and Soviet territory has a common boundary throughout much of Inner Asia, actually the occupied parts of the two countries are remote from each other. This geographic separation by wide expanses of scantily occupied desert and mountain country would not easily be overcome by a single long rail connection.

China's Prospect. Under whatever political regime, China is still faced with a major population problem. The birth rate is one of the highest in the world, averaging between 45 and 50 per 1000. For centuries this high birth rate has been almost balanced by a very high death rate. When medical aid was brought to China by the missionaries, and when the level of living was raised, at least in the port cities, the death rate was lowered. The result was a population explosion. It is estimated that by 1975 the population will have increased to more than 800 million. At first the communist government took the stand that there was no population problem, only a problem of economic development. But by 1958 there were signs that the government had at last accepted the need to develop some kind of a birth control program.

What is likely to happen to China? The Chinese themselves, accustomed to think in terms of a long history of civilized living, are more willing to wait for the outcome of the present communist conquest than are the impatient Westerners. During more than forty centuries China has been conquered many times, but it has always absorbed its conquerors and digested their foreign ideas. The violence of the period after 1950, the "liquidation" of the landlords, is only an incident in the long history of these people. As one Chinese is reported to have said: "After all, things were much worse during the Han Dynasty." It would be difficult for an Occidental, especially a communist, to understand how anyone could hold such a resigned view of the great sweep of history.

There is another aspect of the question that worries the Occidental world. Under a ruthless communist leadership, inspired by purposes unfriendly to the Western nations, an industrialized China with new military strength and with an overwhelming desire for more space for its vast population, could become the world's major military problem. The question then would be to what extent the basic ideas and attitudes of the traditional Chinese culture may have survived the revolutionary change in the economy.

JAPAN

Japan, however, rather than China, was the first Oriental country to develop a strong reaction to the Occidental world. Japan has often been compared with Great Britain, a comparison which is superficially suggested by the similarity of island location off the continental shores. But such comparisons should never be given too much emphasis, for it is a fact which we encounter again and again that each country and each region is unique and requires its own individual analysis and interpretation. In almost every respect, except island location, Japan differs from Great Britain.

Japan before 1868. The Japanese people are diverse in origin. The earliest inhabitants of the islands who have survived to the present time are the Ainus, a Caucasoid people, who came originally from the Asian mainland, and who have been driven from the more accessible parts of the islands to remote and less desirable places by the later invasions of Mongoloid peoples. The groups following the Ainus came from the Asian mainland by way of Korea, and from the southeast Pacific by way of Formosa and the string of small islands connecting southern Japan with Formosa. The racial and cultural heritage brought by the migrants from China and from the south are predominant in present-day Japan. The racial strains which originated in the south make up some 60 per cent of the modern Japanese; although many aspects of the Japanese way of life were carried from tropical regions of Southeast Asia, the contribution of China to the culture of Japan was fundamental. From all these racial and cultural mixtures, however, the Japanese have evolved a fairly uniform society which differs in important ways from other Oriental societies.

Of basic importance in understanding Japan is the fact that for 268 years, from the early seventeenth century to the late nineteenth century, the country remained in seclusion from the rest of the world. To protect their culture from the teachings of the Christian missionaries, the rulers of Japan maintained the strictest blockade against outside contacts. During the period of rapidly expanding empires following the Industrial Revolution in Europe, Japan was inactive. European countries were establishing bases such as Hong Kong along the shores of China while the Japanese were engaged in unifying their own domestic way of life. Not until Commodore Perry in 1853 succeeded in forming personal contact with the Japanese ruler, and not until the Meiji Restoration in 1868 brought in a government with a new policy of participation in international affairs, was the career of modern Japan launched.

Japan before World War II. After 1868 the transformation of the Japanese way of living went on with unexpected rapidity. On a purely self-sufficient agricultural economy, based chiefly on rice, and on a feudal social system in which the individual existed only to serve the interests of the family, the Japanese superimposed an urban industrial economy. The objective of the government was to build a strong military power on the model of nineteenth-century Great Britain. The ideas of the Industrial Revolution were quickly adopted, but in a social environment from which the ideas of the Democratic Revolution were entirely excluded. Huge industrial combinations were built under the control of particular families known as *zaibatsu*. One family built the steel industry; another family was responsible for building and operating the navy, and still another for directing the army. At the top of the hierarchy was the sacred person of the Emperor, to whom every one gave complete loyalty.

The parallel between the position of Great Britain lying off Europe and Japan lying off Asia breaks down at once when we consider the raw material situation. Japan has almost none of the basic raw materials. There are abundant supplies of low-grade coal, but none of it is suitable for use in steel manufacture. Japan does have copper and sulfur, and an abundance of potential water power which has been harnessed by many hydroelectric plants. To build a steel industry, however, it was necessary to import coal and iron. Furthermore, to build a textile industry it was necessary to import cotton and to find outside markets for the manufactured cloth. Japan had, and still has, one great resource: an abundance of cheap and efficient labor, willing to work harder and for lower wages than are the workers of most other industrial countries.

Rice paddies in flood in northwestern Honshu, Japan

In terms of agriculture Japan was also poorly endowed to play the role on which she embarked. Because of the hilly and mountainous nature of the island, only a small part of the total area can be used for rice and other crops. The whole of the potentially useful land was brought into production many decades ago, including not only the small delta plains along the coast, but also the hillsides wherever they could be terraced. This land amounts to not more than 16 per cent of the total area of the four main islands (Hokkaido, Honshu, Shikoku, and Kyushu). And because of the hilly nature of the islands, the construction of huge industrial plants and the expansion of the cities encroach on the very best agricultural land. By 1897 Japan was dependent on outside sources of rice.

In that period the one agricultural product that could be exported to pay for necessary imports was silk. The mulberry trees could be grown on land unsuited to other cultivation, and the abundance of cheap female workers made possible the very low-cost preparation of the silk fiber. The United States offered a huge market for silk. In return, the United States sent large quantities of cotton to Japan. Japan, in turn, manufactured cheap cotton textiles and exported them widely throughout the markets of China and Southeast Asia.

Industrialization profoundly altered the Japanese way of living. While Japan was isolated from the rest of the world the population remained nearly constant—a little below 30,000,000. This was about the number that could be supported by an inefficient feudal system of agriculture; population increase was limited by repeated famines and epidemics. After the Meiji Restoration, however, cities began to grow rapidly. Although the rural population has remained relatively constant, since 1872 the urban population has increased rapidly and at an accelerated rate. In 1920 about 12 per cent of the total population lived in large cities (over 100,000); in 1940, 29 per cent of the people were living in such cities. The major cities which grew so rapidly are located along the southeastern coast of Honshu and around the Inland Sea between Honshu and Shikoku. They include Tokyo, Osaka, Yokohama, Nagoya, and Kobe (map, p. 353). Kyoto is the only great Japanese city with an interior location.

The Japanese leaders, taking their ideas from the Occidental world of the nineteenth century, decided that a strong nation must expand its territory. In 1875 and 1879 they laid claim to the strings of little islands to the north and south: to the Kurile Islands, which reach out toward Kamchatka; and to the Ryukyu Islands, which extend toward Formosa. In 1894–1895 the Japanese attacked China, and had little difficulty in taking Formosa (which they named Taiwan) and in securing a foothold in Korea (which they named Chosen). In 1904–1905 they went to war with Russia, and were successful in gaining control of the Russian naval bases in southern Manchuria and in extending their boundary northward in the southern part of Sakhalin, which borders the Asian coast north of Hokkaido. Soon afterward they declared Korea to be a part of Japan.

As a result of all these conquests, Japan derived important raw material imports. From Korea came large supplies of rice. From the waters to the north around the Kurile Islands came fish, especially salmon and tuna for canning and export. From Taiwan came rice, sugar, and camphor. From Sakhalin came coking coal, petroleum, and wood pulp. From Manchuria came coking coal, iron, soybeans, grain, and timber. Clearly, imperialist expansion paid off.

In 1929, when the great depression hit the Occidental world and the market in the United States for raw silk was enormously reduced, Japan, now inspired by the example of Germany and Italy, declared that the whole of eastern and southeastern Asia was its own area of special interest. This was the East Asia Co-Prosperity Sphere. In 1931 Manchuria was taken from China and set up as the independent state of Manchukuo under Japanese protection. With the aid of Japanese technicians, the industrial raw material resources of southern Manchuria were used as a basis for a vast industrial development. Manchuria became the "arsenal of the Co-Prosperity Sphere." The invasion of China proper began in 1937, and in 1941 and 1942 Japanese armies overran most of Southeast Asia as far south as Burma and Java. The attack on Pearl Harbor in December, 1941, started the participation of the United States in World War II.

Japan's Prospect. Japan's bid for status as a world power ended in disaster. Stripped of all the lands it had acquired by conquest, Japan now includes only the four main islands and a few of the smaller outlying islands. The total area is now only 146,690 square miles. Meanwhile, in spite of the loss of about a million and a half people during

A Japanese village in northwestern Honshu

the war, the total population has continued to increase, reaching 88 million in 1954. Of this number nearly 40 per cent lived in cities. The population density had reached the figure of 583 per square mile of total territory, or 3575 people per square mile of cultivated land. Demographers estimate that population growth will continue until 1990, at which time the population will reach 107 million.

What happens to so large a population in such a strategic situation is of concern not only to the Japanese but also to other nations. With the world divided into hostile segments, the world of the industrial society and the world of the soviet society, Japan's location off the communist-held eastern part of Asia gives it a key position in the world's balance of power. Japan in communist hands would be an even more serious threat to the world's peace than is communist China.

The Japanese, with help from the United States, have been struggling to rebuild a workable economy. There is not much that can be done to increase the cultivated area, although some expansion may be possible in Hokkaido and small marshy places can be drained in the southern islands. It is difficult to see how the yield per acre of rice and other crops can be increased. The hill lands, now used only for the cutting of timber and the making of charcoal, might be suitable for dairy cattle. The difficulty is that Japan's hillsides are covered with a grass that is not edible. The provision of edible pasturage would require the eradication of the native grass and the planting of imported pasture grasses. In 1946 the Land Reform Law took a large area out of family ownership and divided it into individual private properties. This effort to improve the economic condition of the farmers was successful, but most of the Japanese farm properties are still too small to provide a good living. Japan must regularly import some 20 per cent of its food requirements.

Japanese industries face not only a lack of capital to rebuild and modernize the plants but also a serious lack of markets. The demand for silk in the United States has all but disappeared following the development of synthetic fibers. The loss of the Kuriles means that Japan no longer has access to its major source of fish for canning. Although Japan's total catch of fish since the war is once again the largest in the world, this total has been taken from such a restricted area that there is danger that the resource will be exhausted. Japan's steel industry continues to operate on imported raw materials, but at high costs; steel plates, ships, and various kinds of motors are manufactured at costs between 25 and 50 per cent higher than the manufactures of Europe. The items that Japan is able to produce to the greatest advantage include cotton, silk, and rayon textiles, toys, cameras, and optical equipment.

Japan must now find new markets. In many countries there are high tariffs against Japanese manufactures—justified, some say, by the need to protect the living standards of workers in other countries from competition with the low-paid Japanese workers. The traditional market for Japanese manufactures is China; but the present world situation has resulted in reducing China's trade with the Occidental world. Japan is trying to regain its markets in Taiwan, the Philippines, and the countries of Southeast Asia and India, but progress in these countries has been retarded by a deep anti-Japanese sentiment. Without access to markets there is no way of paying for the essential imports of food and raw materials. The temptation to enter the communist bloc and regain the trade with China is to some extent balanced by the fact that Japan would have to play a very minor role at the feet of the new China. The Occidental countries cannot afford to let Japan starve. No easy solution to these problems is apparent.

THREE · OCCUPANCE BY OCCIDENTAL CULTURES

The Group IV areas of Europe and North America, along with the smaller areas of this group in the Southern Hemisphere, constitute the habitat of the Occidental cultures. In Great Britain and around the shores of the North Sea the two great revolutions of our time—the Industrial Revolution and the Democratic Revolution—had their beginnings. From this nucleus both revolutions have spread, but at different rates. Today the effects of these fundamental changes in human life have gone far beyond the regions where they originated.

Occidental culture is now sharply divided into three parts. Where controlled inanimate power has been applied to all kinds of production and transportation, a new kind of economic and military strength has been gained. Where the citizens of a country are given free access to knowledge and are permitted to discuss issues, and where policy is decided by majority opinion, a new kind of political strength is gained—the strength of free men who need no special police to keep them in order. Where the new economic strength has been developed along with the new political strength of the free countries, a new kind of Occidental culture, the industrial society, has made its appearance.

But large parts of the Occidental world are still ruled by privileged minorities and kept in order by police. Some are the original pre-industrial societies, now in process of economic change from an under-developed status. In the soviet society where the Communist Party rules, the liquidation of the privileged classes of the pre-industrial society has been followed by the establishment of a new privileged class of party members, government officials, and army officers. In this chapter on the Occidental occupance of Group IV we are chiefly concerned with the industrial society.

The rise of the industrial society has been accompanied by a great increase in the population, for reasons similar to those we have just described for China. One of the characteristics of the industrial society, however, is the eventual decline of the birth rate and the appearance of a stationary or even declining population at a much higher level of density than existed before industrialization. But as the pre-industrial and soviet countries adopt the technical aspects of industry, they in turn are beginning the cycle of rapid population increase.

The industrial society has also adopted certain attitudes and objectives with respect to the world and its resources that set it off from the pre-industrial society. Self-sufficiency is by necessity abandoned because the locality can no longer provide enough of the materials of food, clothing, and shelter. Earth resources in sufficient quantity to feed the great industrial plants must be gathered from the whole world, not from any one part of it. Self-sufficiency is given up for interdependence. Life becomes richer, more varied, and potentially more secure from the results of natural disasters; but in times of economic or military conflict, when the free flow of commerce is interrupted, the very existence of the industrial society is threatened. For this there is no solution except the wide acceptance of the concept of "one world."

All three of the present major divisions of the Occidental world had their origin in the mid-latitude mixed forest lands of Europe. In this area, today, are the largest concentrations of Occidental people (Plate 4). On a world map of population Europe stands out as one of the areas of greatest density. The key to the problems which beset all Occidental people and which are disturbing the ancient patterns of the Orient is to be found through an analysis of the relation of people to land in Europe.

The Background of Settlement in Europe. Europe is not really a continent at all, except in name. An examination of the globe shows that the great land mass of Eurasia is formed like an isosceles triangle, with its base at the east coast of Asia and its apex in western Europe. No barrier of any sort separates Europe from Asia; in the course of many centuries people have migrated back and forth from the great central heartland of Asia to the various peripheral areas, of which Europe is one.

There is an important difference, however, between the broader eastern part of Europe where it adjoins Asia, and the narrower, western part. West of a line drawn from Leningrad to Trieste most parts of the land are easily accessible to people with ships (map, p. 224). There are three reasons for this. In the first place, the land itself is tapering so that no part of the continental interior is far from the ocean. In addition, the coast line of this part of Europe is deeply indented and has many excellent harbors. And, most important, this part of Europe is crossed by a series of navigable rivers. The Seine-Saône-Rhône system provides a fine route of travel and communication which was of special significance to a people otherwise dependent on transportation overland by horse and wagon. From the Saône, the Gap of Belfort between the Vosges and the Jura gives access to the Rhine, which, in turn, is navigable to the North Sea. The Elbe and the Oder, together with other smaller rivers, connect the North Sea and the Baltic with the heart of western Europe. In contrast, eastern Europe is much less accessible for people with ships, except for the Danube, which leads to the Black Sea.

This difference was of importance to the people who settled in the

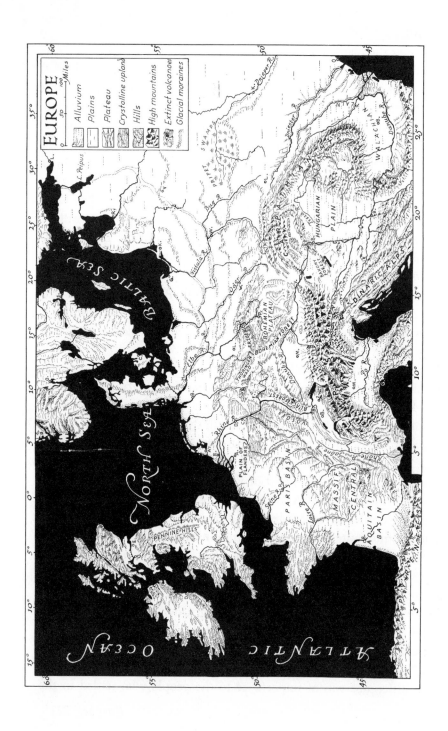

forested regions north of the Alps. The difference in outlook between people close to the sea and people distant from the sea remains even today; and the conflict for power between maritime people and continental people has yet to be resolved.

The People of Europe. Europe was thinly populated north of the Alps when the Romans pushed their conquest across Gaul and into Britain. The Celtic tribes who came very early to the forests near the apex of the great Eurasian triangle were pushed on by later migrants. Today the parts of Europe which are predominantly Celtic are the westernmost islands and peninsulas (map, p. 226). About 2000 B.C. the Germanic tribes were in southern Scandinavia and on the plains between the Rhine and the Oder. Seeking better crop land where summers were warmer, they pushed southward into what is now France, and into the middle valley of the Rhine, and into the upper valley of the Danube. Wherever the soils were easy to drain and to cultivate with simple tools they established settlements and planted crops; but between the settlements were large areas of untouched forest, pictured in German mythology as the dwelling places of gods and demons. To the east were the land-minded Slavs, a pastoral people but recently come from the grassy steppes of the Eurasian interior. They established fixed villages wherever lands could be cleared for pasture. Many of these early villages are marked today by large cities, identified as Slavic in origin by the endings -in or -zig (such as Berlin or Leipzig).

The Romans brought language and many social and political ideas to western Europe. When Roman power collapsed, people in the area west of the Rhine continued to speak a Latin language, but the Germanic language persisted east of the Rhine. English was enriched from both sources. The relation of people to the land, both among the Latin people and the Germanic people, was based on the feudal concepts of the Romans. Feudalism was the basic and widespread way of living in Europe before the rise of the industrial society, and to this day it characterizes the pre-industrial society wherever it is found.

Medieval Europe. Medieval Europe was still not densely populated. There were areas of concentrated settlement, but between them were large expanses of uncut virgin forest, mostly uninhabited. The land was divided into large domains ruled over by lords but occupied chiefly by an illiterate peasantry.

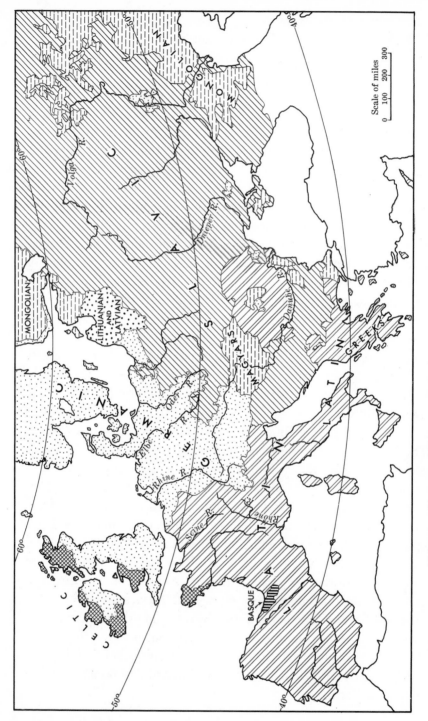

Ethnographic map of Europe before World War II. (*After Bartholomew*)

Essentially each community was a self-sufficient unit of settlement. To be sure, the lord of the land and the retainers who lived with him in his castle and the officers of the army who maintained his rule could make use of foods, articles of clothing, and luxuries brought at high cost from distant places. But the great majority of the people lived on what they produced from the immediate locality.

Under the traditional agricultural system the soils of Europe did not give large yields. The brown forest soils soon declined in productivity when used repeatedly for grain crops without the addition of fertilizers. To cope with this fact the "three-field system" of farming was used. Rye or wheat was planted in a field one year; the following year the same field was used for barley or oats; and in the third year the field was permitted to stand idle or in fallow. Animal manures were not used, even where there were cattle. Under this system the yields of wheat were only six to ten bushels to the acre, and few of the communities were safely beyond the danger of famine caused by local crop failure. The density of population was closely related to the quality of the soil for grain-farming.

The Emergence of the Industrial Society. The emergence of the industrial society and the appearance of modern Europe involved a number of basic changes in the attitudes, objectives, and technical abilities of the people, and with these changes came fundamental differences in the distribution of people and the relation of settlement to the physical earth. The inhabitants of the island of Great Britain played an important role in these changes.

Why should such important cultural developments have appeared first in Britain? There is certainly no one simple answer to this question. It is true that Britain enjoys a stimulating climate, with frequent changes of weather and without great extremes of heat or cold, flood or drought. It is true also that the British people were made up of a variety of ethnic strains. The channel which separates the island from the mainland gave just enough protection from repeated invasion and conflict to permit early political unification and more attention to non-military matters than the people of the mainland could afford. The British people turned to the sea, and their ships sought commercial connections in the most distant parts of the world. The homeland was mostly too wet or too steep to make first-class agricultural land, yet the island was not lacking in products. Traders came very early to exploit the tin ores of Cornwall. In the medieval period wool was sent across the channel to Flanders, where skilled workers made it into clothing. Britain had long been accustomed to dealings with places across the water; and the traders and explorers who blazed the trails to distant places brought back new and stimulating ideas as well as exotic and useful products.

The fact is that the first attack on the traditional way of living of the Occidental world was delivered in Great Britain. The first people to challenge the political and economic power of the landlords over an illiterate peasantry were the British. The first country to become dependent on distant sources of food for the support of all the people was England, which has been dependent on imports of wheat since 1750. The first change in the traditional three-field system of farming was made in England. During the second quarter of the eighteenth century the British farmers adopted a system of crop rotation. A field was used one year for wheat, another year for a cultivated forage crop, and a third year for hay. With the use of more fields for feed crops rather than for human food directly, the acreage in wheat dropped; but the yield rose to between ten and twenty bushels to the acre. This was accomplished through the use of animal manures. The animals greatly enriched the diet of the British, and at a cost low enough so that meat was available not only for the very wealthy but also for a large part of the population. More recently the use of chemical fertilizers has raised the wheat yields of Europe to thirty or forty bushels to the acre.

Inanimate power was first placed under effective human control when James Watt perfected his steam engine in 1769. The technical skill was now at hand greatly to increase the use of power in production and transportation. The age of more and more complex machinery brought about an unprecedented increase in the need of fuels and metals, and it was in Great Britain that the first steps in this direction were taken. The first iron bridge was built in 1779 over the Severn near Coalbrookdale in England not far from the border of Wales. In Coalbrookdale, also, anthracite coal was first used experimentally in the smelting of iron. The traditional fuel for making iron had been charcoal, but the forests of Great Britain were already so seriously de-

The industrial landscape of Halifax, in Yorkshire, England

pleted that a new kind of fuel was urgently needed. The steam engine itself was tried out as a replacement for direct water power, and steam was first used to turn the wheels of a textile factory in 1785. A number of railroads run by animal power or by gravity were in use in England during the eighteenth century for carrying coal from inland mines to the seacoast. Steam engines on wheels replaced animal power on several of these early in the nineteenth century. The first experiment in moving a ship with steam power was made on the Clyde River in Scotland in the first decade of the nineteenth century. These are important events marking the initial steps of the Industrial Revolution.

Changing Patterns of Occupance. Within a relatively few years the significance of the physical features of the earth with respect to the distribution of population in the Occidental world began to require fundamental reinterpretation. Among the many changes in the relation of man to the land which have appeared and are still in process of appearing, we shall discuss four: (1) changes in the pattern of circulation; (2) changes in the significance of barriers to circulation; (3) changes in the location, complexity, and size of cities; and (4) changes in the use of raw materials.

The Patterns of Circulation. One of the distinguishing features of Occidental culture—a feature which has been given new emphasis by the Industrial Revolution—is the movement of people and goods from place to place. This is described by the general term *circulation*. We have already shown that the movement of people and goods is by no means limited to areas of Occidental culture. The caravans crossing the Sahara were described in connection with the Moslem occupance; the connections of ancient China both by sea with India and by land with the markets of Turkestan and Persia, as well as the internal movements within China proper, have been discussed. But in comparison with the volume of movement within the Occidental world these other patterns of circulation are insignificant. A comparison of the patterns of settlement in two Oriental areas (maps, pp. 121 and 206) with those of an Occidental area (map, p. 153) reveals strikingly the contrast in the importance of roads.

The kinds of routes selected in Occidental culture areas have changed with changes in the technology of transportation. In the pre-industrial era of horse-drawn vehicles, canal boats, and small sailing vessels certain kinds of surface and coastal features were important in the selection of routes. But the same features are not so important in the era of railroads, motor trucks, and large ocean ships, and they are quite irrelevant to the patterns of air travel. In many instances the pre-existing patterns have survived the changes in technology because, once established, they could not easily be shifted. However, there are numerous examples throughout Europe of old market towns or ports that have declined because they have been bypassed by the modern routes.

In general, men seek the shortest route from starting point to destination, but they swerve from the straight course to avoid obstacles. Some people, like the Romans, are accustomed to building very straight roads, and are deflected from the shortest lines only by the most serious obstacles; while other people's roads wind this way and that in obedience to the slightest local advantages of travel. Roads are fixed at either end on the surface of the earth, and, to a greater or lesser degree, at other critical points along the way—for example, at passes or low points in hilly country, or at river crossings. In crossing an upland the route which requires the least ascent and descent is usually chosen, but not uncommonly this is modified by the selection of the easiest approaches.

To people crossing a river, firm landing places on either bank are fully as important as shallow water. At such points the roads are fixed in position; but in between they conform to slight local advantages of grade or to stretches of dry soil. In most parts of Europe the natural lines of travel for people on foot or with horses were discovered and utilized by the earliest inhabitants.[1]

Surface features, however, are not the only controls of the road pattern. In many regions the road patterns conform to an arrangement prescribed by the survey of land properties. Whether the property lines conform to the pattern of roads, or the roads assume a pattern determined by the survey of properties, depends on which of these two things came first. The main highways in Europe usually antedate the property lines, and, in fact, form the skeleton to which the latter are articulated. The secondary roads, however, are in many instances fixed in position by the land divisions.

Quite different is the pattern of settlement based on railroads. The route selected for a railroad may or may not follow a route previously selected for a road. By making use of cuts, fills, bridges, and tunnels, a railroad can follow a less devious course through hilly country than can a road, and it is deflected less by swamps and rivers. But because railroad grades cannot be so steep as road grades, rail routes are tied more closely to the major advantages of terrain than are highways.

World Distribution of Railroads. The present world pattern of railroads is the product of only about a century, yet it reveals strikingly the present-day distribution of what we call Western civilization. Since 1825 the strands of the railwebs and railnets have been woven into a closely knit fabric near the great Occidental cities. Away from these cities the fabric has a looser weave, until outside the chief areas of Euro-American settlement only long, isolated tentacles have been extended. This present-day pattern is shown on the map (pp. 232–233).[2] On this

[1] Gordon East, *An Historical Geography of Europe*, London, 1935.

[2] Mark Jefferson, "The Civilizing Rails," *Economic Geography*, Vol. 4 (1928), pp. 217–231. Professor Jefferson suggests the terms adopted here: *railweb* indicates that no part of an area is more than ten miles from a railroad; *interrupted railweb* indicates that a few patches more than ten miles from a railroad exist; *railnet* describes a wider spacing of the railroads in which each twenty-mile zone appears as a distinct band; *rail tentacles* are the isolated lines extending into territory otherwise lacking rail facilities; and *river-links* are those detached bits of railroad connecting two sections of a navigable stream.

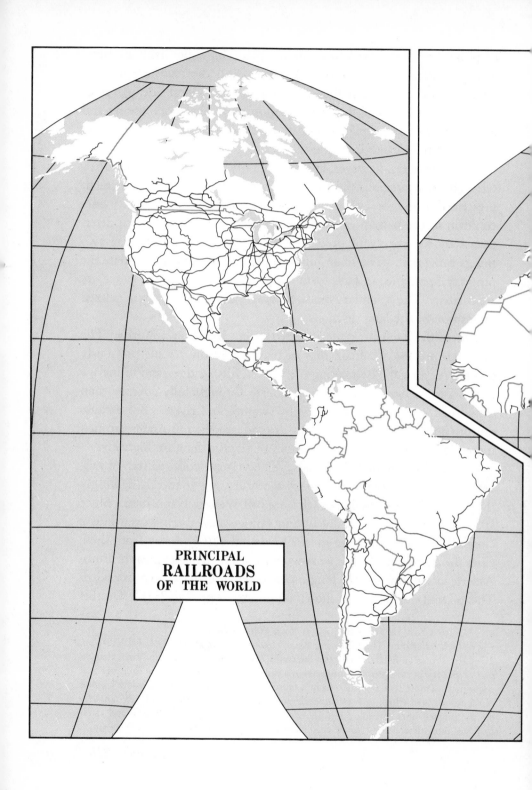

PRINCIPAL
RAILROADS
OF THE WORLD

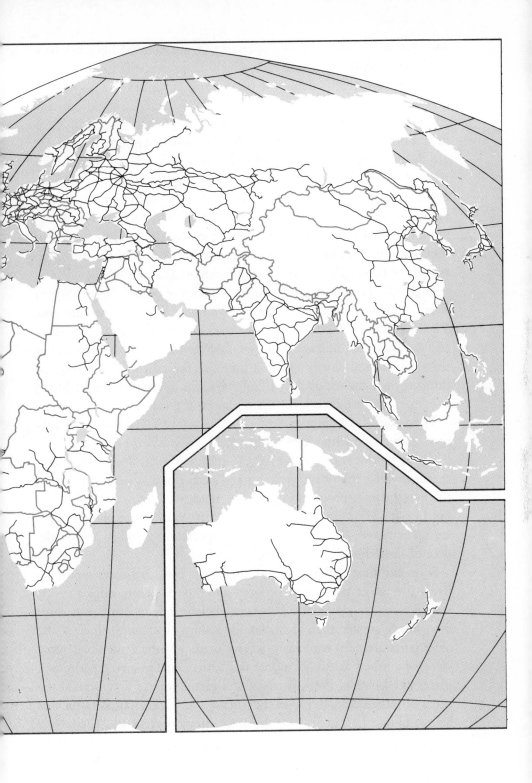

map a zone of ten miles on either side of the railroad lines has been left black. While the actual zone which the presence of a railroad may affect varies with the nature of the terrain, ten miles is a convenient average. Western Europe and eastern North America stand out conspicuously with their closely woven railwebs; other centers of Occidental occupance, chiefly in the different parts of Groups III and IV, are distinguished by interrupted railwebs or railnets; but beyond the parts of the world dominated by the machine culture the rail lines are few and far between. China possesses a net of the loosest weave, and even that is the result of European activities. The railroad is a distinguishing trait of Occidental culture, and its distribution is an excellent measure of the spread of that culture. The importance of the European regions of Group IV in terms of rail transportation is obvious.

Highway Transportation. Motor vehicles appeared before World War I, but it was not until after that war that they became common. The increase in the number of trucks and passenger cars accompanied an increase in the mileage of all-weather paved roads. At first motor trucks were used chiefly to bring goods to the railroads; but little by little, as the network of paved highways was developed, trucks began to compete with railroads for many classes of goods.

The pattern of highways now closely resembles the pattern of railroads in the Occidental parts of the world. The island of Great Britain leads the world in the ratio of road mileage to total area. The high-speed, divided highways with limited access have greatly facilitated the movement of people and goods by motor vehicle for long distances (picture, p. 235). In addition, the fact that even the secondary roads are often paved gives motor-truck transportation a much greater degree of flexibility than transport by rail.

Ships and Ports. Railroads and highways come to a focus on a relatively few large ports, and between these ports ocean ships provide the necessary connections. However, the size of modern ocean ships is so much greater than that of sailing ships that only a few of the older ports are deep enough to receive them. Most of the older ports were established as far inland as navigation on the rivers permitted. Places like London, Paris, Bremen, and Hamburg are now beyond the reach of large ocean ships; so they make use of new outports such as Southampton, Le Havre or Cherbourg, Bremerhaven, and Cuxhaven.

Herkimer Interchange on the New York State Thruway

Smaller ships can still reach these great cities, but the river ports are too crowded to accommodate more than a small fraction of the huge volume of shipping required by the modern industrial society.

If a world map could be made to show the position of every ship on a certain day, it would reveal clearly the pattern of circulation of the Occidental world. Most of the ships would be clustered along the same coasts that show railwebs on the railroad map (pp. 232–233). There would be a great number of ships in the North Sea. Similarly, many ships would be clustered along the eastern coast of North America. In the open ocean the greatest number of ships would be following the North Atlantic route between North America and Western Europe, for the most active movement of people and goods is between the countries of the industrial society. The chief concentration of ships outside the North Atlantic route would extend from

Western Europe through the Mediterranean, the Suez Canal, the Red Sea, to the Persian Gulf and the oil fields of that region. Smaller numbers of ships would be seen following routes to the ports of southern and eastern Asia and of Australia and New Zealand. Ships would also be following routes to Latin America. On vast areas of the oceans there would be no ships at all.

Air Lines. The development of air transportation since World War I has forced people to look at world geography with a new perspective. The old familiar maps of middle and low latitudes, with north at the top and with most of the high latitudes left out, were good enough for people whose only means of oversea movement was by ship. As a result of looking at these maps, however, many geographical errors have crept into popular thinking. One is the peculiar habit of thinking of north as "up" and south as "down," which persists as a kind of geographical illiteracy. Even more serious is the idea that the Atlantic and Pacfiic oceans separate the continents, as well as the failure to see Europe in its new global relationships.

As you look at the world as a whole (which can best be done on a globe), the position of Western Europe takes on a new significance. It is a good exercise in modern geography to pick up a globe and turn it until you find the position which permits you to see the largest proportion of the world's inhabited lands. From such a viewpoint it will be seen that the hemisphere, or half of the earth, that centers on Nantes in France contains almost 90 per cent of the land outside of Antarctica. Only some 10 per cent of the world's lands are on the opposite side of the earth. In the *land hemisphere* (map, p. 237) are to be found 94 per cent of all the people in the world, and 98 per cent of all the world's industries.[1] Western Europe occupies a central position in relation to the global arrangement of lands and peoples, and other parts of the world must be measured in terms of remoteness from Europe. No other great trading area occupies such a strategic position: 94 per cent of the great commercial cities of the world are closer to Europe, on the average, than to any other region of the world. Most of those cities are within twenty-four hours' flying time of Europe.

[1] J. Parker Van Zandt, *The Geography of World Air Transport,* Washington, D. C., 1944.

236 The Mid-Latitude Mixed Forest Lands

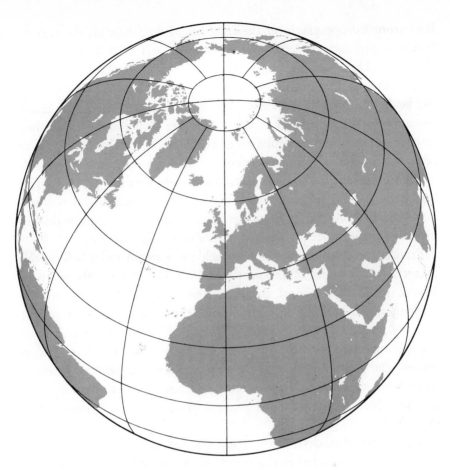

The principal hemisphere

The world's air routes are much freer to follow great circles than are water routes. Air lines connect the chief centers of population and production, just as railroads concentrate in these areas; and from these centers long tentacles are extended to remote places. The high latitudes, long avoided by the world's chief routes of circulation, are now no barrier to high-flying planes. From the chief centers of Europe air routes extend to other parts of the world, departing only slightly from great circles. The air lines to North America pass over the North Atlantic, over or close to southern Greenland, and over Labrador or Newfoundland. From the Scandinavian countries an air route passes over northern Greenland and Canada to western United States. Air lines from Europe pass over the troubled Middle East on the way to southern and eastern Asia, and to Australia and New Zealand. On the way to Latin America the air lines pass over the Sahara, crossing to Brazil between Dakar and Natal.

The Significance of Barriers. What constitutes a barrier to transportation? What features of the terrain are important because they impede or prohibit the circulation of people and goods, or because they offer advantages of military defense? The answer cannot be given without reference to the kind of human society which is present. The search for terrain features which would be advantageous as political boundaries is something which has been of concern in Europe during all the centuries since political boundaries were first drawn.

France, for example, was able to achieve national unity behind the protection of a series of physical barriers. The eastern boundary of France took advantage of the Alps, the Jura, the Vosges, and the Ardennes, along which lines of defense could be maintained against the east (map, p. 224). The fact that there were gaps between each of the hilly or mountainous areas, and that the plains offered easy access around the western end of the Ardennes, has long been of strategic importance to France. In war after war, important and critical battles have been fought in the strategic area between the Ardennes and the sea.

The nature of modern warfare, like the nature of peaceful economic pursuits, has so changed in this period of changing technology that the significance of the terrain is now very different from what it was even during World War I. No longer are ridges and hills of such importance as strong points in defense as they were in that war and earlier wars. With mechanized armies moving rapidly in motor vehicles, the existence of paved roads is more important than the existence of commanding heights. Actually a larger force may be needed to guard the movement of an enemy along paved highways in hills than in level plains because of the many hidden places along the winding roads of the uplands. World War II demonstrated the ease of military movements in the Ardennes, a region long considered as a major strategic barrier. Strong points of defense in that war were offered by the stone houses and narrow streets of the small towns where roads came together and around which it was not possible to pass without leaving the roads (picture below). Now, with the use of air-borne armies and rocket projectiles, the significance of terrain must be interpreted anew.

The Location, Complexity, and Size of Cities. There is an intimate relationship between the pattern of circulation and the pattern of cities. Every urban development of whatever size is the center of converging routes of travel. The area within which the routes converge on a central point is approximately the area that the city serves—the *service area*. But cities, like the means of circulation, have developed in a period of changing technology. Very few indeed are model cities, laid out on previously unoccupied land in accordance with an over-all plan. Most cities have grown without plan or vision, and are handicapped by the forms and features inherited from previous periods of sequent occupance which cannot easily be wiped out for a new start. Most cities are so ill-adapted to modern life that they are frustrating, irritating, and costly for the people who live in them. Most cities are not

The town of Vianden in Luxembourg, in the heart of the Ardennes

The Scotsman Publications, Edinburgh

Edinburgh Castle, once the administrative center of Scotland, now a national shrine and tourist attraction

at all like the dream cities that modern technology and social understanding would make possible.

In medieval Europe there were three kinds of functions for which cities came into being: commercial, religious, and administrative. Most towns started with one of these functions and quickly added one or both of the others. In cathedral towns the church was the commanding structure, visible from afar over the low buildings around it (for example, Köln, in Germany). People came to worship but stayed to trade. In other cases the commanding structure was the castle of the lord of the land, built on a hilltop if one were available, with the town nestled at its base (picture above). From the castle the king or duke carried on the administration of the political area that he controlled. In market towns, the public square in the town center was usually the focus of life. But in any case the medieval towns were compact within their walls, and there was little to distinguish one part of the town

240   *The Mid-Latitude Mixed Forest Lands*

from another. Workshops, salesrooms, and living quarters were all combined in one structure; and the buildings lined narrow, winding streets which were chiefly for the use of pedestrians.

The new technology, which greatly increased the mobility of people and the capacity to transport goods, enlarged and diversified the functions of the urban centers. The volume of commerce grew enormously. Financial and banking services began to concentrate in certain key cities. As the administrative function was extended, government activities were housed in new, imposing buildings, and the castles became museums. A great variety of social functions developed: religious shrines continued to serve people from outside the cities, but there were also university centers for education, centers of art and music, and medical or health centers. In modern life more people seek recreation in cities than in remote rural areas. All these various functions are services performed in central cities for the people of the service areas.

When steam power, and later electric power, was used in factories, large specialized industrial structures made their appearance. The kind of location sought by an industry depends on such factors as accessibility of raw materials and power, supply of labor, and proximity to markets. Industries such as paper manufacture, in which the manufactured product has much less bulk than the raw material, tend to be located close to the supplies of the raw material, often in places where no towns existed before. Industries that are dependent on especially skilled workers tend to be located in previously established cities where workers are available. Industries that turn out products of high value per unit of weight, or products that are perishable, tend to locate close to markets. Since the largest cities are themselves the largest markets and have the largest pools of trained workers, there is a tendency for such cities to grow larger and larger. More and more industries of all kinds are attracted because of all the other services available. Even the basic steel industry, once closely tied to coal supplies, now tends to select locations as close as possible to the largest industrial centers, where steel is used in the greatest quantities.

All these various functions—commercial, administrative, industrial, and social—are often performed in the same city. But now, unlike the undifferentiated medieval city, the new cities are sharply marked off into distinctly different districts. The center is usually a place where the commercial function is focused. This is the *commercial core,* or the *central business district.* Similarly, the other functions are concentrated in distinct *functional areas.* Filling in the spaces around the functional areas, the land in between is occupied by residences which are often built without any over-all plan to guide the development of the urban pattern.

The changes in the technology of transportation made all this development of cities possible. Before the railroad era food could not be brought to any one place in sufficient quantities to support so many non-food-producing urban people. Furthermore, when people had to move about by foot or by horse, they had to live as close as possible to the buildings in which they worked. It was the coming of the electric street-car lines that first made it possible for people to live at some distance from their places of work. For the first time the "journey to work"—a distinctive feature of modern Occidental life—became a problem. Along the street-car lines, or around the stations reached by steam commuter trains, those who could afford to do so left the center of the city and settled in the suburbs. Cities expanded along radiating lines. Later, when the automobile and motor bus permitted commuters to break away from the rail lines, expansion went even farther.

Since the number of new kinds of employment increased to a much greater extent in the cities than in the rural areas, more and more people came to live in cities. Whereas in a country like China less than 10 per cent of the population lived in large cities before World War II, in countries of the industrial society it is not uncommon today to find that 70 to 80 per cent of the total population are city people. The proportion of people employed in agriculture has declined because many people who formerly lived in rural areas now make their living in cities. A large increase in the number of "rural, non-farm" homes has been made possible by the automobile.

The result of these changes has been a rapid increase in the number of great cities in the world. There probably had never been a city with a million inhabitants before London reached that size in 1802. Since then city after city has grown so fast that the present census figures for city populations enumerated within the old political city limits have little real meaning. Geographers define *metropolitan areas,* or *con-*

urbations, as areas which include the connected, continuously built-up suburbs and outlying industrial districts as well as the central city. According to this definition, there were about 20 cities of one million or more in 1920. By 1935 the number had increased to 51, and by 1955 to 71. In 1959 there were well over 80 such cities, and during the next decade many others will reach this size. Table I of Appendix E (pp. 583–584) lists the world's great cities by culture areas.

As cities throughout the Occidental world grew in size and importance, there was a tendency for one city in each country to become pre-eminent. In this one center people could find the greatest variety of goods and services, the rarest articles, the best professional and artistic skills, the greatest development of the business institutions that facilitate trade. To this one center came the most able people because here was the place with the greatest economic opportunity. As the supremacy of one city became more and more apparent, not only traders and business people were attracted to it but also artists, musicians, and people of wealth who wished only to enjoy city life. The result was that one city in each country grew out of all proportion to the other cities. This is what Mark Jefferson calls the "law of the primate city." [1] Among the larger countries of the Occidental world there are eighteen in which the chief city is more than three times the size of the second city; there are twenty-eight in which the chief city is more than twice the size of the second city; and there are very few where two cities of nearly equal size are competing for primacy (as in Canada, Australia, and Brazil).

The Use of Raw Materials. People who live in cities are sometimes seriously ignorant of the relationship between their economy and the resources of the land. Before the Industrial Revolution, however, few indeed were the people, literate or illiterate, who did not appreciate the basic need for forming a workable connection with the land, for in those times economies were closely related to the resources of the immediate locality. The Industrial Revolution has brought a greater and greater capacity to produce goods, and this, in turn, has led to an enormous increase in the volume and variety of the basic raw materials. Water is the raw material consumed in the greatest quantities.

[1] Mark Jefferson, "The Law of the Primate City," *Geographical Review,* Vol. 29 (1939), pp. 226–232.

For industrial purposes it is now used on such a scale that even in rainy parts of the earth many cities suffer from water shortage. More than 250 tons of water are required to make a ton of steel, and the water demands of some other industries are even greater. The world rainfall map (Plate 7) was never more significant than it is today as an aid in understanding the arrangement of people on the earth. But water is only one raw material. In addition to the old, familiar substances, such as coal, oil, copper, tin, iron, lead, and zinc, there are now many newer items such as the hardeners of steel—manganese, tungsten, nickel, chromium, vanadium, molybdenum. Among the other newer natural resources are bauxite, the ore of aluminum, and uranium, used as the basis for nuclear power.

None of these resources is evenly distributed over the earth. Even water, though abundant in some places, is lacking in others. Iron minerals are widespread among the rocks of the earth's crust, and iron ore has been mined in many parts of the world. But the demands of modern industry are so great that no longer is it possible to rely on many small-scale mining operations, which are excessively costly per unit of product. Only by means of large-scale mining operations can the raw materials be produced at low enough cost per unit and in large enough quantities to supply the industrial needs of modern society. One of the basic principles of twentieth-century economic geography is that production of all sorts tends to localize in a few specialized areas. Meanwhile the industrial society has been using up the richer ore bodies at rates even more rapid than the rate of population growth. As lower-grade ores are developed, the cost of production increases—not suddenly, but by small steps. There are some economists who point to the possibility that gradually increasing costs could wipe out the advantages of large-scale production and could bring the industrial society itself face to face with disaster. It seems that the Occidental world is engaged in a race between continued technological progress and resource exhaustion.

Coal is the basic raw material of the industrial society because it is used not only as a source of power but also in the metallurgy of iron and steel, and as a raw material from which many by-products, ranging from aspirin to nylon, are made. Yet awareness of coal as a basic natural resource is relatively recent. In the thirteenth century, when

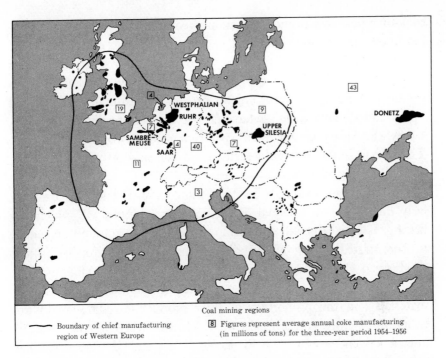

Coal-mining regions and coke production of Europe. (After Chauncy D. Harris)

the forests of the more accessible part of Britain had already been largely cut off, King Henry III gave his consent to the mining of coal at Newcastle. The people of London protested against this new fuel on the grounds that it fouled the air and endangered health. By 1650, however, two sailing vessels were regularly employed in carrying coal from Newcastle to London, and English coal was also being used in Belgium and France. By 1700 there were six hundred sailing vessels carrying coal to London. Coal mining began in France in 1715, and at about this same time coal was used in a small way in England to smelt iron at Coalbrookdale. After 1769 the demand for fuel increased very rapidly. But it was not until after 1859 that the method of using coke made from bituminous coal in steel manufacture led to an unprecedented expansion of coal mining. And it was only then that large numbers of people concentrated in industrial cities located where coal was near at hand.

As a result of these developments, the geography of the world's coal took on a new significance. There proved to be large supplies of high-grade coal in Great Britain and in parts of Europe, especially in the valley of the Ruhr River in Germany (map, p. 245). Later discoveries have indicated that by far the greater part of the world's coal reserves are outside Europe. According to present-day estimates, the United States and Canada together have 64 per cent of the world's coal reserves, the Soviet Union has 21 per cent, and China has 4 per cent. These four countries would seem to have nearly 90 per cent of the coal of the world.

The other raw materials needed by the industrial society are similarly distributed in unequal amounts. For example, oil, which has become essential since the invention of the internal combustion motor, is concentrated in only a few parts of the earth, most notably around the Persian Gulf (Plate 29). Plates 28 and 29 and the table on page 476 show the world distribution of certain important mineral raw materials and the proportion of their production. The world distribution of crops and animals on which the Occidental factories are also dependent is shown on Plates 30, 31, 32, and 33. Some of these maps show the importance of Europe as a source of raw materials, whereas some of them show that there are certain essential raw materials which are not produced in Europe.

The Political Units of Europe. Unfortunately the people and the resources of Europe are divided among twenty-eight sovereign states, and the boundaries between these states are matters of the greatest significance. The rise of the spirit of nationalism accompanied the rise of the industrial society, and, in fact, was largely produced by it. Yet one of the basic contradictions of Occidental thought at the present time is the existence of ideas of international economic interdependence along with ideas of national economic self-sufficiency and international political irresponsibility. The continent of Europe has the physical resources, the technological skills, and the man power to form one of the major aggregates of economic power on the earth, comparable to that of the United States, the Commonwealth of Nations, and the Soviet Union. But Europe is split into separate states, plagued by the fear of foreign aggression, hampered by the urge to achieve economic self-sufficiency, and dominated by the hatreds engendered in two great wars.

Because of the importance of political units in the current period—because, whatever may be our aspirations, the fact is that in the immediate future aggregates of economic and military power within political areas are basic realities which cannot be overlooked—we must analyze the problems of population and the relation of people to the land in terms of national territories. Political geography is a field which attempts to analyze the significance of differences from place to place within political areas, and so to draw conclusions concerning the economic or military capabilities of states. As two examples of the methods used in making such analyses we shall consider in turn the geographic structure of France and of Germany.

France. From behind the string of physical barriers which once offered a degree of protection from invasion, the nation of France emerged from the medieval period. The strongly marked national character of France was not easily created. It is the product of centuries of struggle during which the many separate and contrasted regions of the country were brought together in a closely knit political entity. The map on page 224 suggests the variety of kinds of country existing in this area. There is the warm, sunny Mediterranean coast, the rugged Alps, the rounded, hilly lands of the Massif Central, the cool, rainy hills of Brittany, the limestone areas where surface water is not easy to find, and the flat, muddy plains of Flanders. Physical differences are matched by differences of dialect and differences of product. The question is raised again and again for each generation of Frenchmen: Is this diversity to be a source of strength or of fatal weakness?

Paris is the one great urban center of France. When the Industrial Revolution came to France, Paris had achieved its political and social conquest of the rest of the country. Its commercial conquest was never in doubt. At first its growth was small, for the outline of the city in 1800, shown on the map on page 248, was the result of many centuries of slow population increase. When the fortifications of 1840 were built around the city they included a built-up area only slightly larger than that of half a century earlier, and there was nothing beyond. But the fortifications were soon overrun by the expanding city. They have now been leveled and used for the fine boulevards which surround the central part of Paris. By 1861 the city had more

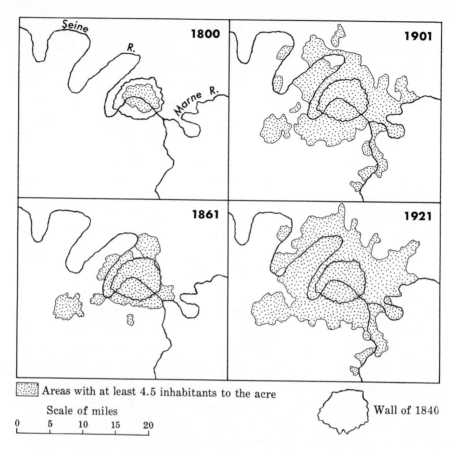

Areas with at least 4.5 inhabitants to the acre

Scale of miles

0   5   10   15   20

Wall of 1840

The growth of Paris. (*After Gallois*)

than a million inhabitants. By 1901 the urban area had expanded up and down the Seine Valley; it had invaded the valley of the Marne, and toward the west it had almost reached the formerly separate Versailles. Today the metropolitan area, which is much larger than the political city, includes a number of once independent municipalities. Paris has become the primate city of France.

Meanwhile France in the industrial society was not so well off in terms of economic and military power as it had been in the pre-industrial society. The country possesses excellent and varied agricultural lands, and it is more nearly self-sufficient in terms of food than is Great Britain. In the pre-industrial world France had the agricultural production to support a numerous population, and it had the advan-

248 The Mid-Latitude Mixed Forest Lands

tages of easy communication along its fine rivers to lead to the development of commerce. But as an industrial power it is handicapped by the lack of coal (map, p. 245). To be sure, France possesses large resources of iron ore in Lorraine; and it has large quantities of potash and bauxite (the ore of aluminum). But the lack of coal meant that in the early days of industrial development in Europe the iron-and-steel-manufacturing centers were in other countries, although a lesser steel industry was set up in Lorraine based on imported Ruhr coal. Industries made use of France's meager supplies of coal in the north along the Franco-Belgian border, in the Massif Central, and in the Rhône Valley around Lyon. A great variety of industries were built on the outskirts of Paris, where the necessary raw materials and fuels could be brought by rail and river boat. France utilized its water-power resources for electricity, and by this means in part compensated for the scarcity of domestic sources of coal. The industrialized areas, however, are mostly located in relatively vulnerable positions from the point of view of military attack.

The import of essential industrial raw materials and fuels was paid for in part by the export of numerous agricultural specialties. France has long been famous for its wines; the various contrasted districts of France have given their names to such well-known types of wine as Burgundy, Bordeaux, Champagne, and others. Other districts have become equally famous through the production of specialized types of cheese, such as Camembert. Most of France is devoted to the raising of wheat, and of grapes and other fruit. In the south there is a narrow zone of wheat and maize farming; and in the north, from Brittany into Belgium, the land is used chiefly for dairy cattle, hay, sugar beets, and apples (map, p. 250).

France was the first country of Europe to reach a static population. In the early eighteenth century, before the beginning of the Industrial Revolution, France had the largest population of any country of Europe. Its soils and location were favorable for a pre-industrial society, and it gained strength in terms of population density. But the significance of soil and location changed with the advent of the industrial society, and France dropped behind. The population of Germany passed that of France about 1870, that of the British Isles about 1900, and that of Italy in 1930. Meanwhile France's population would have

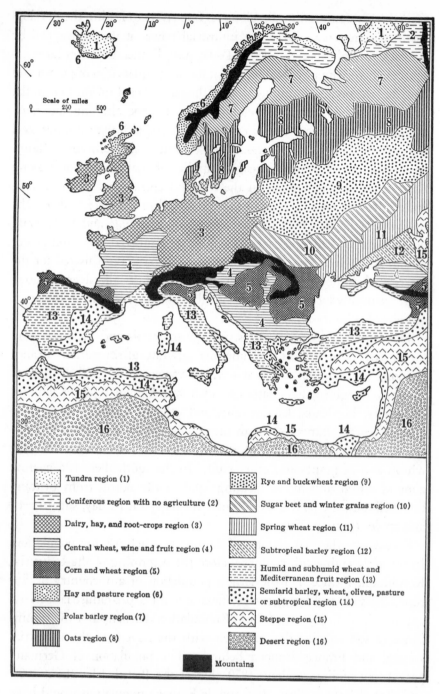

Agricultural regions of Europe. (*After Olof Jonasson*)

Tundra region (1)

Coniferous region with no agriculture (2)

Dairy, hay, and root-crops region (3)

Central wheat, wine and fruit region (4)

Corn and wheat region (5)

Hay and pasture region (6)

Polar barley region (7)

Oats region (8)

Rye and buckwheat region (9)

Sugar beet and winter grains region (10)

Spring wheat region (11)

Subtropical barley region (12)

Humid and subhumid wheat and Mediterranean fruit region (13)

Semiarid barley, wheat, olives, pasture or subtropical region (14)

Steppe region (15)

Desert region (16)

Mountains

actually declined during the period between World Wars I and II had it not been for a considerable current of immigration from North Africa and from other parts of Europe. The population was about 41,900,000 in 1936, and 40,500,000 in 1946; since 1946 it has remained a little more than 40,000,000, but it is estimated that by 1970 the population will have dropped below that figure. France is a country which has gone through the period of increase associated with the arrival of the industrial way of living, and has reached stability at a new level of density. In other words, France is demographically mature. Production is more restricted by man-power shortage than by lack of raw materials.

All France's current intentions, capabilities, and unsolved problems must be interpreted against this background of land and people. Lack of coal is not necessarily a weakness; there are other kinds of specialized production that can bring substantial income and can pay for necessary imports. Dense and rapidly increasing population is not necessarily an asset; there are many advantages for the country which has achieved a stationary population. France suffers from the idea of nationalism (which the French themselves were among the first to develop) not because the love of country is bad, but because the love of country in an industrial society must be illuminated by an understanding of the fact of international interdependence and responsibility. France as an integral part of a federated Europe would be very well off indeed.

Germany. Germany is another country the territory of which is made up of a great variety of contrasted parts; but Germany, unlike France, had no protection along its borders during the early centuries of European settlement. The barriers within the country were greater than those around its margins. It was crossed from east to west and from south to north by major routes of travel. Meanwhile the Germans themselves were pushing eastward at the expense of the Slavs. The German advance followed two chief directions: northeast and southeast. Germans moved along the south shore of the Baltic, establishing commercial towns in the midst of rural areas still solidly occupied by Slavic peasants. A German colony was established even as far east as the Volga River (map, p. 226). The German advance was also channeled down the Danube. Meanwhile Slavs remained solidly entrenched behind physical barriers such as the marshes of western

Poland or the wooded ramparts of the Erzgebirge and the Böhmer-wald (Bohemian Forest) (map, p. 224).

Both the Industrial Revolution and the Democratic Revolution had their first major impact on the Germans about the middle of the nineteenth century. The ideas of the Democratic Revolution made their chief impression on the people of western and southern Germany. The kingdom of Prussia in the north and east remained almost untouched. A revolt against the privileged classes in 1850 was defeated, and as a result there was a considerable emigration to the United States, Brazil, and Chile at that time. Germany remained divided into small kingdoms and principalities until 1870, when the whole country was brought under the rule of the Kaiser, who was also the king of Prussia. Berlin, located in the northeastern part of the country, became the national capital. Nevertheless, Germany still remained divided in sentiment between the west and south, where democratic ideas continued to develop, and the north and east, where the landed aristocracy and the army officers maintained sufficient strength to dominate the whole country. Pre-industrial political concepts gave support to the Kaiser before World War I and to the Nazi dictatorship before World War II. Meanwhile, however, Germany could never have gained its great economic and military strength had it not been for the rapid development of manufacturing industries based on the new technology of the Industrial Revolution.

Industrial development after the middle of the nineteenth century was dependent on the coal of the Ruhr Basin (map, p. 245). Coal had been mined in this district since the thirteenth century, but because of the cost of transportation it was used only locally near the mines. The Ruhr district was a thinly-inhabited and rather poor farming land, for the soils were sandy and not very productive. But after the method of using coke in steel manufacture had been invented in 1859, the value of Ruhr coal as a natural resource was enormously increased. The building of the great industrial complex took place largely between 1860 and 1913, during which period the Ruhr became Europe's major manufacturing center and one of the world's largest concentrations of productive capacity. The present urban development of the Ruhr and neighboring areas is shown on the map (p. 253). The black areas are solidly built up with factories, warehouses, railroads, and residences.

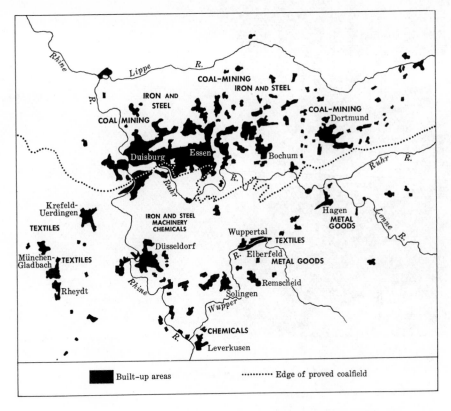

COAL-MINING
IRON AND STEEL

IRON AND
STEEL

COAL-MINING
Dortmund

COAL MINING

Duisburg   Essen   Bochum

Krefeld-
Uerdingen

TEXTILES

IRON AND STEEL
MACHINERY
CHEMICALS

Düsseldorf

Wuppertal

Elberfeld

Hagen
METAL
GOODS

TEXTILES

München-
Gladbach   TEXTILES

Rheydt

Solingen

TEXTILES

METAL GOODS

Remscheid

CHEMICALS
Leverkusen

■ Built-up areas   ·········· Edge of proved coalfield

Urban development in the Ruhr district. (After Chauncy D. Harris)

The Ruhr became the productive heart not only of Germany but also of Europe. In a world of divided sovereign states, Germany had the coal and France had the iron. From the Ruhr came 90 per cent of the bituminous coal of prewar Germany, and about half of all the coal in Europe outside the Soviet Union. Of the coal mined in the Ruhr before World War II, some 48.5 million tons a year were used in the manufacturing industries of the Ruhr itself; 39.6 million tons were sent to other parts of Germany; and 39.6 million tons were exported to the Netherlands, Belgium, France, Luxembourg, Italy, Switzerland, the Scandinavian countries, the Balkans, Spain, and other places. Thus a very considerable part of the productive capacity of Europe was based on Ruhr coal.[1]

[1] Chauncy D. Harris, "The Ruhr Coal-Mining District," *Geographical Review,* Vol. 36 (1946), pp. 194–221.

Heavy industry in the German Ruhr

A great variety of manufacturing industries were established in the Ruhr. Close to the coal mines and the huge coke ovens, blast furnaces and rolling mills turned out great quantities of steel of different kinds. All kinds of plants for making things out of steel were located close to the steel mills. Close by, also, were chemical and dye industries, which used by-products such as coal tar and its numerous components. There were synthetic fiber plants and pharmaceutical industries, all based on the same materials. The present great concentration of people in this area (Plate 4) includes only a small proportion of the total number of people both inside and outside Europe whose economic life is directly or indirectly tied to the productivity of this one place.

Industrial development in Germany before World War II was not restricted to the Ruhr (map, p. 255). There was also the Industrial District of Upper Silesia (map, p. 245) located on the prewar boundary between Germany and Poland. In those days the border cut right through the midst of this industrial complex.[1] There was also the Saar district, located on the border between Germany and France, so persistently claimed by France, but so stubbornly German in sentiment. The Central Industrial District of Germany, between Hannover and Leipzig, was based in part on large deposits of lignite, or brown coal, which could be used for the chemical industries and for generation of electric power. The Ruhr, before the war, produced 68 per cent of Germany's coal (of all kinds) and 73 per cent of Germany's steel. But there were many industries which were built, partly for strategic reasons, in areas not previously industrialized. Germany led the way in the use of new technologies for the manufacture of

[1] Richard Hartshorne, "Geographic and Political Boundaries in Upper Silesia," *Annals of the Association of American Geographers,* Vol. 23 (1933), pp. 194–228.

The industrial regions of prewar Germany. [*From R. E. Dickinson, "The Economic Regions of Germany," Geographical Review, Vol. 28 (1938), pp. 609–626*]

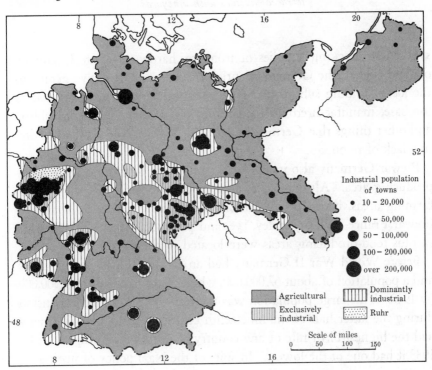

Photo by the author

*A river steamer in the Rhine gorge above Koblenz. In the background are
terraced hillsides with vineyards*

synthetics. Lacking supplies of iron ore, hardeners of steel, bauxite,
oil, and rubber, the German scientists turned their inventive genius to
the job of finding substitutes. The chemical industries, using coal as
the base, manufactured such quantities of gasoline, synthetic rubber,
and other things that Germany's defeat in World War II was not due
to a lack of resources.

Prewar Germany also included in its national territory a large food-
producing area. Although this area lacked the variety of the French
farming areas, it did produce more of the basic necessities than did
prewar France—wheat, barley, rye, and potatoes. Most of Germany's
surplus food-producing areas were located in the east.

Before World War II Germany had an area of 181,699 square miles
and a population of about 67,000,000, which had increased to 69,500,000
by 1940. This large population was the result of very rapid expansion
during the latter half of the nineteenth century. Until 1910 Germany
had the highest birth rate of any country of northwest Europe; but by
1933 it had one of the lowest. In spite of the Nazi policy of urging an

256 *The Mid-Latitude Mixed Forest Lands*

increase in the birth rate, births were still on the decline in 1939. It was estimated that by 1955 the population would have reached a peak of about 72,000,000, and thereafter would start to decrease.

At the conclusion of World War II in Europe, Germany was divided into two parts. In 1949 the western part voted to adopt a democratic form of government. This part is now the German Federal Republic (West Germany), with an area of some 94,000 square miles and a population, in 1955, of about 50,000,000. This is the part of Germany that includes almost all the prewar heavy industries.

The eastern part of Germany remained under the control of a communist government. It is called the German Democratic Republic (East Germany), and has an area of some 42,000 square miles and a population of about 18,000,000. The communists use the word "democratic" to describe a political system in which complete control is in the hands of a minority, the members of the Communist Party. East Germany, like the other so-called satellites of the Soviet Union, has never had a chance to express its political preference in a free election. Its economic problems have been complicated by the fact that the eastern border of Germany was moved westward to the line of the Oder River and its tributary the Neisse (the latter is not shown on the map on page 224). The Germans who used to live east of the Oder (map, p. 226) have been forced to move westward. The shift of boundary took the industrial area of Upper Silesia away from Germany and placed it entirely within Poland. East Germany, cut off

Hay cut and drying in southern Germany. In the background is a field of wheat

Photo by the author

from its traditional market in West Germany and from its source of low-cost steel, suffers from severe economic dislocation. The unification of Germany must remain a major objective of Germans on both sides of the line.

International Co-operation in Europe. Events are beginning to force the European nations toward closer economic co-operation. There is only one solution to the stubborn geographic fact that most of the coal is in one country and most of the iron and bauxite are in another. In 1952 six European countries—the Netherlands, Belgium, Luxembourg, the German Federal Republic, France, and Italy—agreed to pool their coal, iron ore, and scrap metal and to send these commodities freely, without tariff restriction, into any of the participating countries. In 1954 refined steel was added. This is known as the European Coal and Steel Community, developed by what has been called the Schuman Plan. The result was an increased production in all these items.

In 1957 two revolutionary new international agreements were ratified by this same group of countries. These agreements established Euratom and the European Economic Community (the Common Market). Like the Coal and Steel Community, each of these undertakings will be guided by an executive commission responsible to an Assembly of 142 members: 36 each from France, West Germany, and Italy; 14 each from Belgium and the Netherlands; and 6 from Luxembourg. The members of the first assemblies were selected by the parliaments, but in the future members will be elected by the citizens of these countries. There is also a Court of Justice to decide on cases of disagreement. The basic purposes of the two organizations are to pool atomic knowledge and resources, to eliminate tariff barriers and other trade restrictions, and to permit the free movement of capital and workers from one country to another. These objectives are to be reached gradually over a period of some fifteen years.

These agreements will go a long way toward eliminating the artificial barriers which have weakened the economies of the European countries and have led to conflict and war. With Europe operating as an economic unit, a third great power, between the United States and the Soviet Union, will begin to take shape. In 1956 the six participating countries produced 12.5 per cent of the world's electricity, 14 per cent of the world's coal, and 20 per cent of the world's steel. Their foreign trade, taken as a whole, was substantially ahead of that of all the other great trading areas of the world, and some 40 per cent greater than the foreign trade of the United States. With the countries acting as a unit, production and trade will increase rapidly, and the level of living throughout the area will be raised. No part of the world stands to gain more from the development of atomic power. If and when the power of the atom has been effectively harnessed (probably before the year 2000), the whole world picture of raw material strategy will be revised and thus, also, the balance of political and military power. Major changes in world geography are in the making.

NORTH AMERICA

The second of the two major areas of Occidental occupance in the regions of Group IV is in eastern North America. The area of the mid-latitude mixed forest lands of North America is only a little less than that of the similar regions of Europe, but it is occupied by a much smaller population. Within these regions in Europe there are twenty-one cities with more than a million inhabitants; in Anglo-America there are fourteen such cities. In Europe the density of rural population is generally more than 100 people per square mile; in eastern North America the density is mostly between 25 and 50 (Plate 1). But the North American area stands foremost in the whole world in terms of productive capacity, and so in the living standard of its people.

In some ways the eastern part of North America is remarkably similar to western Europe. As Carl Sauer points out, "it would be impossible to cross an ocean anywhere else and find as little that is unfamiliar on the opposite side." [1] The mid-latitude mixed forests of both areas contain many of the same kinds of trees. The climate of both areas is characterized by variable and stimulating weather, and by an abundant, but not excessive, supply of moisture. To be sure, the winters of eastern North America are colder than those of Western Europe, and the summers are hotter; but the difference is not so great that important changes in clothing or housing were necessary. The

[1] Carl Sauer, "The Settlement of the Humid East," in *Climate and Man,* 1941 Yearbook of the U. S. Department of Agriculture, pp. 157–166.

surface of the land, too, was familiar to the Europeans—there are similar landforms resulting from geological processes already observed in Europe. And there is the further element of similarity, which became important after the emergence of the industrial society, in that both parts of the world are abundantly supplied with coal.

The Culture Hearths. The native Indians had been living in the forests of eastern North America for a long time before the arrival of the Europeans. They depended for their food supply on hunting and fishing, supplemented by a shifting cultivation of maize, squash, and beans. In many places the Europeans found openings in the forest where the Indians had made clearings and planted crops. The settlers called these openings "Indian oldfields." Through the forests the Indian trails marked the easiest routes over the hilly terrain for men on foot.

To this thinly occupied land came the English, French, and Dutch settlers during the first few decades of the seventeenth century. The English settled near Chesapeake Bay in Virginia in 1607, and in New England in 1620. The French established Quebec on the St. Lawrence River in 1608. The Dutch settled along the Hudson Valley in 1614; but in 1667 the Netherlands ceded this colony to the British in exchange for the sugar-producing colony of Surinam in the Guianas. In the century that followed these first settlements, four different culture areas developed, in each of which a new and distinctive way of living was forged in an American habitat. Such areas in which cultures have their origin can be called *culture hearths*. The traditions of modern United States and Canada were derived from the mixture of ideas and skills from these different sources and from the original culture hearth in Great Britain. The four culture hearths were: (1) French Canada; (2) New England; (3) the Southern Colonies; and (4) the Middle Colonies.

French Canada. The French colonies were the only ones that were situated where there was an open route of travel to the continental interior (map, p. 261). French missionaries and fur traders from Quebec went up the St. Lawrence River to the Great Lakes. By easy portages they reached the headwaters of the Mississippi system or of the rivers draining northward toward the Arctic. In canoes they traveled widely over the interior, spreading a thin net of settlement

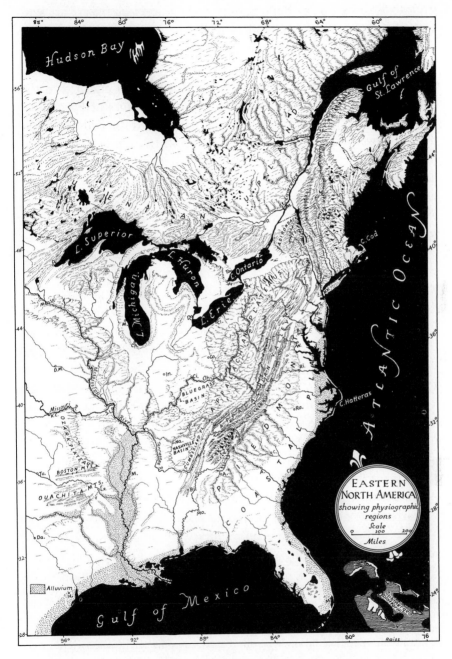

Eastern North America

261

over a vast area. They built trading posts at strategic places, such as Detroit, Chicago, St. Louis, and New Orleans.

Along the lower St. Lawrence River, downstream from Montreal, there was a very different kind of French settlement. This area was occupied by farmers who were firmly and compactly attached to the land. Over the continental interior the chief heritages of French occupance that remain today are the place names, and the culinary tradition of New Orleans. But along the lower St. Lawrence Valley in the Province of Quebec the French farmers developed a way of living that has survived three centuries. The French language and the traditions of rural France have resisted effectively the impact of ideas from other culture hearths. French Canada remains French in language, conservative in politics, Roman Catholic in religion. From it there has been very little outward spread; but the distinctive way of living remains solidly intrenched in the original area of settlement.

New England. The colonists who came to New England in the early years of settlement were seeking religious and political freedom. The beginnings of the Democratic Revolution had met resistance in Great Britain from those who benefited from the old system of privilege. Only by a slow process were the rights of the monarchy being defined by law; only after much bloodshed was the supremacy of the elected House of Commons over the hereditary House of Lords established. But the people who went to America could develop their revolutionary new ideas unrestricted by tradition. The Plymouth Compact of 1620 was the world's first written statement of the principle that government should be by the consent of the governed.[1]

The New Englanders took steps to carry out these principles. In the early years of settlement they built their houses close together in villages. The citizens of the community were brought together periodically for "town meetings," at which problems of public policy were

---

[1] ". . . We whose names are under-written . . . having undertaken a voyage to plant the first colony in the northern part of Virginia, do by these presents, solemnly and mutually in the presence of God, and one another, convenant and combine ourselves together into a civil body politic, for the better ordering and preservation and furtherance of the ends aforesaid; and by virtue hereof to enact, constitute, and frame such just and equal laws, ordinances, acts, constitutions, and offices, from time to time, as shall be thought most meet and convenient for the general good of the colony, unto which we promise all due submission and obedience."

A settlement in the hilly upland of New England

freely and openly discussed and decisions were based on majority opinion. The people of New England recognized the need for wide popular education, and they gathered their children together in schools. They established colleges and universities for higher education.

New England was a harsh habitat for the early settlers. Its severe winters, its cool summers, and especially its sandy or stony soils and many ledges of bare rock made farming difficult. Yet, with great labor, fields were cleared of trees and the stones were piled up in "stone walls." The farmers learned from the Indians how to grow the Indian grain—maize—as well as squash and beans; and they also tried the familiar European grains—wheat, barley, rye, and oats. The chief source of wealth, however, was the sea; there was an abundance of fish. The forests provided masts and timber for shipbuilding. The

New England merchants sent their ships to trade in the ports of the world, and if the ships returned home the profits were considerable.

The Southern Colonies. Quite different were the traditions developed in the South. The first settlements in Virginia were soon followed by others which spread along the navigable rivers of the coastal plain from Maryland to the Carolinas (map, p. 261). The land was laid out in large estates, and the owners enjoyed the status of a "landed gentry." In the mansions of the gentry life was genial and civilized. There was music, literature, dancing. The children of the well to do were educated at home by tutors.

The South was able to develop a commercial farm economy. It happened that the Indian crop, tobacco, and the Indian method of smoking it in pipes and cigars had met with great favor in England. There was a new and increasing market for tobacco. When the tobacco plant was introduced into Virginia it did very well during the hot, rainy summers. But there were not enough workers to clear the land, to plant, cultivate, and harvest the crop, and to prepare the leaf for shipment, until the landowners began to bring in Negro slaves.

In the culture hearth of the South there was strong support for the ideas of the Democratic Revolution. Freedom, however, meant freedom for the free citizens to elect their own government without arbitrary interference from the mother country. The idea that Negro slaves might have equal treatment before the law was disturbing and subversive, for slavery had become the necessary basis of the economic life.

The Middle Colonies. Between New England and the South were the Middle Colonies. They were located in eastern Pennsylvania and bordering parts of New Jersey and western Maryland. To this culture hearth came many kinds of Europeans: Dutch, Swedes, and Germans, as well as English, Scots, and Irish. Many different religious denominations were represented. Most of the colonists settled on small farms, building their homes on the lands they worked. In this frontier land the farm family had to be almost self-sufficient. The parents taught the children to read the Bible, to write, and to do simple arithmetic. Here also democracy flourished. The people of the Middle Colonies were perhaps less interested in theory than were the educated Southerners, and less interested in methods than were the serious-minded New Englanders. But they practiced democracy by treating their neighbors on a basis of equality and tolerance.

From this mixture of people came an amazing series of inventions. The farmers of the Middle Colonies were the first to use the Indian maize to fatten the European domestic animal, the hog. In this part of America maize was first used as a feed rather than directly as a food. The people of the Middle Colonies built the great four-wheeled wagons that later were known as prairie schooners. They invented the long rifle. They adapted the Scandinavian log house to frontier conditions, and they invented the pot-bellied stove to heat it. These were the restless pioneers who provided the main impetus for the westward movement, and who set their stamp on the greater part of rural America.

The Pioneer Movement. From the three culture hearths of English-speaking America settlers spread and mingled. As late as 1700 the areas of settlement along the east coast were still separated by unoccupied country. But by 1790 the colonies had spread along the country east of the Appalachians, forming a continuous belt of settlement all the way from what is now Maine to the border of Georgia. The New Englanders had moved northward into northern New England and westward into New York. But the chief currents of movement had come from the Middle Colonies and the Southern Colonies.

The greatest tendency to advance the frontier of settlement appeared in the Middle Colonies. Pioneers spread first southwestward along the valleys between parallel ridges that mark the eastern side of the Appalachians (map, p. 261). Some of them went up the Susquehanna River and its tributary the Juniata to the east-facing front of the Allegheny Plateau. This was the most serious barrier, which was nevertheless crossed in central Pennsylvania. Beyond, the winding headwaters of the Ohio River brought the pioneers to Pittsburgh. Daniel Boone was the famous person who led the settlers through the Cumberland Gap and on into the Blue Grass Basin of Kentucky. By 1790 settlers from the Middle Colonies had occupied both the Blue Grass Basin and the Nashville Basin of Tennessee, and had established settlements along the Ohio River in southern Ohio and Indiana.

Meanwhile a very different kind of pioneer movement had developed in the Southern Colonies. The planters had been experimenting with crops other than tobacco. They tried rice, indigo, and cotton. But after 1785, when steam power was applied to textile factories in England and when new and improved cotton-spinning and cotton-weaving machines had been invented, the demand for cotton began to rise rapidly. The cotton plant, introduced through Charleston, grew well in the southern climate; but it was still costly to produce cotton for sale. The rise of the South as the world's leading cotton-producing region was made possible by Eli Whitney's invention of the cotton gin in 1793 (patented in 1794), which made it possible for one man to do the work of two hundred in removing the seeds from the fiber. No other part of the world could at that time produce cotton at so low a cost.

Cotton planting in the United States began to spread rapidly from the original area on the piedmont of the Carolinas and Georgia. New plantations were carved out of the forest to the west. Cotton planting swept round the southern end of the Appalachians in Alabama and on to the Mississippi, then across the river onto the black prairie soils of Texas as far as climatic conditions permitted. Cotton planting was tried as far north as Rhode Island. But it was found that where the growing season, or the period between the last killing frost of spring and the first killing frost of fall, was less than 200 days, the yield per acre of cotton was not enough to make it profitable. As a result of the balance of costs and prices, the line marking the northern boundary of the 200-day growing season became a critical climatic limit to the northward expansion of the cotton belt.

Pioneer movements were also bringing new settlers into Canada. After the Revolutionary War there were many people in the newly independent United States who desired to remain loyal to the British king. At this time large numbers of them migrated from New England into Nova Scotia and New Brunswick. From the Middle Colonies many went over to the northern side of Lake Ontario and Lake Erie, forming there the colony, and later the Province, of Ontario.

The part of the Group IV regions lying west of the Appalachians and north of the Ohio River became known as the Northwest frontier. It was occupied by pioneer farmers from the Middle Colonies who pushed northward from the early settlements along the Ohio River. But the people of this frontier region found themselves isolated from the markets of the east. Because the expense of shipping the frontier products back across the Appalachians was prohibitive, they built rafts of lumber cut from the forests, loaded them with bacon and other products, and sent them down the Ohio and Mississippi rivers to New Orleans. Pressure from the people of the Northwest led the United States to make the Louisiana Purchase of 1803, which brought the national territory south to the Gulf of Mexico and added, to the west, a vast area drained by the Missouri and its tributaries. In 1825 the Erie Canal, connecting the Hudson River at Albany with Buffalo on Lake Erie, opened the way for a stream of New Englanders moving westward and a stream of farm products moving back east to markets. The rise of New York City dates from this event. A wagon road was built from Baltimore and Washington across the Appalachians to Ohio and Indiana. Over the National Road, as it was called, the large wagons brought products back east. Today this road is followed almost exactly by U. S. Highway 40.[1] Finally, however, it was the building of the railroads that so effectively connected the settlements of the Northwest with the markets of the east that the major currents of movement have ever since been across the grain of the country—from west to east rather than from north to south.

The westward movement which was initiated in the Middle Colonies, but which included streams of settlers from the other two culture hearths, swept far beyond the western limits of Group IV. It brought the whole western part of North America into the national territory of the United States, changing the regional name of the old Northwest frontier to the modern Middle West. At first, however, this westward spread had jumped over the intervening grasslands (Plate 10). It was only after 1865 that there was a new strong pioneer movement into the regions of Group V. This remarkable period of economic history will be described in the chapter on the grasslands.

Patterns of Population in Eastern United States. The patterns of population that have emerged in the modern period had their origins in these early periods of settlement. The fact that the main current of pioneer movement came from the Middle Colonies into what is now the Middle West, the agricultural heart of the nation, accounts for the prevailing pattern of dispersed rural settlement, the types of rural habitations, even the basic "corn-hog" type of farming. In each region the patterns of settlement have gone through periods of sequent occupance,

[1] George R. Stewart, *U. S. 40* (Boston, 1953), p. 84 ff.

in each of which a particular kind of technology was practiced. The superimposure of the later patterns on the earlier ones preserves in the landscape of today the record of the whole process of settlement.

The details of the pattern of settlement vary from place to place. The series of block diagrams (p. 269) suggests certain characteristic relationships of settlement and underlying terrain that can be observed at many places in eastern United States (except that the rectangular patterns are found only in those areas settled after 1785). Where the valleys are narrow and V-shaped, they are commonly left in forest, whereas the roads and farms are concentrated on the level uplands. In some regions there are discontinuous bits of valley flats along the river with small settlements on them, but the larger area is still on the more continuous uplands. There are other cases where the uplands are discontinuous, but the valley bottoms are the chief farming areas. And there are cases where the uplands are too steep and narrow-crested to permit much settlement.

Along the floodplains of large rivers, such as the Mississippi, the pattern of settlement is likely to take on a crescentic arrangement in harmony with the arrangement of somewhat higher ground along the immediate river channel or former channels (map, p. 270). The farm patterns on the valley bluff which marks the edge of the floodplain and on the higher country back from the river are quite different from that of the river bottoms, a fact which can be observed strikingly from the air. In the United States, where maize rather than rice is the chief grain crop, the floodplains of the rivers are thinly settled, and there are many more people on the higher ground away from the rivers. In a similar situation in China, the rice-growing Orientals have developed the opposite patterns of settlement, concentrating on the floodplains rather than on the country away from the rivers. Furthermore, the chief towns along the larger navigable rivers, which occupy sites perched on the valley bluffs safe from flood waters, nevertheless have been located at places where the river in its meandering swings against the base of the bluff (map, p. 271).

Settlement in eastern United States, as in most Occidental regions, was first established along the main pre-existing lines of travel. The Indian trails and the rivers which were navigable for canoes were the first routes along which settlement advanced. The map of Michigan

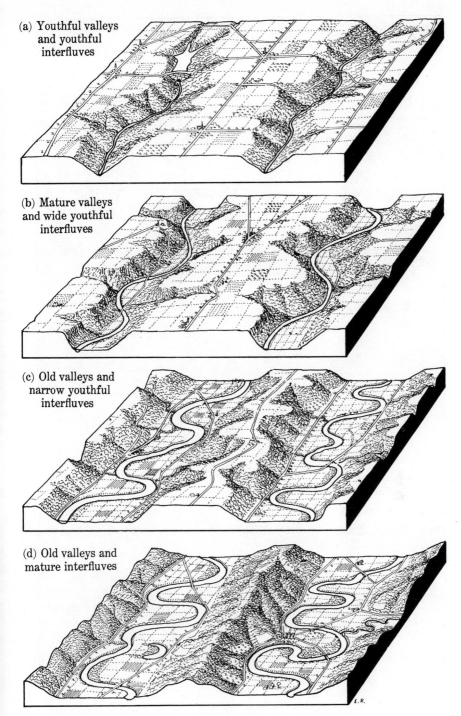

(a) Youthful valleys
and youthful
interfluves

(b) Mature valleys
and wide youthful
interfluves

(c) Old valleys and
narrow youthful
interfluves

(d) Old valleys and
mature interfluves

Relation of Occidental settlement to landforms

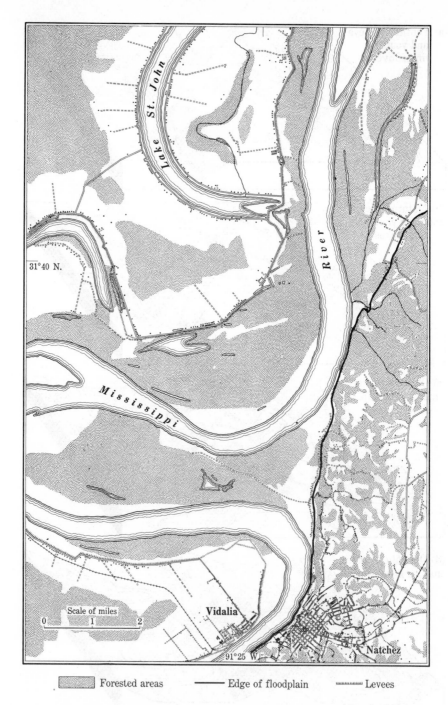

Topography of a floodplain. (*From the Natchez Quadrangle, Mississippi, United States Geological Survey*)

(p. 272) shows the relation of the Indian trails to the terrain, and suggests the extent to which the aboriginal pattern of settlement focused on the same points which later emerged as great cities. Detroit owes its location to the existence of firm gravelly banks which permitted easy landings on both sides of the Detroit River. The Indians used it so frequently that the French placed their trading post there. Many of the main automobile highways of the present day follow very closely the routes first laid down by Indians on foot.

In 1785 the Federal government of the United States adopted a uniform pattern of land survey—a rectangular pattern based on square mile sections (diagram, p. 326). In most parts of the country settled before 1785 there are irregular field boundaries and winding roads. The parts of the country settled after 1785 are dominated by the right-angle pattern, oriented to the cardinal points of the compass. However, in many parts of the forested regions, the first routes of penetration were still the Indian trails, which conformed to no systematic pattern. Main roads, therefore, in many cases cut at an angle across the north-south or east-west roads. The basic pattern, too, is interrupted in places by such natural

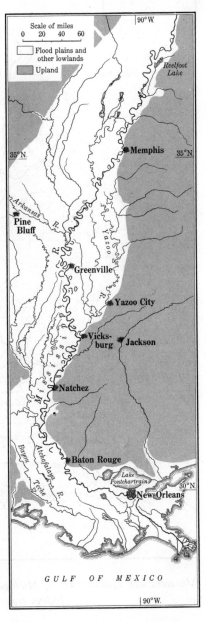

A part of the lower Mississippi floodplain, showing location of chief towns and cities

North America   271

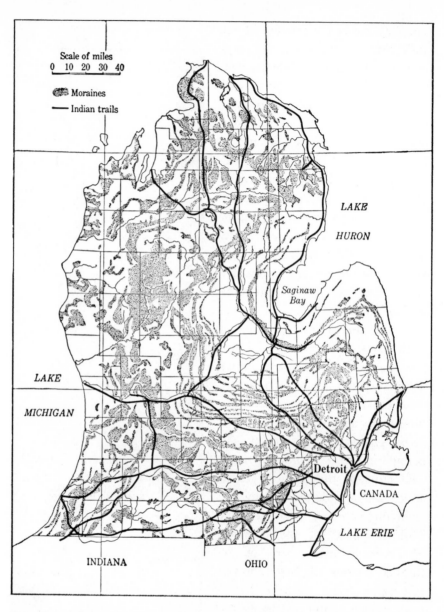

Scale of miles
0 10 20 30 40

Moraines
Indian trails

LAKE HURON

Saginaw Bay

LAKE MICHIGAN

Detroit

CANADA

LAKE ERIE

INDIANA

OHIO

Moraines and Indian trails of Michigan. (Moraines after Leverett and Taylor; Indian trails after Hinsdale)

obstacles as lakes, swamps, rivers, or steep slopes. A detail which illustrates these features is shown on the map on the opposite page.

272 *The Mid-Latitude Mixed Forest Lands*

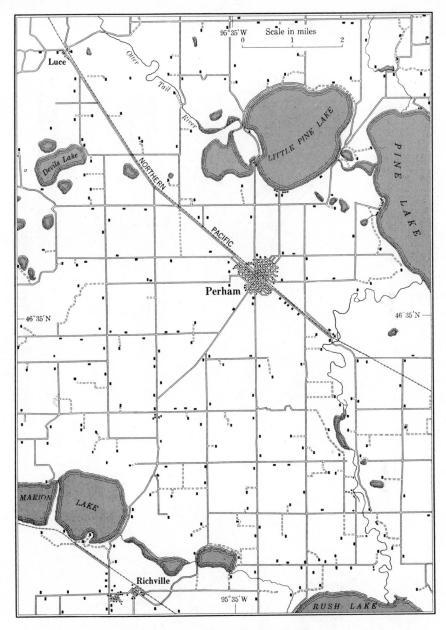

Topographic detail in Minnesota. (From Perham Quadrangle, Minnesota, United States Geological Survey)

273

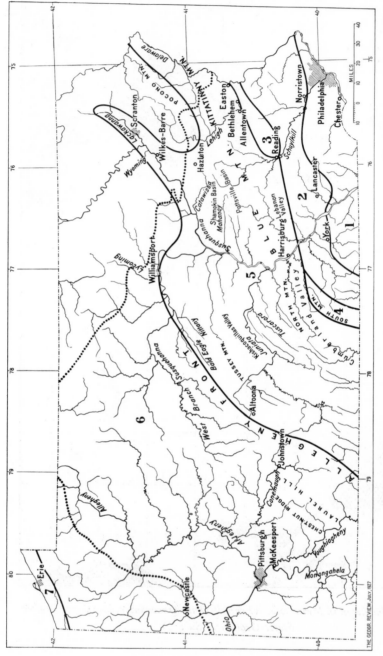

Surface divisions of the state of Pennsylvania. 1 and 2, Piedmont; 3 and 4, Blue Ridge; 5, Appalachian Ridges and Valleys; 6, Allegheny Plateau; 7, Lake Plain. Southern limit of glaciation indicated by dotted line. (Courtesy of the American Geographical Society of New York)

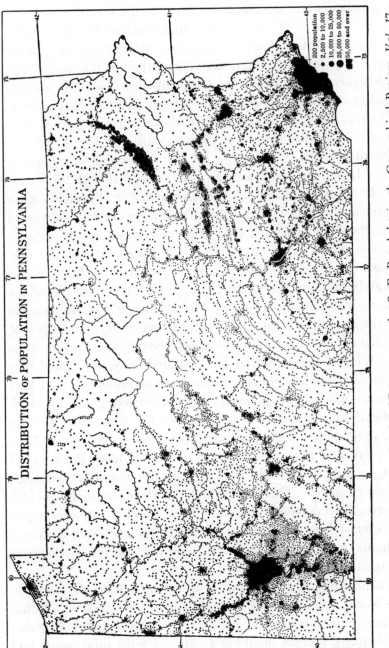

DISTRIBUTION OF POPULATION IN PENNSYLVANIA

200 population
2,500 to 10,000
10,000 to 25,000
25,000 to 50,000
50,000 and over

Distribution of population in Pennsylvania. [*From a paper by C. E. Batschelet in the Geographical Review, Vol. 17 (1927), p. 430*]

The pattern of people in the state of Pennsylvania shows to what extent population and settlement are fitted to the underlying terrain (maps, pp. 274 and 275). Where the parallel ridges and valleys of the Appalachian Highlands develop a strongly annular arrangement of the drainage, the population reflects this characteristic of the land. West of the Allegheny Front, where the Allegheny Plateau is cut by streams arranged in a dendritic pattern, the population also reflects this condition. Even in the great cities the shape of the terrain is a matter of great significance in the development of the urban structure.

In North America, as in Europe, the first settlements were made in the era of horses, and roads were fixed in accordance with the factors previously discussed. Later, when railroads were built, some notable readjustments were made. The best farm lands in the hilly interior of New England are generally, but not in every case, on the uplands. The valleys, filled with sandy and gravelly glacial deposits, are generally poor for agriculture. So the earliest towns were on the uplands—for example, Grafton and Sutton (map, p. 277), on either side of the Blackstone Valley in Massachusetts. The situation at that stage was not unlike the conditions shown hypothetically on block c on page 269, except that the valley bottoms were unoccupied because they were too sandy. When textile industries first appeared in New England they were placed at small water-power sites, such as Millbury. And later the railroads ran through the valleys to avoid the steep grades by which the uplands were reached. Millbury grew; but Sutton and Grafton became sleepy little villages until summer visitors from the large cities not far away came to them for summer homes. In many instances hill towns have declined or disappeared. But the new towns along the railroads have prospered. There are examples of whole communities which have been moved downhill into the valleys. There are other examples of towns which have been extended to nearby railroads, such as Princeton, Illinois (map, p. 278), where the result has been the development of two trading centers.

An essential part of the pattern of settlement as it has developed in eastern North America is the arrangement of trade centers. Within the service areas of towns and cities there are many scattered smaller places—hamlets, villages, small towns—in which the rural people find a variety of urban services. The map of central services performed in

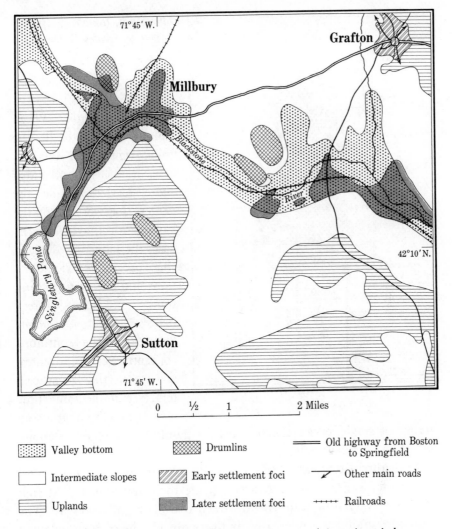

71° 45′ W.

Grafton

Millbury

Blackstone

River

42° 10′ N.

Singletary Pond

Sutton

71° 45′ W.

0 ½ 1 2 Miles

⬚ Valley bottom	⬚ Drumlins	═ Old highway from Boston to Springfield
☐ Intermediate slopes	⬚ Early settlement foci	⬚ Other main roads
⬚ Uplands	⬚ Later settlement foci	┼┼┼┼ Railroads

Sequence of settlement patterns in Massachusetts. (A portion of the Blackstone Valley)

the small trade centers of a part of southwestern Wisconsin (p. 279) illustrates a characteristic feature of the American Mid-West.[1] Twelve different kinds of central services are mapped. The smaller trade centers developed in the period before 1880 when transportation was by

[1] John E. Brush, "The Hierarchy of Central Places in Southwestern Wisconsin," *Geographical Review*, Vol. 43 (1953), pp. 380–402.

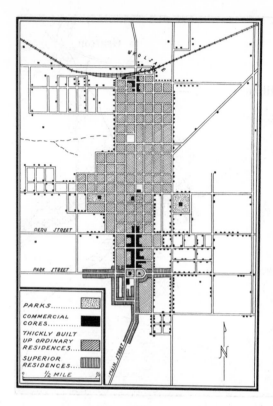

Princeton, Illinois. (After a map by Stanley D. Dodge)

horse and wagon. When railroads were built, the trade centers on the rail lines grew larger and added more services, while the centers that were not on the rail lines declined. In some cases the latter have lost all their previous service functions and are now nothing more than clusters of residences. The automobile has led to the continued concentration of central services in the larger centers; yet at the same time it has brought about a scattering of single-service centers, such as gasoline and service stations, which did not exist before.

Agricultural Regions. Only gradually have the present agricultural patterns of eastern North America made their appearance. At first there was very little difference between one place and another. The European grain crops were tried, but very quickly the colonists adopted both Indian crops and Indian methods. In the course of time, however, certain areas became differentiated from other areas in terms of agriculture. Near the great cities, today, there are concentrations of truck farms and dairy farms. Almost all New England, New York, and Pennsylvania supply fluid milk to New York, Boston, and Philadelphia. In other places there are highly specialized areas where the farmers have found the physical conditions especially well suited to the production of one product; for example, the potatoes of Aroostook County in Maine, the cranberries of Cape Cod, the tobacco for cigar

278 *The Mid-Latitude Mixed Forest Lands*

wrappers of the Connecticut Valley, or the orchards and vineyards of the shores of Lake Ontario, Lake Erie, and Lake Michigan. The Corn Belt, which is one of the major agricultural regions of the United States, has its eastern end in the previously forested areas of Ohio, but its greatest development is in the grasslands farther west (map, p. 328). South of the Corn Belt the farms of Kentucky and Tennessee raise chiefly maize and wheat, with certain specialized districts devoted to tobacco.

Trade centers, showing central services. (*Courtesy of the* Geographical Review)

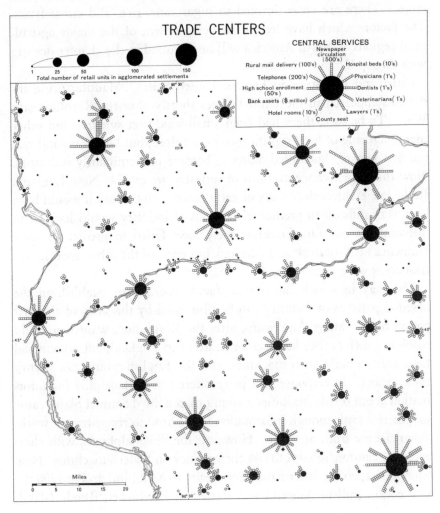

Still farther south is the Cotton Belt, which until the 1930's extended all the way from the Carolinas to Texas. Since World War II the introduction of the mechanical cotton picker to replace the hand labor that was formerly required has again changed the meaning of the land. Cotton has almost disappeared from the hillier parts of the piedmont where the cotton picker cannot be operated. It no longer reaches the 200-day growing season limit. It is concentrated on flat lands: in the east on parts of the coastal plain, on the floodplain of the Mississippi, and on the black prairies of Texas. Along the Gulf coast and in Florida the long growing season permits the growth of tropical or semitropical crops. There are areas devoted to sugar cane, rice, and citrus fruits. The factors which have led to the development of the major agricultural regions of North America will be discussed in the chapter dealing with Group V.

Cities and Industries in Eastern United States. Manufacturing industries appeared in the United States shortly after the Revolutionary War. To be sure, there had been small-scale iron smelters and other manufacturing of local significance long before; but New England was the first part of the United States to become predominantly industrial. Now the largest concentrations of industry are outside New England. In the late eighteenth century or early nineteenth century it would have been very difficult to predict what kinds of industry would localize in different places. One could scarcely have failed to predict the pre-eminence of Pittsburgh and Chicago, but none of the other great industrial areas were so obvious.

The way in which the human factor operates in establishing the original patterns of industry can be illustrated by the story of the first cotton mills. Many Americans, after the Revolution, wanted to build machines such as they had seen or heard of in England, but no one had been able to build such machines, and the English would not permit their export. In response to a prize offered in Philadelphia for information about textile machines a young man named Samuel Slater came to America with enough information in his head to reconstruct a workable machine from memory. However, the Philadelphians, with characteristic caution, refused to risk their money on Slater's machine. New Englanders, on the other hand, were ready to back him; and in 1790 the first cotton mill in America was started in Pawtucket, Rhode Island, near Providence. Thus New England rather than Pennsylvania became the leading cotton textile region of the United States because of the attitudes and temperament of the people, not because of any advantages of location.

Furthermore, the distribution of the textile industry within Massachusetts and Rhode Island was the result of unpredictable historical factors. When Slater showed that machines could be built to produce cotton thread, knowledge of steam engines to furnish the power had not reached America. The only source of power was falling water, used directly through a mill wheel to turn the machinery. Since each factory had to be within a hundred feet or so of the mill wheel, there was room for only one factory at each power site, or at the most two, if both sides of a stream could be used. Small water-power sites were therefore just as valuable as large power sites. Along all the New England streams there are numerous falls and rapids, and at each place where a small dam could be inexpensively built, small industrial towns were established around a mill. Industries were scattered all through the valleys of interior New England.

Scarcely thirty years later the significance of these resources was wholly changed. The application of steam power gave an advantage to mills located at tidewater, for the coal had to be imported by barge along the coast. Within a short time, however, railroads, which were built rapidly after 1830, provided adequate connections for all the scattered little industrial towns. Where canals had been started (as in the Blackstone Valley above Providence), they were promptly abandoned in favor of the cheaper railroads. The many small manufacturing towns were therefore able to survive and to this day can be found in the hilly New England interior.

The study of each industrial concentration brings to light a story similar to that of the early New England textile mills. But once a district becomes known for a specialty and skilled workers become available, there is a definite economic advantage for other similar or closely related industries to select the same locations. So it is that the Providence–Fall River area is the chief center of high-grade cotton textiles in New England today, and has survived even the removal to the South of most of the cotton textile industries which require less skill. Woolen textiles are concentrated north of Boston, and Boston itself is one of the largest of wool depots. Shoe manufacture is localized in eastern Massachusetts. The lower Connecticut Valley is noted for its metal industries and its manufacture of complicated machinery. Holyoke, in Massachusetts, is a center of paper production. In recent years the electronics industry has had a large and rapid growth in various parts of New England. In all these industrial districts of New England, which cover less than 1 per cent of the area of the United States, there are about 5 per cent of the people of the United States, and 10 per cent of the manufacturing in terms of value. More than 75 per cent of the people of New England live in towns and cities, leaving large areas of surrounding countryside almost empty of human inhabitants.

Changes in the pattern of industry are constantly taking place. Consider, for example, the story of steel manufacture. It was only during the second half of the nineteenth century that steel began to replace iron, which was proving inadequate to meet the requirements of the new machines and of the railroads. In 1867, a few years before steel began to be produced regularly in open hearth furnaces, the United States manufactured only about 22,000 tons of steel. In 1900 it manu-

Blast furnaces of a huge steel plant about twenty miles northwest of Pittsburgh on the Ohio River

The sky line of the automobile city of Detroit. The lake boat in the foreground is probably carrying iron ore

factured 10,000,000 tons; and since World War II its steel-producing capacity has passed 100,000,000 tons in some years. Steel has become the most widely used of all manufactured substances.

To produce so much steel requires an enormous volume of raw materials. A century ago coal was the raw material needed in largest amounts, and as a result most of the first steel centers were located where coal was abundant, as in the Ruhr district of Germany. In the United States the Pittsburgh-Cleveland district became the major center of steel manufacture. Coal suitable for making coke was at hand (map, p. 284). At Pittsburgh there was also iron ore, and sources of limestone were close by (picture, p. 282). As the volume of production increased, iron ore was brought by lake boat (picture above) from the great Mesabi Range in Minnesota, west of Lake Superior. The large steel center which was built round the southern end of Lake Michigan used coal from the Illinois fields not far away.

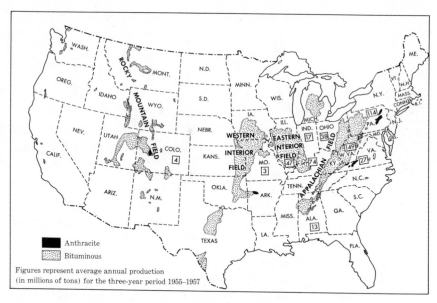

Coal fields and coal production in the United States

The United States was abundantly supplied with high-grade coal, high-grade iron, and limestone, and with deep waterways on which to transport the iron to the coal. But modern steel manufacture requires many other materials which were unknown during the earlier years of the industry; and to supply these materials the United States must reach out to fifty-seven different countries. During and since World War II the reserves of high-grade ore in the Mesabi Range have been exhausted, and the use of ores of lower grade has increased the cost of steel manufacture. Meanwhile new sources of iron ore were being developed in Canada, on the Quebec-Labrador border and in southwestern Ontario, and in Venezuela. Two changes resulted. One was the construction of a canal deep enough to accommodate ocean ships round the falls of the St. Lawrence and Niagara Falls, thus permitting ore boats to bring supplies of ore to the steel centers round the Great Lakes. The other change was the construction of new steel-manufacturing centers on Chesapeake Bay and the Delaware River. No longer was coal a major factor in the location of steel plants. In addition to being accessible to ores brought by ocean ships, the east coast plants are close to the great markets for steel, where there are many industries which manufacture steel products.

Since the beginning of the twentieth century there has been an enormous increase in the volume of manufactured goods in the United States; and during all this time the per capita production of the workers has increased. New centers of manufacturing have developed in parts of the country other than the east coast—notably in the Tennessee Valley, where electric power is abundant; and in the Gulf coast of Texas, where new chemical industries are making use of the abundant resources of oil, gas, and sulfur. The greatest concentration of industries, however, still remains in the great manufacturing belt of the northeast. The map (Plate 21) shows this area extending from New England to Baltimore, and running westward through New York State and along the southern margin of the Great Lakes. It includes western Pennsylvania, Ohio, Michigan, Indiana, and Illinois to the western side of Lake Michigan. At least the eastern part of the Corn Belt can now be better characterized as a manufacturing region than as an agricultural region. About 76 per cent of all the factory workers in the United States are employed in this manufacturing belt of the northeast. In terms of value added by manufacture this belt accounts for 77 per cent of the United States total.

New York. The primate city of the United States is New York. This is the one urban center which stands out above all others, and in it are concentrated many millions of people, many of the most important skills in the United States, and huge aggregates of financial power. The city performs all the urban functions: it is a commercial and financial center of world-wide significance; it has an enormous concentration of manufacturing industry, chiefly of consumer goods; it is a city which provides recreation for many millions of people from distant places; it is a major center of art, music, and literature; and in recent years it has become the seat of the United Nations organization. On it are focused the interests and hopes of the entire world.

The geographical city of New York extends far beyond the political city. In the east it includes politically independent cities at least as far as the border of Connecticut. It includes Brooklyn, Manhattan, and the Bronx east of the Hudson River. West of the river in New Jersey the metropolitan area of New York takes in Jersey City and Bayonne

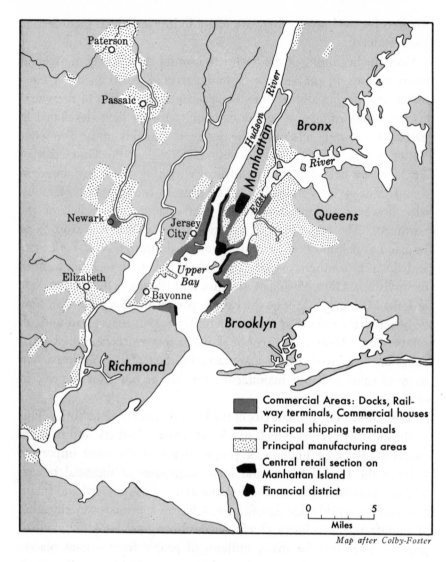

Commercial Areas: Docks, Railway terminals, Commercial houses

Principal shipping terminals

Principal manufacturing areas

Central retail section on
Manhattan Island

Financial district

0   5
Miles

Map after Colby-Foster

The metropolitan area of New York

along the Hudson, and, west of a belt of marshes, Elizabeth, Newark, Passaic, and Paterson. The heart of all this enormous metropolis is Manhattan (map above; picture, p. 287).

New York City owes its location to a variety of factors. The Dutch at an early date recognized the strategic value of Manhattan Island, commanding the outlet of the easiest route of travel across the Appalachians. Warfare restricted the value of this route until after 1812, and its full value was not realized until after 1825. The development of New York's connections to the Middle West took place just at the beginning of the period of great expansion westward. Then, also, few great cities are built on sites which possess such natural advantages. The Hudson River is wide and deep; Manhattan Island and the nearby shores of Long Island and New Jersey are firm and rocky. The East River and the Hudson meet in the Upper Bay, which is large enough to accommodate a vast amount of shipping. The Port of New York has a water frontage of some 770 miles, not all of which is yet developed. But all these advantages could scarcely have resulted in the growth of

Lower Manhattan, the Upper Bay, and the Narrows

Fairchild Aerial Surveys

so large a metropolis were it not for the location of New York with reference to Europe. The exchange of people, goods, and ideas with Europe is a fundamental fact of American life, and New York is as much a reflection of these currents of exchange as it is of local advantages. Nor could New York have appeared at all except for the rise of the industrial society, with all the attitudes, objectives, and technical skills implied by that term.

Canadian Settlement in Group IV. The mid-latitude mixed forest lands of North America are not without national boundaries. Along the northern border of Group IV is Canada, separated from the United States along the "unguarded frontier" which separates two friendly and co-operative peoples. The national territory of Canada stretches far to the north into the regions of Groups VI and VII, and westward into the grasslands of Group V. But most of the Canadian people are concentrated in two separated areas close to the border of the United States, one east of the Great Lakes and the other to the west of them (Plate 1).

Canada, moreover, is strongly divided between two diverse groups. There are the English-speaking Canadians, who are predominant in the country westward from Montreal and in Nova Scotia; and there are the French-speaking Canadians, who form the majority of the inhabitants in Quebec. The attitudes and interests of the two groups are not always easy to reconcile.

Most of eastern Canada is unsuited for grain-farming. The chief use of the land is for hay and dairy products. In the narrow bit of land between Lake Ontario and Lake Erie is Canada's major fruit-raising area. Toward the north the shortness of the growing season, as well as the poverty of the glacial soil, greatly restricts the significance of agriculture. In Nova Scotia, where the proximity of the ocean tempers the length and severity of the winters, apple orchards are of importance.

Canada has no primate city. Montreal, with a population of over a million, is the largest city, and it owes this pre-eminence to its location at the head of navigation for ocean ships on the St. Lawrence River (picture, p. 289). Toronto, on Lake Ontario, is only a little smaller than Montreal. Both cities are important commercial centers, and in both there is a considerable development of manufacturing industries. Manufacturing enterprises are hampered by the small size of the Canadian market and by the restrictions which keep Canadian prod-

Philip Gendreau

Montreal, looking south from Mont Royal across the St. Lawrence River

ucts from reaching the markets of the United States. There are important mining and refining industries, especially in the nickel and platinum area around Sudbury; there are many scattered mills producing paper pulp from Canada's forests; and there are heavy industries manufacturing iron and steel products at several places along the lake fronts. The lack of one great metropolitan center in Canada may be owing in part to the geographic pattern of commerce and industry, which does not point toward the development of one central focus of the domestic economy.

Group IV Regions of Western North America. From a climatic point of view, the part of North America which is most nearly comparable to western Europe is the west coast north of 40°. In North America this part of Group IV has not developed on the scale suggested by the patterns on the generalized continent (diagram, p. 177) because of the presence of high mountains running parallel to the coast. In British Columbia, except for a narrow bit of lowland around Vancouver, the mountains rise from the water's edge (Plate 9). In Washington and Oregon hills or mountains border the ocean; but between the coastal mountains and the Cascade Mountains farther inland there

North America 289

are the Puget Sound Lowland and the Willamette Valley, in which most of the people are concentrated. The whole region is but thinly populated, and much of it is still in the stage of the first exploitation of the most easily utilized resources. Seattle is a port with connections across the Pacific to the Orient and northward to Alaska. As Alaska grows in population and production, now that it has become a state, Seattle will be the chief base and will provide the chief market for Alaskan products. This important city now serves a wide area beyond its immediate surroundings. Abundant electric power from the Columbia River supports many new manufacturing industries.

THE SOUTHERN HEMISPHERE

Mid-latitude mixed forests occur only in small areas in the Southern Hemisphere. There are five separate regions to describe: South Chile; South Brazil; the Durban area of South Africa; southeast Australia; and New Zealand.

South Chile. South Chile is very much like the northwestern part of the United States and British Columbia. The climatic similarity is reinforced by a remarkable similarity in the arrangement of the surface features. The heavy forests of rainy South Chile begin abruptly along the Río Bío-Bío, inland from Concepción (map, p. 148, and Plate 11). To the north, in mediterranean Middle Chile, are the open scrub forests and maquis, the irrigated fields bordered by roads which are dusty in the dry summers. To the south is a land of dense forests in which pioneer settlers have opened clearings in places where rainfall is not too heavy or where the wet ground can be drained. The Spaniards, who were more at home in open country than in the forests, did little more than establish a few ports south of the Bío-Bío; but the southern region was opened to pioneer settlement after 1850, when a colony of Germans was located a little north of Puerto Montt. Since that time a steady movement of new settlers from Middle Chile has moved to the new frontier, where the land is used for wheat and cattle, and the forest is utilized for its lumber. But beyond Puerto Montt and Valdivia the much embayed coast of South Chile, like the coast of British Columbia and Alaska, offers little opportunity for settlement where the rainy mountain slopes come to the edge of the sea. Puerto Montt occupies

The Chilean lake district; in the foreground is Lake Todos Los Santos, and in the background is the volcano Mount Osorno

a position in many respects similar to that of Seattle; but south of Puerto Montt there is no Alaska, and to the west only a vast ocean.

South Brazil. South Brazil is the region which lies in the lower middle latitudes of eastern South America, south of the coffee region of São Paulo. Its climate, its mixed broadleaf and conifer forest, its hilly dissected plateau surface, all combine to form a strong physical resemblance to the southern part of the Cumberland Plateau in Alabama. This part of Brazil was not all divided into large estates by the early Portuguese settlers, because they, like the Spaniards, avoided the heavy forests in favor of the open grasslands. The forests of South Brazil were first occupied during the nineteenth century by colonies of Germans, who established a pattern of small farms in woodland clearings. Later pioneer settlers have included Italians, Poles, and others, as well as Brazilians from farther north. The colonies have been notably successful, and a considerable pioneer expansion has taken place around the original nuclei. No spectacular wealth has been produced in this region, but a sound local economy has been developed based on the sale of hogs and other farm products to small, but growing, urban markets. This is one of the world's largest areas of land suitable for pioneer farm settlement to which immigrants might still come.

South Africa. Little of South Africa belongs in Group IV. There is a narrow fringe of mid-latitude forest along the east coast north of the mediterranean region. Along most of this part of the coast the lower hilly slopes of the escarpment descend to the water, leaving no flat coastal plain for agricultural use (Plate 13 and map, p. 73). The chief town of the area is Durban, a port which acts as the commercial center for the settlements in the interior and along the coast farther north.

Australia. The most important of the Southern Hemisphere regions of Group IV is in southeastern Australia. The mid-latitude mixed forest region extends from north of Brisbane to the southeast coast around Melbourne and to the island of Tasmania. Most of the area is hilly, and northeast of Melbourne the hilly lands are surmounted by the high Australian Alps (Plate 19 and map, p. 170). There are only a few narrow lowlands such as those around Melbourne and Sydney. Wheat farming is concentrated in the eastern part of the Great Plains west of the hilly uplands, where the Murray and Darling rivers flow west toward the dry interior. The extension of farming westward is restricted by the low and uncertain rainfall; the increase of farm land in the humid east is restricted by the hilly terrain. In the south, around Melbourne and on Tasmania, the land is used as pasture for large numbers of sheep.

Like Canada, Australia has no primate city. Both Sydney and Melbourne have more than a million inhabitants. At Sydney, and north of it along the coast, there are numerous industrial establishments based on local sources of coal. Australia looks to London as the major commercial and cultural center of the Commonwealth of Nations.

Australia as a whole is very thinly populated. It is hoped to raise the total number of people from 9,000,000 (1954) to something like 22,000,000, chiefly by bringing immigrants from Great Britain. Although the British can scarcely spare such a large number of their young and most productive people, a considerable current of migration to the member states of the Commonwealth has developed. Among the immigrants, also, are many from other European countries. Australia's territory is mostly too dry for very dense settlement; the larger proportion of the immigrants will be settled on farms in the southeast, greatly increasing the density in this region, and thereby strengthening the whole Australian economy.

New Zealand. New Zealand is mostly mountainous (Plate 19). Its chief areas of settlement are located on the relatively small lowlands around Auckland, Wellington, and Christchurch. Although some wheat is raised around Christchurch, the chief use of the land on South Island is for the pasture of sheep. North Island, which enjoys a somewhat milder climate, has a larger area of good farm land and pastures suitable for cattle. Like Canada and Australia, New Zealand has no primate city. New Zealand, also, is looking for immigrants from Great Britain, and is especially anxious to establish new manufacturing industries to process the raw materials originating on farm and ranch.

Conclusion

The mid-latitude mixed forest lands are occupied by nearly two fifths of the world's population. There are regions within this group with very dense populations; and there are other regions still available for more pioneer settlement. There are populations which have gone through a period of rapid increase during the past century, and are now again approaching an almost static or, perhaps, even a declining condition; there are other populations still growing rapidly; and there are some which stand on the verge of a great era of expansion. In the Orient there are major problems to be solved of the relation of people to the resources of the land—of the means of increasing the supply of food, clothing, and shelter. But in the Occidental world the technical knowledge exists to provide a much better level of living than now prevails: in these countries the major problems to be solved are those of adjusting the institutions and habits of thought inherited from the era of horses and sailing ships to the realities of the industrial age.

But the industrial society cannot be understood against the background of any one of the world's groups of regions. That the chief centers of industry and commerce are in the regions of Group IV is the result of a variety of factors, and the present economic and political pre-eminence of these regions can scarcely be understood without reference to the rest of the world. The industrial society has been evolved in an atmosphere of expansion: the population itself was growing at a rapid rate. and this was providing always larger and larger markets. Pioneer settlers were also moving into new regions, and bringing into economic use a wide variety and enormous quantity of new products. There was wide opportunity for individual initiative and profit. And the greatest profits went to the people who had first developed the new technologies—to the people of the English-speaking world.

A very important part of the process of expansion took place not in the regions of Group IV, but in other parts of the world not previously exploited. This outward movement into new lands brought the Occidental people into contact with many other cultures. We have seen some of the results of Occidental contacts in the dry-land regions of the world, and in the tropical forests. But the greatest expansion was taking place in the grasslands and to a somewhat lesser extent northward in the Northern Hemisphere. We now turn our attention to these other groups of regions in the world and to the penetration of them by Occidentals.

GROUP V

THE GRASSLANDS

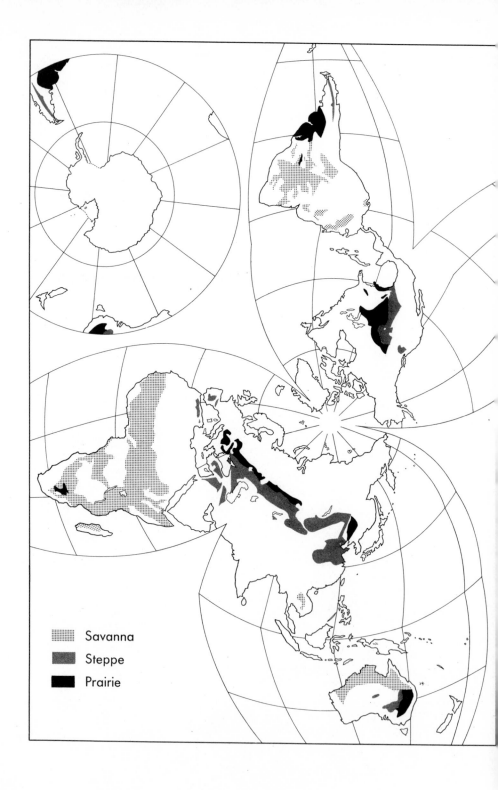

Savanna

Steppe

Prairie

$\mathbf{A}$T THE BEGINNING of historic time some 21 per cent of the earth's land surface had a vegetation cover of grass. On the generalized continent (diagram, p. 177) the grasslands occupy a position intermediate between forests and deserts. They are distinguished from the former by the scarcity of trees, and from the latter by a continuous cover of plants. In many places, however, grass and trees are variously intermingled, especially in the savannas of the low latitudes. Where treeless grasslands occur, it is probable that they were formed by the action of prehistoric man.

If the grasslands occupy an intermediate position among the major regional divisions of the earth, they are nevertheless distinctly marginal with reference to the centers of population. As we have already seen, a large proportion of the earth's human inhabitants occupy the mixed forests of middle latitudes and the light semideciduous forests of the Asian low latitudes. Recently, settlement has pushed out from these forests onto the contiguous grasslands, so that now parts of Group V share with the mixed forest lands those spectacular developments of the machine culture which we have just described. In fact, it is from the more accessible grasslands that the major portion of the grain and meat supply for the support of the great urban populations is now derived. Where the grasslands have been subject to agricultural settlement a transformation of the primitive landscape no less remarkable than that of the forest clearings has taken place. The present distribution of such settlements illustrates once again the vital role played by culture in the establishment of geographic limits.

The Land

VEGETATION AND CLIMATE

Because the grasslands are intermediate in position between the deserts and the forests, the landscapes developed in the various parts of this group represent a series of transitional types between the bordering groups. The gradual change from abundant moisture to aridity, through zones which are sometimes characterized as subhumid and semiarid, is reflected in the character of the vegetation. Three chief types of grassland are commonly recognized. In the middle latitudes the dry margins of Group V are occupied by the *steppes* and the wet margins by the *prairies*. In the low latitudes several kinds of *savannas* reflect the transition from forest margin to desert margin. We shall consider each of these in turn.

The Steppes. The change from the xerophytic shrub vegetation of Group I to the steppe grasses of the cool, semiarid portions of Group V brings a notable difference in the landscape. The actual boundary between the two is not everywhere easy to identify when it is sought in topographic detail, although in some parts of the world the limits are sharp enough for this. Generally speaking, the vegetation of the dry lands fails to form a complete cover over the surface of the land; if grass is present, as in the "desert shrub–desert grass" formation, it grows in bunches with bare ground between the plants. The steppes, on the contrary, are covered with a nearly continuous mat. At maturity the steppe grasses are only a few inches in height, although in unusually wet years taller grasses give the vegetation cover an uneven appearance. Normally the steppes resemble a closely pastured meadow,—a landscape of striking monotony which extends unbroken to the horizon.

The short grasses of these regions are developed in areas deficient in moisture. Like the xerophytic shrubs of the deserts, these plants are adapted to long periods of drought. After a rain they spring quickly into activity, completing the life cycle within a short time and then remaining parched and brownish until the next shower brings renewed life. The water is absorbed by the surface layers of the soil, but very rarely is enough received to penetrate to the water table. Soil moisture is available to the grass roots near the surface for a period after a rain, but underneath this surface layer there is a zone of permanently dry soil. Deep underground, as in the deserts, lies the zone of saturation, replenished at rare intervals by unusual rains. It is the presence of soil moisture near the surface that makes possible the growth of the shallow-rooted short grasses.

In general, the steppes are associated with a semiarid type of climate

An encampment on the Kirghiz Steppe

(Plates 10–20 and 8). However, this relationship is obscured in many places; for the grasslands, which, on the generalized continent (diagram, p. 177) almost completely surround the deserts, are much interrupted by mountains. The mid-latitude margins of the great dry-land area of North Africa and Eurasia are actually bordered by steppes in only a few places: in the northern interior, extending from the western side of the Black Sea eastward beyond Lake Balkhash, including the great Kirghiz Steppe; two small patches in the Far East, in Manchuria and the Ordos Desert; and in North Africa, where there is room for only a narrow band of steppe between the desert and the mountains or the Mediterranean shore (Plate 14).

In the other parts of the world similar irregularities may be observed. In North America the steppes are developed only on the east and north of the dry lands. The Great Plains extend from Texas into southern Canada, and a small steppe area in Washington and Oregon borders the northern limits of the dry lands of the intermontane plateaus and basins. In South America the steppes, like the deserts themselves, are much distorted by the Andes. Along the eastern piedmont of the mountains in Patagonia there is a narrow zone of steppe which widens southward toward the Strait of Magellan. The tall bunch grasses of the Argentine Humid Pampa, which lies east of the desert, are mixed with a dwarf scrub forest known as *monte* along the dry margin, and there is no zone of short-grass steppe between the prairies and the dry lands. Nor is there a steppe bordering the dry-land region of South Africa. In Australia the steppe is limited to the eastern desert border in the basins of the Murray River and the Darling River.

Even in regions where the steppe does form a zone of transition between the arid climates of the desert and the subhumid climates of the wetter lands, the relations to the climatic lines are not always simple. In the classification of climates developed by Wladimir Köppen a formula was devised by which arid, semiarid, and humid climates might be distinguished on the basis of average monthly and annual figures for temperature and rainfall. This formula is presented in Appendix B, section 30. The climates are described by letter: an arid climate is represented by the letters *BW*; a semiarid climate by the letters *BS*. The distribution of climates according to the Köppen system is shown on Plate 8.

A comparison of the outlines of the *BS* and *BW* climates with the observed distribution of vegetation shows a number of important differences of pattern. In many places xerophytic shrub vegetation is found well beyond the area of *BW* climate—as in western China or the western interior of the United States. As a matter of fact, in nearly all the vegetation distributions thus far described, forest as well as desert, numerous departures from the generally related climatic patterns can be observed. In part these can be explained by reference to the edaphic conditions, especially the presence or absence of water. But future field studies may also seek explanations for these irregularities in the distribution and activities of prehistoric man.

The activities of prehistoric man, especially his use of fire, had differing results under different climatic conditions. In arid lands there could not be a sufficiently large accumulation of inflammable material to feed a fire; in wet forested areas fires could not easily spread out of control. But in places where there was enough rainfall to support the growth of an abundant vegetation, yet where there were periods of dry weather long enough to dry out the surface of the ground and the accumulation of organic matter lying on it, fires could get a start and spread widely. The question is, where do extended periods of dry weather occur? The average position of the boundary between humid and semiarid climates may be less important in defining the areas subject to periodic drought than the position of the line defining the dry areas in any one year. The *B* boundary, that is, the boundary determined by Köppen's formula between the semiarid *BS* climates and the bordering humid climates, has an average position which is shown on Plate 8; but it shifts widely from this average position when it is plotted for individual years. In fact, rarely does the actual border between sufficient moisture and deficient moisture in any one year lie close to, or even correspond in trend with, the average *B* boundary. This condition is illustrated by a map of this critical boundary in the United States in a succession of years. During the period from 1915 to 1924, humid years were experienced as far west as the front of the Rocky Mountains, and dry years were experienced as far east as Minnesota (map, p. 302).[1] Russell suggests the possibility that the recurrence of a very dry year (a *BW* year) at not infrequent intervals may serve more effectively to limit the spread of grasslands toward the deserts than does the average condition (map, p. 303).[2]

The Prairies. The prairies are quite distinct from the vegetation types which border them. Unlike the grasses of the steppes, the prairie grasses are tall and deep-rooted. At maturity they reach heights of from three to more than ten feet. The natural grasses of the Argentine Pampa are said to have risen above the head of a man on horseback. Few scenes in the New World so impressed the early travelers from Europe as did the sight of the great expanses of grass billowing in the wind. Around most of these prairies the edge of the forest is sharply defined. Except for the galeria forests along the streams, the prairies, at the beginning of historic time, were entirely treeless.

Toward the steppes the prairies are limited by a fairly definite moisture supply. Where the zone of moist soil extends for as much as two feet below the surface, the tall grasses are able to gain a foothold at the expense of the short grasses. Russell finds that in the United States

---

[1] H. M. Kendall, "Notes on Climatic Boundaries in the Eastern United States," *Geographical Review*, Vol. 25 (1935), pp. 117–124.

[2] R. J. Russell, "Dry Climates of the United States, II, Frequency of Dry and Desert Years, 1901–1920," *University of California Publications in Geography*, Vol. 5, No. 5 (1932), pp. 245–274.

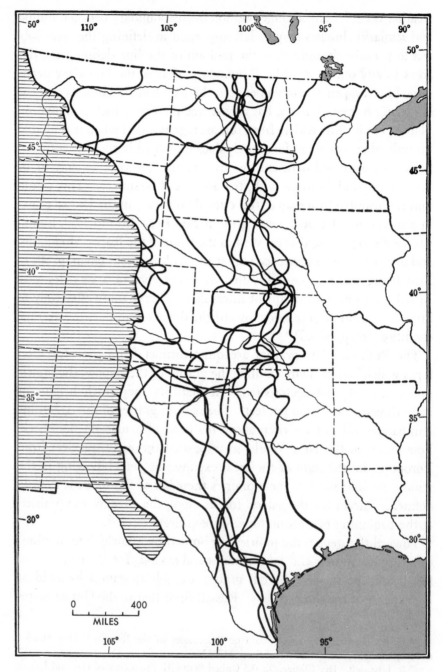

Fluctuations of the semiarid/humid boundary in the central part of the United States, 1915–1924. (*After Henry M. Kendall*)

this condition, and with it the prairie-steppe boundary, corresponds closely to the eastern limit of the area which receives at least one very dry (*BW*) year in twenty (map below). In topographic detail this prairie-steppe boundary is much influenced by edaphic conditions. On sandy soil the depth of the moist surface layer is greater, climatic conditions being equal, than on clay soil. Therefore the tall grasses penetrate well within the areas generally deficient in moisture on sandy soils, but short steppe grasses are found on clay soils well within the humid lands.

The boundary between the prairie and the forest is not so clearly related to climatic or edaphic conditions. In the United States the prairie-forest border bears only a very general relationship to the eastern limit of climates with one dry year (*BS*) in twenty (Plate 10 and map below). The eastward extension of the prairie south of Chicago is well within a climate humid enough for tree growth, and where trees are planted they grow without difficulty. Similar wet prairies occur along the Gulf coast of Texas and Louisiana, in the Humid Pampa of Argentina, in Uruguay and southern Brazil, in Hungary and on the northern side of the Russian steppes, in South Africa, in Manchuria, and in Australia. In all these places the prairies are treeless, except for galerias, and the prairie-forest border is sharp.

That the treeless wet prairies owe their origin to fires set by prehistoric man seems well established. Such fires, started perhaps to aid in the hunting of game or

Frequency of semiarid (BS) *and arid* (BW) *years in central United States.* (*After Richard J. Russell*)

Isarithm of one *BS* year in twenty

Isarithm of one *BW* year in twenty

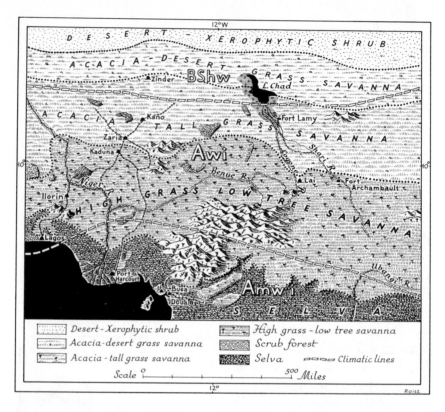

The savannas of the central Sudan. (*Vegetation after Shantz and Marbut*)

to improve the feed for game animals, spread out of control. The intense heat killed the young trees which otherwise might have gained a foothold on the prairies, in the course of time pushing back and sharpening the forest edge. Nevertheless, when man first came upon these prairies in historic time, they had been in existence long enough to have developed as a distinctive natural habitat, with their own peculiar soil types and their own peculiar animal population adjusted to life in a treeless environment.

The Savannas. In the low latitudes a wide zone in which forests and grasslands are intermingled occupies the drier parts of the humid climates and crosses the *B* border to the margins of the deserts. This is the zone of the savannas. Essentially this is a transition between forest and desert, but the landscapes which are developed differ in important respects from those of the mid-latitude transitional grasslands.

304 The Grasslands

Photo by H. V. B. Kline, Jr.

The degraded savanna of western Uganda. Each clump of bushes in the middle distance occupies an abandoned termite mound

Not only are the savannas ribbed with galeria forests along the streams, as are also the prairies and some of the steppes, but the savanna flora includes enough scattered trees so that in only a few places is the horizon visible. The tropical scrub forests merge almost imperceptibly with the savannas. In some parts of the world the scrub forests actually border the xerophytic shrub of the dry lands without any intervening zone of savannas.

The savannas themselves can be divided into a succession of types reflecting the transition from wet to dry. These different kinds of savannas can be illustrated by a study of the Sudan of Africa (map, p. 304).[1] In the south, bordering the selva of the Congo, lies the "high grass–low tree savanna," composed of grasses which, at maturity, reach heights of ten or twelve feet, mixed with a fairly close scattering of low trees, together with numerous patches of thicket. The grasses are coarse and do not form a sod, because each plant stands individually. Farther north, in the direction of decreasing rainfall, this formation gives way to the "acacia–tall grass savanna," composed of grasses growing from three to five feet in height and associated with scattered,

[1] H. L. Shantz and C. F. Marbut, "The Vegetation and Soils of Africa," American Geographical Society, Research Series No. 13, New York, 1923.

flat-topped acacias which stand somewhat farther apart than the low trees of the southernmost zone. Still farther north, extending across the *B* boundary, is the "acacia–desert grass savanna," where the stunted trees stand far apart and the short desert grasses cover most of the surface. Thus representatives of the forest extend all the way to the edges of the desert, while, as we have seen elsewhere, patches of open savanna are found in the midst of the selva. Similar transitional types are found in other parts of the world.

Information regarding the relationship of the savannas to climatic conditions is difficult to obtain. Climatic stations in the savannas are widely scattered, and their records are mostly fragmentary. Certain it is, however, that few parts of Group V suffer such extreme fluctuations of rainfall from year to year or such extreme variations from season to season as do the savannas. Almost every year in the Sudan is abnormal in regard to either rainfall or drought. No doubt more adequate data would suggest the importance of the extremely dry years in establishing the margins of the savanna and the tropical forests. (Compare pictures, pp. 305–308.)

No other parts of the low latitudes exhibit such a marked change in their appearance with the march of the seasons as do these tropical grasslands. During the dry season the coarse grasses become parched and brown, and the scattered trees lose their leaves and stand with bare limbs. The beginning of the rainy season witnesses a most remarkable awakening of the plants; the trees quickly send out a cover-

Hippos in a water hole in the savanna of western Uganda. How many hippos are there?

Photo by H. V. B. Kline, Jr.

Giraffes on an African savanna

ing of new leaves, while the tender young shoots of grass give the ground a carpet of velvety green.

SURFACE FEATURES AND DRAINAGE

Most of the grasslands are developed on relatively level surfaces,— either plains or plateaus. Although in some cases these lands may be gently rolling, only rarely can they be classified as hilly. Most of the hilly areas which interrupt the grasslands receive more plentiful rainfall than the surrounding plains, and are forest-covered.

On the vast level surfaces of the grasslands the transitional character of the rainfall is faithfully reflected in the drainage features. The rivers, especially in the savannas, have a marked seasonal rise and fall. During the dry season they slowly lose volume, in part by the loss of tributaries which dry up, in part by evaporation. As they lose volume

Surface Features and Drainage 307

A tropical savanna in the rainy season—Goiás in Central Brazil

and velocity they drop a large part of their load, and this accumulates in the river channels, forming a maze of sand bars. When a river is choked with its alluvium, it may split apart into many small rivulets, producing a typical braided channel. Near the arid boundary, if the river is flowing toward the desert, this accumulation becomes so great that the river tends to spread out and form an extensive shallow marsh. All three of the rivers of northern Africa which cross the savannas toward the Sahara behave in this way. The rivers in a semiarid climate, being exotic, receive few tributaries, for no local streams can rise within the regions of deficient moisture.

The seasonal contrast is especially great in the savannas. The glistening white sand banks of the streams are speedily submerged when the rainy season begins. Unlike the rivers in the forest lands, these streams are so clogged with silt that the waters cannot easily drain off, and therefore vast areas of lowland may be inundated. From brown, parched drought to widespread flood is a seasonal change which rivals the snowy winters and verdant summers of the higher middle latitudes.

Especially in the savannas, the effect of these seasonal drainage contrasts is determined in large part by the type of country. Where the rivers lie close to the surface, as on the Shari Plain or on the llanos of the Orinoco, the rainy-season floods cover a vast extent of territory. In contrast, where the streams are incised in youthful or mature valleys in a plateau, as in the plateau of Brazil or of South Africa, the floods are confined to the immediate valleys. While the first type of country may suffer from rainy-season floods, the latter type is more exposed to dry-season droughts. The distribution of these types of surface is indicated on the accompanying maps (Plates 9–19).

SOILS

Some of the most fertile soils in the world are in the grasslands, especially the prairies. The contrast between the dark-colored prairie soils and the lighter soils of the neighboring forests of Group IV is very great. In order to understand the pre-eminence of the grassland soils we must turn briefly to a review of the soil-making processes.

A Review of the Soil Processes. The development of a regolith is the first step in the construction of a soil. Under the influence of the atmosphere the process of weathering results in the disintegration and decomposition of the exposed rock material at the earth's surface. To be sure, the character of the climate affects the nature of this weathering process; for chemical decomposition, producing a fine-textured regolith, is emphasized in hot and moist climates, while physical disintegration, producing a relatively coarse regolith, is emphasized in dry climates, especially those with a temperature range that crosses the freezing point. But the differences of texture and composition of regolith in any climate are closely related to the nature of the parent material. The geologic map furnishes the pattern for the map of regolith.

The production of a soil on the surface of the regolith is the result of three processes. The percolation of water through the surface layers on its way down to the water table is responsible for the first two of these: leaching and eluviation (pp. 105–106). Leaching, like all other chemical processes, is at a maximum in hot and rainy climates; eluviation also goes on most rapidly where an abundance of water is moving down through the regolith. Both leaching and eluviation cease where there is no percolation of water, whether this is due to a desert condition, to a permanently waterlogged condition as in a swamp, or to a permanently frozen condition as in the polar regions. These processes are only retarded, of course, in places where droughts, floods, or frosts recur seasonally. Under any given type of climate, however, both leaching and eluviation proceed much more rapidly where the regolith is coarse in texture than where it is fine and compact.

The third soil-making process is the accumulation of humus. This goes on most rapidly not only where the largest amount of organic litter is provided by the vegetation but also where the destruction of this litter by bacteria is not too rapid. Bacterial action is at a maximum in hot, moist climates, and declines with lower temperatures or decreased moisture. Although the tropical forests supply a considerable amount of litter in the form of dead leaves and twigs, the bacteria, together with the destructive activity of ants and other small animals, quickly destroy this material. The rate of humus accumulation in the forest lands increases as one proceeds toward cooler climates. Whereas the tropical forest soils as well as those of the lower middle latitudes are characteristically light-colored, those of the higher middle latitudes (north of Chesapeake Bay in eastern North America) are somewhat darker in color. No forest vegetation, however, can supply such an abundance of organic material as can a grass cover, with its yearly increment of dead stems and its mat of fine roots. The grassland soils are black or dark brown in color.

As these soil-making processes continue they produce a gradual change on the surface layers of the regolith. In the course of time three horizons become more and more clearly distinguished. The surface, or *A horizon,* is one which has felt the maximum of leaching, has been rendered somewhat coarser in texture than the original regolith by the process of eluviation, and has been mixed with whatever amounts of humus are available. The *B horizon* is a zone of accumulation, rendered finer in texture than the original material by the addition of the fine particles brought down from above. Underneath is the *C horizon,* the unleached and uneluviated parent material. The depth and character of these horizons reflect the balance of the soil-making processes as controlled by the climate and the cover of vegetation. Not until the first signs of these horizons appear, however, is the regolith said to have a cover of soil. As the horizons become more and more clearly defined the soil is said to become mature. Theoretically, given a long enough time, the soils lose the characteristics imparted to them by the underlying parent material, and throughout the broad regions of similar climate and vegetation cover the mature soils all take on the same kind of profile. The patterns of soil distribution which are related to the underlying geology are gradually obscured by the broader patterns related to the climate.

Mature soils, however, can only develop where the regolith is undisturbed. On steep slopes where creep or flow is active the A and B horizons are stripped off as fast as they are formed, and fresh regolith is brought to the surface. On river floodplains fresh alluvium is laid down before any soil horizons can be formed in the older deposits. Similarly, in areas of active loess accumulation mature soil profiles should not be expected. Mature soils can develop only on level or gently rolling surfaces free from active deposition and exposed to the soil-forming processes for a sufficiently long period of time. In hilly lands only minor portions of an area can have mature soils; nowhere but on the more level plains are any extensive areas of such soils to be found.

Grassland Soils.[1] Over the wide expanses of rolling to level plains in Group V, however, the soils are able to reach maturity and to reflect closely the transitional features of the climate. A succession of soil types, from the humid forest margins across the prairies and the steppes to the dry lands, conforms to the changes in moisture and vegetation cover. On the rainy margins of the prairie a deep soil is formed which is so abundantly supplied with organic material that it is dark-colored

---

[1] See the classic treatment of the Great Plains of the United States: C. F. Marbut, "Soils of the Great Plains," *Annals of the Association of American Geographers,* Vol. 13 (1923), pp. 41–66; J. B. Kincer, "The Climate of the Great Plains as a Factor in Their Utilization," *Annals of the Association of American Geographers,* Vol. 13 (1923), pp. 67–80; H. L. Shantz, "The Natural Vegetation of the Great Plains Region," *Annals of the Association of American Geographers,* Vol. 13 (1923), pp. 81–107; O. E. Baker, "The Agriculture of the Great Plains Region," *Annals of the Association of American Geographers,* Vol. 13 (1923), pp. 109–167; see also F. Shreve, "Rainfall, Runoff and Soil Moisture under Desert Conditions," *Annals of the Association of American Geographers,* Vol. 24 (1934), pp. 131–156.

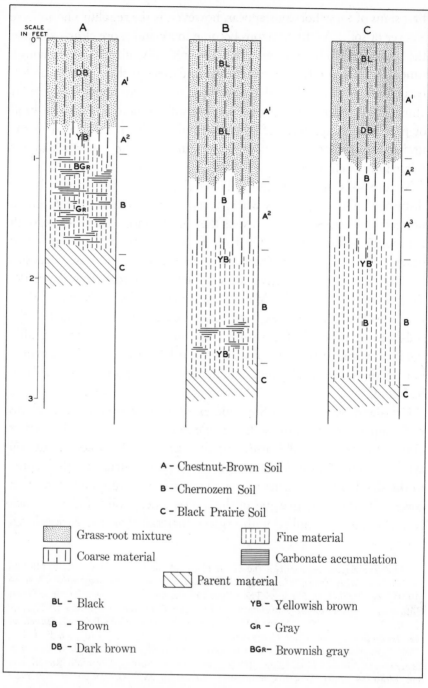

A - Chestnut-Brown Soil

B - Chernozem Soil

C - Black Prairie Soil

Grass-root mixture   Fine material

Coarse material   Carbonate accumulation

Parent material

BL - Black   YB - Yellowish brown

B - Brown   GR - Gray

DB - Dark brown   BGR - Brownish gray

Generalized mature soil profiles developed under grasslands. (After Jenny)

even in the B horizon (diagram, C, p. 312). This is the *black prairie soil*. But near the dry margin of the tall-grass prairies a very important change in the moisture conditions takes place, a change which is critical in soil formation. No longer, except at rare intervals, does enough rain fall on the ground to percolate through to the ground-water table. Whereas the black prairie soils are subject to leaching like all other humid soils, the soils on the dry margins of the prairie cannot be similarly robbed of their soluble constituents. The minerals which are dissolved near the surface are carried down to the B horizon, but no farther. The result is the accumulation of these soluble minerals in the subsoil.

Two soil types share this peculiarity of having mineral accumulations, chiefly lime, in the B horizon. The first of these, occupying the dry margins of the prairies, is known as the *chernozem* (diagram, B, p. 312). The color of the chernozem is even darker than that of the black prairie soil, and its fertility is increased by the decreased effectiveness of the leaching process. The humid boundary of the chernozem is not easy to identify, for this type grades almost imperceptibly into the black prairie soil through a zone where the small and scattered lime concretions occur only here and there in the subsoil. The dry boundary of the chernozem, on the other hand, is quite distinct. It coincides with the prairie-steppe boundary, where, because the depth of the moist surface soil becomes less than approximately two feet, the tall grasses give way to the short grasses. The smaller supply of humus from the short grasses is reflected in a change from the black color of the chernozem to a chestnut-brown color; and the more active evaporation and shallower penetration of the rain water result in the formation of a continuous layer of lime salts much closer to the surface than in the case of the chernozem (diagram, A, p. 312). This is the *chestnut-brown soil*.

The soils of the tropical grasslands are little known.

The distribution of these soil types, where they have been adequately studied, conforms closely with the vegetation and climatic patterns. The black prairie soils are apparently rather unusual; the largest area of these, probably, is in the United States. The chernozems and chestnut-brown soils in both North America and Eurasia, where they have been carefully mapped, straddle the boundary between humid and semiarid climates.

The Occupance

The occupance of these grasslands provides numerous illustrations of the way in which different cultures have reacted differently to the same complex of physical conditions. To most primitive peoples armed with few agricultural implements the grasslands have not yielded an abundance of resources. On the other hand, nomadic peoples with domestic animals find in the open plains a favorable, although at times uncertain, habitat. The large-scale occupance of the grasslands, however, is a recent phenomenon. Various kinds of machines have in numerous ways made possible the development of the mid-latitude prairies and steppes as surplus grain-producing regions, and from these lands now comes a large part of the food supply for the Occidental urban centers. But even today the penetration of the tropical savannas by white people is uncertain and experimental.

AGRICULTURAL OCCUPANCE BY SIMPLE CULTURES

The fact that the grasslands are unattractive to primitive agriculturists is not difficult to understand. The clearing of grass presents great difficulties for workers armed with few implements. For them the partial clearing of a forest is much easier than the removal of tall grass. On the steppes, where the short grass is less of a problem, the decrease of moisture becomes critical, especially for people who do not possess the machinery or techniques to reach dependable supplies of water.

The few cases of the establishment of sedentary agriculture on the grasslands by peoples of simple cultures are all the more remarkable because they are exceptional. The chief examples seem to have resulted from contacts with more complex cultures. For example, when the Scythian nomads of the Russian steppes so radically changed their mode of life as to become wheat farmers, it was under the influence of the Greek colonists who had established themselves on the northern shore of the Black Sea.[1] Yet from this region came the greater part of

[1] E. C. Semple, *Geography of the Mediterranean Region,* New York, 1931, p. 357.

the grain supply for the support of ancient Athens—an extraordinary preview of the type of occupance which, some twenty-five centuries later, is dominating this and analogous regions.

The Negro tribes of the African Sudan have also established a sedentary agricultural occupance on the savannas. Although the moderately dense populations (Plate 3) of Nigeria and the French Sudan have been built up rather recently, still, long before the European conquest, agriculture was well established in parts of this region. To what extent the cultural traits of these tribes (including the smelting of iron, the making of iron tools, and an excellent dry-farming technique) had been introduced by the Arabs, and to what extent these things really are native to the Negro cultures, is not known. The subsistence agriculture in these regions is based on rice, grain sorghums, millet, maize, peanuts, and a number of other crops.

THE NOMADIC OCCUPANCE

While most of the world's grasslands have not favored agricultural settlement by simple cultures, those peoples who possess domestic animals have been able to gain at least a precarious existence. But before the spread of the Europeans, knowledge of domestic animals was limited to only one of the world's great areas of grassland. It is a remarkable fact that of the thirty animal species which are of chief importance to mankind, all had been domesticated before the dawn of written history, and all but four originated in eastern, southern, or central Asia and in the neighboring regions of Europe and Africa. Except for the ubiquitous dog, the only animals of importance which were domesticated outside these parts of the world were the reindeer of the polar regions of Eurasia and the llama of the Peruvian Andes.[1] Only on the grasslands of the Old World—those of North Africa and Eurasia—is a non-European nomadic occupance based on domestic animals to be found (picture, p. 316), and even in these regions this type of life is rapidly disappearing as the range of movement of the nomads becomes more and more restricted. The Soviet Union has largely eliminated nomadism from the Asian steppes and from Outer Mongolia (Mon-

[1] Ellsworth Huntington, "The Distribution of Domestic Animals," *Economic Geography*, Vol. I (1925), pp. 143–172.

Long-horned Ankole cattle grazing on the degraded savanna of western Uganda. An abandoned termite mound is at the right, and others appear behind the cattle

golian People's Republic) by establishing fixed settlements for the pastoral peoples. Where nomadism is still found, sheep and goats are of primary importance (picture, p. 317), although cattle predominate in a few especially favored localities. Horses and camels also play a vital role in the nomadic life. We have already described the effect on the Berbers and Arabs of the importation of the dromedary, without which ally their conquest of most of northern Africa would have been impossible.

The word "nomad" implies the absence of a fixed location. Nomadic peoples are free from the close attachment to the earth which of necessity characterizes the agriculturists. To be sure, certain of the forest dwellers, carrying on migratory agriculture, establish only temporary attachments to the land which are periodically broken; and other peoples, making use of the resources of contiguous regions, may make more or less regular seasonal migrations from one locality to another. Such peoples may be termed *seminomadic*. But the true nomad at no time thinks of his encampment as in any sense fixed; and even if the passage of the seasons finds a nomadic tribe moving regularly back and forth between neighboring areas, as between a mountainous region and the plains close by, the routes of travel are seldom the same, except, perhaps, where a mountain range enforces the use of a certain pass, or where the crossing of a large stream is possible at only one point. A map of the distribution of nomadic peoples would show always the same pattern of scattered groups, but the position of the groups would be ever-shifting.

The nature of the nomadic occupance enforces this freedom. The wealth of the nomad is represented solely by the number and condition of his animals. He has no other possessions that he cannot quickly pack and move on the backs of his horses or camels. From his flocks and herds he gets the material for his clothing, his house, his rugs, and his implements; from them he gets his meat and milk; from them he derives a surplus to exchange with the sedentary agriculturists for grain, dates, tea, or other agricultural products; and it is on his animals that he relies for the mobility which is an essential part of his life. In these lands of uncertain rains the pasturage is dependent on the scattered showers. When the nomad hears of a rain, he must be ready

A shepherd with sheep on the steppe in Iraq

Courtesy of G. B. Cressey

quickly to move his animals into the section which has been moistened, in order to take advantage of the brief period of rich growth which will follow. Rainy years to these people mean years of plenty, even of luxury.

Not uncommonly, nomadic peoples take advantage of complementary regions. The people of the Kirghiz Steppe, for instance, move their flocks into the high plateaus of the Altai Mountains during the summer, returning to the grasslands for the winter. Many of the nomadic peoples of the Sahara, who claim ownership of the various oases, enter the deserts only during the winter, leaving them either for the high pastures of the Atlas Mountains or for the savannas south of the desert during the summer months.

In comparison with their numbers, the steppe nomads have wielded a very great political power. For various reasons they have since time immemorial established their control over the neighboring sedentary agriculturists. These two contrasted groups of people, so necessary to each other, are traditional enemies. The nomad, because of his military organization and his mobility, is usually the conqueror; but the agriculturist, because of his permanence and the strength of his attachment to the land, has always survived and at last absorbed his conquerors.

The recurring cycles of dry years, which are so characteristic a feature of the steppe climate, have played a very important part in the history of the nomads. Dry years bring distress, and when they are too severe or are continued too long the nomad is brought face to face with disaster. Under the scourge of drought the great nomadic conquests of the neighboring lands have taken place. Around the margins of the steppes from China and India to Europe and Africa, history has been punctuated by repeated invasions from the grasslands. One of the greatest of these was the "barbarian" invasion of Europe which contributed to the downfall of the Roman Empire. These great migrations are thought to have been caused by cycles of dry years of more than usual severity, when the nomadic tribes were forced to flee from the steppes.[1]

[1] Ellsworth Huntington, *The Pulse of Asia,* Boston, 1907; Isaiah Bowman, "Our Expanding and Contracting 'Desert,'" *Geographical Review,* Vol. 25 (1935), pp. 43–61.

THE OCCIDENTAL OCCUPANCE

Before the middle of the nineteenth century the grasslands held little attraction for the European or American colonists. Only in the black-earth belts of European Russia and western Siberia was settlement extensive at an earlier date. In North America, when the settlers reached the prairies they hesitated and built their homes on the edge of the forest. For a long time the chief penetration of the grassy plains was by the hunters who followed the wild game, such as the buffalo in North America. Later, domestic animals were introduced, and these regions were used as natural pastures. Cattlemen on the North American plains, on the Argentine Humid Pampa, and in Uruguay adopted a seminomadic existence with their enormous herds of cattle, horses, and mules. A market for these frontier products was to be had in the settlements of eastern North America or, in South America, in the mining communities of the Andes. But the roads to these markets were long and difficult.

A stretch of plains in Saskatchewan, Canada

National Film Board of Canada

Cow punchers rounding up their cattle on the ranges of the Great Plains in Texas

The Advance of Settlement onto the Grasslands. Meanwhile the mechanical inventions were appearing which have so radically transformed the Occidental mode of life. Railroads and steamboats were the first of these to affect the grasslands by providing them with access to the growing urban markets. When the prairies of the United States were reached by through railroads from the eastern cities, between 1850 and 1860, the immediate result was an enormous stimulation of the cattle trade. In Argentina, too, railroads reached inland from Buenos Aires (1857) and Rosario and redirected the currents of trade from the centuries-old route to Bolivia. When the first refrigerator ship reached Argentina in 1877, the fact was established that frozen meat could be sent across the equator to the markets of Europe.

Almost at once, however, fundamental changes in the mode of occupance of the grasslands began to appear. With the railroads came a stream of settlers. The steel plow, first manufactured about 1837, was making the removal of the thick prairie sod a relatively easy task, the machinery for digging deep wells was making it possible for the settlers to reach dependable supplies of water, and the invention of

320   The Grasslands

barbed wire (1873) was making feasible the low-cost fencing of large fields. The Homestead Act in the United States, originally passed in 1862 to permit new settlers to occupy farms of not more than one hundred and sixty acres practically without charge, was a great stimulus to settlement. Increasing numbers of farmers moved onto the grasslands, fenced off their fields, built their homes, and planted crops. No longer could the cattle graze at will on the unfenced range. The ancient struggle between nomadic herders and sedentary agriculturists was renewed; but this time the picturesque cattlemen found themselves unable to face the more effective occupance of the farmers, and step by step they were pushed out of existence.

A stream of settlement has followed the construction of railroads on all the world's mid-latitude grasslands, one after the other. First, on the prairies of the United States the chief wave of settlement came after the Civil War. On the Argentine Humid Pampa the largest numbers of immigrants, chiefly from southern Europe, arrived between 1880

Crowded conditions at the old docks at Buenos Aires. A large new port has been built north of this area

and 1910. In Australia the conflict between the "squatter" cattlemen and the farmers began about 1860, and by 1884 the farmers were victorious. In Russia a renewed stream of colonists poured eastward along the black-earth belt following the construction of the Trans-Siberian Railroad, which was started in 1891. This eastward migration was especially strong from 1907 to 1912. Still more recent is the settlement of the Canadian steppes.

The Transformation of the Grassland Landscapes. As a result of the Occidental occupance of the grasslands, the landscapes of these regions have been profoundly modified. Before the arrival of settlers in any important numbers the "balance of nature" remained virtually undisturbed. There was an equilibrium between the various forms of plant and animal life living together in the same area. The native grasses were those which had developed a resistance to the hazards of the environment; the native animals had established a balance between their natural rate of increase, the food supply, and the depredations of their enemies.

Into this organized community came man. First he killed off, either for sport or for food, many of the larger native animals. Then he plowed up large areas of the native grasses and replaced them by cultivated grasses. But the effects of these simple acts went much farther than could have been predicted. Certain of the native animals of the region enjoyed either an elimination of their natural enemies or an increase in the supply of food, or both, which made possible a sudden and large increase in their numbers. The killing off of certain birds, for instance, was followed by a rapid increase in the gopher population. Some of the insects which had previously maintained a bare existence on the native grasses now found the nonresistant wheat or maize much more to their liking. The chinch bug, for example, probably fed on the native bunch grasses, whither it returns, even now, to pass the winters; but during the summer season this little native of the North American plains plays havoc with the maize, wheat, and oats. Among the native plants the sunflower, which now rapidly covers an idle field, once maintained itself precariously in competition with the prairie grasses. Thus many of the insect pests and weeds which, as a part of the natural grassland region, were effectively held in check by the competition of their enemies, were suddenly freed from this competition, so that their numbers increased enormously and they came to form hazards against which man's agriculture now has to contend.

There are spectacular stories of the introduction of new species into these regions. The Hessian fly, for instance, is a grass-feeding insect which was introduced accidentally into the United States from Europe. The great wheat fields of the North American prairies provided an ideal environment for this insect, and it multiplied at a rapid rate. Lacking any natural enemies in these new surroundings, it encountered little to check its ravages until special resistant varieties of wheat were developed. Even now the Hessian fly each year takes its toll of the American wheat crop. Still more extraordinary was the effect of the introduction of rabbits and prickly pears into Australia. Both of these, in a new environment essentially free from natural enemies, found conditions ideal and multiplied at enormous rates until both became a national menace. The prickly pear has been brought under partial control by the aid of a parasite, the cochineal scale; but every year more and more grazing land and even cropland is ruined by the rabbits.

The introduction of trees was the cause of a change of another kind in the grasslands. Around the farmsteads and villages forests were planted, so that today the buildings are all but hidden in the foliage during the summer months. On the prairies, where settlement is close, trees have been added to the landscape in such numbers that no longer is the horizon visible. At first glance these modified grasslands seem closely to resemble the cleared forest lands. The landscapes of the Corn Belt of the United States, whether in the eastern, previously forested part or in the western prairies, are strikingly similar. Yet there is a difference. The relict woodland patches in the eastern part are not uncommonly left in the centers of the sections, away from the roads (map, p. 324); but in the prairies the planted wood lots are mostly located around the farmsteads, close to the roads (map, p. 325).

Settlement of the Grasslands of the United States. The patterns and problems of settlement vary in each grassland region in accordance with the culture of the settlers. The sequence of events in the United States during the movement of the frontier of agricultural occupance across the prairies is of the utmost importance in understanding the rise of this country to pre-eminence as a world power.

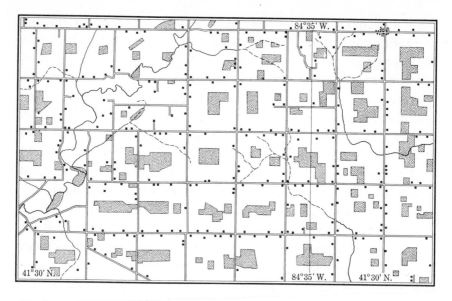

North American Corn Belt landscape in a previously forested region. The wood lots are relict patches of the native oak-hickory forest. (From the Pioneer Quadrangle, Ohio-Michigan, United States Geological Survey)

At first the grasslands were used only for the grazing of vast herds of half-wild cattle. The farmers, accustomed to the forests, hesitated when they came to the edge of the open prairies where there was no shelter. The frontier of settlement in the United States had been pushed westward to the western edge of the forest by the time of the Civil War; but beyond was the land of the cattlemen. Market towns, to which the cattle were brought from the open range, were located on the forest margins—such places as Chicago, St. Louis, Minneapolis–St. Paul, and Kansas City.

The movement of the frontier of farming settlement across the grasslands after the Civil War was a major factor in the building of the modern nation. This period of occupance came at a unique time in economic history: the eastern cities were developing rapidly as large-scale manufacturing centers, supported in part by immigrant workers from Europe; the urban markets were in need of continuously increasing supplies of bulky foods, especially wheat and meat, and the railroads were providing the means of sending such supplies from the

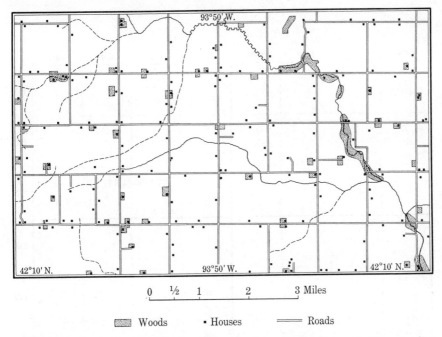

North American Corn Belt landscape in a prairie region. Some patches of relict galeria forest follow the streams, but most of the wood lots have been planted around the farmsteads. (From the Boone Quadrangle, Iowa, United States Geological Survey)

distant grasslands at costs low enough so that the whole arrangement was profitable; and as the urban industries expanded, there was a continuous demand for their products on the frontier—for steel rails, barbed wire, windmills, lumber, agricultural machines, and many other things. Then, as the settlers made good the claims to their homesteads and new communities made their appearance in the rapid elaboration of settlement, each land property increased in value. Some of the original settlers sold their farms and moved westward, but the general and rapid rise of property values continued. To be sure, there were business recessions and price declines; but the trend as a whole was upward, and there seemed no reason to believe that the trend would ever stop.

This increase in land value resulting, not from the labor of the individual owner, but from the general rise in the economic life of the community, is known by the economists as "unearned increment." It

R4W	R3W	R2W	R1W	R1E	R2E	R3E	R4E	

$\begin{pmatrix} T3N \\ R4W \end{pmatrix}$ — T3N

EAST — *Meridian* — 1 — T2N

BASE — TOWNSHIP 1 NORTH — T1N

LINE — T1S

Principal — RANGE — T2S

6 Miles — $\begin{pmatrix} T3S \\ R4E \end{pmatrix}$ — T3S

NW 40	NE 40
SW 40	SE 40

½ Mile

Diagram of a
quarter section
divided into "40's".

NW ¼	NE ¼
SW ¼	SE ¼

1 Mile

Diagram of a section,
divided into four
quarter sections
of 160 acres each.

6	5	4	3	2	1
7	8	9	10	11	12
18	17	16	15	14	13
19	20	21	22	23	24
30	29	28	27	26	25
31	32	33	34	35	36

6 Miles

Diagram of a Township,
showing division into 36 sections
of one square mile each.

*Diagrammatic layout of the General Land Office survey of the United States.
(The survey is governed in various parts of the country by a number of different
principal meridians and base lines. Sample description of a forty-acre property:
the NE forty of the NW quarter of section 17, township 2N, range 4E of the
fifth principal meridian)*

326

was collected by many small landowners throughout the grassland region of central United States; it was spent for many of the manufactured products which in turn brought prosperity to the urban centers. Unearned increment made the Middle West of the United States one of the most prosperous economic regions of the world, and gave the American people an attitude of optimism toward matters of economic development which even today distinguishes them from people who have been less fortunate. It was amazing luck to approach the settlement of an essentially empty region of such potential productivity at just such a time in the history of mankind.

The patterns of settlement developed in this period are remarkably uniform over large areas. This is owing in part to the absence of strongly marked relief features, but also in part to the ease with which roads in a grassland can be shifted to conform to a general settlement plan. On forested plains the first lines of travel away from the rivers, which developed even before the stage of pioneer settlement, are more or less fixed as the framework to which later settlement is joined. Even where the standard survey of properties was later applied, the persistence of the first roads along the Indian trails is notable, as is illustrated by the map of Perham (p. 273). But in the grasslands the roads are not so rigidly fixed because they are not hemmed in by trees. Even where a regular line of travel exists across a prairie, a well-defined road is not necessarily impressed upon the landscape. As the ruts of the wagon wheels score the prairie sod too deeply, a new way is picked to one side. The result was that when the uniform pattern of properties was established the shift of the roads to conform to the right-angle lines was easy. Because the tradition of the dispersed settlement had become established west of the Appalachians, for reasons previously described, this same pattern was carried on westward into the grasslands.

Agriculture. Maize and wheat are the basic crops of the grasslands of the United States. Both were grown first in the forested areas of Group IV farther to the east, and the patterns of crop distribution have gone through stages of development, gradually emerging in the agricultural regions we know today (map, p. 328).

The Corn Belt is unique in the whole world. In other mid-latitude grasslands there are large areas devoted to the surplus production of grains and meat; but, as we shall learn, no other region shares the

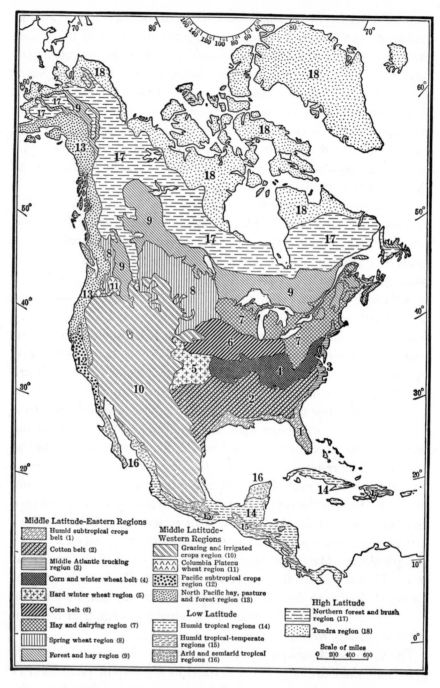

Middle Latitude–Eastern Regions

⬚	Humid subtropical crops belt (1)
⬚	Cotton belt (2)
⬚	Middle Atlantic trucking region (3)
⬚	Corn and winter wheat belt (4)
⬚	Hard winter wheat region (5)
⬚	Corn belt (6)
⬚	Hay and dairying region (7)
⬚	Spring wheat region (8)
⬚	Forest and hay region (9)

Middle Latitude–Western Regions

⬚	Grazing and irrigated crops region (10)
⬚	Columbia Plateau wheat region (11)
⬚	Pacific subtropical crops region (12)
⬚	North Pacific hay, pasture and forest region (13)

Low Latitude

⬚	Humid tropical regions (14)
⬚	Humid tropical-temperate regions (15)
⬚	Arid and semiarid tropical regions (16)

High Latitude

⬚	Northern forest and brush region (17)
⬚	Tundra region (18)

Scale of miles
0   200   400   600

Agricultural regions of North America. (*After O. E. Baker*)

J. C. Allen, from Ewing Galloway

A Corn Belt farm in Iowa

remarkably favorable qualities, both physical and economic, of the Corn Belt. From this one region comes half of the world's production of maize. Very little of it, however, is marketed directly as human food; most of it is fed to hogs and cattle. From this region comes more than half of all the pork and beef consumed in the United States.

The accompanying series of maps (pp. 330 and 331) show the distribution of maize in the United States at various periods since 1839. By 1859 there was already a suggestion of maize concen-

Philip Gendreau

Grain elevators along a railroad in Oklahoma

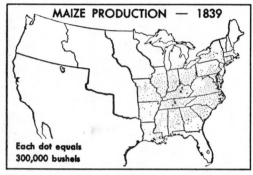

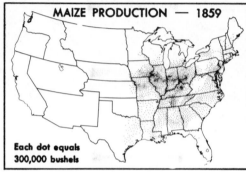

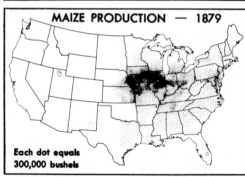

Development of the North American Corn Belt, 1839 to 1879. (Courtesy of the United States Department of Agriculture)

tration in Ohio, Indiana, and Illinois, but the outlines of the Corn Belt scarcely appeared until after the Civil War, and at that time the only cattle concentrations were on the plains of Texas (map, p. 333). By the end of the century, however, the outlines of the Corn Belt were distinct.

The advantages of the Corn Belt, so eagerly seized by the settlers during the nineteenth century, are both physical and economic. Maize is a tropical plant which, like most other crops, produces best near its cold limits. Because of a continental position, the Corn Belt enjoys very hot summers in spite of fairly severe winters. A little farther north the climate is poor for maize as a grain, and beyond the isotherm of 66° average temperature for the three summer months maize can be grown only to cut green as a hay. Furthermore, although much of the Corn Belt is only moderately rainy, the greater part of the rains come in the warm season. The resulting hot, showery, almost tropical summers are ideal for maize. The Corn Belt has been extended westward as far as the isohyet of eight inches in the summer months. The great productivity of this region, however, must be laid primarily to the vast area of level to gently rolling surface, little broken by steep slopes, and to the remarkable and sustained fertility of the dark-colored soils.

Nature can provide only opportunities; these same grasslands remained quite inhospitable to settlement before the era of machinery and big markets. The rise of the Corn Belt cannot be interpreted without reference to the growth of the great cities and to the expansion of the railroads which gave access to these cities. Nor can the particular kind of economy practiced in this area be understood without reference to the traditions of the American people, who demand meat rather than "corn bread."

Crop Combinations in the Corn Belt. In previous chapters the effect of trans-

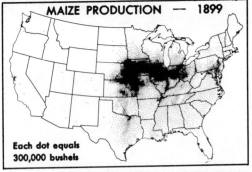

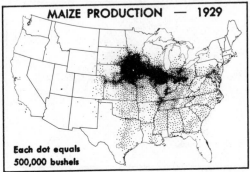

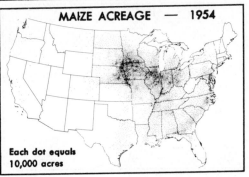

Development of the North American Corn Belt, 1899 to 1954. (Courtesy of U. S. Departments of Agriculture and Commerce)

portation development in causing a localization of crops in areas best suited to them has been pointed out. We have seen how certain vegetables and fruits have become established and have been intensively cultivated in those localities where the combination of climate, soil,

The Occidental Occupance 331

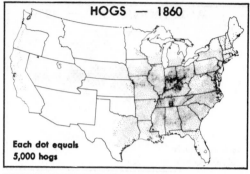

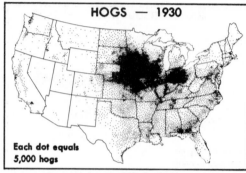

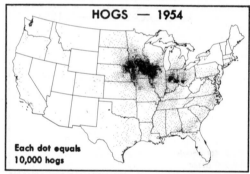

Hogs in the United States, 1860 to 1954.
(Courtesy of the United States Departments
of Agriculture and Commerce)

surface, and drainage is peculiarly favorable. We must now amplify this principle; for although maize exhibits a notable localization in the Corn Belt, this region is also ideally suited to other crops which are not similarly concentrated there, and although this is one of the chief maize-producing regions of the world, only about 25 per cent of the area and 42 per cent of the cropland are used for the chief crop. Maize is associated with oats, wheat, and hay; and much of the total area is in permanent pasture.[1]

There are certain tendencies in agricultural land use leading toward a specialization of crops, and there are other tendencies leading toward a diversification. We have seen that, with nothing more adequate than horse-drawn vehicles, each community is forced to depend on local sources of the basic supplies; there is little opportunity for specialization. Only very valuable products, for which the cost of shipment represents but a small

[1] See the discussion of the Corn Belt in Clarence F. Jones and Gordon G. Darkenwald, *Economic Geography,* Revised Edition, New York, 1954, pp. 266–273.

332 The Grasslands

part of the total cost, can become localized in places where the conditions of land, labor, or capital are particularly favorable. The development of railroads and steamboat lines results only in a relative change in the operation of this economic principle. Still it is the crops having the larger values per unit of weight which respond most clearly to the forces leading to localization. Such are most of the crops produced by Occidental plantations in the tropical forests: sugar, cacao, coconuts, coffee, bananas, and others. Such, also, are the fruit and vegetable crops, previously described as examples of localization. The sugar beets and potatoes which in certain parts of the Corn Belt interrupt the prevailing crop combinations have become localized in response to this principle. These very valuable products take precedence over maize, and where they are grown there is little diversification.

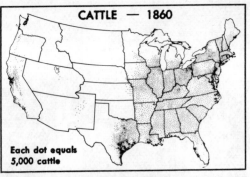

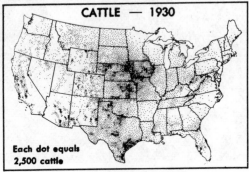

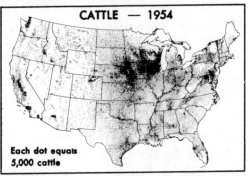

Cattle in the United States, 1860 to 1954. (Courtesy of the United States Departments of Agriculture and Commerce)

Specialization of crops is also apparent in the zones around the urban centers. In these places, however, localization is brought about by the high value of land near the cities rather than by any special quality

The Occidental Occupance 333

The corn harvester removes the ears from the stalks, husks them, and chops the leaves and stalks—all in one operation

inherent in the soil. Where land is expensive, only those crops can be grown which bring large returns in money income. Truck-garden zones are established on the periphery of most cities of the world, in many cases despite adverse conditions of climate, soil, or slope.

Among the more bulky products, such as the grains, it not uncommonly happens that two or more crops are in competition for the same territory, all of them finding especially favorable physical conditions. This is the situation in the prairies of the Corn Belt, where both maize and wheat find excellent conditions of growth. In these circumstances, provided there is a market for all the competing crops, those which are otherwise most narrowly limited by physical requirements generally get the first choice of the land. Thus, in the American Cotton Belt, although maize grows there excellently, cotton, which is more narrowly limited by moisture and temperature, occupies the best lands. In the Corn Belt, maize, being unable to grow as far coldward or as

J. I. Case Company

A cotton picker on the Mississippi floodplain in Mississippi. This machine does not work on hilly land

far toward the dry lands as wheat, has first choice of the land and tends to eliminate competing crops.

The diversification of crops arises chiefly from two causes. In the first place, experience has shown that soil fertility, quickly exhausted by such crops as maize or wheat, can be maintained by a rotation of crops and by the application of animal manures. During the last century, as we have seen, crop rotation and domestic animals have become important features of Occidental grain-farming. Then, too, the most efficient use of labor throughout the year is gained by crop diversification. In a one-crop system the work of planting, cultivating, and harvesting is concentrated at certain times of the year, and periods of relative idleness intervene. But the labor demands of different crops are spread differently over the seasons, so that a more uniform distribution of work is possible in regions of diversified agriculture. For these reasons other crops are associated with the dominant crop in the Corn Belt.

The operation of these various principles leads to the appearance of such specialized agricultural regions as the Corn Belt. The outlines of the region represent an adjustment between these economic principles and the physical qualities of the land. The land, however, remains as a relatively permanent basic factor; it does not become a positive force in the man-land equation unless it is significantly changed during the course of settlement—unless it is destroyed, perhaps, by wasteful

The Occidental Occupance 335

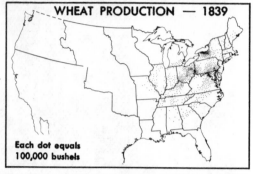

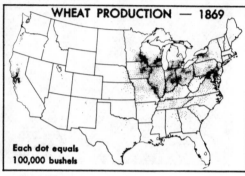

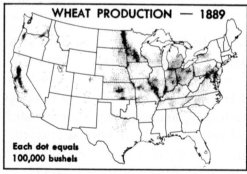

Development of the wheat regions of the United States, 1839 to 1889. (Courtesy of the United States Department of Agriculture)

farming methods. Otherwise, the positive force is the balance of costs and prices determined by the economic conditions from year to year. Outlines of the Corn Belt are threatened with change owing to the development by agronomists of a "hybrid corn," from the use of which the yields per acre may be increased by as much as 100 per cent. The widespread use of this new variety could result in the reduction of the proportion of land in maize, especially on the poorer soils or the marginal areas.

The Wheat Regions of the United States. Wheat, unlike maize, is mostly used directly as a human food. It is stated that this grain provides between 25 and 50 per cent of the fuel value of the food eaten by white people. It is therefore not marketed in the form of fattened animals, but must be shipped as grain. Wheat is well adapted to this method of marketing, for the hard, dry kernels can stand rough handling and can be shipped even through the rainy tropics without deteriorating.

Wheat was carried onto the grasslands of North America along with

336 *The Grasslands*

maize, but before 1870 it showed little tendency to concentrate (map, p. 336). In the decade between 1870 and 1880, however, the binders and large power-driven threshing machines were invented, making possible large-scale farming. The settlers advanced onto the drier grasslands in three places: in the Red River plains of Minnesota and North Dakota, in southern Nebraska and Kansas, and in the Columbia Plateau portion of Washington and Oregon. The next decade witnessed an enormous increase of production in these areas, especially on the Red River plains. The pattern of distribution as outlined by 1899 has remained essentially the same except for amplification of its details (map at right).

Advantages of the Grasslands for Wheat. To interpret wheat distribution it is necessary to consider

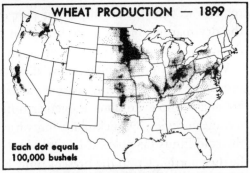

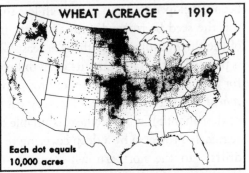

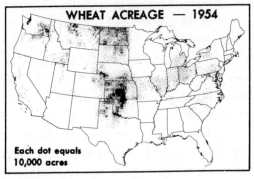

Development of the wheat regions of the United States, 1899 to 1954. (Courtesy of the United States Departments of Agriculture and Commerce

briefly the advantages which parts of these grasslands possess for wheat production, advantages which have led to the establishment of wheat as a chief crop. We are not concerned here with those areas where wheat is a minor crop, as in the Corn Belt, although these regions account for an important part of the world production. On the dry margins of the prairies and on the steppes wheat is not only dominant but, in places, occupies nearly all the cropland.

Wheat will grow under many different climatic conditions. By a process of seed selection numerous varieties have been developed which are adapted to conditions altogether different from those of the Mediterranean region. Quick-maturing varieties, for instance, have pushed the cold limits far poleward. Only barley and potatoes can be pushed farther north. Up to the present time, however, no kind of wheat has been developed that can mature in less than ninety frost-free days. Nor can the seed be ripened with certainty unless the average temperature of the three summer months is at least 57°. Most of the world's wheat is planted in the fall, starts its growth before winter sets in, and is ready for the harvest early in the following summer. This is known as *winter wheat*. Where the winters are very cold (averaging below 20° in the coldest month), winter wheat is unable to survive unless the ground is regularly protected by a deep covering of snow which is not blown into drifts. In the northern wheat areas—the Dakotas and part of the Washington-Oregon area—wheat is planted in the spring after the frost is out of the ground and is harvested in the late summer. This is called *spring wheat*.

In its native habitat wheat is adapted to cool, moist winters and hot, dry summers. The largest yields of wheat are associated with a cool, moist period in the early stages of growth; but a hot, dry harvest season is required for the best quality of grain. Although very large yields are produced in western Europe, the resulting wheat is soft and starchy and is considered to be poorer in quality than the hard, protein-rich varieties, which require hot, dry summers.[1] In regions of heavy rain-

---

[1] Early in its growth the wheat plant sends up additional stalks from buds near its roots. Only as many heads are developed as there are stalks. Branching is promoted by cool, moist weather during the early period of growth, a condition which is best provided by the cool marine climates of the continental west coasts. The largest yields of wheat occur in these regions, but the much-desired hard wheats, with their high protein content, do not thrive in these wetter climates. The following table gives the average yields of all varieties of wheat in bushels per acre:

Cool summers		Hot summers	
Denmark	44	Kansas	13
Belgium	36	Hungary	16
New Zealand	31	Argentina	12

United States Department of Agriculture

Harvesting wheat on the steppe lands of eastern Oregon

fall, too, wheat is subject to numerous diseases. The rainfall limits within which the crop is grown vary with the temperature. On the poleward side the wheat concentrations lie between the 10-inch and 40-inch rainfall lines, but in the warmer wheat-producing regions the rainfall limits become 20 inches and 70 inches. Wheat is grown both above and below these amounts, however.

The grasslands, then, especially those with severe winters, do not possess the best of wheat climates. They do possess one feature in common, however, which makes wheat-growing possible on a large scale: the great expanses of level land permit the use of machinery, and wheat is now essentially a machine-cultivated crop. As the decreasing rainfall or the increasingly unfavorable winters result in diminished yields per acre, machinery makes possible the cultivation of more acres per farm. Thus, wheat has become established on the chernozem belts of the world, where the climatic conditions have made it possible to

The Occidental Occupance 339

compete on more even terms with maize, and where the deep, rich soils have maintained their productivity in spite of continued use.

The Dry Margins. The settlers who pushed the agricultural frontier westward across the grasslands of the United States usually raised wheat at first, and only changed to maize later. But as the wheat farmers moved westward they did not stop at the western margin of the chernozem belt. The chestnut-brown soils beyond lured the pioneers on with promises of quick wealth, especially after a series of wet years. In the northern Great Plains three years of more than normal rainfall from 1914 to 1916, and especially in 1915, started a wave of settlement. Far out on the steppes the pioneers plowed up the short-grass sod and planted wheat. From the virgin soils large yields were gained, and, aided by wartime prices, the settlers found themselves prosperous beyond their hopes. But then came the inevitable cycle of dry years, from 1917 to 1919—all years of crop failure. Many of the farmers who managed to survive the drought, with their farms heavily mortgaged, were ruined by the drop of land values which followed the conclusion of World War I. The fields were left to grow up in weeds; the tide of abandonment was almost as strong as the tide of settlement.

Eroded land in the spring wheat area of South Dakota—on the dry margin

Soil Conservation Service

A similar story can be told for western Kansas. In one county the total income from wheat farming for a 640-acre farm for the whole period from 1912 to 1934 was $21,167. This means an average income of about $1000 per year for a farm of this size. But such a statistical average is far from the actual income per year. The fact is that of the total income quoted above, $20,472 was received in one year, 1920, when the farmers in that county enjoyed a rare combination of favorable rainfall and high prices. Obviously this is a system of farming which is entirely speculative, and one which requires a considerable outlay in the form of relief funds from the government.

The farmers on the dry margin who have managed to survive have learned a number of important lessons. A different agricultural tech-nique was necessary on these dry margins in order to make permanent settlement possible. It was found that by allowing the land to lie fallow for a year enough moisture might be stored up to permit the production of a crop the following year. Thus a part of the cropland is left bare each year,—carefully plowed and harrowed to reduce the evaporation. Wheat grown with such *dry-farming* methods may yield only from six to ten bushels to the acre, although in wet years the yield may be much more than this. But, aided by machinery, the farmers ceased to care about the yield per acre, provided they could cultivate a sufficient number of acres. The Homestead Act had been changed in 1909 to permit settlers to occupy a maximum of 320 acres, and in 1916 the limit was further raised to 640 acres. Recent studies in Montana lead to the conclusion that 1280 acres, or even twice this number, are needed to provide security.[1] Furthermore, it has been found that on the steppes farming and cattle-ranching ought to be combined, so that in the dry years range cattle can provide some income to compensate, at least in part, for the crop failure (picture, p. 342).

Even with the best techniques, however, the settlement of the dry margin of the Great Plains remains precarious. No part of the region is free from the threat of drought, and no one has yet found a way to predict with accuracy when a drought will begin or end. Sometimes

[1] See the studies of pioneer settlement in I. Bowman, *The Pioneer Fringe*, American Geographical Society, Special Publication No. 13, New York, 1931; and *Pioneer Settle-ment* (by twenty-six authors), American Geographical Society, Special Publication No. 14, New York, 1932.

Cattle grazing on the steppes of eastern Montana

droughts last for only a few months; sometimes a number of years pass without a single shower. Sometimes the farmers of one county watch in despair as a heavy shower drenches a neighboring county. Sometimes, when the air is very dry, a shower forms, but the rain evaporates before it reaches the ground. From 1950 to 1956 there were large parts of the southern Great Plains which had no rain at all. The drought was so prolonged that even the cattle had to be moved away. With the droughts come the dust storms that blow the fertile topsoil from vast areas of plowed land being used for dry farming (pictures, pp. 340 and 343). As a result, only ruined land and abandoned buildings remain.

Settlement of the Canadian Grasslands. In many respects the process of grassland settlement in Canada has been similar to that in the United States. There is the same pattern of dispersed farms, the same articulation along the railroads, the same profit from unearned increment, and the same speculative insecurity along the dry margin. The economy in Canada is based on the production of spring wheat, for the wheat regions there are mostly too cool and have too short a growing season for winter wheat or maize. The chief movement of pioneer settlement west of Winnipeg came after 1900. In general, the densest population is established along the margin of the forest and along the mountain front, forming a crescent from Winnipeg in the east to Edmonton and Calgary in the west. The drier steppes are only thinly populated (Plate 1).

Settlement of the Argentine Humid Pampa. The Humid Pampa of Argentina forms the heart of the Argentine nation. Around its great city, Buenos Aires, is grouped more than three quarters of the productive capacity of the country. The Humid Pampa has become one of the world's leading producers of grain and meat, and Argentina leads the world in exported maize. But the story of settlement on the Argentine grasslands is very different from that in the United States and Canada (map, p. 344).

A dust storm approaching in the western Great Plains

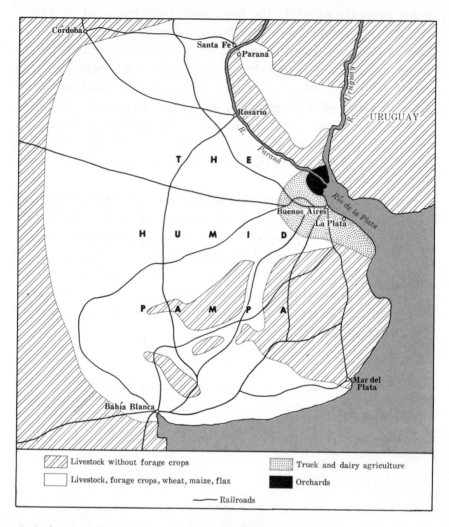

Agricultural divisions of the Argentine Humid Pampa. (*Adapted from Preston E. James,* Latin America, *Revised Edition, New York, 1959*)

The basic difference is the result of the attitude of the native Argentine toward land ownership. In most parts of Spanish America the pre-industrial tradition of the large private estate prevails. When the Argentine Humid Pampa was opened for settlement after 1857 (when the first railroad was built), it was quickly partitioned among a relatively small group of people. Within some 30 years the greater part of the region had been divided among 300 families. The estates were of vast size—100,000 acres or more. Furthermore, the people who owned the land were primarily interested in raising cattle, horses, and sheep, and not at all in agriculture except as it was necessary for the preparation of good pasture.

The development of the Humid Pampa was paid for largely by investments of British capital. The British built most of the railroads, they furnished the refrigerator ships to carry meat to Britain, and they sent out coal to supply Argentina. British and North American interests built the packing plants, and financed many other developments in Buenos Aires and other cities. The British wanted fat beef—not the lean meat that came from the traditional Argentine herds. They introduced high-grade beef animals to Argentina.

A succession of events followed the introduction of the new beef cattle, and these events have resulted in the emergence of modern Argentina. In the first place, the beef animals had to be fed from a cultivated crop because they could not exist on the native Pampa grasses. Alfalfa proved to be the ideal feed crop, for the climate and ground-water conditions, as well as the soils, of the Humid Pampa are excellent for this crop. But to clear the grass and prepare the land for alfalfa it proved to be necessary to plant wheat, at least for a few years. To do this the landowners hired immigrant tenants, who produced wheat for a share of the crop, agreeing that after a specified number of years they would plant alfalfa and move away. Except for an area around Rosario in the northern part of the Humid Pampa, where maize is more important than wheat, and a truck-farming area around Buenos Aires, over 50 per cent of the land is used for pasture throughout the remainder of the region, and in the southeastern part more than 80 per cent is used for pasture. Alfalfa and wheat are the crops, the latter raised by tenant farmers who remain temporarily on the land. The basic and permanent interest which determines the pattern of Argentine farm economy is the raising of high-grade animals.

As a result, the unearned increment has been collected by a very small proportion of the people. There are great differences between the wealthy landowners and the workers. But on the dry margins, where the large owners can go in or out of wheat production with

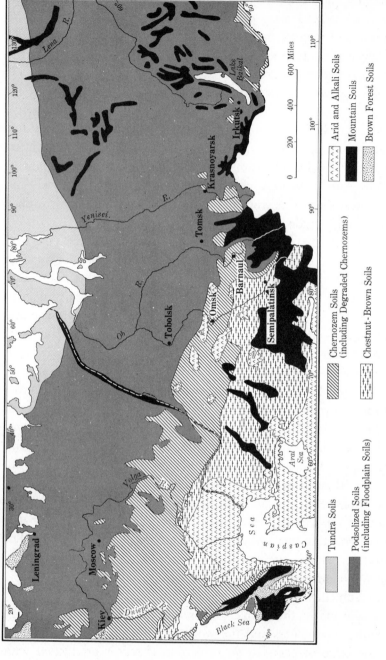

Soils of the western part of the U.S.S.R. [Adapted from the "General Map of the Soils of Europe," Warsaw, 1928; and "Soils of the U.S.S.R." in Pioneer Settlement (New York, 1932), p. 248]

Tundra Soils

Podsolized Soils
(including Floodplain Soils)

Chernozem Soils
(including Degraded Chernozems)

Chestnut-Brown Soils

Arid and Alkali Soils

Mountain Soils

Brown Forest Soils

0   200   400   600 Miles

great ease, there is much greater flexibility of adjustment to market prices and rainfall than is the case in North America. There is a strong tendency to reduce the number of tenant farmers by increasing the use of machinery, and as this process goes on there is a movement of rural people back into Buenos Aires. Here manufacturing industries are being developed, and large numbers of displaced tenants who might otherwise create a serious unemployment problem are converted to industrial workers. The difficulty is that Argentina, more than most countries, is dependent on overseas trade. It would be impossible to consume all the potential production of grain and meat in Argentina. Furthermore, Argentina lacks coal and other sources of power. The country is struggling with problems arising from the concentration of land in the hands of a few people, the very profitable development of commercial agriculture, and the subsequent restriction of international commerce. In Buenos Aires, too, the industrial way of living is making its appearance; Argentina is in the throes of the transition from a pre-industrial to an industrial society.

Settlement of the Russian Steppes. Within the territory of the Soviet Union there is a third major area of grasslands. The chernozem soil which lies under the prairie is the famous "black-earth belt" of Russia, extending from the northern side of the Black Sea northwest of Odessa eastward to the edge of the mountains near Barnaul, and in scattered patches even as far as Irkutsk near Lake Baikal (Plate 18 and map, p. 346). The black-earth belt forms a narrow band between the forests farther north and the steppes and deserts to the south. This is the chief agricultural area of the Soviet Union, and also the part with the greatest density of population (Plate 5). The Russian grasslands, un-like those of the United States, occupy that part of the world pattern that borders the dry lands in the north (diagram, p. 177). In this position they are comparable to the prairies and steppes of Canada.

The climatic hazards that farmers must face in this region are serious. Agriculture is limited to the north by cold and by the shortness of the growing season, and to the south by lack of rainfall. But within the black-earth belt, and the forest margin to the north of it, both cold and drought are frequently experienced. During the winter, cold air masses from the northern interior of Siberia and from the Arctic pour unimpeded across the open plains, bringing very low temperatures. Because

The Occidental Occupance 347

cold air masses are very dry and the winds are strong, the little snow that may have fallen on the black-earth belt is blown away or evaporated, thus depriving the soil of much-needed moisture for the spring planting. During the growing season the whole area is frequently visited by droughts. Records indicate that serious droughts occur, on the average, once every two or three years. Only in the westernmost part of the black-earth belt does the rainfall average more than 20 inches a year. These climatic hazards are only partially compensated by the excellence of the soil.

The grasslands of European Russia were the first such regions in the world to be successfully occupied for grain farming. In accordance with the pre-industrial tradition the land was divided into large private estates, and the work was done by the labor of serfs. Armed only with the most primitive agricultural implements, the prairie sod was broken largely by the power of human muscles supplemented by domestic animals. Under a system of virtual slavery, work was accomplished which elsewhere proved impossible until the age of machinery. After the freeing of the serfs, a small proportion of the peasants were able to acquire farms of their own, but most of the agricultural workers were employed on the lands of the large owners. The average size of the peasant farms was between seven and ten acres, which is too small for the support of a family in the grasslands.

Wheat was raised on the black-earth belt, not as a food for the peasants, for they generally ate rye bread, but for export. The grain was carried by wagon to the Volga River, and thence by river and canal to St. Petersburg (now Leningrad), where it was loaded on foreign ships for export to other European countries. In 1891 the Trans-Siberian Railroad was started, and a stream of pioneer settlers spread eastward into western Siberia, following the advance of the rails. Between 1897 and 1917 the population of Siberia doubled, and most of the new settlement was in the black-earth belt.

The Soviet government has reorganized the agricultural system. The first step was the elimination of the inefficient small private farm, and the combination of farm properties in large collective or state farms. This change involved no rearrangement of the people, for the rural population has traditionally been grouped in compact rural villages (map, p. 349). In 1958 there were some 78,000 collectives, averaging

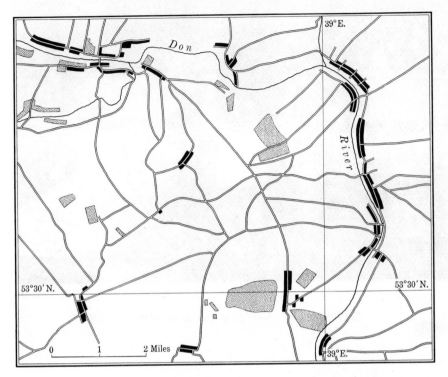

Topographic detail on the Russian steppes. Location is about 170 miles southeast of Moscow. [From Kurkina and Chernova sheets (N 37–90 and N 37–91), Geodetic Survey Committee, U.S.S.R., 1928]

more than 3000 acres in size. They were operated by work brigades, using new machinery supplied from the factories. There were also 5000 state farms, run by the government, having an average size of 6000 acres. In 1954 there were 124 new state farms laid out on a vast area of steppes in western Siberia.[1]

The agricultural regions are still approximately those shown on the map (p. 250). In the west the land is used for winter wheat and sugar beets, with rye and buckwheat becoming more important toward the north. In the drier and colder climates to the south and east, spring

[1] Theodore Shabad, "The Soviet Union: Demographic and Economic Aspects," in W. G. East and A. E. Moodie (editors), *The Changing World*, New York, 1956, pp. 385–409.

Fertilizing sugar beets on a state farm in the U.S.S.R.

wheat is grown rather than winter wheat. In 1940 wheat made up 43 per cent of all grains, but by 1952 it made up 61 per cent. Other crops included rye, barley, oats, potatoes, and sunflowers. Since 1950 there has been some increase in the number of dairy cattle near the big cities, and in the number of beef cattle pastured on the steppes. On the drier steppes there has been a considerable increase of sheep-grazing and wool production. The government has been enlarging the irrigated areas of the steppes by diverting water from the Dnieper and the Volga, and has been experimenting with the planting of trees to reduce wind erosion.

The Occidental Occupance of the Savannas. The Occidental occupance of the low-latitude grasslands has not gone so far as that of the prairies and steppes. The difficulties of tropical settlement are yet to be solved. As a matter of fact, the problems of colonization in the savannas are in many respects similar to those already discussed in connection with Group II. There are the same medical questions to be solved, the same difficulties of providing access to the high-altitude settlements, the same problems of the political and economic control of native peoples, and the same necessity of basing the settlement on a product of commercial value.

There are numerous natural handicaps, especially on the lowland savannas, which impede the occupance by Europeans or Americans. The insect pests are even more of a menace to health than they are in the tropical forests. They spread disease not only among the human inhabitants but also among the domestic cattle, which seem peculiarly susceptible. Only poor, scrawny cattle can be produced in these regions without a very expensive transformation of the entire scene. The natural grasses are very poor as feed, so that artificial pastures of planted grasses must be prepared. Then, too, because of the seasonal alternation between flood and drought, not only must these pastures be protected by drainage systems, but they must also be irrigated during the long dry season. Although a few such developments have been carried out—for example, in the Orinoco llanos in Venezuela and on the scattered ranches of northern Australia—they represent only a negligible fraction of the savanna area.

The savannas of the Sudan present the additional difficulty, for Occidental occupance, of being already inhabited by a native population. In these regions European political or economic control may be continued, but actual settlement by Europeans in any numbers is unlikely.

In two places, however, Europeans have made serious attempts to occupy the savannas. These are southern Africa and northern Australia. Southern Africa, as we have seen, is a plateau of sufficient elevation to bring cool climates well northward toward the equator. In the analogous climatic position in southeastern Brazil a year-round rainfall supports a tropical forest; but on the Plateau of South Africa various types of grassland form a concentric pattern around the margins of the Kalahari (Plate 14). For hundreds of miles south of Johannesburg the vegetation cover is a pure grassland much like a tall-grass prairie (map, p. 73); to the north is a scattered tree savanna. The colonization of this area is still in the pioneer stage of experimentation. The settlements are arranged along the axes of the railroads. As yet there has been little elaboration except near Johannesburg.[1] It is not yet established what crops will provide the best support, although the

[1] K. M. Buchanan, "The Union of South Africa," in W. G. East and A. E. Moodie (editors), *The Changing World,* New York, 1956, pp. 757–783.

beginnings of a concentration of maize are visible around Johannesburg and Pretoria.

The European occupance of the savannas of northern Australia is also very much of an experiment, and, in general, one which seems to be unsuccessful. Of all the savanna regions this one is in many ways the most difficult to occupy. There are no mountain areas in the interior of Australia of sufficient size to give rise to large rivers. No permanent stream crosses the savannas. Furthermore, although the average annual rainfall along the north coast is heavy (about 62 inches at Darwin), it is very unevenly distributed during the year. Most of it falls between November and April during the time of the onshore summer monsoon, the average for January at Darwin being about 16 inches. From May to September there is almost no rain. Irrigation would be essential for permanent settlement, yet there are no streams to supply water. At present there is a widely scattered population of sheep ranchers who maintain contact with the outside world by radio and airplane. The prospects for the occupation of this region by additional settlers are not good; in fact, the tendency is for the numbers to diminish as ranchers move away to more favorable parts of the country.

THE ORIENTAL OCCUPANCE

In all the great grassland regions of the world the experience of man in his attempt to form permanent fixed settlements has been similar. In a general way there are the same problems of securing water, of clearing the grass sod, of combating insect pests, of building houses to withstand the extremes of weather in a land without the shelter of trees or hills, and of finding a suitable form of economy to make the settlement workable. But in each region we have described, differences in human culture—in the attitudes, objectives, and technical abilities of the settlers—have produced different relationships between people and land. Underlying the broad similarity of all the regions of Group V are the detailed differences which make each area and its problems unique.

This is illustrated with special force in the story of the Oriental occupance of Manchuria, another of the great mid-latitude grasslands of the world. Manchuria (map, p. 353) is a region of long and very cold,

Japan and the neighboring portions of Asia. (For definition of climatic symbols, see Appendix B, section 30)

Manchurian roads become all but impassable in the summer rainy season

dry winters and short, hot, rainy summers. At Harbin, now called Pinkiang, the average temperature of January is $-1.7°$. From October to April the ground is frozen and generally bare. The roads at this time of the year are easily passable. When the short summer comes (from May to September) the weather is hot and rainy, vegetation springs to life, the landscape changes from brown to green, and the roads are deep with mud and all but impassable (picture above). Into this region, once occupied only by pastoral nomads, came the agricultural Chinese.

Chinese Settlement. The Chinese settlement of Manchuria began over a century ago; for between 1821 and 1851 colonies were established as far north as the Sungari River. Not until 1878, however, was colonization given official sanction. During the last two decades of the nineteenth century a slow but steady movement of Chinese was filling the southernmost parts of Manchuria. When the railroads were built, after 1900, the stream of settlement, as in the Occidental grasslands, was rapidly augmented. It was not until 1926, however, that the numbers of immigrants into Manchuria became spectacular. From 1926 to 1928 over a million people a year moved northward, probably the greatest migration in human history. Most of these colonists came from the famine zones of North China, chiefly from Shantung. After their arrival in Manchuria a few took advantage of the railroads, but the greater number struggled northward on foot to find room for settlement.

The Chinese mode of expansion on this frontier is quite different from the expansion on Occidental frontiers. The North American pioneers, for instance, traveled far beyond the margins of established settlement and located their homesteads in a zone of very thin and scattered population. Similarly, the older Russian expansion eastward along the black-earth belt sent colonies far out in advance. Not so the Chinese. This frontier spread northward "like a drop of oil," presenting a solid front of dense settlement against the unsettled grasslands beyond the frontier, still occupied by pastoral nomads.[1]

The story of settlement in Manchuria is greatly complicated by the fact that this region is of interest not only to the Chinese but also to the Soviet Union and to Japan. For some 2000 years, up to the end of the nineteenth century, Manchuria was important chiefly as a marginal part of China. To the Chinese it is known as the "three eastern provinces," and only the foreigner uses the name Manchuria. In 1896, however, the Chinese government permitted Russia to build the Chinese Eastern Railway to serve as a shortcut on the Trans-Siberian line to Vladivostok. The Russians, seeking an ice-free port, built a branch southward from Harbin (now Pinkiang) to Port Arthur (now Lüshun), near Dairen (now Talien). The activities of the Russians brought them into conflict with the Japanese, who desired both protection from the advance of the Russians into eastern Asia and also the right to exploit the mineral resources of Manchuria, which include both coal and iron ore. As a result of the Russo-Japanese War of 1904-1905, Japan took over the southern branch of the railroad and renamed it the South Manchuria Railway.

These railroad lines were administered by essentially independent corporations, which therefore made them lines of Russian and Japanese

[1] R. B. Hall, "The Geography of Manchuria," *Annals of the American Academy of Political and Social Science,* Vol. 152 (1930), pp. 278–292.

penetration into Chinese Manchuria. The corporations were responsible for the policing of zones on either side of the rails, and they built mines and factories and developed cities. When the Japanese seized Mukden (now Shenyang) in 1931 and set up a puppet government for "Manchukuo," the chief purpose was not to find new lands to colonize, but rather to have a free hand to develop and utilize the commercial resources of the country. In comparison to the millions of Chinese, few Japanese ever came to Manchuria. But the Japanese developed the coal mines, especially the mines at Fushun near Mukden, where the thickest coal seam in the world (417 feet) is located. At Anshan, south of Mukden, large iron and steel works were built. For Japan, poor in coal, the control of Manchuria seemed essential. As a result of World War II many of these industrial establishments were destroyed or removed.

Since the rise to power of the communist government in China, the situation in Manchuria has changed again. No longer can Japan exert influence in this area. With the help of the Soviet Union, the Chinese have rebuilt the big steel plant at Anshan and have reopened many of the mines that were destroyed during the war. From the Manchurian base the communists gave support to North Korea in its war against the forces of the United Nations. The communist line was pushed almost as far south as Seoul (map, p. 353). Manchuria is still a focus of conflicting

Each dot equals 2,500 acres

No record

0   200
MILES

N. MURAKOSHI

Soybean acreage in Manchuria [1]

[1] From *Land Utilization Maps of Manchuria*, by Nobuo Murakoshi and Glenn T. Trewartha. Courtesy of the *Geographical Review*, published by the American Geographical Society of New York.

356   *The Grasslands*

interests. As one or another of the interested countries becomes relatively stronger or weaker, the balance of influence in the region is shifted.

The Agriculture. Settlement in Manchuria was formerly based on subsistence grain-farming. Even today the most important subsistence crops are a giant sorghum known as kaoliang, millet, and wheat. Before World War II, however, the soybean had become more and more of a commercial crop, after the mode of the Occident. This remarkable plant is a native of eastern Asia and has been cultivated in China for many centuries. Its introduction into Manchuria was very successful. In 1908 a shipment to England found an overseas market, and until World War II exports of soybeans, bean cake, and bean oil brought a steady cash income. The soybean had become particularly important to the Japanese as a fertilizer for their heavily overworked agricultural lands. The distribution of soybeans in Manchuria just before the war is shown on the map (p. 356). The influence of the railroads on the crop pattern is clear. Since the war Japan has lost this valuable import.

Conclusion

From Manchuria across Siberia to Europe and Africa, from the tropical savannas to the prairies of the Americas, different peoples at various periods of world history have sought to establish themselves on the grasslands. For some people success was never attained. The spread of tropical grasses into the overworked clearings of the forest dwellers was a signal for the abandonment of the land. In only a few places could hoe cultivators wage a victorious battle with the grass,—chiefly where they could occupy the lands in great numbers, as the Chinese have done. The cultures with domestic animals maintained themselves perilously on the steppes of the Old World; but, scourged by the recurring cycles of drought, these nomadic peoples have poured periodically into the neighboring regions in great waves of conquest and migration which have punctuated the course of history of all the nations from China and India westward into Europe. For a time the Europeans also established a nomadic or seminomadic occupance of the grasslands. Then, as the machinery of the Western world made it possible to ship products from distant places and also solved the chief difficulties of permanent grassland settlement, namely, grass and scarcity of water, a wave of colonization brought a rapid and far-reaching transformation of the grassland scene. Occidental agriculture became established in accordance with the principles which govern the economics of the Western world. The conquest of at least a part of the grasslands seems to be secure. Who can predict that some of the experiments now being tried in the tropical grasslands may not also prove successful and pave the way for a new migration?

GROUP VI

THE BOREAL FOREST LANDS

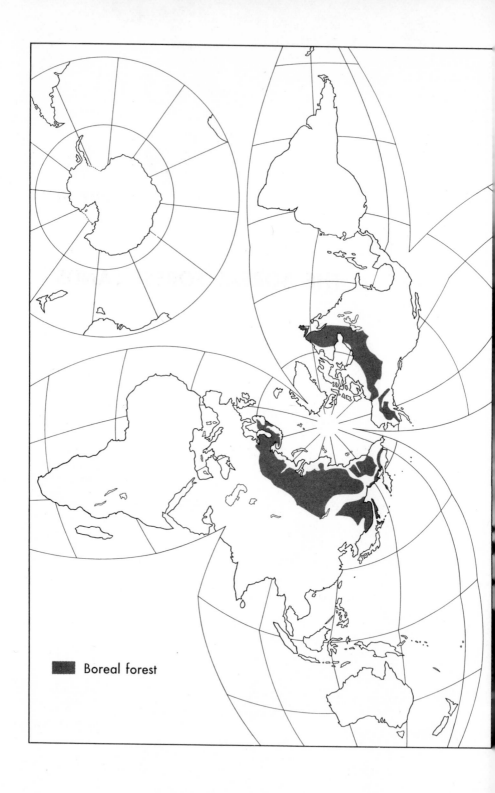

Boreal forest

Seasonal change reaches a maximum in the boreal forest lands. In no other part of the world does the aspect of the face of the earth undergo such a radical transformation rhythmically, in the course of the year, as in these forest lands of the higher middle latitudes of the Northern Hemisphere. The intense cold and long hours of darkness during the winter enforce on the vegetation a long period of rest. During this time the contour of the land is smoothed by a blanket of snow, and the rivers and lakes are locked in a casing of ice. At first the longer hours of sunlight in the spring seem to make little impression on the frozen land; but suddenly, in May or June, the bare ground is revealed, the ice breaks up and is carried downstream in great thundering, chaotic masses, and the long-slumbering vegetation almost bursts into vigorous life. A carpet of flowers quickly covers the ground left bare by the melting snow, and the air is filled with myriads of insects. This is the brief period of breathless activity for all the inhabitants of the forest,—all except man, the intruder, who finds travel difficult when he tries to penetrate the thick forests and bogs away from the navigable rivers. Only where agriculture is attempted is this a busy period for the human inhabitants. With the first touch of fall the broadleaf trees turn yellow or red, the insects disappear, and the land animals seek a shelter for the long winter hibernation. Great numbers of migrating animals, especially birds, start southward. First with a touch of frost, then more firmly with a grip of ice and snow, winter fastens its fingers on the land. The long, dark night sets in. Then, from their summer refuge near the rivers, men move out into the forest, traveling easily on skis or snowshoes or sledges over the snow-covered surface or along the smooth ice-covered rivers. These are the hunters, trappers, and lumbermen who extract from the forest at this time its toll of timber and furs (picture, p. 365). No landscapes, not even those of the tropical savannas, could change more than this in the course of a year.

The climatic background of this seasonal change is related to an extreme continental position. Great temperature ranges are associated with wide land expanses, for only at a distance from the oceans can great contrasts between warm summers and cold winters be developed. Range of temperature, we have said previously, increases with increasing latitude and distance from the sea. Since all the continents taper to the south, no large expanses of land occur in the middle latitudes of the Southern Hemisphere; only north of the equator is land and water distribution effective in producing extreme continental climates. The northern lands where these extreme climates prevail are the regions of Group VI.

The Land

VEGETATION AND CLIMATE

The boreal forests which extend from west to east across the continents of the Northern Hemisphere, poleward of the deserts and grasslands, are dominantly coniferous. Farther equatorward on both the eastern and the western sides, as we have seen, lie the mixed forests of Group IV. The predominance of conifers north of the mixed forests does not mean that the rigorous climatic conditions of the higher middle latitudes are more suitable to these trees, for actually conifers grow much better in regions of milder climate. But only in the north are they freed from the serious competition of broadleaf species.

The Taiga.[1] The northern coniferous forest, or *taiga,* can be contrasted in almost every respect with the tropical selva. To be sure, both are evergreen; but this resemblance is only superficial, for the evergreen conifers of the taiga do not enjoy the year-round growing season of the evergreen broadleaf species of the tropics. Then, the taiga is composed of a few simple associations instead of a great variety of kinds of trees. Spruce, fir, larch, and pine are the chief conifers, and these are combined with such broadleaf species as aspen, birch, beech, maple, and willow. These forest regions, except in northern Manchuria, lie north of the range of the oaks. Among the most common associations are the spruce-fir forests of North America, with larch (tamarack), cedar, and maple occurring along with spruce and fir in the swamps; or the fir, birch, and aspen forests of western Siberia; or the larch and fir

---

[1] "Taiga" is a Russian word referring to the northern virgin forests.

Floating logs down a Siberian river

forests of eastern Siberia. Pure stands of pine are found on some of the sandy soils, much as on the similar lands farther south in Group IV. The conifer forests are interrupted by broadleaf enclaves along the river banks or in some of the swampy areas, or where these species have sprung up as second-growth forest after the conifers have in one way or another been removed.

The density of the stand of trees in the taiga varies greatly from place to place, but even in the most favored spots these forests do not form such a thick cover as the selva. Although many valuable stands of timber are found, probably the greater part of the land is covered by poor, stunted, and knotted trees having little value as timber. At the

Vegetation and Climate 363

northern limits of the forest single mature trees, centuries old, have reached only the stature of small bushes. In marked contrast to the selva, the forest floor in many areas is littered with fallen trunks and branches or with bundles of upturned roots, which, because of the high pitch content of the wood and because of the cool climate, decay very slowly. Especially in the swampy places the underbrush is so thick that passage through the forest may be extremely difficult.

The pitch content of the conifer renders it peculiarly liable to destruction by fire. Where lumbering operations are being carried on, sparks from the mills or camps frequently catch in the piles of slashings. In dry weather fires start very quickly, and once well under way are almost impossible to check. Few, indeed, are the northern forests in which charred trunks do not give evidence of at least one destructive fire.

The clearing of the taiga, whether by extensive lumbering or by fire, is not followed by a rapid return of the original species. At first only a low growth of bushes appears among the stumps. Then, instead of conifers, the first trees to gain a precarious foothold on the land are the broadleaf types, chiefly birch and aspen. In Siberia this second-growth enclave of broadleaf types is called "white taiga," as opposed to the dark-green fir forests, which are called "black taiga." Only after a long period of time does the slow growth of conifers reproduce the climax forest (pictures, pp. 370 and 376).

The Native Animals of the Taiga. In another respect the taiga differs from the selva. Instead of lacking large ground animals, it is the habitat of an animal population of extraordinary variety and number—an animal population which derives most of its food supply from the aquatic life in the numerous rivers, lakes, and swamps. In fact, in the more northerly sections the forest animals are of much greater value as a resource than the timber which shelters them. In these forests roam the world's chief fur-bearing animals; minks, martens, muskrats, foxes, wolves, badgers, bears, beavers, squirrels, sables, and ermines are included in the long list. There are also several large ungulata, chief of which are the deer, the moose, the caribou, and the close relative of the caribou—the reindeer.

The Climate. Temperature is the most significant climatic element in these regions. Fundamental in the production of the boreal forest

Trappers making camp in northern Quebec

landscapes, with their marked seasonal contrast, is the alternation of long, severe winters and short, cool summers. Especially in the continental interiors very large ranges of temperature between the average of the coldest and warmest months are experienced. For example, Winnipeg, in Manitoba, has a range of 70.3°, between an average of $-3.9°$ in January and 66.4° in July; and Dawson, in the Yukon, has a range of 82.4°, from $-23.1°$ in January to 59.3° in July. As might be expected, the most extreme ranges of all are found in the interior of the largest land mass, Eurasia. The little town of Verkhoyansk, in northeastern Siberia, holds the world's record for the range between the average temperature of its coldest and its warmest months. January averages $-58.2°$, and July averages 59.9°—a range of 118.1°. The lowest temperature ever recorded at Verkhoyansk is $-90°$; but at this same place a July temperature of 93.5° has also been recorded. Even lower winter temperatures have been reported from a

Vegetation and Climate 365

place called Oymyakon. Both these places are located in valleys among the low mountains of northeast Siberia where air drainage during calm, clear nights produces exceptionally low temperatures. Generally the winter temperatures in the northern parts of Group VI are not quite so low as these extremes: $-78°$ at Fort Yukon in Alaska, $-81°$ on the lower Mackenzie River in Canada, $-88°$ on the lower Lena River in Siberia. At all these places summer temperatures in the 90's are normal.

The winter temperatures are by no means so critical as the summer temperatures and the length of the growing season. Even though the summers are short, this is more than compensated by the long hours of sunshine. Poleward of latitude 55° or 60° N. the number of hours of possible sunlight per day during June increases rapidly to a maximum of twenty-four hours near the Arctic Circle (map, p. 367). At these latitudes it is not sufficient to measure the growing season in terms of frost-free days. Instead, it must be measured by the total number of hours of sunlight which come while the air temperature is over 42.6° (below which the vegetation growth ceases). Because of the very rapid rate of growth resulting from the long hours of sunshine, wild plants and crops extend considerably farther toward the north than might be expected.

The forests of Group VI, like those of Group IV, run diagonally across the continents (diagram, p. 177, and Plates 10 and 18). On the west coasts the boreal forest is more than 10° farther north than on the east coasts. The southern limit of the forest in Alaska is about 55° N., and in Scandinavia about 60° N.; in northern Maine and in eastern Siberia the southern limit is south of 45° N. The diagonal arrangement is owing, as we have seen, to the contrast of warm and cold ocean water on the two sides of the continents in higher middle latitudes. There is an important difference to be observed, however, between the northern limit of the boreal forest in Europe and North America. In Europe the warm North Atlantic Drift runs northward along the coast of Norway into the Arctic Ocean, bringing ice-free conditions around northern Norway and even some distance beyond (map, p. 397). But the barely submerged range of mountains which forms the Aleutian Islands shuts out the warm Kuro Siwo from Bering Sea. As a result the boreal forest does not reach the coast of Alaska, which is tundra-covered even in the Aleutian Islands well south of 60° N.

The boreal forest is not broken by the dry lands in the continental interiors, as are the forests of Group IV. It extends all the way across the Northern Hemisphere continents north of the grasslands. Its limits are closely related to the temperatures of the summer months. The northern limit, where the boreal forest borders the arctic tundra, corresponds closely to the isotherm of 50° average temperature for the warmest month. The southern limit, where the boreal forest borders the mixed forests of Group IV, is very close to a line drawn through places which have three months averaging over 50° and a fourth month which averages just under 50°. Where four months average over 50° the summers are long enough so that the oaks and other trees characteristic of the forests of Group IV can compete successfully with the conifers except on areas of porous soil.

The rainfall over most of the boreal forest regions is low. Only on the continental margins is the total annual precipitation greater than 10 inches. Furthermore, most of the rain comes in summer, and the winters are characteristically dry

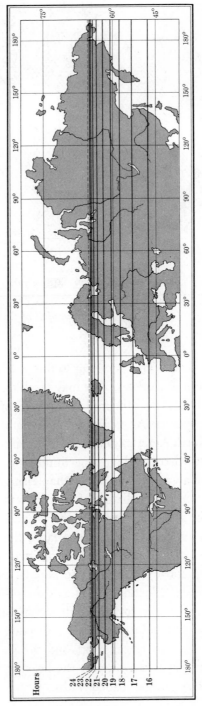

Hours of sunshine north of 45° on June 21. Based on sun's center and corrected for refraction. (Computed by A. D. Maxwell)

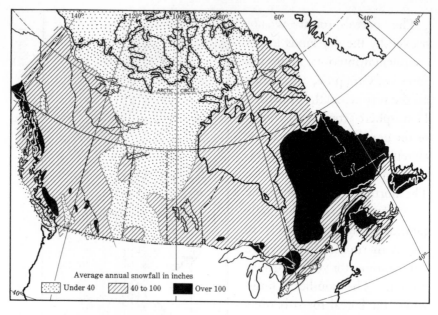

Mean annual snowfall of Canada. (*After Koeppe*)

and clear. This is owing to the position of these regions in the world pattern of climates. We may recall that the cold air masses which move southward over the middle latitudes of the Northern Hemisphere originate over the Arctic Ocean, Greenland, and the higher middle latitudes of North America and Eurasia in winter. Although there may be heavy frosts where cold air is accumulating, there can be no precipitation because air is settling rather than rising. The skies are cloudless, which promotes the radiation of heat from the ground and the further chilling of the air in contact with the ground. During the winters the area of cold air accumulation is so large that no warm air masses can bring moisture to it. Only on the continental margins is there much snowfall (map above). Contrary to popular belief, supported generally by the "movies," Siberia in winter is a land of little snowfall; the ground is mostly bare or covered with accumulations of frost. Because of the intense cold and the lack of a protecting blanket of snow, the small rivers and marshes freeze solid, and the ice on lakes and larger rivers is so thick that it can support the heaviest trucks and machines, even locomotives pulling loaded trains.

The average annual rainfall of the regions of Group VI is much less critical than the temperature, however. Because even in summer the temperatures do not average very high, the evaporation is never very great. At Verkhoyansk, for example, where the average annual rainfall is only 5.2 inches, the evaporation is so low that crops can be raised with no thought of irrigation. Actually a large part of the area of Group VI is covered by marshes and bogs, some of them permanently frozen underneath. In summer, when the ice melts and the surface of the ground thaws out, large areas become all but inaccessible for people who must travel on the land.

SURFACE FEATURES AND DRAINAGE

The prevalence of lakes and marshes in Group VI, however, is not solely the result of low evaporation. The surface features and drainage also contribute to this condition. Two chief processes have been at work in sculpturing the landforms of these regions: glaciation and running water. In both cases, for reasons we shall see, lakes and marshes are commonly produced.

The Surface Configuration of Group VI. On both sides of the North Atlantic Ocean, in northeastern North America and northwestern Europe, there is a remarkably similar development of the surface features (Plates 9 and 17). This part of North America is occupied by the Laurentian Upland, in the midst of which is found the great indentation of Hudson Bay. The southern end of this hilly region in southern Canada and in parts of the United States is within the borders of Group IV. In Europe the Scandinavian Upland occupies part of Finland and most of Sweden and Norway. In the midst of this upland is the Gulf of Finland. Both uplands are made up of knobby hills rising above extensive marshy or lake-filled valleys. Within the uplands major terrain features are formed by long and sharply-marked escarpments following old fault lines through the ancient geologic formations here exposed at the surface. Both uplands rise gradually from the continental interiors toward rims which face the Atlantic. The sea face of this escarpment in Labrador and in Norway is steep and rugged, forming what looks from the sea like a range of high mountains; yet only in southern Norway and in northern Labrador can it be classified

J. Allan Cash, from Rapho-Guillumette

Lake and boreal forest in Norway, fifty miles north of Oslo

as mountainous, for elsewhere, on climbing to the top, one finds a rolling hilly surface sloping gradually inland. Both uplands are bordered around their margins by cuestas which mark the upturned edges of the resistant sedimentary formations.

Bordering these hilly uplands and their marginal cuestas are vast plains which extend from the lower middle latitudes of both North America and Eurasia northward to the Arctic Ocean. These lowlands in the north are drained by three great north-flowing rivers: the Mackenzie, the Ob, and the Yenisei.

Immediately east of the Yenisei in Siberia, the moderately-dissected plateau of eastern Siberia rises abruptly from the lowlands of the west. This vast level-topped upland fills most of the area between the Yenisei and the Lena, reaching from the mountains of central Asia to the shore of the Arctic Ocean. A similar kind of terrain is found in the Yukon Valley of Alaska between the Alaska Range and the Brooks Range. The Yukon and its tributaries pass through this plateau in steep-sided valleys.

Northeast Siberia, east of the Lena Valley, is composed of ranges of high mountains, rising distinctly above a low mountain country. Along the arctic coast there is a wide coastal plain, and another narrowly confined lowland connects the Bering Sea with the Sea of Okhotsk north of Kamchatka.

The Extent of Glaciation. These various natural divisions of Group VI have been sculptured in detail by two quite different processes. A considerable area was never covered by the ice of the continental glaciers, and here the landforms have been produced chiefly by the work of running water. Glacial landforms, however, have been only very slightly modified by postglacial erosion in the other parts of the group.

Since glaciers can be formed only where so much snow falls during the winter that it does not all melt away during the summer, the places most favorable for ice accumulation are in the regions either of heavy snowfall or of cool summers, or of both. Such places are found in the high latitudes or on the snowy continental margins of higher middle latitudes. It is believed that a climate not radically different from that of today was needed to produce the continental ice sheets of the Pleistocene.

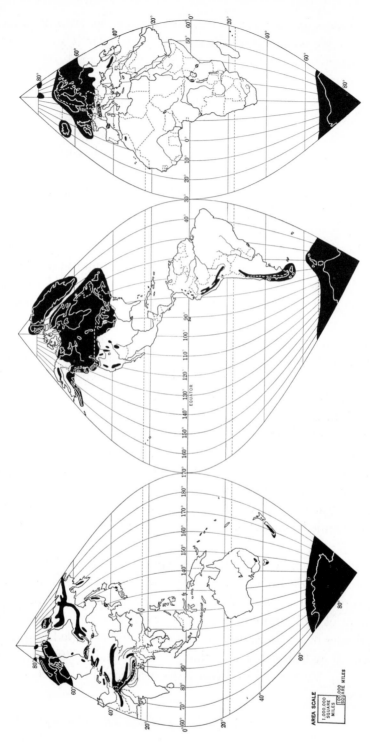

Major areas of Pleistocene glaciation. [*After E. Antevs, "Maps of Pleistocene Glaciation,"* Bulletin of the Geological Society of America, *Vol. 40 (1929), pp. 631–720*]

The areas of the world covered by Pleistocene ice are shown on the map (p. 372). In North America the chief centers of accumulation were in the far west on the snowy mountains of the west coast, and on the Plateau of Labrador, east and south of Hudson Bay. From these centers the ice spread chiefly south, east, and west. The Labrador ice sheet extended as far south as Long Island. Its southern boundary crossed the Appalachians north of Pittsburgh, and thence followed roughly the line of the Ohio and Missouri rivers into the central part of the continent. A small area in Wisconsin was never covered by the ice, although it was at one time entirely surrounded. The ice crossed Hudson Bay and covered the plains of central Canada as far north as the Arctic Ocean, but the Yukon Plateau was never glaciated. Ice still covers Greenland and parts of Ellesmere Island. In Europe the chief center of ice accumulation was the northern part of the Scandinavian Peninsula and Finland, from which the ice spread southward over most of the British Isles and, on the Continent, as far as the mouth of the Rhine and the highlands of central Europe. Eastward, however, glaciation probably extended only a short distance beyond the Urals. Most of the great interior of Siberia, with its light snowfall, was never glaciated. In the Southern Hemisphere glaciation was extensive in the southern Andes and the New Zealand Alps. The largest area of accumulation was the Antarctic Continent, which is still ice-covered.

Lakes and Swamps. In glaciated territory, whether the landforms are dominated by the processes of erosion or of deposition, innumerable depressions, large and small, are formed. If these are deep enough, they hold lakes. On the crystalline rocks of the hilly uplands the ice carved a surface of alternating low rocky ridges, smoothed and bare of soil on top, and bog-filled or lake-filled hollows. The similarity of the landscapes developed chiefly by glacial erosion on the crystalline rocks of the Laurentian and Scandinavian uplands is striking. In Finland alone, for example, there are some thirty-five thousand lakes, covering nearly a tenth of the total area of the country (map, p. 563). In North America a series of large lakes have been formed along the margin between the crystalline rocks and the sedimentaries. In the south are the Great Lakes. Northward, arranged along this geologic boundary, are Winnipeg, Athabaska, Great Slave, and Great Bear lakes. In addition to these larger water bodies, smaller lakes or marshes nestle in almost every depression. Travel by airplanes, equipped in summer with pontoons and in winter with skis, is an easy matter in these regions, where landing places can be found every few miles (picture below).

On the lowlands the glacial landforms are chiefly those of deposition. Here the greatest variety and confusion of surface topographic features appear, marked by only a vague festooning of the moraines. Some of these areas contain even more lakes and swamps than the hilly uplands.

In whatever manner lakes may be formed, they are only temporary features of the land in point of view of geologic time. Not only are their outlets being cut down, thus lowering the level of their waters, but also their basins are being filled with material washed into them. Throughout these glaciated regions all stages in the extinction of lakes can be found, from open water bodies to marshy flats from which all signs of open water have disappeared. Along with the gradual filling of such depressions, there is a fairly definite succession of vegetation (diagram, p. 375). First, water lilies and sedges grow on the margins of the open water. These gradually form a floating bog which extends out from the solid shore. The floating bog becomes thicker until it

A seaplane at Uranium City, Saskatchewan

fills in sufficiently to form a marsh, and various shrubs and bushes crowd out the sedges. The first trees to appear are usually larch (tamarack) in pure stands; later, as the marsh becomes more solid, in the regions of Group VI spruce follows and crowds out the larch. These various elements in the succession can all be identified in more or less concentric arrangement around lakes in process of extinction.

Rivers in Glaciated Territory. The drainage patterns in glaciated country are very different from those developed by more normal processes. Because of the blocking of preglacial valleys and the character of the surface left after the retreat of the ice, the rivers in such country are extremely irregular and winding in their courses. In many cases

Diagram to illustrate the filling of a pit lake by vegetation. (After C. A. Davis)

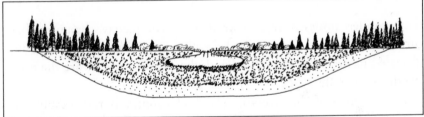

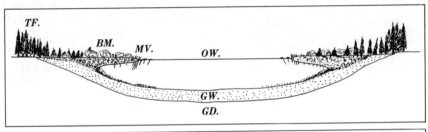

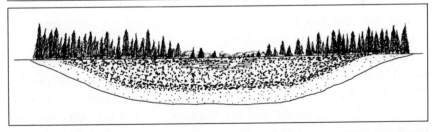

| **TF.** = Taiga | **MV.** = Marginal vegetation | **GW.** = Glacial Wash |
| **BM.** = Bog meadow on floating bog | **OW.** = Open water | **GD.** = Glacial drift |

Surface Features and Drainage 375

A coniferous forest in western Canada

they wander aimlessly from lake to lake, completely changing their direction of flow as they proceed downstream (map, p. 377). In unglaciated territory, on the other hand, the stream patterns are the usual dendritic or trellis types.

The regimen of the rivers in glaciated country is remarkably uniform. The many lakes regulate the flow of water so that only a protracted drought can have much effect, while sudden rains must be excessive to produce much of a rise.

Floodplain Swamps. An exception to this statement, however, is found in the cases of the great north-flowing rivers of this group—the Mackenzie, the Ob, the Yenisei, and the Lena. These rivers are subject to extensive spring floods, and the lowlands, even where they are not glaciated, do not dry out rapidly after the water recedes. This irregular regimen arises from the conditions of the spring thaw. Since the

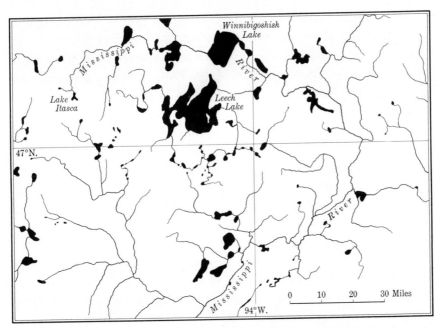

Irregular drainage of a glaciated area: the headwaters of the Mississippi River in Minnesota. (United States Geological Survey)

headwaters are freed earliest, while the lower portions of the rivers are still incased in ice, great jams are the result, and behind these jams the water backs up over a large territory. The floods of the Ob are as much as thirty-five miles wide in some sections. Permanently water-logged surfaces, in many places underlain by peat, are common in all these regions, covering as much as 75 per cent of the total area in the lowlands north of Tobolsk. In Canada the name "muskeg" is applied to such surfaces.

THE SOILS

The mature soils of Group VI are well developed only in the un-glaciated areas. In the regions covered by glacial deposits the time that has elapsed since the retreat of the ice has permitted only the beginnings of soil development. In both glaciated and unglaciated territory, moreover, no mature soils can develop in swampy places.

The Soils 377

The soil type toward which the immature regoliths are developing, and which is represented in mature form over much of Siberia, is the *podsol*.[1] The podsol profile is distinctly shallower than any of the other mature profiles (diagram, A, p. 197), in few places reaching depths greater than from eighteen inches to two feet. Soil development is slow because of the long period each year when the land is frozen. For various reasons, notably the absence of earthworms, the humus layer on the surface is not mixed with the soil, but remains as a very black, highly acid accumulation. The lower part of the A horizon in mature podsols is leached to a gray or even white color. The B horizon is reddish from the accumulation of part of the leached material, and is very compact. These soils quickly lose their fertility under cultivation.

In parts of Group VI there is a permanently frozen subsoil. This is the case in the far northern part of European Russia, in Siberia east of the Yenisei, and in parts of Canada and Alaska—all regions of light snow cover and intense winter cold. This frozen subsoil, by prohibiting the percolation of water, is a further reason for the extensive development of swamps. Because the removal of the vegetation cover has in some places resulted in the thawing out of this ice, it is thought that perhaps this phenomenon has been inherited from the intense cold of the glacial epoch. It is known as *permafrost*.

The Occupance

The boreal forest lands rival the deserts in their scantiness of human inhabitants. Although these regions comprise 10 per cent of the world's land area, they are occupied by only about 1 per cent of the world's population. Furthermore, most of the inhabitants are recent comers who have, for one reason or another, migrated to these more remote regions. The Asian steppe nomads, fleeing from the periodic droughts of the grassland regions, not only pushed westward into the forests of Europe and eastward into China but also northward into the taiga, where certain of the steppe tribes sought refuge from their warlike neighbors. More recently the Occidentals have extended their frontiers of settlement into these regions, and scattered outposts of

[1] A Russian word meaning "ash-colored underneath."

Westerners are found in the most isolated places, supported by such extractive industries as mining, lumbering, fishing, and trapping.

OCCUPANCE BY NONOCCIDENTAL CULTURES

The several different tribes which were pushed northward into the Siberian taiga from the steppes of central Asia have readjusted their modes of life to this new environment in various ways. Some have given up their horses in favor of cattle; others, such as the Samoyeds of northwestern Siberia, have adopted the reindeer and have remained pastoral nomads. Perhaps the most adaptable of all these "native" peoples are the Yakuts, who occupy the basin of the Lena River, in the heart of the world's "cold pole." They have learned to supplement their cattle with fish and game, to raise agricultural products and sell them to the Russian settlements, and even to act as traders between the Russians and the more remote forest tribes along the Lena and its tributaries. The still more primitive peoples of the Canadian forests, who live by hunting and fishing only, are believed to have migrated from Asia through Siberia and Alaska into the New World before mankind had advanced to the domestication of other animals than the dog.

Contacts with the European and American settlements or trading posts have seriously disorganized the native ways of living. In Siberia only the Yakuts are still increasing in numbers. In both Siberia and Canada the Occidental demand for furs has led to an increase of winter trapping. Men with their families start out into the wilderness in the fall and establish themselves in remote and isolated places, where they spend the winter in gathering a supply of pelts. With the melting of the snow in spring, when travel is limited to the rivers, they return to the trading posts and there exchange their skins for articles manufactured in the Occident, such as foods, rifles and ammunition, clothing, and strong drink.

OCCIDENTAL OCCUPANCE

This fur trade of the Europeans with the inhabitants of the taiga, both in Siberia and Canada, is now many centuries old. As early as the eleventh century the merchants of Russia were carrying on trade with the inhabitants of the Ob Valley. Trading posts were established during the sixteenth and seventeenth centuries, mostly at the mouths of the rivers down which the "natives" brought their loads of skins in the spring. The famous Hudson's Bay Company received its charter from King Charles II in 1670, and proceeded to locate posts first around the shores of James Bay and later along the western shore of Hudson Bay (map below). For some time the Company did not find it necessary to penetrate inland, as the Indians brought their furs over great distances in order to purchase the white man's products. Competition with other fur-trading companies, however, forced the establishment of posts in the interior, mostly at important river junctions or at portages between river systems. Meanwhile the Russians had pushed their trading activities across Asia and into Alaska, and even southward along the Pacific coast to the Spanish settlements in California. Only the moun-

Chief trading posts and routes of a portion of Canada

380 *The Boreal Forest Lands*

A gold dredge at work in a stream of the Yukon Plateau

tains separated them from the domains of the Hudson's Bay Company. Through the activities of these big trading companies vast areas of the boreal forest lands came under the control of two nations: Great Britain and Russia. In 1867 the United States purchased Alaska from Russia. Today railroad tentacles have been extended into these regions, and the posts at the railheads are the chief points of concentration of the fur traders.

Mining and Lumbering. Meanwhile other types of Occidental occupance have appeared which have done more to transform the landscapes of the forest lands than have the isolated trading posts or the activities of the trappers. These are the mining and lumbering settlements. Mining camps associated with the precious metals commonly grow with mushroom rapidity, and after a period of feverish existence are entirely abandoned. Furthermore, it is not much of an exaggeration to say that no place is too isolated or too remote from the developed means of transportation to prohibit the establishment of a mining settlement for the exploitation of such minerals as gold, platinum, and uranium, provided the ore bodies are sufficiently rich. Placer gold was exploited as early as 1830 in the territory just west of the mountains of

Occidental Occupance 381

central Asia between the headwaters of the Ob and the Yenisei. Other gold camps sprang into being, flourished, and declined. Today the chief centers of placer gold-mining in Siberia are located along the valley of the upper Lena and its tributary, the Vitim, northeast of Lake Baikal (map, p. 384). Placer gold, too, was the cause of the great gold rush of 1898 into Alaska. Auriferous gravels are widely distributed throughout the Yukon Valley and its tributaries (map, p. 386).

Somewhat more permanent are the mining settlements based on veins in the bedrock, such as the nickel, platinum, gold, and silver mines of the Sudbury-Cobalt Region of Canada. Most of the vein minerals, as in this case, are located in the upland areas of ancient crystalline rocks. Since prospecting must be done in summer, when travel away from the rivers is especially difficult, it is little wonder that the supposed mineral wealth of such regions as the Laurentian Upland

An open pit mine in the Mesabi Range, from which high-grade ores have now been completely removed

Ewing Galloway

of Canada should remain even today so little developed. The discovery of the ores at Sudbury in 1883 resulted from the digging of a cut along the new railroad line then being extended westward. Since the invention of methods for the use of uranium in atomic fission, this mineral, known to occur in several places in the Laurentian Upland, has been made the subject of widespread search. Where uranium ores have been found, large mining camps have been established, as at Port Radium.

Other mining regions require even closer connections with the industrial cities of Group IV. The iron mines of the Mesabi Range, west of Duluth, are very fortunately located at the end of one of the world's finest inland waterways, leading directly to the industrial cities farther south. The Kiruna iron district of Sweden (Plate 28) is not so fortunately located, for a railroad line is necessary to connect the mines with Narvik, on the other side of the Scandinavian Highlands. Ore bodies in Siberia, including iron and coal, are at an even greater disadvantage. Although the rivers of this part of the world are navigable during the summer, they lead northward to an ocean which is open, if at all, for only a few months each year; in other words, these rivers are oriented, as is Lake Baikal, at right angles to the desired lines of travel. Yet coal fields are being worked along the line of the Trans-Siberian Railroad, chiefly south of Tomsk and west of Irkutsk (map, p. 384).

Lumbering operations in these regions are similar to mining in that they carry on the "destructive exploitation" of a resource which is not replenished. As the forests are cut over, the lumber camps must move on. Many are the towns of Canada, such as those along the northern shores of Lake Huron, which flourished for a time and then declined as lumbering operations were shifted to other areas of virgin timber. Now some of them are feeling a renewal of prosperity, perhaps less temporary, with the rise of the paper-pulp industry, which does not require such high-grade stands of timber. The paper and match industries, utilizing the abundant water power, are of importance in the forests of Sweden and Finland. In northern European Russia the Soviet government has established several lumbering settlements, supplemented by enough agriculture to make them self-supporting.[1]

[1] See the various studies of pioneer settlements in the boreal forest lands contained in *Pioneer Settlement*, Coöperative Studies, American Geographical Society, Special Publication No. 14 (New York, 1932); especially pages 236–239.

Agricultural Settlement. Agricultural settlement in the boreal forest lands has been pushed far to the north, even beyond the Arctic Circle, yet the areas of such settlement are small and isolated. They represent inhabited islands in the midst of the thinly peopled forests. Like all Occidental pioneer settlements, they are located along the chief lines of travel—the navigable rivers or the rail tentacles.

The chief axis of settlement in Siberia is the Trans-Siberian Railroad (map below). This follows the black-earth belt of the grasslands until it enters the forest in the neighborhood of Tomsk. Clearings along this line in Group VI are scattered from Tomsk to Irkutsk, and beyond Lake Baikal in the valley of the Amur and its tributaries as far as Vladivostok. Penetration into the taiga to the north follows the valleys: along the Dvina nearly to Arkhangelsk, along the Ob to Tobolsk and beyond, and along the middle portion of the Lena to Yakutsk. Isolated spots of settlement are found in the valleys even within the Arctic Circle, the most northerly of these being Verkhoyansk.

In Canada the chief axes of settlement have been the St. Lawrence

Occidental settlement in the northern U.S.S.R. (After P. Camena d'Almeida)

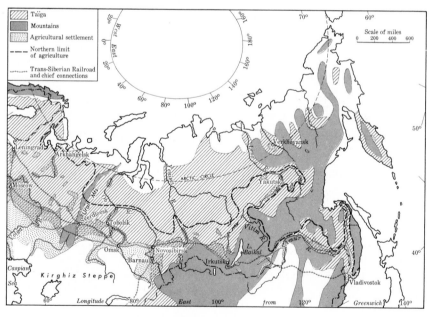

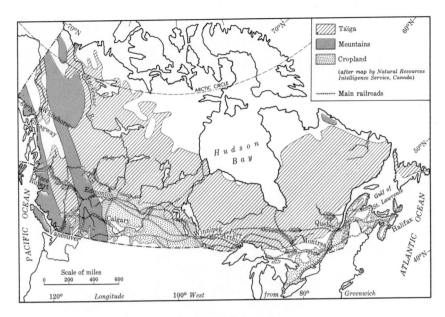

Cropland of Canada

River in the east and the railroad lines across the grasslands beyond Winnipeg in the west (map above). Penetration of the forests to the north by agriculturists has been successful only in isolated localities. The occupance of the Laurentian Upland has been especially difficult, in spite of the proximity to the large cities along the St. Lawrence. Only in the Lake St. John lowland, and in the clay belts south of James Bay which have been opened up by the railroads, as around Cochrane, have agricultural settlements persisted. As in Finland and northern Sweden, this region seems little suited to agricultural occupance. The clearings north of Edmonton along the Peace River, however, are analogous to those of the Siberian taiga.

Agricultural settlement in Alaska has also been slow in developing. Although agricultural products of good quality have been raised at Fairbanks on the Tanana River (map, p. 386), the difficulty of reaching a market has proved very great. During the decade before World War II, a new pioneer colony was established in the Matanuska Valley around Palmer, along the railroad north of Seward and Anchorage.

Though the patterns of occupance on this northern pioneer fringe

Occidental Occupance 385

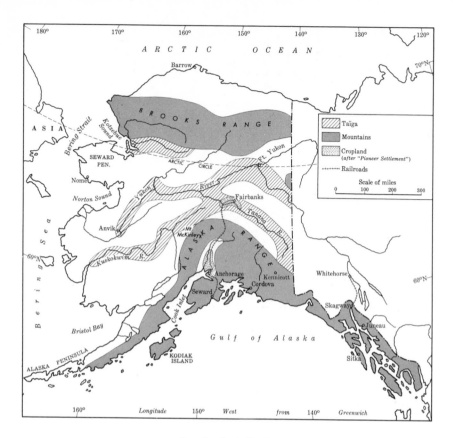

Cropland of Alaska

resemble those of the early stages of Occidental settlement in the other
forest lands of the world, it is not at all certain that they can be elaborated as the others have been. Agriculture is handicapped in the boreal
forest lands in numerous ways. The severity of the winters, the shortness of the growing season, the isolated and spotty distribution of the
areas of favorable soil, and the difficulty of reaching a market are all
major obstacles to this form of occupance. As the climate becomes more
rigorous toward the north the importance of the edaphic elements in
limiting the areas of potential settlement becomes greater. In spite of
the optimism expressed in some of the propaganda, there is considerable doubt as to whether these isolated forest clearings can ever be in-
corporated in the main area of Occidental settlement by the conquest

386 *The Boreal Forest Lands*

of the surrounding territory. This may be possible in certain areas along the southernmost margin of the taiga, but in most of the lands of Group VI widespread agricultural settlement under present conditions will probably not be feasible.

Animals and Crops. The pastoral and agricultural products which might support pioneer settlement in the boreal forests are numerous. Most important at present are the animals raised for meat or dairy. In terms of acreage the feed crops are more important than the food crops, and many of the grains are cut for hay and stored for winter feeding. Although cattle can scarcely compete for the large city markets in the regions of Group IV, they can be marketed in nearby lumbering or mining communities. Reindeer, however, might well compete with cattle raised in places closer to the markets. Reindeer do not need to be sheltered or fed on stored hay during the winters, for they can take care of themselves. Reindeer meat has actually been successfully sold in the United States, as it has been for a long time in the Scandinavian countries. It was so successful in the United States that a storm of protest from cattle-raisers was aroused. Stefansson [1] believes that the far northern pastures can, in fact, be developed to provide an important additional source of meat. But a pastoral economy supports only a small total number of people.

In a few parts of the regions of Group VI the production of spring wheat has provided economic support for settlement. The Peace River District of Canada, for instance, has been organized around the production of this grain, as have also the similar clearings in southwestern Siberia. An increase in the demand for wheat in the world markets would perhaps result in an extension of these wheat-growing communities; for wheat can be raised on favorable soils as far as the limit of ninety frost-free days and as far as the isotherm of 57° average temperature for the three summer months. If suitable soils can be found, the temperature conditions would permit the development of wheatlands even north of the Peace River District and in certain small areas in Alaska (map, p. 386). However, the production of wheat in these areas must remain marginal both in the economic and in the geographic sense.

[1] Vilhjalmur Stefansson, "The Colonization of the Northern Lands," in *Climate and Man,* 1941 Yearbook of the U. S. Department of Agriculture, pp. 205–216.

Beyond wheat other crops reach the farthest limits of agriculture. The hardiest of all the grains is barley; in the most northerly agricultural settlements of Siberia, Canada, and Alaska the usual crop combination is composed of barley, hay, and potatoes (map, p. 250). Vegetables and berries of rich flavor find suitable conditions of growth at these high latitudes and, with the establishment of canneries, might conceivably provide a commercial basis of settlement. Vegetable gardens are planted even on the delta of the Mackenzie River not far from the margins of the Arctic Ocean.

Conclusion

Man is still the intruder in these regions. Various cultures, driven by necessity to seek a refuge in the forests, have been able to maintain themselves, even if they have succeeded in doing little more than this. The Occidentals, in their search for the primary materials with which to fashion the structures and implements of their civilization, have established mining and lumbering centers even where all the necessary foodstuffs have had to be brought in from other regions. They have done the same in other parts of the world. These regions have now also been penetrated by the fringes of Occidental settlement. In especially favored places the isolated communities of pioneer farmers may prove permanent, but they are not likely to lose the flavor of the frontier for a long time.

THE POLAR LANDS

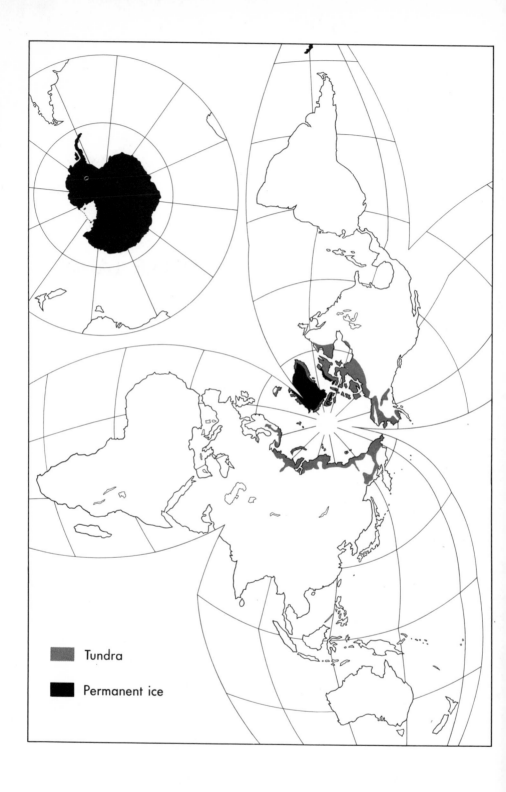

Tundra

Permanent ice

COLD WEATHER, even in summer; sparse vegetation or no vegetation at all; snow and ice visible in the landscape, at least in patches, throughout most of the year,—these are the outstanding characteristics of the polar lands. All these things can be experienced at one or another place and time in various parts of the world; but nowhere else, save on the poleward margins of the neighboring groups, can one find the long winter nights when the sun never comes above the horizon, or the long summer days when there is no darkness.

The polar night of the lower arctic latitudes, with its strange beauty, has been vividly described by the explorer Nansen:

The sky is like an enormous cupola, blue at the zenith, shading down into green, and then into lilac and violet at the edges. Over the ice fields there are cold violet-blue shadows, with lighter pink tints where a ridge here and there catches the last reflection of the vanished day. Up in the blue of the cupola shine the stars, speaking peace, as they always do, those unchanging friends. In the south stands a large red-yellow moon, encircled by a yellow ring and light golden clouds floating on the blue background. Presently the aurora borealis shakes over the vault of heaven its veil of glittering silver—changing now to yellow, now to green, now to red. It spreads, it contracts again, in restless change; next it breaks into waving, many-folded bands of shining silver, over which shoot billows of glittering rays, and then the glory vanishes. Presently it shimmers in tongues of flame over the very zenith, and then again it shoots a bright ray up from the horizon, until the whole melts away in the moonlight, and it is as though one heard the sigh of a departing spirit. Here and there are left a few waving streamers of light, vague as a foreboding—they are the dust from the aurora's glittering cloak. But now it is growing again; new lightnings shoot up, and the endless game begins afresh. And all the time this utter stillness, impressive as the symphony of infinitude.[1]

How very different are these same scenes during the polar day! The colorful beauty of the night is lost in the white glare of the brilliant yet heatless sunshine. Instead of the awe-inspiring displays of light and shadow on white snow surfaces, the day brings pale skies, a horizon veiled in fogs, and a foreground of barren rocks and patches of ice or snow now pitilessly revealed in the daylight.

[1] F. Nansen, *Farthest North,* New York, 1898, pp. 252–253.

The Polar Lands   391

Near the northern limit of the taiga in Alaska

For the whole twenty-four hours of the earth's revolution the sun circles the horizon, bringing real warmth only to the slopes which are steep enough to receive its rays nearly perpendicularly. In the shade, on the north-facing slopes at noon, or on the south-facing slopes at midnight, the air is cold. Bare ground appears from beneath the melting snow, and the ice on the polar seas breaks up in jumbled masses. In the far north sheltered places, warmed by the reflection from neighboring cliffs, are filled with a luxuriant cover of quick-flowering plants. Near the southern margins of the arctic regions, where the summer temperatures climb well above freezing, the land is covered with a mat of mosses, lichens, grasses, and flowering plants. Here only the surface thaws out, soaking this mat of vegetation like a sponge and providing breeding places for swarms of mosquitoes.

Except for the cool summers and cold, dark winters, the two polar regions of the earth are very different in character. The arctic is composed of a deep ocean basin, bounded by the northern coastal plains of

North America and Eurasia, with their fringes of island clusters. Just the opposite condition is found in the antarctic; for here there is a continent five million or so square miles in area, larger than Europe, which is bordered by the stormy southern oceans. Whereas the arctic shores are sparsely inhabited by men, the Antarctic Continent is totally uninhabited.

The Land

VEGETATION AND CLIMATE

In many respects the polar lands resemble the dry lands. Both are deserts in the sense of being largely uninhabited and also in the sense of possessing a meager cover of vegetation. The one is a desert of drought; the other, a desert of cold. Both of them, moreover, are bordered by a margin of semi-desert, a transition zone which separates them from the world's forest lands. Around the dry deserts are the grasslands of Group V; around the cold deserts are the tundras.[1]

As in the dry lands, there are few places in the polar lands which are entirely without vegetation. Glaciers present to the eye a glittering white surface without vegetation cover; and there are many areas of bare rock. But even the bare rock, on closer examination, usually proves to support mosses and lichens and scattered plants.

Every Arctic traveller remembers his surprise and delight when for the first time in high latitudes he came on meadows of rich grasses, bright with tall, yellow buttercups, luxuriant saxifrages, violet cuckoo flowers, blue polemoniums, or many other flowers; moorlands purple with saxifrage as a Scottish hillside is with heather; peat bogs white with myriad tufts of waving cotton grass; dry banks with their hundreds of sturdy white and yellow poppies, clumps of red and yellow saxifrage, dryas, campions, and other blooms; or some wind-swept summit on which the Arctic poppy triumphantly flowered.[2]

The Tundra. The characteristic vegetation of the polar regions is the tundra; but the tundra itself, like the grasslands, is composed of

[1] For the convenience of classification the tundra and polar deserts are included together in one group, and the dry deserts and grasslands, with their varied modes of occupance, are placed in separate groups. There can be no argument for this except expediency.

[2] R. N. Rudmose-Brown, *The Polar Regions,* New York, 1927, p. 112.

transitional types. From the margins of the taiga, northward to the absolutely barren polar desert, three chief kinds of tundra are recognized: these are the *bush tundra,* the *grass tundra,* and the *desert tundra.*

The first of these is found on the edge of the taiga and in a few especially well-sheltered spots farther to the north. Here the flora is composed of dwarf trees, chiefly willow, birch, alder, and mountain ash. Where conditions are particularly favorable a scrub forest of birch is found, as in southernmost Greenland; but mostly the tallest individuals rise no more than three feet above the ground. The bush tundra grades off rapidly into the broader zone of the grass tundra, which is composed of a nearly continuous mat of sedges, mosses, and lichens, mixed with bushes which lie prone on the ground. This grass tundra, like the other polar types, rests on a permanently frozen regolith; and when the surface thaws out during the summer the water does not drain away, but is soaked up by the spongy vegetation. Summer travel over these tundras is described by the expressive term *mushing.* Still farther poleward the grass tundra breaks up into detached "oases" in the sheltered hollows, separated by expanses of bare rock or regolith. This is the desert tundra (picture, p. 395).

The Animals of the Polar Lands. In view of the severity of the polar winter the richness and variety of the fauna of the arctic regions are remarkable. Many of the land animals of the taiga migrate northward onto the tundra during the summer months. The reindeer of Eurasia and the similar, but smaller, caribou of North America are the most important of these. Another large herbivore found far within the arctic is the musk ox, or ovibos, generally now surviving only in isolated herds which graze on the more luxuriant patches of desert tundra. Two small herbivora—the arctic hare and the lemming—are also widespread in the arctic.

Following the herds of reindeer, caribou, or musk ox are a number of predatory animals, such as the wolf and fox. Most of these carnivora, however, belong typically to the taiga fauna and are intruders in the polar lands. The drift ice of the polar sea or the immediate coastal margin is the habitat of the polar bear, which preys chiefly on marine life—the seal and the walrus.

Birds and insects are particularly numerous. Mosquitoes are prob-

Bear hunters on the tundra in Alaska

ably present in greater numbers in summer over the tundra than anywhere else on earth and are a terrible plague to the human and animal inhabitants, although not as carriers of disease. Bees and butterflies perform their usual function of the fertilization of flowers. Flies are abundant, especially near human habitations. Attracted in part by this abundance of insect life, many a migrating bird in summer makes the tundra its goal. The rocky shores of the arctic seas provide breeding places for a great number of the birds well known in middle and even low latitudes. The land birds which remain in the regions during the winter include the ptarmigan, the snowy owl, the gerfalcon, the raven, and the snow bunting.

Sea life is rich. Although reptiles, amphibians, and fresh-water fish are either entirely absent or very rare, the inhabitants of the polar

Vegetation and Climate 395

oceans are varied and numerous. The seal, the walrus, the whale, the narwhal, and the sea elephant are among the most typical forms of sea life.

In the antarctic regions a land fauna is practically nonexistent, although the sea life is abundant. The largest known land animal on the Antarctic Continent is a wingless mosquito, found in only one single protected locality. There are no land mammals; no land birds. Because of the absence of predatory animals, the penguins find conditions on the coasts and on the isolated islands of the southern oceans ideal as breeding places. These birds, unable to fly and awkward on the land, could scarcely exist in the presence of a land enemy.

The Polar Climates. These various zones of vegetation with their associated faunas correspond closely to the summer temperatures. All the polar climates average less than 50° in the warmest month. In the Northern Hemisphere this isotherm corresponds to the boundary between the taiga and the tundra. The continuous vegetation cover of the bush and grass tundras is found mostly within the regions which have warmest-month temperatures between 50° and 41° (map, p. 397). Where the temperatures drop below 41° in the warmest month, only the desert tundra can exist. The polar desert, including the areas covered by ice, corresponds with the places where the warmest month averages below 32° (in the Northern Hemisphere only Greenland and possibly a portion of Ellesmere Island).

In the Southern Hemisphere very little of the Antarctic Continent extends far enough northward to reach the isotherm of 32°. Only in these few places is any vegetation found (map, p. 398). A very peculiar type of polar climate exists in southernmost South America and some of the islands of the South Atlantic and South Pacific oceans. Here, although the warmest month averages under 50°, the coldest month is over 32°. This is an extreme of marine conditions—the result of great expanses of open sea. Tierra del Fuego, in spite of its position with reference to the isotherm of 50° for the warmest month, is covered by a broadleaf forest, mostly of antarctic beech.

The polar climates are not necessarily colder in winter than are the climates of higher middle latitudes. The lowest air temperature ever recorded at the surface of the earth was observed at an altitude of more than 10,000 feet at the South Pole. But close to sea level the tempera-

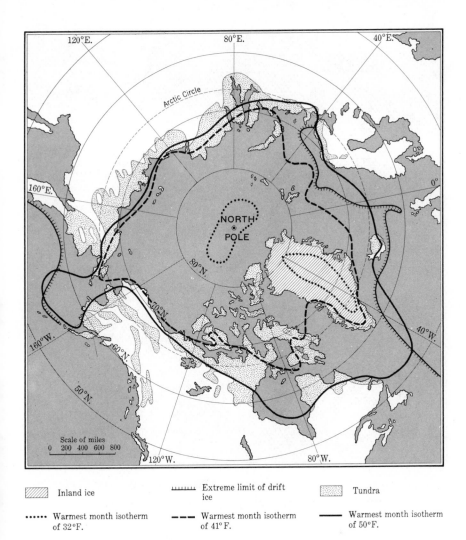

The north polar regions. (After Nordenskjöld and Mecking)

tures are not so low as those of Siberia. From both Greenland and Antarctica, especially the latter, come great outblasts of cold air which move at high velocities and blow along great quantities of snow. Mawson names the Antarctic Continent "the home of the blizzard." The neighboring oceans in the higher middle latitudes of the Southern Hemisphere are among the stormiest in the world.

Vegetation and Climate 397

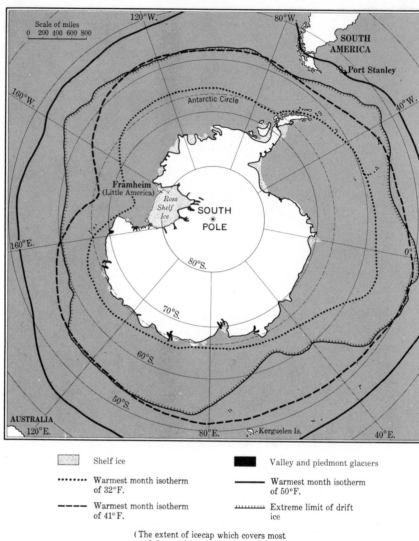

The following labels appear on the map:

Scale of miles
0 200 400 600 800

120°W. 80°W.

SOUTH
AMERICA

Port Stanley

160°W.

Antarctic Circle

40°W.

Framheim
(Little America)
Ross
Shelf
Ice

SOUTH
POLE

160°E.

80°S.

0°

70°S.

60°S.

50°S.

AUSTRALIA
120°E.

80°E. Kerguelen Is.

40°E.

▨ Shelf ice		▮ Valley and piedmont glaciers	
•••••• Warmest month isotherm of 32°F.		—— Warmest month isotherm of 50°F.	
———— Warmest month isotherm of 41°F.		⊥⊥⊥⊥⊥ Extreme limit of drift ice	

(The extent of icecap which covers most
of the continent is largely unknown)

The south polar regions. (After Nordenskjöld and Mecking)

SURFACE FEATURES

The surface features of the polar lands include all varieties of relief,
from low, swampy coastal plains to high ice plateaus and glaciated
mountains. In the Northern Hemisphere the Arctic Ocean is bordered

for the most part by the Eurasian and North American coastal plains (Plates 9 and 17). These lowlands are interrupted by the Urals, a chain of low mountains which extends into the polar ocean through Novaya Zemlya, and by the highlands of Greenland and the neighboring islands. Part of the Canadian arctic archipelago is composed of low-lying detached pieces of the North American coastal plain, underlain by horizontal stratified rocks; but the easternmost coasts which face Greenland, notably of Ellesmere and Baffin islands and of Labrador, stand up as ice-scoured hills and low mountains still partly covered by glaciers. The ice-free coasts of Greenland are similarly composed of heavily glaciated uplands. Iceland and Svalbard are also mountainous and harbor small accumulations of ice. But none of these existing glaciers is

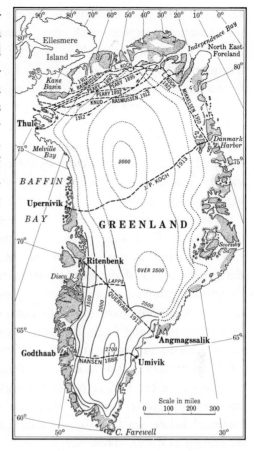

Greenland, showing the configuration of the inland ice (elevations in meters), the ice-free areas (stippled), and the routes followed by explorers crossing the inland ice. (After De Quervain: courtesy of the Geographical Review, *published by the American Geographical Society of New York)*

so extensive as the inland ice which masks the greater part of Greenland (map above). In the Southern Hemisphere the continent of Antarctica is covered by the world's largest existing icecap.

Landforms. In contrast to surfaces exposed to a tropical rainy climate, which are attacked dominantly by chemical decomposition and are speedily covered by a thick mantle of fine-textured regolith, the surfaces in the polar regions are attacked dominantly by physical disintegration, the exposed rock being shattered and broken into angular fragments by frost action. Nowhere else, except on the summits of high mountains above the timber lines, is frost action so potent a force in fracturing the rock surfaces. The lower slopes of cliffs broken up in this way are covered with accumulations of rock fragments, much as in the deserts. Plateau surfaces not covered with ice are mantled with angular blocks of rock loosened by frost action, forming a very rough surface known as a *rock field*. In the course of time such rock fields may be modified by continued frost action until a coarse, gravelly regolith is produced.

Erosion is carried on by processes very different from those of the rainy lands. Even more than in the case of the dry lands running water is limited to the exotic rivers. River valleys exist, to be sure, along the courses of the north-flowing rivers of Canada and Siberia. Except for summer streams pouring from the front of melting glaciers, however, other streams in the polar regions are poorly developed. As a result the water from the melting snow and ice during the arctic summer forms extensive ponds and marshes on the surface.

Glacial erosion is at a maximum. Where the formerly more extensive glaciers of the ice age passed through mountain valleys they produced typical glacial troughs. Near the coast, where the valleys were deepened below sea level by ice scour, the drowned glacial troughs are known as *fiords*. However, while the ice had the effect of smoothing the hills and deepening the valleys, it seems to have had little effect on high-level plateaus; in fact, it seems to have preserved them from weathering. The high-level surfaces of Labrador and Norway are little touched by erosion; instead, they are mantled with rock fields apparently of postglacial origin.

Along the coasts a feature common in the polar regions is the *strand flat*. This is a marine terrace bordered on the landward side by an abrupt sea cliff and extending seaward in a fringe of rounded, polished islets known as *skerries*. In some places the strand flat broadens out to ten or twelve miles in width; in other places it may be very narrow or entirely lacking. The flat-topped rock ledges and the partially submerged skerries are persistent elements of the arctic coastal landscapes of the hilly or mountainous sections.

In addition to the landforms produced by glacial action, there are also vast lowlands which were never ice-covered (map, p. 372). These are monotonously flat and poorly drained.

The Occupance

Man in the polar regions maintains his existence only by continuous effort. Along with the driest deserts, these regions are among the world's least favorable habitats; and along with the deserts, the polar lands have been the least penetrated by Occidental settlement. When Occidentals did enter these regions they found two chief native cultures, and the patterns of population distribution developed by these contrasted modes of occupance were quite distinct. The Eskimos, chiefly of North America, were the only people who established themselves permanently in the arctic lands. Since their occupance was based on the hunting of the seal they were nomadic or seminomadic, and they never placed their villages far from the seacoast. On the other hand, the Eurasian tribes, whose occupance was based on the domesticated reindeer, were pastoral nomads, living on the tundras only during the summers and seeking refuge in the forests during the winter months. Their summer villages were placed back from the coast. Occidental contacts with these peoples at first were largely through the activities of traders, explorers, miners, and missionaries, and more recently have come from the establishment of air bases and from other military activities. The result has been the virtual annihilation of these native cultures.

The population of the polar regions is entirely limited to the Northern Hemisphere. The great Antarctic Continent is surrounded by a stormy, ice-filled ocean which has so effectively barred the access of man that until the airplane could be used for exploration large parts of its coast were unknown.

OCCUPANCE BY THE ESKIMO CULTURE

The Eskimos occupied the margins of the polar seas from the extreme northeast of Siberia across northern North America to eastern Greenland and Labrador. Their present distribution, and the whole territory over which the signs of Eskimo occupance have been found, are

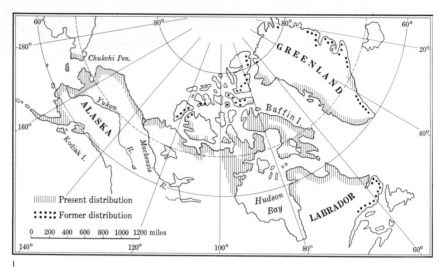

The maximum distribution of the Eskimo culture, with an indication of the lands from which the Eskimos have withdrawn. (From Ludwig Mecking, Die Polarländer, Leipzig, 1925)

shown on the map above. Over these many miles of arctic coast there are scattered some 50,000 Eskimos; of these nearly 23,000 are in Greenland and nearly 16,000 are in Alaska.[1]

The Eskimo culture represented an amazing adaptation to the harsh conditions of arctic living. Agriculture was entirely lacking, and very few of the products of the plant world were utilized in any way. The seal provided the basic support; from this animal came clothing, food, implements, and even fuel. Only a very few small tribes of Eskimos lived inland and depended on the migrations of the caribou. Hunting was a serious business; for, in spite of a high degree of skill and almost continuous effort, game was not always plentiful and starvation was the consequence of failure. The best season of the year for seal-hunting was the winter, except for the darkest period in December. The surface of the polar sea is frozen, and travel long distances by dog sled was relatively easy. The Eskimos learned that if the nearer hunting grounds were visited too frequently the game would be driven away; during the

[1] G. H. T. Kimble and D. Good (editors), *Geography of the Northlands,* New York, 1955.

Eskimos in their kayaks along the coast of Labrador

winter, therefore, they frequently traveled for weeks at a time to distant places where seals were reported to be plentiful.

The seal, however, had to be supplemented with other game. Numerous sea animals were hunted during the summer with the aid of the kayak, or skin boat. At this season also the large land animals, especially the caribou and the musk ox, were sought; for although their meat was less satisfactory than that of the seal or the walrus, owing to the small amount of fat it contains, nevertheless it provided a pleasant variety and a much needed supplementary supply to be "cached" as a provision against later want. Birds and birds' eggs were also much

Occupance by the Eskimo Culture 403

prized as offering a change in the steady diet of seal meat. Yet through-out the year the Eskimos ate little else but meat: meat eaten cooked but more often eaten raw, or frozen, or rotten; meat served without salt.

Eskimo Settlements. The nomadic or seminomadic type of life was essential in such a culture. Migrations of the game were closely fol-lowed by migrations of people. Only in the places where water and ice conditions were especially favorable for the seal—so favorable that a dependable supply of that animal was certain year after year—could the Eskimos become in any way sedentary. Even the land animals in the territory of Eskimo occupance have been the cause of migrations. The absence of both sea game and land game from the outermost islands of the Canadian arctic archipelago was reflected in the absence of Eskimos in this region.

Yet the Eskimos were not without attachment to certain sites. Dur-ing the winter they gathered together in villages near the water known to be frequented by seals.[1] The immediate locations of these villages de-pended on such features as ease of approach over the sea ice, protection from high winds, supplies of drinking water (usually from stranded icebergs), and other local factors. In all the centuries during which the Eskimos occupied the shores of the polar seas, they re-

Eskimo girls dressed in their fancy parkees

Machetanz, from Three Lions

[1] See the description of the life of the "Polar Eskimo," the north-ernmost of the world's human in-habitants, who occupied the penin-sula of Thule in western Greenland north of latitude 76° N., in W. Elmer Ekblaw, "The Material Re-sponse of the Polar Eskimo to Their Far Arctic Environment," *Annals of the Association of American Geographers,* Vol. 17 (1927), pp. 147–198, and Vol. 18 (1928), pp. 1–24.

Native sod dwellings north of the Arctic Circle in Alaska

turned to these same places again and again. The stone houses used during the winter were first built before the memory of the oldest inhabitants; they had been repeatedly abandoned and reoccupied. The movements of these people, therefore, were between points more or less definitely fixed.

During the summer the Eskimo became more completely nomadic. With his skin tent he traveled along the coast to visit the summer sealing grounds or the cliffs on which great numbers of birds breed. Small groups, too, traveled inland to hunt the caribou and the musk ox, so that at this season the distribution of people was less rigidly attached to the coast or to any particular sites.

Contacts with Occidentals. Contacts with Europeans and Americans have completely transformed the traditional Eskimo culture in all but the most remote places. The Eskimos have been described for years

Occupance by the Eskimo Culture 405

in elementary geography texts as an example of the close adjustment of a way of living to the meager resources of the polar lands. The Eskimo culture belonged to the Stone Age, but it was one in which a certain few skills were developed to perfection. When contacts with European traders and missionaries brought the rifle to the Eskimos so that they could hunt the seal much more effectively than with a spear or harpoon, the first result was an unprecedented abundance of food. Hunting the land animals in summer was also made easier. The Eskimos seemed to be well off indeed. After a time, however, the seals began to leave their accustomed waters, and so the Eskimos had no product of great value that they could sell to the traders. The seal on which the Eskimos depended for food, clothing, and heat is the hair seal. (The furs used for making sealskin coats come entirely from the large herd of pelagic "fur seals"—*Callorhinus alascanus*—which returns every year to breed on the Pribilof Islands, off Alaska.) When the hair seals were killed off too rapidly by hunters with rifles, the Eskimos could no longer occupy their arctic homes. Here is a case where a technical change resulted in a decrease in the habitability of an area. The Eskimos began to decline rapidly in number so that by 1920 there were probably not more than 33,000 of these interesting people left.

Now the process of cultural change has gone a step farther. Some individuals among the Eskimos have had a capacity for making a fundamental change in their way of living. Not every person can give up traditional ways and learn entirely new ways; but among every people, even the most primitive, there are some who can do this. In Greenland the Eskimos have moved into the settlements of the ancient Norse and the Danes, in many cases have intermarried, and are today scarcely to be distinguished from other Greenlanders. Likewise, many native Indians in the United States are no longer distinguishable from other Americans.

OCCUPANCE BY THE EURASIAN CULTURES

Probably the whole Eurasian tundra does not support more than thirty thousand people, and during the winter the population is much less than this. The various peoples of the taiga, chiefly the Samoyeds

Winter travel by dog sled in the Siberian tundra

and the Chukchi, who have domesticated the reindeer, migrate north-ward with these animals during the summer, much as the wild herds of reindeer used to migrate and as the caribou of North America still migrate. These nomadic peoples have no permanent villages, either in summer or in winter, but move their herds from place to place to take advantage of the slow-growing pasturage. When the snow begins to fly, they move into the taiga and abandon their skin tents in favor of pits dug in the ground. These Siberian tribes are therefore only partly dependent on the polar habitat. Their diet of meat is supplemented by fish from the rivers and by berries, roots, and nuts from the forest. Furthermore, the possession of domestic animals frees them from the fortunes of the chase. They are not so close to the margin of existence as the Eskimos used to be, nor are they so harmoniously adjusted to the conditions of arctic living.

Contacts with the European traders have been as detrimental to most of these peoples as in the case of the Eskimos. Among all the Siberian forest and tundra tribes, only the Yakuts are increasing in number. Apparently none of these cultures can survive except in greatly modified form—perhaps organized for the production of a meat surplus from the reindeer herds in exchange for which the white man's industrial and agricultural products can be purchased.

OCCIDENTAL OCCUPANCE

There is little to record concerning the occupance of the polar regions by Europeans and Americans. While these regions have attracted parties of explorers since classical antiquity, little permanent settlement by white men has ever taken place. The trading posts, which are the only permanently inhabited spots along the Eurasian arctic littoral, are engaged in the handling of the products of the taiga (chiefly furs) and are located at the mouths of the north-flowing rivers. A number of similar posts in North America have been established within the polar lands, but they are not supported by polar products.

Whaling and mining have also attracted Occidentals to these regions and have led to the establishment of settlements. The whaling industry, so important before the days of mineral oil, shifted from the vicinity of Svalbard to the more remote parts of the world as the whales were killed in increasing numbers. Modern mechanical equipment threatens the final exhaustion of this resource. Until recently the whaling industry required land bases for the extraction of the oil, and such bases were established where protected harbors provided shelter for the whaling fleet. A number of these stations were located in the arctic, as at Herschel Island off the mouth of the Mackenzie River, and in the antarctic, as at Stanley, on the Falkland Islands. With the invention of the modern whaling ships, which are, in reality, floating packing plants where the carcasses are turned into a variety of products, the land stations have declined in importance.

Mining too has supported more or less permanent settlement in a few localities in the north. The coal mines of Svalbard are perhaps the most important, although gold in Alaska continues to provide a somewhat unsteady basis for such communities as Nome.

A landing strip on the Mackenzie River near Aklavik, Northwest Territories

The airplane now makes any part of the arctic or antarctic regions more easily accessible than it ever could be by land travel. Polar enthusiasts foresee regular air routes that cross the polar regions; but an examination of the arctic regions on a globe shows that the actual air routes connecting major concentrations of people cross only the margins of the polar lands. The air routes from the United States to eastern Asia pass over southern Alaska; those from eastern United States and Canada to western Europe may pass over the southernmost tip of Greenland. However, two vital needs—the need of defense in the arctic regions, and the need of scientific observation in both the arctic and antarctic—have resulted in the establishment of permanent or semipermanent settlements in the polar regions. A system of military air bases and radar warning nets stretches for 3000 miles across the arctic regions of North America, and it may be assumed that similar systems have been built in Northern Siberia. A large number of bases have been set up in the polar regions for the observation of meteorological phenomena and other matters of interest to students of the physics of the earth.

Occidental Occupance 409

Conclusion

The Occidental peoples have not yet found a resource by which permanent polar settlement can "pay its way." Hitherto occupance has been based on resources of other regions seeking an outlet through the arctic, or on temporary extractive industries, such as whaling and mining. Agriculture being physically impossible, permanent settlement would have to rest on pastoral activities, probably those associated with the reindeer. But the permanence of the arctic pastures under heavy grazing has yet to be demonstrated. The native cultures, so intimately adapted to the region, have been disorganized by the introduction of Occidental tools and foods, and are threatened with annihilation. On the whole the landscapes of the polar lands have been modified by human occupance to a lesser degree than those of any other group.

THE MOUNTAIN LANDS

Mountains

Most people think they know what a mountain is. Yet when we compare such relatively small and inconspicuous features as the Turtle Mountains of North Dakota with such imposing heights as the Berkshire Hills of Massachusetts, we find that we cannot depend on popular impression and terminology for our definition of mountains. The dictionary says that a mountain must rise to sufficient elevation and with sufficient abruptness to stand out conspicuously from its surroundings; also that it must have a relatively small summit area, as opposed to a plateau, which has a large summit area. This definition admits of considerable range of interpretation, for the feature which would stand out conspicuously on the plains of North Dakota would remain quite incidental in a hilly land such as New England. Nor is elevation above sea level a safe guide to the definition; for there are many examples of mountainous surfaces at low elevations, and many plains which rise gradually to high elevations. As a matter of fact, any definition must be arbitrary because no sharp distinction exists in nature between high hills and low mountains. There is a complete series of steps from almost featureless plains to plains with many steep slopes but of slight relief, to low hills, to high hills, to low mountains, and finally to the highest mountains. Only in certain places do mountain fronts stand imposingly above extensive plains. For the purposes of classification in this book we have adopted as a working definition of "conspicuous" the concept that the elevation must be sufficient to bring about a vertical differentiation of the vegetation cover. We shall explain this definition and its limitations more fully as we proceed.

The mountain lands differ from the other seven landscape groups in several important ways. In the first place, the chief criterion for the recognition of mountain areas is the surface configuration, whereas the other groups are recognized primarily by the various kinds of vegetation. The characteristic features of mountain landscapes are associated with ruggedness of terrain. According to the definition we

The Mountain Lands 413

have adopted for mountains, vertical differentiation of vegetation types is an essential characteristic. The occupance also is commonly arranged in layers. In other words, the major landscape differences are found in Group VIII by ascending or descending the slopes; not, as in the other groups, by traveling horizontally north, south, east, or west. Another characteristic of mountain geography is the intricacy of the patterns of distribution as compared with the relative simplicity of the patterns developed on more level lands. To follow the winding course of an isotherm, for example, through the valleys and around the ridges of a mountain region requires a much larger-scale map than is necessary in order to observe the same degree of accuracy in plotting the relatively simple course of the isotherm on a level surface. Unlike the monotonously similar landscapes over large areas on the plains, the mountain landscapes are spotty; they are arranged in a mosaic of small units, each contrasted sharply with the surroundings, resembling the patterns on a crazy quilt. Still another characteristic of mountain lands is the difficulty of moving over their rugged surfaces or steep slopes. As a result these regions are isolated and offer places of refuge for the survival of relict flora or fauna or even cultures; they are areas of survival of ancient ideas and modes of life, not areas where new ideas originate. As a further result of the difficulty of movement over them, mountains play the role of barriers to the spread over the earth of plants, animals, and man. Mountains cover 12 per cent of the earth's land area, and of the world's population about 12 per cent occupies the regions of this group.

Distribution of Mountains. Mountains are major lineaments of the face of the earth, and their distribution controls even the shape of the several continents. The essential features of mountain distribution have already been described (map, p. 26). From the central knot in southeastern Asia the world's high mountains extend in three directions: southeastward through the East Indies to New Zealand; northeastward and around the northern and eastern margins of the Pacific Ocean to the southern end of South America; and westward through southern Asia, southern Europe, and northern Africa to the Atlantic. Only a few more or less isolated mountain areas exist which are not attached to this basic system (Plates 9–19). We may now turn to an examination of the characteristics of these regions.

The Land

SURFACE FEATURES

Of fundamental importance in producing the intricacy of the distribution patterns in mountain regions are the surface features. Mountain surfaces are of the greatest variety not only in their topographic details but also in their broader aspects. Nevertheless, in spite of this variety, certain characteristic designs are repeated in almost all the world's high-mountain regions. For example, there is a tendency for the ranges to take on an arcuate, or festoon, arrangement. Commonly, also, the mountain arcs are backed on their concave sides by more or less extensive tectonic basins; and off the middle of the convex sides there are usually rift depressions, in many cases ocean "deeps." [1] With few exceptions, too, the distribution of volcanoes coincides with that of the ranges of high mountains (map, p. 416).[2]

These general patterns, characteristic of all mountain regions, are the result of certain basic similarities of geologic origin. By pressures and strains developed in the earth's crust, the rocks are crushed, folded, wrinkled, broken, and pushed up along certain zones of crustal weakness. These zones of weakness form the three-line figure described above. The various kinds of structures, or tectonic forms, developed in these zones are described briefly in Appendix C, and are made the subject of more intensive study in courses in geology.

As soon as rock structures are lifted above the sea they are exposed to the various processes of destruction or denudation (see Appendix C). Exposure to the weather results in the breaking of the surface of the rock into fragments, so that eventually a mantle of loose rock debris is formed which we have previously described as a regolith and on the

[1] These various tectonic features have their geological explanations. See, for example, W. H. Hobbs, *Earth Evolution and Its Facial Expression* (New York, 1921), pp. 135–158.

[2] Ocean deeps on map (p. 416) based on Sir John Murry (and Dr. Johan Hjort), *The Depths of the Ocean* (London, 1912), map II. Volcanic areas based on Joseph P. Iddings, *The Problem of Volcanism* (New Haven, 1914), map. Earthquake regions based on F. de Montessus de Ballore, *Les Tremblements de terre: géographie séismologique* (Paris, 1906), maps I and II.

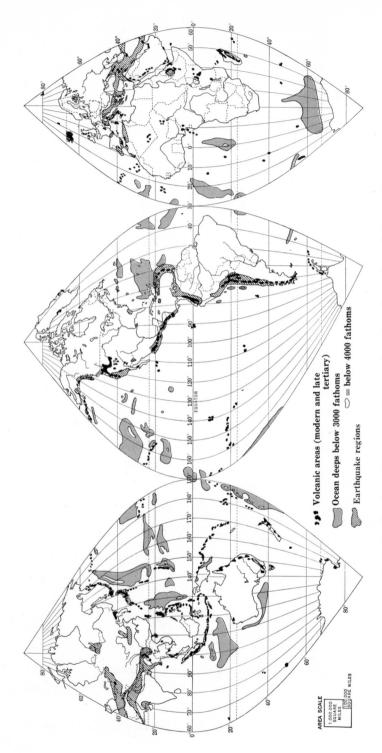

AREA SCALE
1,000,000
SQUARE
MILES
100,000
SQUARE MILES

Volcanic areas (modern and late
tertiary)

Ocean deeps below 3000 fathoms

= below 4000 fathoms

Earthquake regions

Areas of volcanic activity, ocean deeps, and earthquake regions of the world

surface of which soils form. Rain falling on the sloping surfaces of upraised areas runs off over the surface and forms rills, gullies, valleys, and canyons; furthermore, as the rivers continue over long periods of time to carve the upraised surfaces, the valleys pass through a sequence of stages to which William Morris Davis gave the descriptive terms: youthful, mature, and old. The youthful valleys are V-shaped, and the rivers which pass through them are torrential. When the valley bottoms have been cut down almost to the level of the body of water into which the stream flows they cannot be lowered any more, and the stream expends its energy in widening the valleys; the valleys with flat bottoms but steep sides are said to be mature, a stage in which there is the maximum amount of relief. After very long periods of time the intervening heights between the valleys, the interfluves, are also worn down, and the rivers meander freely across wide floodplains; this is the stage of old age (see diagram on page 554 in Appendix C). The most important process of denudation which produces the landforms in upraised portions of the earth is that of running water.

There are many other processes, however, which produce strongly marked surface features in places where they have been in operation. Glaciers form on high mountains wherever the snowfall of winter is so deep that it does not all melt off during the summer. They are therefore most common in climates which have heavy precipitation and cool summers. The climates of higher middle latitudes on the continental west coasts fill this description most fully, and in these regions glacial landforms are most conspicuous; but even on the equator, if one climbs high enough, one finds the mountaintops permanently covered with snow. The various landforms produced in mountain areas as a result of glaciation are shown in a series of block diagrams in Appendix C (p. 566). Since the ice was everywhere more extensive in the Ice Age, these various forms are to be observed where glaciers no longer exist. The places where mountains or mountainous escarpments border the sea, and where the ice-deepened valleys are drowned, are today clearly visible, even on small-scale maps, as fiorded coasts. The map of a part of the coast of South Chile (p. 419) illustrates this feature. Similar coasts are to be observed in British Columbia and South Alaska, in Norway, in Labrador, and in New Zealand. Glacial landforms in the interior are similar to those near the coast except that

Photo by the author

A glacier on Süsten Pass, in the Swiss Alps. In the foreground is a lateral moraine, and in the background a glacial cirque

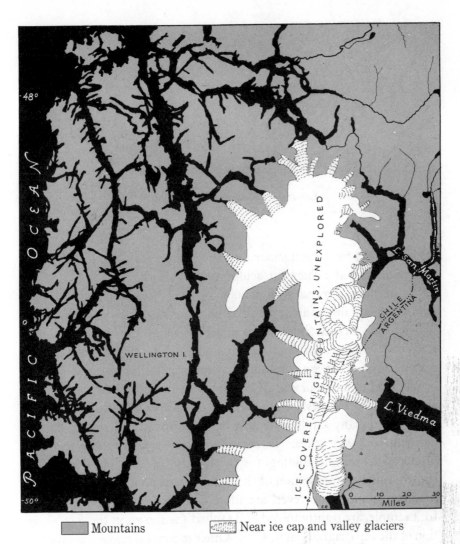

| Mountains | Near ice cap and valley glaciers |

A near icecap in the southern Andes, with detail of the fiorded coast of South Chile. (From the Map of Hispanic America, published by the American Geographical Society of New York)

more of the valley bottoms and sides are visible. Long, narrow marginal lakes, however, are commonly found along the edges of glaciated mountains, such as those of the Italian piedmont, or the eastern front of the Rocky Mountains in Montana (Glacier National Park). Some

Landforms produced by landslides [1]

of the world's most spectacular mountain scenery is to be found where glaciers have had a chance to sculpture the surface.

Of the other processes of denudation which work on the sloping land of mountainous areas we need only mention the work of gravity which produces rock slides and avalanches. In mountain regions where steep valley slopes are subjected to soaking and drying with the passing seasons, avalanches are common, and the scars of ancient slides are to be observed in many places. The characteristic landforms produced by recent and older slides are suggested in the drawing above.

All these many kinds of landforms are infinitely varied by the underlying rock structures. In some mountain areas the structures are produced by simple folding (as in the case of the Jura Mountains, shown in the *a* cross section of the top diagram on p. 421). Most high mountain regions, however, are more complex than this. The Alps, for example, are tightly folded and faulted (as shown in the *b* cross section of the top diagram on p. 421). Other mountain regions are formed by block faulting, in which large masses or blocks of the earth's crust are broken and lifted or dropped in relation to bordering blocks. Rocks, therefore, are broken and contorted into very complex structures, and in many places these structures are masked by a covering of volcanic material—old lava flows or deep accumulations of ash. Each kind of rock formation differs in its resistance to the forces of denudation.

[1] Reproduced from a drawing in W. M. Davis, "The Lakes of California," *California Journal of Mines and Geology*, Vol. 29 (1933), pp. 175–236.

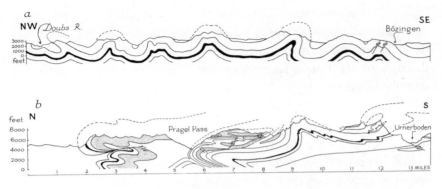

a NW Doubs R.   SE
                                                              Bözingen

3000
2000
1000
0
feet

b   S
feet N
8000   Pragel Pass   Urnerboden
6000
4000
2000
0   1   2   3   4   5   6   7   8   9   10   11   12   13 MILES

(*a*) *Cross section of the Jura Mountains;* (*b*) *cross section of the Alps* [1]

Some rocks are weak and easily eroded; others are resistant. As the processes of denudation work on the underlying structures the work goes forward rapidly on weak rocks, whereas resistant rocks stand out boldly as cliffs or still uneroded heights. The result is the extraordinary complexity of mountain terrain.

In many of the mountain regions of the world, areas which are nearly flat or gently sloping occur in the midst of steeper and higher surfaces. These are intermont basins, which are distinguished on the plates (Plates 9–19) by solid black. The block diagram which is shown below suggests two ways in which intermont basins can form: on the left where a downfold of the rock structures forms a basin; on the

[1] Generalized from A. Heim, *Geologie der Schweiz*, Leipzig, 1919–1921, Vol. I, Table 23; Vol. II, Table 18.

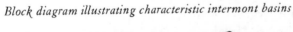

Block diagram illustrating characteristic intermont basins

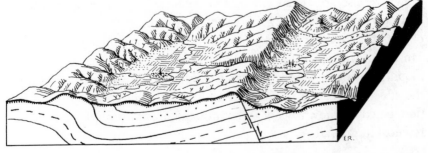

Surface Features   421

right where a depression between two mountain blocks is partly filled with alluvial material washed down from the higher slopes. Intermont basins are formed upstream from places where the rivers pass through resistant rock formations and where, as a consequence, the downward cutting of the valley is retarded. They are formed where volcanoes block earlier river-cut valleys with flows of lava or falls of ash. In these and many other ways intermont basins are formed, some of large extent, others too small to show on the maps.

It is important to notice that the major ranges of mountains in the world in most places do not form the divides between river basins. A close examination of the maps will reveal example after example of rivers which rise outside of mountain areas and pass through the mountains in gorges. An outstanding example is the Danube, where it passes through the Iron Gate on the border of Romania and Yugoslavia. The Yangtze and the Columbia are two other examples among many. Such rivers are said to be *antecedent* because they were established in their courses before the mountains rose across them, and as the mountains were slowly lifted up they were able to continue their downward cutting. The Amazon is an example of a river which was unable to maintain its course because the Andes rose so fast; as a result it turned and found a way out to the Atlantic, but its valley is still widest along the eastern front of the Andes and gets narrower downstream.

CLIMATE AND VEGETATION

Climatic distribution in mountain areas is also extremely complicated. Although most of the major types of climate found in other parts of the world occur in mountain regions, the significance of these types in Group VIII is largely obscured by the many important local variations. Nowhere else are "local climates" developed in such large numbers, and nowhere else do they exert such a critical effect on the character of the landscape. Yet this seeming confusion of climatic distribution can be understood through the interplay of two of the principles of mountain geography: the principle of vertical differentiation, based on the effects of change in altitude; and the principle of spotty distribution, based on the effects of different exposures to sunlight and of differences in rainfall.

Vertical Differentiation. The most important climatic element leading to the vertical differentiation of landscapes in mountain areas is temperature. Generally speaking, lower temperatures may be found either by traveling along the surface of the earth toward the poles or by ascending vertically above the earth. However, one would have to travel many miles along the surface to find as great a contrast of temperature as is concentrated in only a few miles of vertical distance (diagram below). The isotherms which reach sea level in high or middle latitudes rise steeply toward the margins of the low latitudes, gaining their greatest altitude between 20° and 30°, especially over the hot deserts. Although sagging somewhat over the equator, they remain high between the tropics. So it is that mountains on the equator rising to fifteen thousand feet can reach all the average temperatures which are spread over the thousands of miles of horizontal distance between the equatorial and polar regions.

We must not suppose, however, that because a place at a considerable elevation in the low latitudes has the same average temperature as a place at sea level in middle or high latitudes, it also has the same climate. At high altitudes on tropical mountains none of the climates of middle and high latitudes are found. There are none of the cyclonic storms or associated weather changes which are essential characteristics of the middle latitudes. Furthermore, with increase of altitude, there is a decrease of the range of temperature between summer and winter. This effect is most noticeable in the low latitudes, where temperature ranges are small even at sea level. The average monthly temperatures

Vertical arrangement of the average annual isotherms. (After Clayton and Ramanathan)

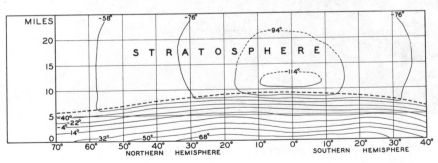

The Uspallata Pass between Chile and Argentina

at Quito illustrate this condition (Appendix E). Quito is located nearly on the equator in the Andes of Ecuador at an elevation of 9350 feet. Its average annual temperature is 54.6°, but its range between the average of the coldest and warmest months is no more than 0.3°. In middle-latitude and high-latitude mountains, on the other hand, the ranges of temperature are not so low as in the tropics, and seasonal change is an important feature.

Snow Lines and Tree Lines. As a result of these vertical distributions of temperature, almost all the landscape features which are affected by temperature not only have horizontal limits bounding their areas of distribution but also vertical limits. One very important altitude limit is the snow line, the boundary of the area covered by permanent snow or ice. Horizontally, the areas of permanent snow and ice are restricted to the polar regions; but the vertical limits are reached by the higher mountain summits even on the equator. As in the case of all altitude limits which are governed in whole or in part by temperature, the snow line corresponds in pattern to the vertical arrangement of the isotherms (diagram, p. 423). It rises to its greatest elevation near

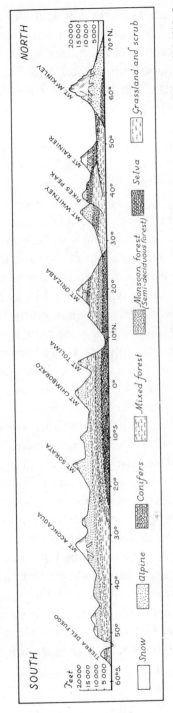

Diagrammatic cross section through the mountains of North and South America, showing vertical zones of vegetation. (Modified from J. Paul Goode)

the margins of the low latitudes and declines to its lowest elevation in the high latitudes. Near the equator it is necessary to climb about 15,000 feet to reach the snow line—a little higher than this on Mount Chimborazo near Quito, and a little lower on Mount Ruwenzori in Uganda. Southward along the Andes the snow line rises to about 16,000 feet near Lima and to more than 20,000 feet at the Tropic of Capricorn in Northern Chile. South of this, however, it drops rapidly. In Middle Chile it is between 11,000 and 14,000 feet. In Tierra del Fuego it lies a little below 2500 feet. The snow line, however, is obedient not only to temperature but also to snowfall and other things. At any given latitude it lies somewhat lower on the wetter sides of the mountains and somewhat higher on the drier sides, and it descends farther on shady slopes and remains higher up on sunny slopes.[1]

The altitude limits of the various types of vegetation also correspond to the pattern of vertical temperature distribution. Roughly, the same succession of types is found in ascending mountains near the equator as is found on proceeding poleward along the continental east coasts. The tropical forests occupy the lower slopes; higher up are the mixed forests of broadleaf types; and beyond the upper limit of trees but below the snow line is a zone of alpine meadows not unlike the tundra of the polar margins. Conifers do not appear at higher altitudes south of Nicaragua. Since tree lines are generally higher in rainy mountains and lower in dry mountains, whereas snow lines vary in just the opposite way, it follows that the zone of alpine meadows is widest in dry regions and narrowest where the rainfall is heavy (map, p. 427).

As far as vegetation and other forms of life are concerned, the vertical differentiation reaches a maximum in the low latitudes. Here we find the greatest variety of zones. Vertical differentiation remains a conspicuous feature of mountains in the middle latitudes, but it disappears altogether in the high latitudes. The criteria suggested in the introduction to this chapter for the recognition of "conspicuousness" in mountains can be used, therefore, only in the middle and low latitudes, not in the polar zones (diagram, p. 425).

Other Climatic Elements. Certain of the other elements of climate act to reinforce the effects of temperature in producing a vertical dif-

[1] See W. Heybrock, "The Interval between Tree and Pasture Lines and the Position of Their Extremes," *Geographical Review,* Vol. 24 (1934), pp. 444–452.

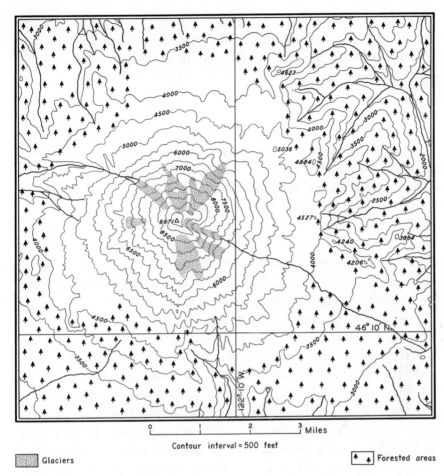

0   1   2   3   Miles

Contour interval = 500 feet

Glaciers   Forested areas

Topographic detail on Mt. St. Helens, Washington. (From Mt. St. Helens Quadrangle, Washington, United States Geological Survey)

ferentiation. Rainfall, for instance, develops something of a vertical zoning. Up to six thousand or seven thousand feet in the middle latitudes, and somewhat higher in the low latitudes, the rainfall on mountain slopes increases; but above this zone of maximum fall the amounts diminish. At higher altitudes the specific humidity of the air becomes very low. Unbroken ranges of high mountains are very effective barriers to the passage of moisture.

Pressure is another climatic element which decreases with increasing altitude. Its results, however, are of less significance than those of

Climate and Vegetation 427

temperature and rainfall. At elevations above twelve thousand or fifteen thousand feet many human beings are affected by altitude sickness, and at very high altitudes the difficulty of breathing forms a distinct limit to occupance. Decreased pressure also lowers the boiling point of water so that the cooking of foods by boiling takes much longer, or may become altogether impossible without pressure cookers. When Marco Polo observed this phenomenon in his journey across high Tibet, he explained it as the result of the low temperatures. "Even the fire," he wrote, "is not hot enough to cook foods."

Spotty Distribution Patterns. The vertical differentiation of mountain landscapes, resulting from the variation of these several factors with altitude, is greatly modified by the irregularity of the terrain. Steep slopes oriented at various angles to the sun's rays; narrow valleys with winding courses; mountain-rimmed bits of flattish valley floor or delta plain: all these features combine to add complexity to the otherwise simple arrangement of things in vertical zones.

Local contrast in exposure to sunlight is one of the important causes of spotty landscape patterns. Slopes which face toward the sun not only absorb much more heat than those which receive the sun's rays more obliquely, but they also enjoy many more hours of sunshine. In the Northern Hemisphere the north sides of east and west valleys, such as the upper Rhône Valley in Switzerland, are much warmer than the south sides at the same altitude, and these temperature differences are reflected in striking landscape contrasts—contrasts in natural vegetation, in occupance, and even in landforms (picture, p. 429). So great are these differences that the two sides have been distinguished by the names *adret,* meaning "sunny side," and *ubac,* meaning "shady side." [1]

The adret and the ubac are generally not arranged symmetrically on the two sides of the valley, however; for where towering peaks cast shadows over the neighboring terrain the patterns of light and shade are amazingly intricate. A map of the average daily hours of sunlight

[1] "The matter of sunlight is so dominant that each dialect of European mountain peoples has a set of terms for sunny side and shady side. Thus the German, *Sonnenseite, Schattenseite; Sonnenberg, Schattenberg;* French, *adret* (Latin, *ad directum*), *ubac* (Latin, *ad opacum*); *endroit, envers;* Italian, *indritto, inverso; adritto, opaco;* Catalan, *sola, baga; solana, ubach; soula, umbaga.* One may so name a village or a shady portion of a village, as Envers de Fontenille or Inverso Pinusca." From R. Peattie, "Height Limits of Mountain Economies," *Geographical Review,* Vol. 21 (1931), pp. 415–428.

Looking up the Vorder-Rhine Valley in Switzerland. Note the contrast between the ubac and the adret

in the valley of Barcelonnette, in the French Alps, suggests at least one reason for the characteristic spottiness of mountain landscapes (map, p. 430). The resulting temperature contrasts from place to place may be sufficient in any locality to wipe out quite completely the general decrease of temperature with increase of altitude, and so to obscure the vertical zoning.

Another climatic element which contributes to the intricacy of mountain patterns is rainfall. While it is true that rainfall exhibits a certain vertical arrangement,—increasing, as we have pointed out, up to a zone of maximum, and decreasing beyond that,—still in most mountain areas this feature is only vaguely developed. Vertical zoning of rainfall is most apparent on mountain sides which present a relatively unbroken

Climate and Vegetation 429

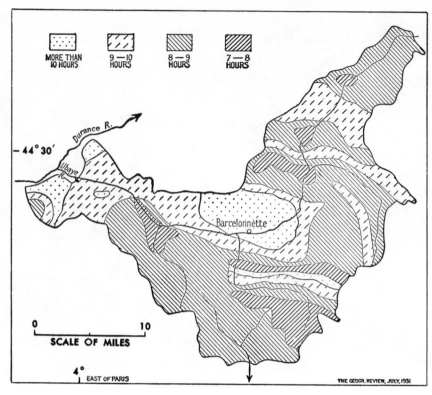

Hours of sunlight in the valley of Barcelonnette. (*By A. Levainville; courtesy of the* Geographical Review, *published by the American Geographical Society of New York*)

wall to the air currents, as the eastern slopes of the Andes, the southern slopes of the Himalayas, and the western slopes of the Sierra Nevada of California. In most mountain areas the great contrasts in the amount of rain received, even on neighboring slopes which are oriented some-what differently to the rain-bearing winds, make it difficult or impossible to observe any general increase or decrease with altitude (map, p. 431). As we have seen, the world's heaviest rainfalls occur on the windward slopes of mountains up which warm, moist air is rising buoyantly (Kauai and Cherrapunji). Where the mountains are high, the windward slopes are generally much wetter than the lee slopes, which lie in a *rain shadow;* but where the mountains are lower, the clouds which form over them may drift to leeward and bring more rain to that side. Basins and deep valleys into which the wind must

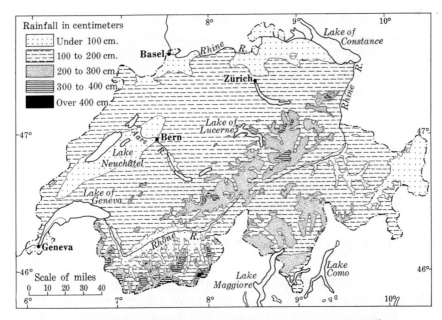

Rainfall of Switzerland. (*After J. Maurer and J. Lugeon, 1928*)

descend are usually dry; but, on the other hand, where the wind blows up through a valley, it may bring copious rainfall. The actual rainfall distribution in a rugged mountain region composed of slopes standing at various angles to the winds forms a pattern which is even more intricate than that of the hours of sunlight. Furthermore, these two patterns in no way correspond; so that the landscape features, which are in part conditioned by sunlight and in part by rainfall, find in mountain regions the most extraordinary number and diversity of combinations of these elements. If to these things is added the variety of edaphic conditions, we can appreciate the basic reasons for the spottiness of mountain landscapes.

The Occupance

Mountains resemble the deserts in the persistent effect they exert on the distribution of the human occupance. In most parts of the world the character of the occupance patterns is largely determined by the culture which produces them, and a succession of cultures in any one area may result in a series of occupance patterns which are radically different one from another. In the mountain lands, on the contrary, the location of settlements and the routes of travel established by different cultures are as closely fixed by the rugged terrain as they are in the dry lands by water. Only in topographic detail can they vary. The general characteristics of mountain distribution patterns may be illustrated not only from the physical elements but also from elements of the occupance. Vertical differentiation appears in many forms; spotty arrangement reflects the diversity of habitat background; and the barrier nature of mountains leads to the convergence of routes on the passes and to the historical persistence of these routes.

VERTICAL DIFFERENTIATION

The vertical differentiation of occupance is developed in almost all the mountain regions which have gone beyond the pioneer stage. Even early in the progress of settlement, when the main routes of travel are of chief importance in guiding the arrangement of population, a vague altitude zoning is usually apparent; but as settlement is elaborated, vertical zones, differing from one another in the modes and forms of occupance, become more and more sharply differentiated. While this stratification is an almost universal feature of mountain regions, the actual modes of occupance at the various levels differ from place to place. In the low latitudes, for instance, the occupance has a tendency to become static, with little movement from one altitude to another; but in the middle latitudes in most mountain regions a regular seasonal migration up and down the slopes is developed. Throughout the world the differing cultures of the mountain dwellers find expression in the many and various methods in which the resources of the several altitude zones are utilized. In other words, while some form of vertical arrangement appears in the occupance of almost every mountain region, the ways in which this arrangement is worked out are in large measure unique for each group of people.

Altitude Limits. The altitude limits of the various forms of human settlement are in many respects similar to the horizontal limits of these same forms in the other landscape groups. In most cases such limits are a reflection more of the culture of the people than of rigidly im-

Sheep in the Peruvian Andes

posed natural barriers. However, in general, the same crops reach the upper limits of agriculture as reach its poleward limits, and there is a similar sequence of crops down the slopes or equatorward.

The extreme upper limits of settlement differ in the various mountain regions not only with such natural features as the snow line and tree line but also with the historical and cultural background of the inhabitants. The highest human habitation is reported by Bowman in the Andes of southern Peru, at an elevation of 17,100 feet,[1] only a little below the snow line. Settlement at this great elevation, however, is the

[1] See the chapter on the Andes by I. Bowman, in J. Brunhes, *Human Geography,* Chicago, 1920, pp. 453–498; reference on page 468.

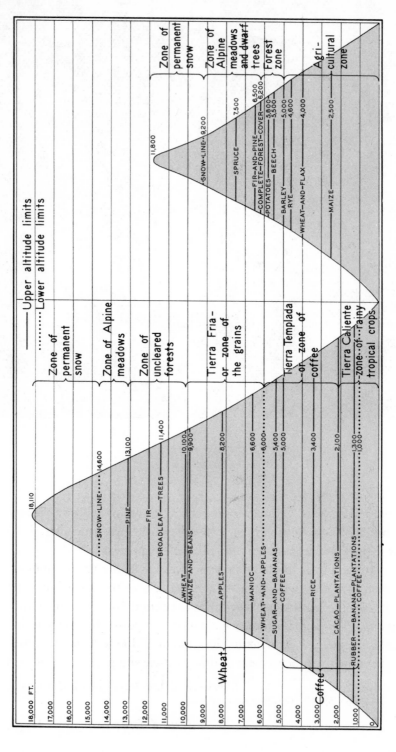

Altitude limits and vertical zones on Mount Orizaba, Mexico (19° N.). (After Sapper)

Altitude limits in the Ötztaler Alps, Austria (47° N.). (After Sapper)

result of certain peculiarities of the occupance in this region. Neither of the major culture groups in the Peruvian Andes, namely, the Indians and the Europeans, would, if left to itself, have established a permanent settlement at such an altitude. But the European has appropriated the better lands at altitudes suitable for his commercial crops, and the poor Indian has been forced to seek refuge at still higher altitudes where a scanty pasturage for his sheep and llamas may be had. In each mountain region the upper limits of settlement represent a compromise between the traditional mode of occupance, the historical background of the people, and the peculiarities of the local terrain. We may say in general, however, that the highest settlements are usually associated with mining; in fact, some mining communities have been established above the snow line. The next highest settlements are commonly supported by the pasturage of domestic animals. Lower down, the various types of agricultural settlement appear.

Both the animals and the crops which support these settlements show fairly distinct upper limits in any one region. Because sheep can exist on much scantier pasturage than cattle, they are the domestic animals which are driven highest in the mountains. Cattle and horses usually occupy the richer pastures lower down. Of the crops, the potato reaches the highest altitudes, just as it reaches the highest latitudes. Lower down, the various grains arrange themselves in the expectable sequence: barley, rye, wheat, maize, and rice in descending order. The tropical crops occupy the lower slopes of low-latitude mountains.

Vertical Zones. Most mountain people recognize in the region they inhabit fairly definite zones of altitude, to which they give distinguishing names. For the reasons previously suggested, the number of these zones is greatest in the low latitudes. In any region, however, these popularly recognized zones, when analyzed, prove to represent a generalization of a considerable number of altitude limits: crop limits, limits of various types of settlement, even limits of racial groups. A few specific examples will illustrate this more clearly.

On the slopes of Mount Orizaba in Mexico, at about latitude 19° N., six vertical zones are given popular recognition (diagram, p. 434).[1]

[1] Karl Sapper, *Allgemeine Wirtschafts- und Verkehrsgeographie,* Berlin, 1930, pp. 66–67. The altitudes on the diagram on p. 434 and in the corresponding parts of the text are translated from the metric system to the nearest round numbers of feet.

The two upper zones are simple concepts, each based on one dominant feature. At the top is the zone of permanent snow, lying above 14,600 feet (to the peak at 18,110). The zone of alpine meadow lies between 13,100 feet and the snow line. The forest zone is not so simple as the upper two, for it is differentiated by the altitude limits of the various trees into three parts: a lower part of mixed broadleaf trees and conifers, a middle part of pine and fir, and an upper part where pine alone can exist. The upper limit of agriculture as practiced on Orizaba lies about 10,100 feet above sea level. This corresponds to the upper limit of wheat. At various altitudes below 10,100 feet are found in succession the upper limits (in some cases the lower limits) of the various crops. As a result of certain typical combinations of crops, however, the agricultural occupance is divided into three zones. The *tierra fria* (roughly from 6000 to 10,100 feet) is essentially the zone of wheat cultivation. Manioc, apples, maize, and beans are associated with wheat at the bottom of this zone, but all these other crops disappear, one after another, as one ascends. Below the *tierra fria* is the *tierra templada* (from 2100 to 6000 feet). This is primarily the zone of coffee culture, although coffee does not quite reach the top, nor does its cultivation stop at the bottom. Associated with coffee up to their respective altitude limits are sugar, bananas, and rice, as well as maize, manioc, and beans. The lowest zone is the *tierra caliente*. This is the zone of rainy tropical crops: cacao, bananas, rubber, sugar, rice, maize, manioc, and beans.

The vertical zones recognized in the Ötztaler Alps in Austria, at the head of the Adige Valley, are similarly composed of various individual limits (diagram, p. 434). The zone of permanent snow is above 9200. Below this lies the zone of alpine meadow and dwarf trees, within which, however, pine, fir, and spruce have their successive upper limits. The zone of continuous forest cover begins about 6200, while the upper limit of the agricultural zone is about 5000 feet. Within the forest zone are found the upper limit of broadleaf trees (beech) and the upper limit of crops (potatoes). Only one agricultural zone is recognized, although it is diversified by the limits of barley, rye, flax, wheat, and maize. There is no *tierra templada* or *tierra caliente*.

In many of these mountain regions there is a stratification of people as well as of crops. We have already pointed out that in the Peruvian

A basin on the high altiplano of Bolivia, near La Paz—elevation over 12,000 feet

Andes the Indians, with their domestic animals and their subsistence crops of potatoes, barley, wheat, and maize, are now concentrated at the higher altitudes, while the Europeans, with their commercial crops of cotton and sugar, occupy the lower slopes and the coastal desert. Similarly, in Colombia the Indians are most numerous at the higher altitudes, where they have been forced by the white man's appropriation of the better lands lower down. The Spanish Americans for various reasons avoided the hot, humid, unhealthful lowlands in South America and Middle America, concentrating their settlements in the zones of grain cultivation and of coffee cultivation. Meanwhile the *tierra caliente* has been occupied chiefly by Negroes, the descendants of former slaves who, upon being freed, sought what was to them a more congenial climate at the lower altitudes. As in the case of the low-latitude

Vertical Differentiation 437

A branch of the Sogne Fiord, Norway, latitude 61° N., in summer

plateaus, discussed in Group II, the occupance of the mountain basins above 2000 or 3000 feet provides freedom from the ravages of malaria and yellow fever, but at the same time it raises seriously the problem of mountain transportation. Most of these settlements suffer from difficult accessibility to markets—an item of the greatest importance to Occidental peoples, for whom a commercial connection with the economic world is one of the necessities of successful colonization.

Contrasts between the Low and Middle Latitudes. In the low-latitude regions regular seasonal movements up and down the mountain slopes are of relatively minor significance. Not that such movements never occur. There are places where people move uphill to escape summer heat (Rio de Janeiro to Petropolis, Manila to Baguio), or downhill to get warm (Mexico City to Cuernavaca); but one may suspect that the social life is as much a factor as temperature. In other places there is a shift of the agricultural occupance up and down the slopes in

The same scene as on page 438 in winter. The fiord is not frozen over

harmony with the rains (as on the eastern slopes of the Andes).[1] Such movements, however, are of small importance. On the whole, the stratification of people and crops in the low-latitude mountains is static. In fact, the vertical contrasts in occupance become well enough established so that locally important currents of trade are developed between the lowland dwellers and the highland dwellers, based on the vertical differentiation of products.

There are two reasons why the occupance in most middle-latitude mountains does not achieve this permanence of stratification. In the first place, there are fewer vertical zones and so less opportunity for the development of different layers of contrasted types of occupance. There are no zones of tropical products or of coffee below the zone of grain-farming; and as one proceeds poleward, even the zone of grain-farming is forced to lower and lower altitudes until it disappears altogether,

[1] I. Bowman, *The Andes of Southern Peru*, New York, 1916.

and the forest zone descends to sea level. In the second place, the marked seasonal change, which is lacking in the low latitudes, renders the higher mountain slopes productive only at certain seasons. There is a tendency, therefore, for the mountain peoples to establish their homes at the lower altitudes and to ascend each summer with their domestic animals to take advantage of the excellent pasture lands of the alpine meadows.

Transhumance and Seasonal Seminomadism. The movements up and down the slopes of middle-latitude mountain ranges in response to the rhythm of the seasons are of two chief kinds. There are movements involving only the herds or flocks of domestic animals accompanied by a small number of attendants, and there are movements involving not only the animals but also the whole human group. These kinds of movement are called, respectively, *transhumance* [1] and *seasonal seminomadism.* Transhumance is a widespread phenomenon. It is reported from nearly all the lower middle-latitude mountain regions of the world, with one striking exception to be described later. The flocks of sheep of the pastoral nomads of inner Asia are driven into the mountains during the summer, and a similar combination of transhumance and nomadism is practiced in the southern Andes of Argentina and Chile. In the North American mountains transhumance without any form of nomadism is the rule; sheep are driven to the higher pastures above the timber line, and cattle and horses to the pastures at lower elevations, many of them in the open forests of these regions. Similar movements of animals are reported from Australia and New Zealand.

Transhumance combined with seasonal seminomadism was formerly an outstanding feature of mountain occupance in Europe, especially

---

[1] "Transhumance" is a word borrowed from the French. It is derived from a combination of *trans,* meaning "across" or "over," and *humus,* meaning "the ground." As a term, "transhumance" denotes the periodic, or seasonal, movement of flocks or herds of domestic animals between two areas of different climatic conditions. Such climatic differences within relatively short distances are found in mountains, and the term "transhumance" is therefore associated with the seasonal movements of domestic animals in mountain areas. A distinction is made between the Greater Transhumance, involving movements between a mountain region and its surrounding lowlands or plateaus, and the Lesser Transhumance, which includes movements within the mountain region from lower to higher slopes. E. H. Carrier, *Water and Grass, a Study in the Pastoral Economy of Southern Europe,* London, 1932.

southern Europe, where the nomadic tradition was a culture trait of the mountain peoples. These movements of the people as well as of the animals continue even today, but in a form much modified by modern transportation. In some of the mountain valleys of the Alps an exceedingly complex series of migrations up and down the slopes takes place. After passing the winter in stables in the valleys, the animals are started up the mountains early in the spring. They are driven first to the lower pastures (known as the *voralps*), and then, as the snow melts, they proceed by stages to the pastures above the tree line (known as the *alps*). Meanwhile the human group carries on various activities at different levels—now climbing to harvest a crop of hay from the alpine meadows, now descending to care for grains or vegetables planted in the valleys, now ascending again to make cheese at the settlements on the alps.

The most complex of such movements was described by Brunhes in the Val d'Anniviers, a tributary of the Rhône in Switzerland.[1] In this valley the inhabitants have several permanent villages at different altitudes, and some of the people can be found at almost all times of the year ascending or descending the mountain roads between their different habitations. Their activities extend from vineyard cultivation in the Rhône Valley to cheese-making in the alpine meadows near the snow line. This very active and self-sufficient community, however, is now being changed considerably by the establishment of tourist hotels in the upper part of its valley. The economic life will suffer a profound modification as a result of this closer contact with the outside world.

The Lack of Transhumance in Japan. Japan is a notable exception to this general rule of mid-latitude mountain occupance. Until recently there was little or no pastoral utilization of the mountain slopes to supplement the intensive agricultural use of the valleys and coastal lowlands. The Japanese culture contains no traditional familiarity with domestic animals, for other than draft purposes, to suggest the use of the mountain pastures; nor are the pastures of much value in the high mountain area of Japan, owing to the growth of nonedible bamboo grass and sedge. A distinct vertical zoning is developed which remains

[1] See Chapter VIII in J. Brunhes, *La Géographie humaine,* Paris, 1925; and also P. Arbos, "The Geography of Pastoral Life," *Geographical Review,* Vol. 13 (1923), pp. 559–575.

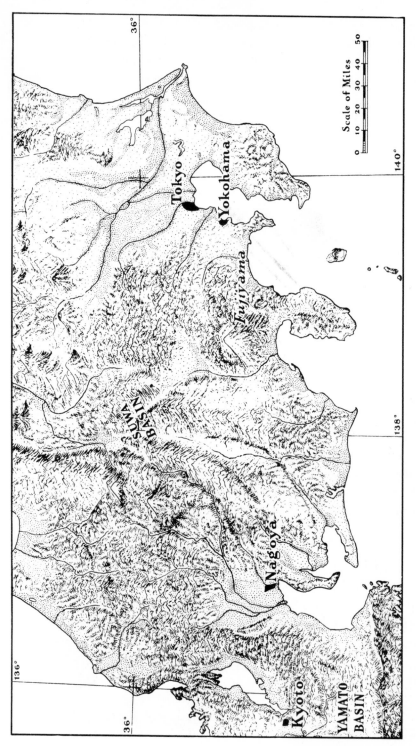

Surface features of central Honshu, Japan. (Map by Guy-Harold Smith from Notes on a Physiographic Diagram of Japan, by Glenn T. Trewartha. Courtesy of the Geographical Review, published by the American Geographical Society of New York)

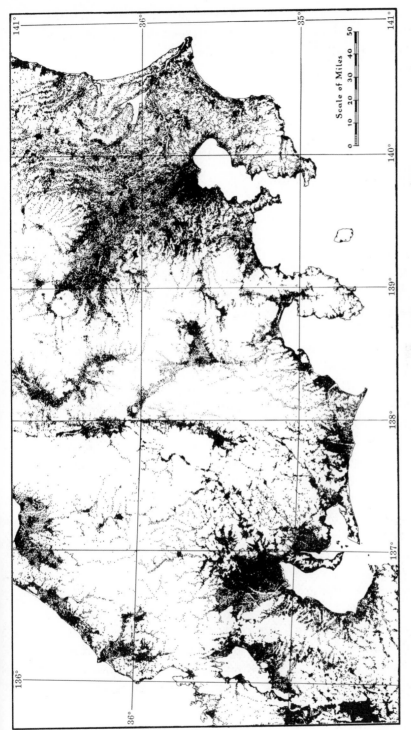

Population of central Honshu, Japan. Each dot represents two hundred people. (From map by K. Tanaka and K. Yamamoto, based on 1925 data)

undisturbed by important vertical movements, in spite of the rhythm of the seasons. Agriculture, based primarily on rice, is concentrated in the valleys, the intermont basins, and the coastal lowlands (maps, pp. 442 and 443). Certain dry-land crops, such as tea or mulberry, are planted on the lower slopes. Above this zone of cultivation the Japanese mountains are forest-clad, and into this zone come a few charcoal-makers during the summer months. Still higher are the unoccupied alpine meadows, just below the snow line.

SPOTTY DISTRIBUTION

The mountain lands resemble the dry lands in the prevailing scantiness of population. Yet, as in the dry lands, there are in these regions numerous small areas of very dense population,—some of the densest in the world. The concentration of the occupance in the valleys, basins, delta plains, or other bits of flattish land at appropriate altitudes is an outstanding feature. The resulting patterns of occupance are no less spotty than the background of the physical setting. The areas of concentrated settlement are of various sizes and shapes, but each community is more or less isolated from other communities by uninhabited slopes over which communication is very difficult.

Relation of Settlements to Landforms. Among the mid-latitude mountain regions there are many illustrations of the concentration of people and their settlements in the small areas of favorable land. The densely populated lowlands, with their big cities, form a striking contrast to the scantily populated highlands in such small countries as Switzerland and Austria. The canton of Zürich in Switzerland, a lowland canton, has more than seven hundred people per square mile, whereas the canton of Valais, in the highlands, has only about sixty per square mile, and these are mostly in the valley of the upper Rhône (map, p. 455).

A map of the land utilization in Andorra brings out these relationships quite clearly (map, p. 445). Agriculture in this mountain state in the Pyrenees is limited to a few cultivated crops and to hay cut from untilled meadows. The agricultural lands follow the valley of the Río Balira and its tributaries. The sequence of widened intermont basin and narrow, steep-walled gorge, which is characteristic of mountain

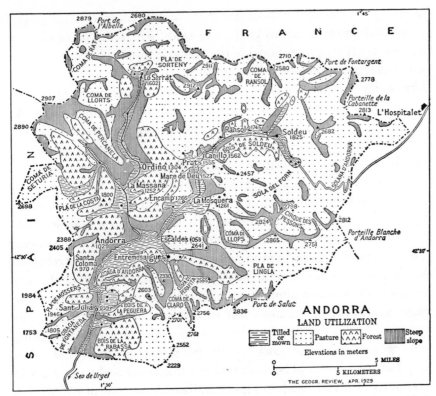

Land and settlement in Andorra. (By R. Peattie; courtesy of the Geographical
Review, *published by the American Geographical Society of New York*)

streams descending over rocks of varying degrees of resistance, is revealed in the pattern of the agricultural land. The concentration of the
small villages in these basins can be seen, and also the location of the
chief town, Andorra, in the midst of the largest basin. Only a small
proportion of this little country is devoted to agriculture; much more
of the area is alpine pasture with a few patches of forest. But the various parts of the territory are divided into small units by slopes too steep
for any kind of use,—slopes which follow either the sides of the main
valleys or the mountain crests.

The relation of population distribution to areas of relatively level land
is also illustrated by two maps of the central mountainous part of the
Japanese island of Honshu (pp. 442 and 443). The number of people

Spotty Distribution 445

in any given territory is in rather strict proportion to the size of the plains and basins, much as in the dry lands, where the population of an oasis is strictly proportional to the available supply of water. Tokyo and Yokohama occupy the Kwanto Plain, the largest in Japan. Other large cities, such as Nagoya and Osaka, occupy other plains of considerable extent. Many small villages and towns are strung along the coast on the smaller delta plains and coastal terraces, while back in the mountains each intermont basin and narrow valley bottom stands out clearly on the population map. Yet the greater part of the territory is only scantily inhabited, so rugged are the slopes.

Although this tendency to concentrate on the lowlands is repeated by various cultures in the mountain lands, there are a few regions where the lowlands have been avoided in favor of the higher intermont basins. This is notably the case in most parts of Spanish America. So common is the concentration of settlement in the highlands, leaving the low coastal regions almost uninhabited, that many writers have insisted that this was a result of the avoidance of the hot lowland climates. The historical fact is that the Spaniards came to the New World seeking gold or other sources of quick wealth, and also large numbers of sedentary Indians who could be converted to Christianity and set to work in the mines or fields. Such groups of Indians at the time of the Spanish conquest were to be found in the intermont basins of Mexico, Guatemala, Colombia, Ecuador, Peru, and Bolivia. To these places the Spaniards directed the main streams of settlement. But where the largest number of Indians were found in the lowlands, the Spanish settlements were also established in the lowlands, as in the Dominican Republic and in Nicaragua. The Mexicans in the high Basin of Mexico found the continuously cold climate so tiresome that they established a resort city, Cuernavaca, in the *tierra templada* close by. In other words, the kinds of places sought for the establishment of settlements in mountain regions depends on the cultural traditions of the people; but in any case, the chief areas of concentrated settlement are to be found on the relatively gentle slopes (picture, p. 447). Settlements on very steep slopes are usually associated with mining, or are found to be places of refuge, such as Machu Picchu in Peru.

Relation of the Settlements to Local Climates. Few generalizations can be made concerning the relation of settlements to the various local

The Cochabamba Basin, Bolivia, is about 15 miles long by six wide, at an elevation of about 8500 feet. It is occupied by more than 300 people per square mile

climates of these mountain lands. In dry mountains, for instance, the rainy places are preferred; but in rainy mountains the inhabitants commonly seek the sunny, dry, lee sides, as in the Hawaiian Islands. In the mid-latitude regions the sunny slopes are usually so much more desirable than the shady slopes that a definite separation of the wealthier people from the poorer people takes place, the former occupying the adret, the latter the ubac. In the low latitudes, on the other hand, the shady side is chosen first, and the poorer settlements occupy the sunny slopes. The greatest variety of local adjustments is possible. Thus there may arise not only a vertical stratification of people, as in the Andes, but also a complex rearrangement within the same vertical zone to conform to the different details of slope and local climate.

MOUNTAINS AS BARRIERS

Because of the steep slopes, the narrow valleys, and the rigorous climates of high altitudes, especially in the middle latitudes, mountains have played the role of barriers to the movement of people on the earth. The mountains tend to isolate and separate the communities within the mountain regions, and also the peoples on either side.

The Isolation of Mountain Communities. The isolation of mountain communities is difficult to overcome. Steep slopes require the construction of zigzag trails which cling precariously to the ledges of the valley side. Avalanches, especially on the rain-soaked valley sides of tropical mountains, frequently obliterate parts of the trails and render communication uncertain. If the trails reach considerable altitude, the obstacles of snow, high winds, and low temperatures are added to the difficulties of rugged surface. Yet, in spite of these difficulties, it is quite commonly easier to gain access to an intermont basin by climbing over its mountain rim than by attempting to follow the narrow, steep-walled gorges along the river. It is in such places that anthropologists look for survivals of older races and cultures, which, without the protection afforded by the isolation, would have been submerged.

The resources of mountain lands, moreover, are in many regions insufficient to pay the huge cost of railroad and highway construction. Those mountain basins which happen to lie close to a pass route may find the problem solved with relative ease, but the more remote Occidental communities must pay their own way if they are to be connected with the urban centers. Probably the chief support for railroad development away from the pass routes has come from mining and lumbering. Industrial development—especially of such industries as the manufacture of paper or matches, which can make use of both timber supplies and water power—has resulted in railroad construction. More recently tourist establishments have supported the building of railroads and highways.

Pass Routes. Mountain ranges, also, play the role of barriers between the territories on either side. In this capacity mountains have shaped the course of history at many critical times. The importance of the Alps and Carpathians in shielding the growing cultures of the Mediter-

448 The Mountain Lands

ranean lands, or of the Himalayas in shielding India, can scarcely be overemphasized, although both these barriers were crossed at one time or another by conquering peoples. Because mountains are barriers the interests of the inhabitants of a wide extent of territory are focused on the pass routes. These become nodal points of great strategic importance, not only from the military point of view but also from the commercial and political points of view.

Pass routes across mountain ranges are developed not only as a result of the existence of an easy natural line of travel, but also in response to a demand for communications. Many easy natural passes are followed by little-used trails, as in the southern Andes, because the arrangement and needs of the people on either side bring about no insistent demand for a line of travel. On the other hand, many of the actual roads or railroads which cross mountain barriers in places where the demand for communications from a large territory is concentrated follow very difficult routes. Fortunate, indeed, are those few places

A zigzag route through the Hindu Kush Mountains

Western approach to Süsten Pass, Switzerland, near upper limit of pasture

where world routes of travel come to a focus on a relatively easy pass, such as the Isthmus of Panama. In any case, few pass routes bear any relation whatsoever to the local resources of the mountain area; they are developed in response to conditions elsewhere in the world. The greatest contrasts may therefore be found between the settlements along the routes themselves and the settlements of the mountain dwellers only a short distance away.

Considering the arrangement of the mountains in the world as a whole, we can place pass routes in two categories. There are the passes which cross the mountainous rim of the Pacific Ocean, and there are the passes which cross the great east-west mountain barrier of southern Asia and Europe. But the rim of mountains around the Pacific is broken in the north and south and especially in the southwest. There is no barrier problem involved in sailing from the Indian Ocean into the Pacific. In Asia also the chief difficulties standing in the way of overland communication between China and the Western world are not those of mountains but, rather, those of aridity combined with low winter temperatures. The mountain rim of the Pacific is most effective as a barrier in the great north-south extent of the American ranges. To illustrate the development and historical importance of pass routes over these great barriers, let us consider a few examples.

The Panama Route. The importance of the Panama route is especially great because, at least up to the present, this route has no competitors close by. Not only the great width of a large part of the continents of North and South America, but also the height of the passes over the western mountains, has helped to emphasize the focus of lines of travel on this point in the barrier. In the country of Panama the mountain backbone of Middle America drops to such a low elevation, while still retaining the characteristics of steep slopes and narrow valleys, that a passage from one side to the other may be had by a climb of only two hundred and eighty-five feet through the Culebra Pass. The surface here has been deeply eroded under rainy tropical conditions, resulting in steep slopes, deep clay soils, and the danger of frequent landslides. The whole region was originally covered with a selva.

Inevitably the Isthmus became the focus of transportation routes. A road from Portobelo, on the Caribbean (northwestern) side, crossed the mountains by the Culebra Pass and descended to the Spanish colonial town of Panama, on the Pacific (southeastern) side. Panama was the base from which proceeded the conquest of western South America; and later the entire trade between Spain and its South American colonies was limited by law to the route by way of Panama. Boats from Spain brought goods to Portobelo; thence the goods were carried by mules over the Isthmus to Panama and there were reshipped south. The road across the pass, used chiefly by mules, served until about 1850, at which time the stream of American gold-seekers, on their way from the eastern part of the United States to California, stimulated the construction of a railroad.

In 1876 the French, encouraged by their success in Suez, sent a mission to Panama to survey a route for a canal. In 1881 a French company started work near Colon, attempting to dig a waterway like the Suez, without locks. Two things blocked success. The construction of a canal at sea level was much more difficult in Panama than at Suez, for in the latter case there was no mountain range to cross, but

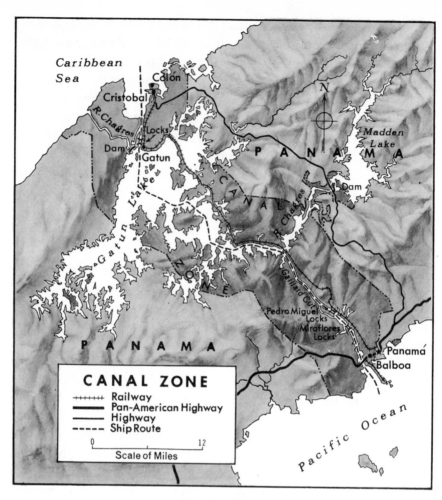

The Canal Zone

only a low ridge; and the rainy tropical climate of Panama, with its disease-carrying mosquitoes, was very different from the desert climate of Suez, where there is little penalty for poor sanitation. But the canal project was too important, considering the geographical position of the Isthmus, to permit its abandonment. In 1904 a project under the control of the United States was undertaken, beginning with an expensive and widespread program of sanitation. The draining of swamps and the clearing of luxuriant vegetation cost too much for the average tropical community; but if yellow fever, malaria, and other diseases now

An air view of the Miraflores Locks in the Panama Canal

common only in the tropics are to be eliminated, it must be by the elimination of breeding places for the mosquito. The new canal project included the construction of a huge dam at Gatun and the flooding of the valley of the Río Chagres. Access to the lake, which is some 40 feet above sea level, is gained through locks. The Gaillard Cut carries the canal across the divide to the Pacific side, and here two sets of locks are used to permit descent to sea level (map, p. 452; picture above). The work was completed in 1914, the first boat passing through the Canal on August 3 of that year.

In return for its independence and the defense of its territory, Panama, formerly a part of Colombia, has leased to the United States a strip of land ten miles wide known as the Canal Zone. Within this zone the usual tropical landscapes, many of them still primitive, have been transformed by the magic touch of money and commercial interest. Instead of being left in the wild confusion of a tropical forest or being closely packed with the squalid wooden houses of an isolated tropical city, the country has been cultivated like a park, and the cities of Cristobal (on the Atlantic side) and Balboa (on the Pacific side) are built with wide, paved streets, shaded by trees and bordered by widely spaced white bungalows, and are kept scrupulously clean. The contrasts are extraordinary between the landscapes, both rural and urban, which result from centuries of occupance in Panama, and the landscapes in the Canal Zone, which reflect unlimited financial backing at a focal point in world trade. From the results attained in the Canal Zone, however, it is not possible to conclude that all tropical lands can be similarly developed.

The Brenner Pass. The Brenner Pass, across the Alps, is not so significant to the world as a whole as the Panama route; nor is it so important a crossing of the European mountains as either the Bosporus and Dardanelles straits in the east or the Rhône-Saône Valley in the west (map, p. 224). The Brenner Pass, however, has played a very important historical role. From Verona in Italy to Munich in Germany the crossing of the Alps by this route requires an ascent of 4470 feet (map, p. 455). From the Plain of the Po the Adige Valley, a broad glacial trough, provides an easy route of approach to the divide. From the crest the descent by way of the Inn Valley is only 2767 feet. In this way the Alps may be crossed by a single climb, although elsewhere more than one range must be crossed through higher passes with steeper approaches. As a result the Brenner Pass has been of importance from an early period in history. By this route the Cimbri invaded the Po Valley; and later the Roman forces, marching out to the frontier posts on the Danube, followed it, building a road so that supplies could be sent out to them. Over this pass came the amber from Germany on its way to Rome in exchange for fabrics and wines. The German emperors of the Middle Ages invaded Italy over the Brenner Pass, and later the road through the pass was traveled by people from the north attracted by the culture of Venice. The trade which was carried on over this pass from Venice resulted in the early flourishing of such cities to the north as Augsburg, Ratisbon, Nürnberg,

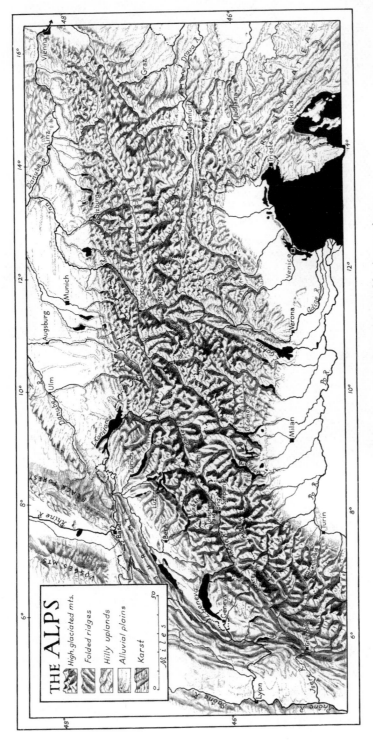

The surface configuration of the Alps and neighboring territory

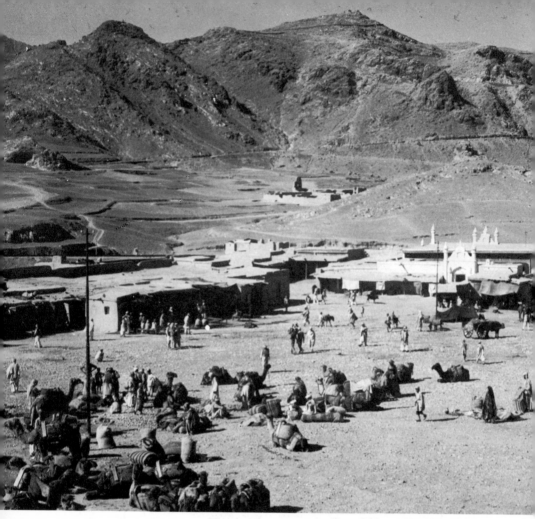

This village in Khyber Pass is a stopping place for passing caravans

and Leipzig. The first carriage road over the Alps, and later the first railroad, followed the Brenner route. To this day the Brenner is one of the chief lines of travel between central Europe and Italy. Within the mountain area there are only glistening steel rails traveled by heavily loaded trains, and highways over which motor cars or wagons pass back and forth; yet the effect of the pass is felt in the lowlands on either side through the growth of the pass cities—Verona to the south and Munich to the north.

The Khyber Pass. Many mountain ranges cannot be crossed by a single pass like the Brenner. Instead, several ranges must be crossed by means of long, tedious ascents and equally difficult descents. Thus the caravans from the oases of Tashkent and Bukhara seek the markets of India over the ranges of the Hindu Kush by a series of difficult passes (map below). From the Amu Darya and the piedmont oasis of Mazar-i-Sharif, they cross several lesser divides, finally surmounting the main range of the Hindu Kush Mountains over the Hajikhak Pass at 12,188 feet. Thence they cross the Paghman Mountains by the Unai Pass to Kabul at 5740 feet, and finally, after passing through the narrow gorges of the Kabul River and the Khyber Pass at 6825 feet, they

The pass route between the Indus Valley and the oases of inner Asia on the margins of the Turkestan

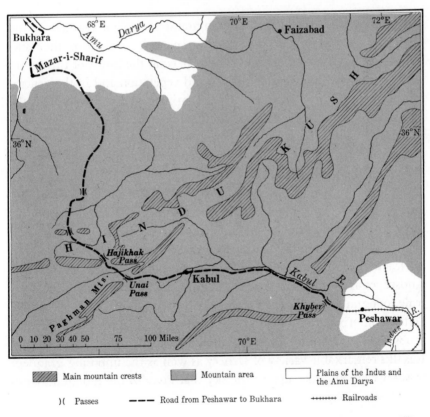

descend to the town of Peshawar and the Indus Valley. Over this and neighboring routes have come the repeated invasions of India which, in the course of history, have peopled that land with such a variety of races. Until recently, in addition to the dangers and difficulties of the road, the pass was dominated by Afghan tribesmen, who for centuries collected toll from the passing caravans and not infrequently resorted to pillage. Across this series of passes there is no railroad—only a road with steep grades and sharp turns, traveled in large part by loaded bullocks. However, at either end of the pass cities have grown up; Peshawar and Kabul are the two places which are most directly dependent on the Khyber Pass. Farther on, Bukhara is the focus of pass routes, not only from the south but also from the high basins of inner Asia to the east.

Conclusion

In more than a surficial sense mountains are major features of the earth's face. Not only do they stand out conspicuously from their surroundings, but their influence is felt far beyond the limits of this group in the continental patterns of climate and vegetation and in the general arrangement of the occupance. On a continent without mountains the major patterns of the landscapes would be simple; the areal scene could be painted, as it were, with broad sweeps of the brush. But mountains complicate the picture. The differences between the simple patterns shown on the generalized continent (diagram, p. 177) and the actual patterns on the face of the earth are to some extent the result of irregularities of coast line; but in large part they are the result of the distortion of climatic lines by mountain barriers. These effects are felt beyond the mountain borders: within the mountain regions there is an intricacy of design not equaled in any other parts of the earth. The landscapes are composed of such a complexity of detail that only large-scale topographic studies can reveal their essential qualities. A general vertical differentiation of the landscapes can be discerned, but this fact is obscured in detail by the spotty design of all the landscape elements. It is this remarkable variety of scenery as well as the imposing grandeur of snow-capped peaks against the sky that gives to the mountain lands their fascination.

REVOLUTIONARY CULTURAL CHANGE, POLITICAL SOVEREIGNTY, AND THE POPULATION PROBLEM

Ghana becomes an independent state and member of the Commonwealth of Nations. The Duchess of Kent represents the Queen

$\mathbf{D}$URING THE LAST FIFTY THOUSAND YEARS or so of man's occupance of the earth he has spread from his original tropical or subtropical habitat into all the various groups of regions in the world. In so doing he has learned more and more about the nature of his habitat, and he has developed new skills for creating useful things out of earth materials. Only yesterday, in the human time scale, he learned how to use inanimate power and machinery to do the work he had long done himself or with the aid of his animals. And only yesterday he began to learn how to organize a society in which every last individual might be treated with dignity and in accordance with law.

How is it, then, that the contemporary world is filled with fear and insecurity? How is it, in spite of the newly acquired ability to produce the necessities of life in abundance and to move vast volumes of things rapidly from place to place, that the great majority of the world's peoples are still hungry and getting hungrier?

The Industrial Revolution and the Democratic Revolution have brought fundamental changes to those areas they have reached. Both started in the same part of the world, and both have been in process of spreading. In the freedom of North America, Australia, and New Zealand—and also of Scandinavia and certain other parts of Western Europe—both revolutions have advanced rapidly. Elsewhere, however, the spread has been retarded. As the new technologies and the new concepts regarding the status of the individual were brought into new areas, they encountered new sets of conditions. They entered regions with different resource endowments; they came into contact with people of different cultural traditions. Few parts of the earth, however remote, remain truly untouched by these changes; but the ways in which the changes have affected life in different parts of the world are by no means uniform. The world can be divided into *culture areas,* in each of which these twin revolutions have reached a different stage and are creating different kinds of reactions.

It is now theoretically possible to create such an abundance of the

Cultural Change, Political Sovereignty, Population Problem 461

necessities of life that, with present technology, it would be possible for the world to provide proper support for "at least three or four times the present population."[1] Modern technology, however, demands acceptance of the principle of interdependence and co-operation among the world's peoples. In a world divided into sovereign states, aligned in antagonistic groups, such co-operation is denied.

In this concluding chapter we shall examine the population pattern on the earth from three points of view. First, we shall define the major culture areas, in each of which the two great revolutions have developed a unique set of reactions. Second, we shall discuss the world from the perspective of political sovereignty, as seen by each of the three "Great Powers." And third, we shall outline the problem of population and the means of supporting the world's people.

CULTURE AREAS

A culture area is a portion of the earth's inhabited lands which is occupied for the most part by people with similar attitudes, objectives, and technical skills, among whom the processes of revolutionary change have produced a series of related reactions. Seven such culture areas can be defined in the world as a whole (Plate 22).

European. The European Culture Area includes the European countries that are not dominated by the Soviet Union. (Yugoslavia occupies an intermediate status.) This culture area includes the original nucleus around the North Sea within which the two revolutions originated. But this area was also the chief center of development of the pre-industrial Occidental culture, with its landed aristocracy, its politically powerful army, and its many illiterate peasant farmers. Here the pre-industrial ideas of national sovereignty and self-sufficiency were developed. Here, also, two world wars have done irreparable damage not only to material structures and resources but also to the human resources. In this area the hopes of a majority of the inhabitants for a rapid rise in the general level of living have been so frustrated that there is widespread disillusionment, even with the ideals of the Democratic Revolution itself. Minorities, impatient at the

[1] L. Dudley Stamp, "Some Aspects of Applied Geography," in W. G. East and A. E. Moodie (editors), *The Changing World,* New York, 1956, p. 1010.

need to persuade majorities, attempt to seize power by force. The European Culture Area remains the world's chief center of conflict and readjustment, the major arena in which new attitudes and new objectives must be formulated in harmony with the radical changes in technology.

American. The American Culture Area includes the countries of the Western Hemisphere. The basic cultural traditions were imported from Europe but have developed in the relative freedom of the New World. The area is sharply divided, however, between Anglo-America and Latin America. In Anglo-America both revolutions have moved forward most rapidly and most successfully, creating an unprecedentedly high material level of living and an atmosphere of individual freedom never before known. In Latin America the revolutions have been retarded, in part by the presence in some countries of large numbers of native Indians; and in part, also, in some countries by the resistance of pre-industrial privileged classes to changes in the status of the individual. Today the new technology is being rapidly adopted, but groups resisting the Democratic Revolution are in bitter conflict with other groups supporting this revolution.

North African–Southwest Asian. The North African–Southwest Asian Culture Area includes the countries of the great belt of deserts and desert margins that stretches from Morocco in the west to Pakistan in the east. All these countries are concerned with the problems of supporting life in a dry-land habitat. Otherwise there is considerable contrast among them. Most of the people are Moslems; but Moslems are found outside this culture area. Most of them speak Arabic; but Arabic is not the language of Turkey, Iran, Afghanistan, or Pakistan. Exceptional both in language and in religion are Christian Ethiopia and Jewish Israel. An industrial society has recently been created in Israel; but the chief impact of the new technology has been felt in those states that produce oil and in those states involved in the shipment of oil. The Democratic Revolution takes the form of a growing demand for the withdrawal of European political rule and for equality of national status among the world's nations. Internal conflict arises from three conditions: (1) European contacts have greatly increased the contrast between the wealth of the ruling minorities and the poverty of most of the people; (2) the oil needed by Europe is produced by one group of countries, whereas the routes over which the oil must be moved to Europe are controlled by another group of countries; and (3) in the midst of the most sensitive part of the area is the newly created state of Israel, the existence of which does more to unite the otherwise disunited Moslem countries than any other factor.

Oriental. The Oriental Culture Area includes the countries of southern and eastern Asia and the bordering islands. The traditional powers of the Oriental area are India and China. But Japan, adopting pre-industrial ideas of imperialism from nineteenth-century Europe, attempted to force the whole of eastern and southeastern Asia to accept its political domination and economic leadership. Japan's effort, defeated in World War II, had the effect of jarring the Oriental countries free from domination by Europe. Now the imperialism of the Soviet Union and of China has replaced that of Europe and Japan. The result is that the ideas of the Democratic Revolution, little understood in the Orient, where the individual has never coveted a change of status, are in conflict with those of communism. What happens in this area is of vital concern to the rest of the world because of the huge numbers of people involved.

Soviet. The Soviet Culture Area includes the Union of Soviet Socialist Republics and the satellite states subordinated to it. These various countries were pre-industrial when power was seized by the Communist Party (in 1917 in the Soviet Union; after World War II in the other countries). This seizure of power was successful even where the Democratic Revolution had gained some acceptance, as in the Czech part of Czechoslovakia and in Poland. The new technology of the Industrial Revolution is being rapidly applied to the development of heavy industries as a basis of military strength. It is not correct to describe the soviet society as communist, for it has never even aimed at the creation of a classless society, nor does it bestow economic rewards on the basis of need. Rather it is a socialist society in which economic rewards are given on the basis of work, and in which there is a strong central government, a strong police force, and a new hierarchy of power and privilege.

African. The African Culture Area includes the whole of Africa south of the Arabic-speaking countries of North Africa and south of Ethiopia. The great majority of the inhabitants are Negro, but there are certain areas where white Europeans have established colonies. For the Negro majority in this area the Democratic Revolution means equality of status with the white minority. But in some places, especially in South Africa, where the Negroes were imported as laborers, this is frustrated by the determination of the white minority to retain political control. In the world-wide struggle for men's minds, communism is offered as a quick means to end the dominance of the privileged classes, and this seems quite attractive to a people ignorant of the Soviet method of establishing a new privileged class.

Pacific. The Pacific Culture Area includes Australia and New Zealand, and the clusters of islands in the southwestern part of the Pacific Ocean. The native inhabitants of this culture area were neither numerous enough nor sufficiently advanced in technology to withstand the invasion of the Caucasoid people. In Australia and New Zealand, and also in the Hawaiian Islands, the new ways of living were developed with little hindrance, as they were in Anglo-America. But in the smaller islands there are many problems of readjustment which seem to spell the doom of the traditional ways of living.

THE GREAT POWERS

The whole problems of culture change and the capacity of the earth to support its human inhabitants is infinitely complicated by the existence of national sovereignty. The world is divided into political areas, each administered by a government which is committed to act on the basis of what are conceived to be its own interests. Not that national loyalty or patriotism should ever be lost; rather, the basic human attitude of group solidarity should be enlightened by an understanding of what is necessary for survival. In the pre-industrial world, states had to be supported largely on their own national territories. Imperialistic expansion meant gaining control of additional territory at the expense of some other country. But the industrial society cannot gain control of enough territory to supply all its needs, for nothing less than the surface of the entire earth would be needed as a base. Some kind of a code of international conduct must be developed even if this code seems to restrict the absolute freedom of action of any one state, just as national laws are adopted for the good of society even though they restrict the absolute freedom of the individual.

National sovereignties still exist, however. No attempt to provide a geographic basis for the understanding of modern problems would be complete or realistic without an analysis of the significance of the geographic structure of the major political units of the world. It is on the basis of these facts of world distribution that we must go forward either to war and disaster or, ultimately, to world organization and peace.

Three great powers emerged from World War II. These powers are the Commonwealth of Nations,[1] the United States of America, and the Union of Soviet Socialist Republics. The first two of these include the part of the world dominated by English-speaking people and by the ideas of the industrial society, which are largely British and American in origin. The third includes the part of the world dominated by the Communist Party and by the ideas of the soviet society, which are largely German and Russian in origin.[2] We shall outline the major features of the political geography of each of these in turn.

THE COMMONWEALTH OF NATIONS

Area and Location. The Commonwealth of Nations differs from the other great powers in that it is composed of sovereign states which are geographically scattered throughout the world, voluntarily associated for the common good, and symbolically united by loyalty to the Crown (map, p. 467). The original nucleus of the British Empire— the United Kingdom of Great Britain and Northern Ireland—is very small indeed compared to the vast territories in other parts of the world that are included among the separate Commonwealth nations and their dependent areas or colonies. In the original nucleus of England, Scotland, Wales, and Northern Ireland there are some 94,000 square miles, and in the rest of the Commonwealth about 12,000,000.

---

[1] The term British Commonwealth of Nations, as used in the reports of the Imperial Conference of 1926, refers to the self-governing lands of the British Empire. However, the term Commonwealth of Nations is used by some writers synonymously with the whole British Empire, whether self-governing or colonial. It is so used in this book.

[2] F. S. C. Northrup, *The Meeting of East and West*, New York, 1946.

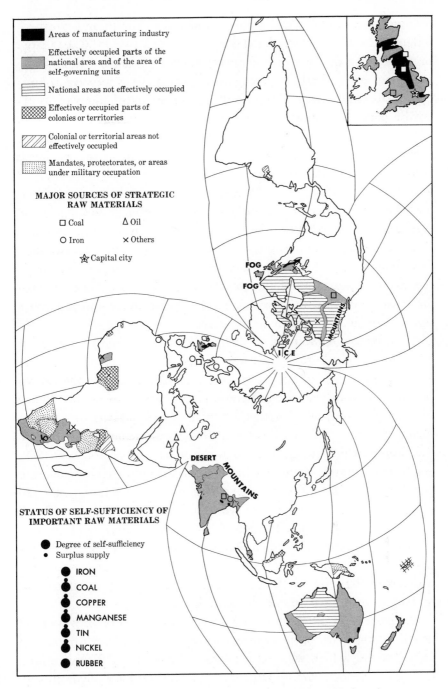

The following labels appear within the map figure:

Areas of manufacturing industry

Effectively occupied parts of the national area and of the area of self-governing units

National areas not effectively occupied

Effectively occupied parts of colonies or territories

Colonial or territorial areas not effectively occupied

Mandates, protectorates, or areas under military occupation

MAJOR SOURCES OF STRATEGIC RAW MATERIALS

□ Coal   △ Oil

○ Iron   × Others

☆ Capital city

STATUS OF SELF-SUFFICIENCY OF IMPORTANT RAW MATERIALS

● Degree of self-sufficiency
· Surplus supply

IRON
COAL
COPPER
MANGANESE
TIN
NICKEL
RUBBER

FOG
FOG
I C E
MOUNTAINS
DESERT
MOUNTAINS

Geographic structure of the Commonwealth of Nations

467

Population. In 1958 the population of Great Britain and Northern Ireland (the United Kingdom) was a little less than 51,000,000; but the population of the whole Commonwealth was about 640,000,000—nearly a quarter of all the people in the world. It is important, however, that within Great Britain only the great conurbations of southern England are increasing in population. Already about 80 per cent of the population of England and Wales is urban, and the clustering of people round London, Liverpool-Manchester, Birmingham, and Leeds is increasing. Northern England, Scotland, and Wales have suffered a net loss of population since World War II. From Britain as a whole there has been a steady current of emigration, especially to Canada and Australia, and since World War II this current has grown stronger. The loss to Britain resulting from this emigration cannot be measured in numbers alone, for the persons most likely to emigrate are those possessing the qualities of imagination and a sense of adventure that are most needed in the home country. Britain today suffers from a shortage of labor, especially in industry.

Attitudes and Objectives. The people of the Commonwealth are ethnically and culturally diverse. Within Great Britain itself there are local differences of culture and dialect which loyalty to the Crown resolves only superficially. There is a persistent demand for "home rule" in Scotland, and Northern Ireland already has its own parliament. At the same time there is a strong sentimental attachment to the Crown, which stands as the symbol of nationality and continuity —a curious example of the redefinition of a pre-industrial institution to provide a focus of loyalty in a democratic society. Britain has suffered severely from the losses in two world wars and from the continued current of emigration. The people of Britain today tend to seek security of employment rather than progress in technological innovation. It is difficult, also, to adjust to the bitter fact that, without the widespread territories of the Commonwealth, the mother country can no longer be counted among the world's great powers.

There are great differences among the attitudes and objectives of the people in other parts of the Commonwealth. In Canada, Australia, and New Zealand, which were settled largely by people of British origin, there are three outstanding attitudes: (1) continued and vigorous support for the ideas of the Democratic Revolution; (2) eager acceptance of technological progress in the interest of increased production per capita and of the achievement of still higher levels of living; and (3) loyalty to the Crown as the symbol of nationality. In South Africa there are three antagonistic groups, each with its own distinctive attitudes: (1) a minority of British settlers; (2) a larger group of Boers, descendants of Dutch settlers who still speak a Dutch dialect (Afrikaans); and (3) a majority of Negroes who were originally brought to this region from farther north to work in the mines and on the farms. Between Negroes and Europeans are the Coloureds (part white, part Negro) and the Indians. Racial antagonism is so strong that even the ties to the Commonwealth are threatened. In India, an attempt is being made to spread the ideas of democratic responsibility for political policy among an illiterate and very poor peasantry. In other parts of the Commonwealth the effort to experiment with the new ideas regarding the status of the individual is only just beginning. Nevertheless, Britain has adopted the policy of bringing the various parts of the former Empire forward to political independence within the Commonwealth as rapidly as possible.

Resources. The natural resources of the earth have been widely developed by British capital. During the period of the expansion of the Empire the people from Great Britain showed uncanny judgment regarding the parts of the world likely to yield the richest rewards. The regions of Group IV and Group V outside Europe, generally neglected by the other European colonizing nations, were eagerly occupied and developed by the British. Argentina almost became a British dominion, and until recently the domination of that country by British capital was such that its economy was closely tied to that of Great Britain. British capital also developed the resources of many of the tropical parts of the world, especially southern and southeastern Asia, and Central, East, and West Africa. However, the currents of trade which were developed were greatly to the benefit of the people of Great Britain, and to a much lesser extent, if any, to the people of the colonies. Serious problems of population pressure developed in such places as India, Egypt, and the West Indies; but meanwhile no part of the world enjoyed such spectacular economic development as did the industrial and commercial cities of Great Britain. London became the primate city not only of Great Britain but of the Commonwealth.

The Commonwealth of Nations 469

During the period of expansion it became evident that the population of Great Britain could no longer be supported by an economy of self-sufficiency. The basic resources were at hand for the beginnings of the Industrial Revolution. There was coal of high quality; and for many years exports of British coal paid for a large part of the imports of food and raw materials. There was iron ore of good quality. There was wool from British sheep. But above all there was the technological skill of the British people. At the beginning of the twentieth century Britain was importing most of the raw materials for its industries, adding value by the process of manufacturing, and exporting the greatest variety of products. Very high yields of the raisable crops had been achieved by British farmers; and in the period after World War II the cultivated area of Great Britain was increased 140 per cent over the prewar area. Nevertheless, because of the high standard of living gained as a result of industrial progress, Britain must continue to import most of its foods, most of its fibers, most of its fuel, and almost all the raw materials used in its industries. Even its coal is no longer adequate for home needs in view of the increasing costs of production as the better deposits are worked out.

Within the various parts of the Commonwealth many of the more important raw materials, both mineral and agricultural, are produced. The Commonwealth is well off as to coal, iron, the hardeners of steel, and tin, but there are certain other key items which are lacking. The most serious deficiency is in oil, for which essential fuel the Commonwealth is dependent chiefly on the area round the Persian Gulf and on Venezuela. The Commonwealth is more than abundantly supplied with food because its various members, scattered throughout the world, embrace many varieties of climate. It is an old saying that the sun never sets on the British wheat crop. Almost every kind of plant and animal product is to be found somewhere in the Commonwealth.

Productive Capacity. During the nineteenth-century development of the British Empire, all these varied resources in different parts of the world were discovered, developed, and exploited by British capital. As a result the general level of industrial production increased enormously in the original nucleus of Great Britain. British manufacturing industries trebled their output between 1860 and 1910. Raw materials were brought to Great Britain in British ships, and the manufactured products were sent to distant oversea markets. London became the financial center of the world, providing the capital for the development of commercially profitable enterprises in every continent.

In the course of time, however, other commercially advanced parts of the world felt the desire to build their own industries. The United States rose as Britain's major competitor, and during the period when British industrial capacity was increasing three times, American industrial capacity increased twelve times. Also, the British dominions began to recognize the desirability of building their own industrial structures instead of simply supplying raw materials to the home country. Even Argentina arose to declare its independence of Britain's factories. In 1949 Great Britain was producing 10.50 per cent of the world's income, and the rest of the Commonwealth was producing 8.32 per cent.

More serious, however, was the relative decline in the productive capacity of Great Britain itself. In coal production, the British output was 225,000,000 tons in 1900 and 244,000,000 tons in 1930; but after World War II it dropped to 192,000,000 tons, and by 1953 it had been increased only to 1900 levels. Meanwhile the cost of coal production has increased so much, owing to the deepening of the mines, that Britain can no longer sell its coal abroad. In fact, its production is not sufficient for its own needs. Although in 1957 the British steel industry had a capacity of about 25,000,000 tons per year, this was less than the steel capacity of West Germany. British scientists and engineers still stand foremost in the world in technological skill; but resistance to the use of the new technology by both management and labor has meant the decline of British productive capacity not only relative to the world as a whole but also relative to the prewar capacity of Britain. Such resistance has also meant that many of the technological innovations developed by British engineers have been eagerly adopted in other countries. On the bright side of Britain's picture is the rapid construction of thermonuclear plants for the generation of electric power. It is estimated that before 1975 half of Britain's energy requirements will be met in this way.

Strategic Position. In terms of modern strategy the Commonwealth has become highly vulnerable. The widespread distribution of its parts, which is a source of strength in a peaceful world, becomes a source of danger in a world at war. As long as the British navy remained unchallenged on the sea, Great Britain could maintain its connections with the sources of raw materials from all over the world. The British life line, protected by Gibraltar, Malta, Cyprus, Suez, Aden, Ceylon, Singapore, and Hong Kong, was impregnable. But with the development of land-based air power, and after Egypt was successful in forcing the British troops out of the Suez area, the whole strategic situation was changed. Although the figures for the Commonwealth as a whole are impressive, none of the parts—and now not even the original nucleus—is any longer able to defend itself alone.

The Commonwealth of Nations, shaken by the destruction caused by World War II, stands today in a precarious position, its future obviously tied to a solution of the problems of international organization. This original nucleus of the industrial society, perhaps the industrial society itself, cannot long survive a divided and conflicting world.

THE UNITED STATES OF AMERICA

Area and Location. The United States differs notably from the Commonwealth of Nations in that it is chiefly concentrated in one compact territory (map, p. 473). In the main group of forty-eight states there are some 3,022,000 square miles of area. The only large outlying state is Alaska, with 586,000 square miles. Hawaii has an area of only 6400 square miles; and the "freely associated" Commonwealth of Puerto Rico has only 3400 square miles. For this reason alone the foreign policy of the United States must differ from that of Great Britain.

Population. Most of the population of the United States is concentrated in the main group of forty-eight states. In 1957 these states had a total population of 171,800,000, Alaska had only 210,000, and Hawaii had 551,500. The most densely crowded outlying area was Puerto Rico, with 2,308,000 inhabitants.

Attitudes and Objectives. The ethnic and cultural make-up of the United States is much more nearly uniform than is that of the Commonwealth. From the British the people of the United States have inherited the basic ideas of the Democratic Revolution and most of the early technological innovations of the Industrial Revolution. For

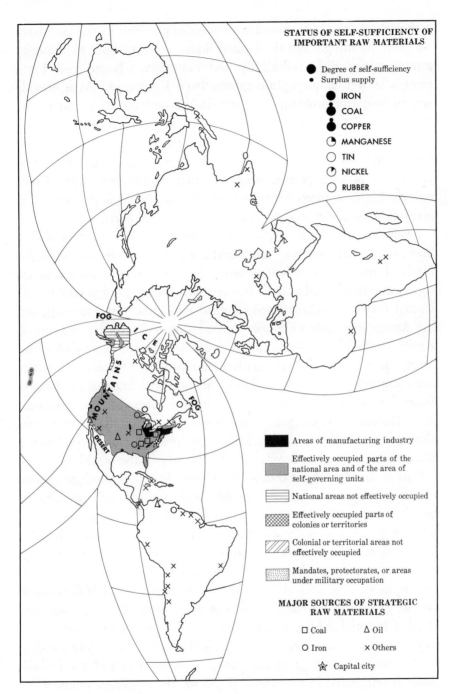

STATUS OF SELF-SUFFICIENCY OF
IMPORTANT RAW MATERIALS

● Degree of self-sufficiency
• Surplus supply

● IRON
● COAL
● COPPER
◑ MANGANESE
○ TIN
◔ NICKEL
○ RUBBER

■ Areas of manufacturing industry

▦ Effectively occupied parts of the
national area and of the area of
self-governing units

▤ National areas not effectively occupied

▨ Effectively occupied parts of
colonies or territories

▧ Colonial or territorial areas not
effectively occupied

▒ Mandates, protectorates, or areas
under military occupation

MAJOR SOURCES OF STRATEGIC
RAW MATERIALS

□ Coal   △ Oil

○ Iron   × Others

☆ Capital city

Geographic structure of the United States of America

both powers the resources and opportunities provided by the land have the same meaning. But the United States is not without its minority groups which differ ethnically and culturally. Negro and Latin groups, as well as immigrant groups from Europe and Asia, provide serious minority problems not only in the outlying areas but in the main part of the United States as well. An important minority of the population in the United States does not wholly subscribe to the basic principles of the Democratic Revolution (see page 16). The proportion of such people, while less than in the case of the Commonwealth, is of more serious concern to the United States because it involves the nuclear area and not just the outlying parts.

Resources. As we have pointed out in the several chapters of this book, few, if any, parts of the world are so richly endowed with the kinds of resources and lands needed by the people of an industrial society as is the United States. Not only was the territory of continental United States remarkably well supplied with basic raw materials, but the American people were able to create an extraordinary amount of wealth by the unearned increment resulting from the process of settlement, for the land was essentially unoccupied in advance. As settlement progressed across the country, the industrial heart of the United States developed in the northeast, in a highly urbanized area extending from Boston to Washington along the coast, and inland to St. Louis, Chicago, and Minneapolis–St. Paul. The primate city of the United States, New York, has become the largest city in the world.

Within the territory of continental United States are produced many of the more important raw materials, both mineral and agricultural, but there are certain key items which are lacking. No country in the world has such a large proportion of the world's coal reserve as has the United States. To be sure, its enormous iron ore deposits are nearing exhaustion, but other large reserves are available within the Western Hemisphere. The United States is well off in oil; but it is dependent on foreign sources for the hardeners of steel, for tin, and for a number of other essential industrial raw materials. No other part of the world, except the Argentine Humid Pampa, includes land so highly suitable for the production of grain and meat. The Corn Belt of the United States is unequaled in the whole world for the sustained yields of its rich soils and for the large area of its high-grade lands. Yet because of the position of the national territory of the United States on the climatic pattern of the world (diagram, p. 177), only a minute part of its area is suitable for the raising of tropical crops such as rubber. For these things, also, it is dependent on foreign sources. To supply the missing raw materials or the materials which may be exhausted in the predictable future, the United States must reach out to Canada and Venezuela for iron; to Malaya for tin and rubber; to the Middle East for oil so that it can utilize its own reserve at home; and to other parts of the world for raw materials of small total bulk and value, but of essential importance in industry.

Productive Capacity. Even before World War II, the United States was the most productive country in the world, and its people enjoyed the highest standard of living of any large nation. With the productivity of much of Europe destroyed or decreased by the war, the proportion of the world's total income produced in the United States has increased to almost 50 per cent. In 1946, while Great Britain was producing 192,000,000 tons of coal, the United States produced 520,000,000 tons; while Great Britain was producing 7,800,000 tons of iron, the United States produced 41,000,000 tons. Because of the renovation of manufacturing equipment during World War II, the productive capacity of the United States, unlike that of Great Britain, was greatly increased. The productivity of labor in terms of output per man-hour gained approximately 20 per cent. In the postwar world there is great need for the products of industry: need not only in parts of the world actually devastated by war but also in the many substandard areas of the United States itself. However, a large proportion of mankind is too poor to pay the cost. The solution of this dilemma involves much more than the profits of the owners of capital: it involves inevitably the very survival of the free institutions of the industrial society.

Strategic Position. The United States is not so vulnerable as is the Commonwealth of Nations. It has the advantage of a vast area which would make actual invasion difficult and costly. And even in the age of air power and atomic weapons, no conflict can be concluded until the territory of the defeated country is occupied by the victorious army. But air power and nuclear weapons have greatly changed the significance of the geographic position of the United States. Because the productive heart of America is concentrated in great urban centers in

PERCENTAGE OF WORLD MINERAL PRODUCTION FROM THE MORE IMPORTANT SOURCES
(Figures are an annual average over a recent three-year period)

Bauxite (1953–1955)
Surinam 20.7
British Guiana . 16.2
Jamaica (ex-
  ports) 13.4
United States . . 11.6
France 8.3
Hungary . . . 8.3
Other producers. 21.5

Chromite (1952–1954)
Turkey 22.1
Union of South
  Africa 18.8
Soviet Union . . 15.8
Philippine Re-
  public 13.6
Southern Rho-
  desia 11.1
Yugoslavia . . . 3.5
Other producers. 15.1

Coal (1954–1956)
United States . . 20.9
Germany . . . 19.4
Soviet Union . . 17.6
United Kingdom 10.4
Other producers. 31.7

Copper (Smelter production) (1954–1956)
United States . . 31.0
Chile 12.6
Northern Rho-
  desia 11.2
Soviet Union . . 10.6
Germany . . . 8.7
Canada 7.9
Belgian Congo . 7.2
Other producers. 10.8

Iron (1954–1956)
United States . . 26.9
Soviet Union . . 20.2
France 13.9
Sweden 4.8
Germany . . . 4.8
United Kingdom 4.7
Other producers. 24.7

Lead (1954–1956)
United States . . 23.1
Soviet Union . . 10.5
Mexico 10.4
Australia . . . 10.2
Canada 7.6
Germany . . . 6.6
Other producers. 31.6

Manganese (1952–1954)
Soviet Union . . 38.4
India 18.3
Union of South
  Africa 9.2
Gold Coast
  (Ghana) (ex-
  ports) 7.8
French Morocco. 4.8
Cuba 3.3
Belgian Congo . 2.8
Brazil 2.6
Other producers. 12.8

Mercury (1953–1955)
Italy 29.1
Spain 27.3
Mexico 10.5
United States . . 9.6
Yugoslavia . . . 8.1
Other producers. 15.4

Molybdenum (1953–1955)
United States . . 91.0
Chile 4.4
Other producers. 4.6

Nickel (1953–1955)
Canada 64.8
Soviet Union . . 19.0
New Caledonia . 8.2
Cuba 5.9
Other producers. 2.1

Petroleum (1954–1956)
United States . . 45.2
Venezuela . . . 14.5
Soviet Union . . 8.9
Kuwait 7.0
Saudi Arabia . . 6.5

Iraq 4.4
Other producers. 13.5

Phosphate (1953–1955)
United States . . 54.9
French Morocco. 20.3
Tunisia 8.7
Other producers[1] 16.1

Potassium (1954–1956)
United States . . 27.5
West Germany . 25.7
France 17.8
Other producers[2] 29.0

Sulfur (1953–1955)
United States . . 86.7
Italy 3.1
Japan 3.0
Mexico 2.8
Other producers. 4.4

Tin
Malaya 34.3
Indonesia . . . 18.5
Bolivia (exports) 15.5
Belgian Congo . 8.4
Other producers. 23.3

Tungsten (1953–1955)
China 24.5
United States . . 16.7
Soviet Union . . 10.5
Korea 9.1
Portugal 6.6
Bolivia (exports) 6.3
Other producers. 26.3

Vanadium (1953–1955)
United States . . 86.0
Southwest Africa 10.2
Peru 3.7
Other producers. 0.1

Zinc (1954–1956)
United States . . 31.5
Soviet Union . . 10.8
Canada 8.3
Belgium 8.1
West Germany . 6.7
Other producers. 34.6

[1] Exclusive of Soviet Union.   [2] Exclusive of Soviet Union and East Germany.

the northeast, it is peculiarly exposed to attack and serious damage. The protection afforded by wide expanses of ocean under the effective control of a friendly power can no longer be counted on to preserve the United States from immediate contact with the destructive force of modern warfare.

The attitude of the people of the United States on questions of foreign policy was shaken by World War II. There was a sudden awareness that the country could not hope to exist in isolation. The principle that an industrial society cannot exist in isolation even in times of peace is still not widely understood; but people now realize that in time of war they are no longer invulnerable. Many Americans, looking at the geographic relations across the polar regions for the first time, are beginning to think in terms of a round earth, not of an earth made up of separate continental islands. The United States possesses enormous power, basically because of its geographic position, its wealth, its productive capacity, its command of potential resources, and the technical genius of its people. But can this power be used so wisely and in accordance with such high moral principles that this country can lead the way to world peace and to a new world order? In the American system of free institutions and popular government, this leadership can depend not on the rise of one great statesman, but only on the intelligent and informed currents of public opinion in which everyone has a share of the responsibility.

THE UNION OF SOVIET SOCIALIST REPUBLICS

Area and Location. The Union of Soviet Socialist Republics differs from the other great powers in that all of its territory makes up one continuous geographic area (map, p. 478). There are 8,602,000 square miles of Soviet territory, and an indefinite number of additional square miles of dominated territory in eastern Europe and eastern Asia; but there are no oversea possessions. Furthermore, this great expanse of land area lies farther to the north than does the main part of the United States: its position on the generalized continent places it mostly north of the dry lands, and mostly outside the regions of Group IV (diagram, p. 177). Moreover, most of its coasts are frozen and inaccessible in winter, except for those along the Black Sea.

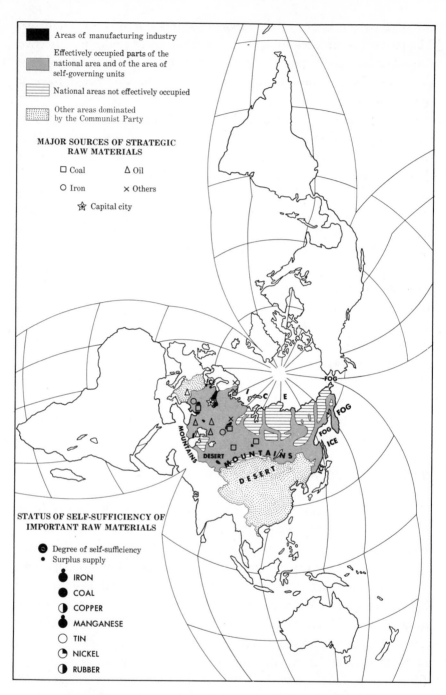

Geographic structure of the Union of Soviet Socialist Republics

Population. The population of the Soviet Union in 1956 was about 200,000,000, or approximately the same as the combined populations of Great Britain and continental United States. But because of the relatively large proportion of young people in the Soviet population it is estimated that for the next several decades the population will increase very rapidly. By 1970 it is probable that the Soviet population will exceed that of Great Britain and continental United States combined.

Attitudes and Objectives. The people who make up the Soviet Union are ethnically and culturally diverse. About 58 per cent of the total are Russians. Ukrainians make up another 16 per cent. The remaining percentage is made up of many different ethnic and culture groups. In the revolution of 1917 an essentially pre-industrial society was abruptly brought under the control of the Communist Party, and the soviet society, based on the ideas of Karl Marx, was brought into being. With respect to three basic ideas of the industrial society, the soviet society thinks along entirely different lines: (1) free speech and majority decisions can be enjoyed only by those who accept the basic premises of communism, and dissident elements within and outside the country are to be removed not by persuasion, but by whatever means seem most expedient; (2) the ownership of earth resources and the tools of production rests with the government, which acts for the people but is not of them or by them; (3) economic values are determined not by demand on an open market, but by the proportion of the total socially necessary labor which was devoted to the production of the particular commodity. Obviously, for people whose basic habits of thought are so different as are those of the soviet society and those of the industrial society, words do not have the same meanings, and the elements of the physical land do not have the same significance.

Resources. What are resources, then? Certainly not something that can be developed for individual profit. The only cost accounting must be in terms of work expended; there is no reason to suppose that, because it would be uneconomic for people of the industrial society to develop certain mining activities, or to plant certain kinds of crops, or to build industries in certain locations, it would also be uneconomic in the soviet society. The attempt to understand the operation of the soviet economy must therefore be about as difficult for us as it would be for a Russian to understand the operation of a capitalist economy.

The Union of Soviet Socialist Republics 479

Even with this difficulty of understanding, however, it is possible to say of the Soviet Union that within its territory are produced many of the more important raw materials, both mineral and agricultural, but that there are certain key items which are lacking. The Soviet Union possesses sufficient coal for its needs, even if the reserves are not so impressive as are those of North America. It also possesses large supplies of iron ore and of most of the hardeners of steel—especially manganese. It is well off in oil, but with proved reserves which seem to be less than those of the United States. In the black-earth belt extending from the Ukraine into southwestern Siberia the Soviet Union possesses agricultural lands of great productivity, but subject, more than those of North America, to the shortness of the growing season. There are, however, key minerals and key agricultural products which the Soviet Union lacks. It has no rubber, no tin, no sulfur, and by no means enough of the things which must be grown in the warmer parts of the earth, such as cotton. As the Soviet Union builds modern industrial plants for the production of the kinds of goods needed by the people, it must also gain access to the sources of raw materials in other parts of the earth. Even in a soviet society the technical needs of industry are such that they can be supplied only from the whole world.

Productive Capacity. Building on the miserable productive capacity of Czarist Russia, the government of the Soviet Union has accomplished marvels of economic growth. Since 1928 the production of coal and steel has been enormously increased. In 1956 Soviet steel production was greater than that of Germany and Great Britain combined, although only about half that of the United States. The total steel capacity was less than half that of the United States. The people were not well off, however. In 1956 the minimum monthly wage for 199 hours of work would buy one pair of leather shoes and a pair of socks; whereas in the United States the minimum monthly wage for 173 hours of work would buy not only shoes and socks but also a man's wool suit, nine cotton shirts, a pair of women's shoes, a woman's suit, six cotton dresses, and a table radio. Soviet economic policy did not give high priority to consumer goods.

Strategic Position. In many ways the strategic position of the Soviet Union resembles that of the United States. The invulnerability given by vast area has been demonstrated a number of times, notably by both

Napoleon and Hitler. Yet the airplane has reduced the significance of this invulnerability, just as it has in the case of the United States. The productive heart of the Soviet Union lies fairly close to the southern border—to Turkey, Iraq, and Iran. Therefore, quite aside from the oil resources of these countries, the Soviet Union would like to control them for security reasons. But there is still another reason: the Soviet Union has inherited from Czarist Russia the frustrated desire for a warm-water port, for without such a base no naval power could be maintained. Although the Soviet territory may be relatively invulnerable from the point of view of invasion, this very invulnerability makes emergence from the national territory difficult. Only by the conquest of western Europe or the Middle East can the Soviet Union reach ice-free water close to its centers of production. In so far as the Soviet Union hopes to remedy its difficulties by physical conquest, the quest for access to the ocean must remain a major interest.

THE WORLD'S POPULATION

The geographic fact underlying all these problems of strategy and national sovereignty is the pattern of population. Where are people located on the earth, and in what densities? In what parts of the world are there no people? Plates 1 to 6 show population density on a world scale. But the information on which a more detailed picture must be based is available only for a few places. We need to distinguish between areas which are thinly peopled and areas which have no people at all. Lester E. Klimm has suggested a method for outlining empty areas on a topographic scale.[1] From such detailed studies as his, the larger empty areas visible on small-scale maps could be identified. From maps of habitations, visible on air photographs, population maps can be constructed even where census data are poor. To make a map of people is one of the essential first tasks in any geographic study that involves man and his activities.

Population Growth. The population map is a picture of the distribution of man at a particular moment of time. In order to understand the significance of the map it is necessary to examine the process

[1] Lester E. Klimm, "The Empty Areas of Northeastern United States," *Geographical Review*, Vol. 44 (1954), pp. 325–345.

of population change, to look at the population historically as well as geographically.

We find that changes in population density are closely related to changes in culture, especially in the technology of production and in the organization of society. When prehistoric man found out how to cultivate plants and to domesticate animals, a large population increase became possible in those habitats that were suitable for crops and animals. In other words, the population could increase because more people could be fed. When, at the dawn of written history, man found out how to organize society under codes of law, an increase in the production of food was made possible and, again, population could increase.

Changes in technology do not always mean that population can increase in any one area. We have seen what the importation of the rifle did to the food supply of the Eskimos. When the plow replaced the hoe in certain agricultural societies, it was found that hilly lands could support fewer people than before. The meaning of the features of the physical earth changes, especially when they are examined in topographic detail. Although population as a whole is permitted to increase as a result of technological change, such change may also lead to a rearrangement of people in relation to the land.

Even when technological changes and changes in social organization permit population increase, however, growth does not always follow. During the long history of man on the earth, the death rates have risen and fallen suddenly and unpredictably. Famines, due perhaps to fluctuations of climate, are not predictable, nor are epidemics. Population increases when the death rate is lowered; it decreases when there is a rise in the death rate. Throughout long periods of time the ratio between the death rate and the birth rate has been so closely balanced that the net population growth has been very slow. The three chief factors that affect the death rate are hunger, disease, and war. These are what Malthus called the positive checks to population growth, which operate to keep the population in balance with the food supply. Of these, hunger (including famine and malnutrition) and disease are the most important. War causes a rise of the death rate because of the decrease of the food supply or the spread of disease rather than because of the actual slaughter of people in battle.

The changes in technology during the past two centuries include advances in the knowledge of medicine. At first medical knowledge increased less rapidly than did the methods of controlling the earth's physical resources. In the first half of the nineteenth century the control of disease and even the understanding of the causes of disease were beyond man's science. Little by little, scientists such as Louis Pasteur uncovered the causes of disease. Since 1900 both understanding and skill have increased enormously. In 1900 the chief causes of death were tuberculosis, pneumonia, infant diarrheas, typhoid fever, scarlet fever, diphtheria, yellow fever, and malaria. By 1950 these diseases were largely under control wherever modern medicine was applied. The chief causes of death in the United States were cancer, heart disease, and hypertension. All of this meant that more people survived to old age. In England and Wales, for example, a man born in 1880 might expect to reach the age of 44; a man born in 1945 might expect to live beyond the age of 65.

Population Growth since 1650. Very little exact information exists regarding the world's population. As late as 1800 most population data were based on estimates. The census taken every ten years since 1790 in the United States is almost unique in the world. Even today the methods of gathering data in different countries vary so greatly that the census of one country is seldom comparable with that of another. Figures for birth rate and death rate based on actual count are available for only 30 per cent of the world's population. Nevertheless, more or less reliable estimates of the world's population have been made for the period since 1650.[1] These estimates are presented in the table on page 484.

According to the table, the population of the areas of Occidental settlement began to increase rapidly after 1800 and continued to increase during the nineteenth century. Although the concentration of people in the European regions of Group IV began to appear only after 1800, the population of Europe as a whole increased 119 per cent during that century. In the same period the population in all the parts

[1] A. M. Carr-Saunders, *World Population: Past Growth and Present Trends,* Oxford, 1935; W. F. Willcox, *Studies in American Demography,* Ithaca, New York, 1940; *The Determinants and Consequences of Population Trends,* Population Studies No. 17, United Nations, New York, 1953.

of the world occupied by people of Occidental culture increased at least three times as fast as in those parts occupied by other cultures.

The most rapid growth of population ever achieved by any large area of the world was recorded in the United States in the nineteenth and early twentieth centuries. In 1775 there were only 2,500,000 people in the colonies; and to the west the whole expanse of the continent as far as the Pacific Ocean was only thinly occupied by Indians, fur trappers, and Spanish cattle ranchers. The westward movement of the frontier, including the occupance of the grasslands, was accompanied by the rapid growth of large cities and urban industries. This era of rapidly-expanding economy resulted in the creation of a vast amount of widely-distributed wealth, and left an attitude of optimism clearly stamped on the American character. The westward movement was supported by the arrival of millions of immigrants, some of whom came freely from Europe and other continents, and some of whom came from Africa as slaves. Most of the immigrants came to America

ESTIMATES OF WORLD POPULATION BY REGIONS, 1650–1950

Population in Millions

DATE	WORLD	ANGLO-AMERICA	LATIN AMERICA	AFRICA	EUROPE *	ASIA **	OCEANIA	OCCI-DENTAL COUN-TRIES ***
1650	545	1	12	100	103	327	2	118
1750	728	1	11	95	144	475	2	158
1800	906	6	19	90	192	597	2	219
1850	1171	26	33	95	274	741	2	335
1900	1608	81	63	120	423	915	6	573
1920	1834	115	92	136	485	997	9	701
1930	2008	134	110	155	530	1069	10	784
1940	2216	144	132	177	579	1173	11	866
1950	2406	166	162	199	594	1272	13	935

From Carr-Saunders and United Nations

* Including U.S.S.R.

** Excluding U.S.S.R.

*** Including Anglo-America, Latin America, Europe including U.S.S.R., and Oceania.

484 Cultural Change, Political Sovereignty, Population Problem

because they had heard that it was a land of opportunity; and because they came it *was* a land of opportunity.

In the late nineteenth and early twentieth centuries great changes began to appear in the death rates of the Occidental world. It was at about this time that medical science began to gain control over the ravages of childhood diseases. More recently the discovery of sulfa drugs and antibiotics, and the use of DDT in the control of disease-carrying insects, have resulted in a still greater drop in the death rates in those parts of the world where modern health measures have been put into operation. Death rates as low as 10 or 12 per thousand can now be achieved.

There has also been a drop in the birth rate in the areas of the industrial society. This decline has been especially noticeable among those who live in cities. In the United States the birth rate, which had dropped below 20 per thousand in the 1930's, rose again to nearly 25; and the death rate was brought to 9. In the pre-industrial society birth rates remained generally above 40, and death rates were only a little lower. In the industrial society the present trend is toward a situation characterized by low birth rates and low death rates, which is in striking contrast to the high birth rates and high death rates of other parts of the world.

The Population Prospect. The question is what will happen to the populations of countries not now included in the industrial society when the new technology of the Industrial Revolution is adopted and when the methods of modern medical science are applied to the improvement of public health. Demographers, who are students of population processes, warn against the idea that the cycle of events that took place in the industrial society will necessarily be repeated elsewhere. It is clear that in countries like China a decrease in the death rate must be followed by a "population explosion." How long might it take such a country to achieve a low birth rate–low death rate situation? Sociologists believe that declining birth rates are associated with a relatively high level of economic well-being. This was brought about in the industrial society by increasing the production of goods and services at a faster rate than the increase of population. But in the industrial society the Industrial Revolution came just at the time when settlers were entering new and previously almost unoccupied lands which had been rendered highly productive by new inventions. The advance of the frontier onto these new lands accompanied the rise of the cities and the development of manufacturing industries. Markets expanded as production increased. Can a similar situation be created again through a series of new inventions that will change the potential utility of the present thinly-peopled or empty areas of the world? No certain answer to this question can be given; yet on it hinges the population prospect of the decades ahead.

As a result of the revolutionary changes brought about by the new technology and by the new concept of the status of the individual, all the world's cultures are going through various processes of rapid readjustment. This is a time of conflicting values; but it is also a time of opportunity for anyone with the courage to face such changes and to seek solutions for the inevitable conflicts. All kinds of economic, social, political, and military problems have arisen which demand the closest attention of the world's wisest people. These problems need to be approached from as many different points of view as possible.

To make application of the geographic point of view to an understanding of these problems of our time, four fundamental facts are required. First is the population pattern—where people are located on the earth and in what density. The second is the arrangement of the significant features of the habitat, the resource base. The third is the pattern of contrasted cultures, or ways of living. And the fourth is the division into political areas. It is from an understanding of the complex areal relationships of population, habitat, culture, and political area that all kinds of modern problems of readjustment can be approached geographically. The geographic analysis of the meaning of the observed areal relationships must proceed from a knowledge of the processes of change that are going on. Such analysis can throw new light on the causes of poverty, hunger, insecurity, and conflict, and on the methods of combating them.

APPENDIXES

A · MAPS

By Hibberd V. B. Kline, Jr.

1. The word "cartography" by its derivation means the making or drawing of maps or charts. To the geographer it is the content of maps that is significant. The full and accurate understanding of content must, however, be based on sound knowledge of the advantages and limitations inherent in cartography. These are related to the basic considerations of space and distance, to map "projections" which present the spherical form of the earth on a two-dimensional surface, and to symbols which stand for facts and ideas.

2. **The Map as a Tool for Analysis and for Synthesis.** The cartographical method serves the geographer as a tool or instrument for analysis. On the map he can record any phenomena, physical or cultural, which are observed on the face of the earth. It must be remembered that the framework upon which these facts and inferences are plotted is that of the earth, or a part of the earth, itself. The geographer may derive his data from original observation in the "field," which in a sense is his laboratory, or from secondary sources. No matter what the derivation, he plots his information on the map. It is thus reduced to comprehensible size and concreteness. The cartographical method also serves the geographer as a means of synthesis and generalization. By use of the map he may combine two or more phenomena for study, or present their relationships to each other. The map is a method of summing up spatial phenomena that have two or three dimensions. The geographer, whose interests are in the significance of differences from place to place, therefore finds the map to be both a means and an end in his field of study.

I. Basic Requirements of a Map

3. **Direction.** We may consider the map to be a representation of the earth itself or of selected items that have areal distribution over the

earth. To be more than a diagram or picture, a map must show measurement of distances, and position or direction with reference to the points of the compass. Direction may be represented in several ways, all of which are based upon a convention commonly accepted by all the nations of the world today. That is, direction is given with reference to an imaginary grid related to the axis of rotation of the earth. This grid of latitude and longitude gives the four cardinal directions of N. E. S. and W. and permits direction from any given place to be considered in terms of arcs of a circle, according to any of the systems for dividing a circle. Direction, then, becomes a matter of stating how a line drawn on the face of the earth trends with relation to the grid of the earth or to a circle drawn around some point on that line. Direction in a circle is measured in terms of an arc, or azimuth.[1]

The instrument most commonly used to determine direction is the compass. Since the magnetic compass conforms to the magnetic lines of force of the earth's field, which is not in perfect correspondence with the axis of rotation of the earth, a correction must be applied in most places to convert magnetic readings to azimuths, or to bearings.

4. **Scale.** Distance is based more simply on a direct comparison between linear measurements on the earth and on the map. A map that is the same size as the portion of the earth it represents would be similar to a pattern used by a dressmaker or toolmaker. Maps are not patterns and are therefore, without exception, smaller in size than the size of the corresponding segment of the earth. It is obvious that a ratio must exist between a linear measurement on the earth and its facsimile on the map. This ratio is *scale*. Any distance on the map is taken as unity, or 1. The corresponding number of units which this same distance has on the earth provides the remainder of the ratio (or the denominator to the numerator of 1). Thus a scale of 1:10,000 is a ratio in which one unit on the map (in inches, centimeters, spans, pipestems, or any other measurements) equals 10,000 of the same units

[1] Azimuth is stated in degrees from 0° to 360°. Two systems are in common use, reading clockwise from either the north or the south point. Bearings are stated in quadrants (quarter circles), using the nearest meridianal point and the direction from it. For example, S. 75° E. is the bearing of azimuth 105° (from north point) or azimuth 285° (from south point).

on the earth. A scale of 1:1 would be "pattern-size." A scale of 1:100,000 is ten times *smaller* than 1:10,000 because the unit on the map stands for 10 times as many units on the ground. Scale may be written as a fraction (1/10,000), sometimes designated as R.F. or representative fraction. Scale also may be expressed in words that translate the ratio of like units into other equivalents. For example, a scale of one inch to one mile has a ratio of 1:63,360 (viz. 5280 feet in one mile × 12 inches in one foot = 63,360 inches in one mile). Therefore, if one unit is one inch in the numerator, the 63,360 units in the denominator equal one mile. Scale may be expressed also as a line drawn on the map and divided into distances representing the distances on the earth. This is an appropriate convention because it makes measurement possible by direct comparison with the subdivided line.

It must be emphasized that scale is a linear comparison between map and earth. The greater the disparity between these two measurements the smaller is the scale. This may be readily appreciated and remembered by recalling that ½ is larger than ¼, and thus 1:10,000 is larger than 1:100,000. Areal comparisons between scales, in accordance with the principles of geometry, are in terms of the squares of their linear measurements. Thus, in the last example above, the linear difference is 10 times but the areal difference is 100 times, since area implies the measurement of two directions at right angles to each other.

5. **Position.** The third attribute that makes a map, that of position, is a consequence of distance and direction, and it is often expressed in terms of the other two (so far in such a direction from a known point). Absolute position may be stated as an intersection of the geographical grid lines in terms of latitude and longitude;[1] for example, Washing-

---

[1] Latitude is the distance north or south of the equator expressed in degrees from 0° at the equator to 90° at each pole. Lines measuring latitude extend east and west around the earth parallel to and including the equator. These lines, therefore, are "parallels of latitude." Longitude is the measurement of distance east and west on the earth. Since no obvious starting point for such measurement exists, an arbitrary line must be selected. Many such "prime meridians" have existed, but today the meridian of Greenwich, England, is commonly accepted as zero. The north and south "meridians" marking the intervals of longitude are numbered from the prime meridian westward to 180° and eastward to 180° to complete the circumference of the earth.

ton National Observatory 38°55' N., 77°04' W. Other systems of co-ordinates may be used, such as the town and range systems of the U. S. Land Survey (see diagram, p. 326); the arbitrary co-ordinates of a military grid; and the network lines on an atlas page.

A map, then, is a representation of the surface of the earth, or some portion of it, in which directions, distance, and position are shown as truly as possible, or with sufficient accuracy for the purposes of the representation. That perfect representation from a mathematical point of view is impossible will be demonstrated subsequently.

II. Measurements for Mapping

6. **Base-Line and Triangulation.** Maps have their origin in the measurement of the earth. Since most maps either are concerned with the land and water bodies of the earth, or relate their subject matter to this distribution, it is apparent that this primary distribution must be determined. The precise determination is known as surveying. The basic concepts of surveying are simple, although the exact methods and applications may be exceedingly complex. Surveying is based on straight lines. A straight line is most easy to sight along, to measure, and to draw. Therefore, direction (line-of-sight) and distance (along the line) may be simulated by a proportionately smaller straight line drawn upon a piece of paper or map. The place where two or more straight lines intersect is a fixed position, which also may be plotted upon the map.

Surveying, or sighting along straight lines, takes two fundamental forms. The first is the *traverse,* in which, starting from a known position, the direction and the distance is measured along each of a succession of straight lines. Points of positions not on these lines may then be related to this framework by additional straight lines drawn and measured to them. The second method is *triangulation.* In this method the measurement of angles takes the place of the measurement of lines, except that at the beginning a *base-line* must be measured carefully. Triangulation makes use of the triangle, or three-sided geometrical figure. Given the measurements of the angles of a triangle and the length of one side, the lengths of other sides can be determined by the simple trigonometry to which virtually every school child in the Occidental culture is exposed. Thus triangulation is the building of triangles in which the directions of the sides are known and the distances are computed after measuring the angles between sides. It has an advantage over the traverse in that many observations can be made from one point and in that the tedious and exacting measurement of lines is avoided, save for the necessary base-line. This method, like the traverse, supplies a framework of known lines and positions to which other detail can be added by further sighting and measurement.

Complexities are added to these simple methods by the fact that instruments are not perfect and man is not infallible; by the irregularly oblate spheroidal shape of the earth, which introduces problems of spherical trigonometry; by the influences of gravity and magnetism, which differ from place to place; by the presence of vegetation, atmospheric refraction, and other handicaps to observation; and by the irregularities in altitude and slope that occur on the surface of the earth.

7. **Elevation.** The measurement and mapping of the surface irregularities of the earth require that some point be chosen to which to relate places of higher, lower, or equal elevation. This point is most often the ocean at some aspect of its level (as "mean sea level" or "lower low water"), and the point is transformed into a geometrical figure of area to become the "datum plane." Since the distance from the center of the earth to the surface of any ocean is affected by gravitational differences from place to place, and since all the oceans have differing "levels," the altitudes obtained from different datum planes are not directly comparable.

Elevation with reference to the datum plane is measured by a procedure called "leveling." Leveling consists of determining the altitude of points the horizontal position of which is known by surveying. The method is to measure the distance between points and their differences in vertical angle from each other. This may be done with a number of different instruments for measuring these two elements. In the United States the telescopic alidade and the leveling rod are commonly employed. The former is focused on the latter. The number of marked intervals on the rod intersected by the cross hairs in the lens of the telescope gives the distance. The angle of the instrument focused on the rod is given by a measuring arc in terms of degrees of elevation or depression from the horizontal. The two figures entered into a table give the difference in elevation between the known position and the new position. The map representation of differences in elevation and the form of the surface require the use of symbols.

8. The techniques of surveying and of leveling have been modified and supplemented, but not supplanted, by photography—both terrestrial and aerial. It is possible to take pictures of the land surface and from those pictures to construct the horizontal and vertical measurements of a portion of the earth. However, photographs alone will not suffice, for they must be related to positions established by work on the ground. This use of surveying and of leveling establishes "control points" by which the pictures can be oriented and be corrected for the irregularities of scale and other errors inherent in pictures. Aerial photography, in particular, has captured the imagination because of the rapidity, precision, and relatively low cost with which work may be done. The quality of aerial surveying, however, can be no better than the control upon which it is based.

III. Map Projections

9. **The Properties of Map Projections.** Reduction of measurements made on the face of the earth to scale representations on the map is a simple procedure provided that only a few square miles of the land surface are involved. Areas of greater extent are more complex because the curvature of the earth's surface and the flat plane of the surface of the map are different geometric forms. The whole earth, or any major segment of it, cannot be simulated to scale except by a globe or a part of a globe, any more than a ball or other round object can be flattened without distortion. By acknowledging and understanding this distortion, the earth spheroid can be represented on a plane surface. This is the *map projection* [1] in which the geographical grid (latitude and longitude lines) of the earth is systematically arranged on a plane surface in order to achieve some desired qualities or properties. The properties that may be obtained are:

[1] The term "projection" is in good repute even though most projections are mathematically computed and are not true perspective arrangements of the geographical grid "projected" onto a geometrical figure.

a. Conformality (orthomorphism), in which angles formed by inter-secting lines are the same on the map as on the globe. This quality results from right-angle intersection of meridians and parallels on the map (as they are on the earth) and the same scale along these lines (not necessarily the true scale) at the intersection.

b. Equivalence (equal-area), in which the ratio between any area on the earth and the corresponding area on the map is constant. This quality is obtained by adjusting the spacing of parallels and meridians so that the area enclosed by any quadrilateral composed of these lines is of the same size proportionally to the similar area on the earth, as is any other quadrilateral. Equivalence applies to the whole map, although shapes must be distorted on any equal-area map in order to keep areas in the same proportion to the earth everywhere.

c. In conjunction with either of the above properties, another quality known as *azimuthal* (or zenithal) may be obtained. Azimuthal projec-tions are those in which direction is truly represented from the center of the projection.

d. Some projections fail to possess any of the above properties, but are *compromises* which sacrifice exactness in order to attain the ap-proximate appearance of the earth, or part of it.

e. The property of showing curved lines on the globe as straight lines on the map.

The variety of map projections that it is possible to construct is almost infinite. However, a limited number of projections are commonly used. The following pages are devoted to those which are commonly encountered, although two pure, but extreme, perspective forms of little actual significance are used to introduce some of the principles involved.

10. **Cylindrical Perspective Projections.** The basic concept of the "perspective" projection is that the geometrical figure upon which the geographical grid is "projected" must be developable. That is, the fig-ure must be one that can be flattened out into a plane surface without distortion. One such figure is the cylinder which, after cutting, may be unrolled. A paper cylinder may be wrapped around a globe repre-senting the earth, and the geographical grid may be transferred from

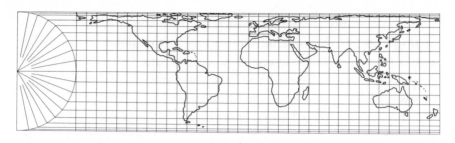

Cylindrical equal-area projection

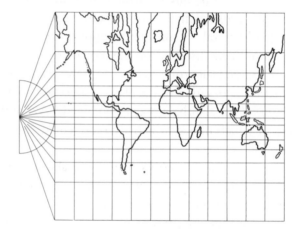

Central cylindrical perspective projection

globe to paper. If a paper cylinder tangent at the equator (the usual case) is of the same height as the diameter of the globe, and if it is intended to represent the whole globe, then a map projection such as the upper one on this page is obtained. This is the *cylindrical equal-area projection,* in which the lines of perspective are assumed to come from infinity as parallel lines. Clearly the equator is truly represented, since the length of the equator on the globe is the same as on the tangent cylinder. However, the poles, which on the globe are points, are elongated by this perspective projection into lines the same length as the equator. This results in great east-west stretching in high or polar latitudes as well as crowded parallels. Observe that half the circumference of the globe is compressed into the distance representing the length of the diameter of the globe, and that the spacing between parallels decreases away from the equator. This projection, then, is so objectionable in high latitudes as to be little used.

The cylinder of paper may once more be wrapped tangent to the equator of the globe, and the origin of the perspective lines transferring the geographical grid to the paper may be placed elsewhere. If the origin be placed in the center of the globe, *the central cylindrical perspective projection,* shown by the lower diagram on page 496 results. Once again the equator is truly represented, but obviously the poles can never be shown, since they lie parallel to the tangent cylinder. High latitudes are so grossly exaggerated in area and shape that this is hardly a satisfactory projection.

11. **Mercator.** Using the ideas contained in the above projections, it is possible to construct other cylindrical projections that do have significance. Gerhardus Mercator in 1569 published one which bears his name. It had great significance in the age of exploration by sea, and it is the best known projection today. It is also most commonly misunderstood. Mercator compromised between the cylindrical equal-area and the central cylindrical perspective projections by spacing the parallels not according to any perspective arrangement but mathematically, so that expansion of the area north and south of the equator is at the same scale as expansion east and west in any given latitude. For example, the parallel of 60° latitude is, on any cylindrical projection, just twice as long as on the earth, and 80° latitude is six times as great. Mercator made his distortion in the N.–S. direction in these same proportions. The projection is, therefore, conformal, but of increasing scale and decreasing fidelity of larger shapes away from the equator; and the poles cannot be shown (Plate 7).

The Mercator projection owes its fame to the fact that a *straight line* upon it cuts all meridians at the same angle and is a *rhumb line,* or line of true compass direction.[1] It is not necessarily the shortest line between

[1] A line of true or constant direction on the globe that trends in one of the cardinal directions (E. W. N. or S.) is a straight line since it is a parallel or meridian of the geographical grid. Any line trending in any other direction must cut across the geographical grid and, on the globe, follows a spiral path, or *loxodrome,* which curves toward the nearest pole, but theoretically never reaches it. The spiral path of the loxodrome may be demonstrated by drawing a line on the globe that everywhere trends northeast, for example.

two points on the earth (unless they are on the same meridian or both are on the equator), but it is one the direction of which is easily ascertained, and also it can be steered by compass in a ship or airplane. Therefore, navigators generally use the Mercator map or chart to determine their direction of movement. *Great circles,* or shortest routes between widely spaced points, are often approximated by traveling along a series of rhumb lines obtained from the Mercator projection, rather than trying to steer a constantly changing compass course. The Mercator projection has obtained the sanction of established use to such a degree that it is often misused where equal-area projections or other projections of the whole world would be more appropriate. Much confusion over the size and positions of areas on the earth, such as the relative areas of Greenland and South America (compare the lower projection on page 500 with the lower one on page 496), or the idea that North America is located between Europe and Asia arises from the inappropriate use of the Mercator projection.

12. **Elliptical Projections.** The tangent cylinder lends itself to other perspective and mathematical projections.[1] A related class consists of those oval or elliptical projections of the whole earth in which the meridians are not parallel to each other, but are less widely separated toward the poles. In these projections the diameter of the globe forms the N.–S. axis, while the E.–W. axis is taken as twice this value. This relationship of distance from pole to pole, being one half the distance along the equator, is the same as on a globe and is the basis for equality of area. Three equivalent projections on this scheme are shown on page 499. *Mollweide's homolographic* and the *Sanson-Flamsteed sinusoidal* projections both possess meridians equally spaced on the parallels, and the latter are truly parallel as on the globe. They differ from each other in that the homolographic diminishes the interval between parallels toward the poles, thereby expanding E.–W. the shapes of the lands in the high latitudes; the sinusoidal expands the interval between parallels toward the poles, thereby contracting the E.–W. extent of lands in high latitudes. The *Aitoff* projection (p. 499) effects a compromise by departing from the parallelism of the parallels of the globe. De-

[1] O. M. Miller, "Notes on Cylindrical World Map Projections," *Geographical Review,* Vol. 32 (1942), pp. 424–430.

spite the curved parallels, equivalence is maintained by decreasing the spacing of the meridians toward the margins of the projection. The result is a pleasing projection in which shapes of land areas are well shown.

Mollweide projection

13. A drawback to all the oval projections is that only the areas adjacent to the central meridian have good shapes. One solution is to lengthen the points that represent the poles to lines parallel to, but not as long as, the equator. Such projections are those of *Eckert* and *Denoyer's semi-elliptical.* They may be made equivalent, but they introduce their own errors of shapes, for, obviously, the poles cannot truly be shown as lines.

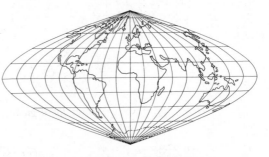

Sanson-Flamsteed projection

Aitoff projection

14. A second rationalization consists of "interrupting" the world projections so as to create several central meridians around each of which is plotted a segment of the geographical grid. This reduces the errors of shape very materially while retaining equality of area. Carried to its extreme, these interruptions would be the "gores" of paper with which an inexpensive globe is covered (upper map, p. 500). One interrupted projection is *J. Paul Goode's homolosine* projec-

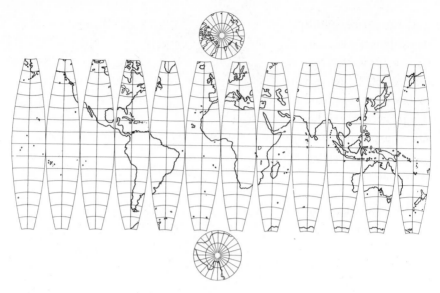

Gores for a globe

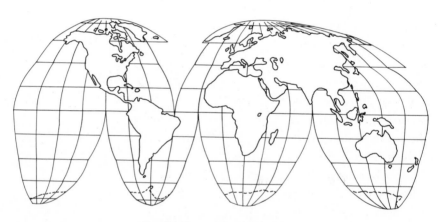

Goode's homolosine projection

tion. Close examination of the lower map above will reveal that Goode
has used Mollweide's homolographic projection from 40° to the poles,
and the sinusoidal between the equator and 40°, in order to get the best
shapes for each area, and that he has "interrupted" the oceans to maintain the continents as units. Another edition of this projection interrupts the continents to give continuity to the oceans. V. C. Finch has
provided a useful interruption of the Aitoff projection by eliminating

some of the landless areas of the earth and fitting the Australian–New Zealand segment into the position normally occupied by the Indian Ocean (Plate 22). A common reaction to these interrupted projections is objection to the fragmentary appearance of the geographical grid. Once it is appreciated how the various fragments fit, the realistic shapes and equivalent areas must be acknowledged to be an advantage over other world projections.

The sinusoidal projection is used in this book with a three-lobed interruption (see map, p. 372). The lobe containing Europe and Africa uses the central meridian of 20° E., but each of the other two segments has a different central meridian north of the equator from that south of the equator because the land mass of South America is distinctly east of North America and the center of Australia is about 40° east of the approximate center of Asia.

15. **Projections to a Plane.** Another group of projections is derived by the perspective extension of the geographical grid from a globe to a plane that is tangent to that globe. Since a plane is used, and not a cylinder, only one half or less of the earth can be depicted. Moreover, these projections are azimuthal, since all great circle lines that pass through the tangent point (center of the projection) are straight lines and therefore directions are truly shown from the center of the projection. Three points are commonly chosen as the origin of the perspective lines: infinity, to produce the *orthographic projection;* the circumference of the globe at the point diametrically opposite the tangent plane, giving the *stereographic projection;* and the center of the globe, called the *gnomonic projection.* These projections may be prepared in three different forms or cases: *equatorial* (*normal*), with plane perpendicular to the equator; *polar,* with plane perpendicular to the pole; and *oblique,* with the plane in some intermediate position.

16. The orthographic projection shows considerable compression of the marginal areas of the hemisphere (upper map, p. 502), just as perspective lines from infinity compress the high latitudes of the cylindrical equal-area projection. However, this is a useful projection because it has approximately the appearance of a globe, viewed from a distance, or a photograph of a globe. It is not exactly the same because neither the human eye nor the camera is at infinity.

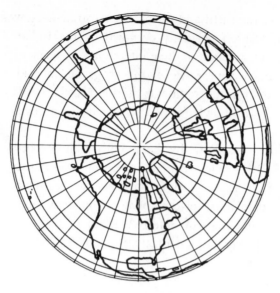

Orthographic polar projection

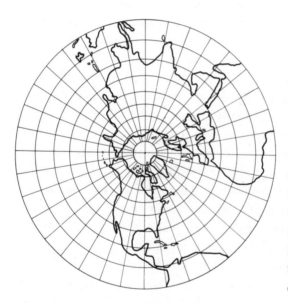

Stereographic polar projection

17. The stereographic projection below has a geographical grid which expands away from the tangent point. It is conformal, but exaggerates areas near its margins as do all projections that show angles correctly.

18. On the gnomonic projection (p. 503), with perspective lines derived from the center of the globe (similar to the central cylindrical perspective projection), the margins of a hemisphere cannot be shown since they lie in a plane parallel to the tangent surface. Indeed only a small part of a hemisphere can be shown without excessive expansion of shapes and sizes of areas. There is one unique property of the gnomonic projection which makes it useful in spite of its obvious defects. This is the fact that all straight lines drawn on the projection are great circle routes (i.e. great circle or circumference lines on the globe become straight lines on the projection). It is therefore possible for the navigator to determine readily the shortest distance between

two points by plotting them on the gnomonic chart and connecting them with a straight line. Points along this line can be transferred to the Mercator chart (where they will form points on an arc unless they lie wholly on the equator or on a meridian) to obtain azimuths or directions (rhumb lines) by which to steer to approximate a great circle course.

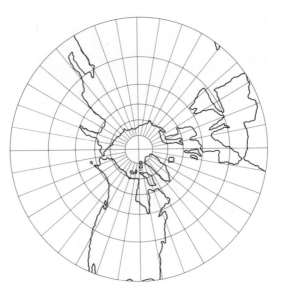

Gnomonic polar projection

19. The principle of the tangent plane may be used with the perspective lines originating elsewhere than stated above. It also may be followed in mathematically locating the geographical grid without recourse to perspective. Two well-known projections of the latter type were constructed by the French cartographer Lambert in the 18th century. *Lambert's Azimuthal Equal-Area* projection gives satisfactory shapes to large areas of approximately equal dimensions and is therefore well adapted to use for continents, as in the plates in this book (Plates 13 and 19 are in the equatorial case; Plates 15 and 17, the oblique case). It is sometimes employed for hemispheres, but here the distortion of the peripheral areas becomes noticeable as in the map on page 237.

20. The *Lambert's Azimuthal-Equidistant* projection derives its name from the fact that any line drawn outward from the center of the projection not only has a true azimuth but also is true to scale throughout its length (maps, pp. 397 and 398). Since these are the two properties desired, shapes and areas cannot be considered important, and the projection may be extended to contain the whole world within its circumference. If this projection be plotted around the North Pole (map, p. 504), Antarctica occurs everywhere around its periphery, since all direc-

Azimuthal-equidistant polar projection

tions are south from the North Pole and must inevitably lead to the South Pole; and, on this projection, the South Pole is at its true scale distance— the radius of the projection. If plotted around a point between pole and equator, both poles will be shown as centers from which the geographical grid curves and loops outward (map, p. 505). This projection has practical value, for example, to radio engineers, since radio waves travel along straight lines outward from the center of propagation.

21. **Conic Projections.** When map-makers and map-users are interested in areas of less than hemisphere proportions, they may employ parts of the foregoing projections or they may turn to a series of projections based on the concept of another developable geometric figure placed tangent to the globe. This new figure is the cone, which is a surface intermediate between a cylinder and a plane and may be "unrolled" to become a plane. Commonly the apex of the cone is considered to lie on the polar axis of the earth extended into space, so that the cone is tangent to a selected *standard parallel*. Following the analogy of the cylinder, this parallel must be of true length and scale, since it is a line on the globe and the cone both. When the cone is unrolled and opened out into a plane surface, the standard parallel becomes an arc of a circle. All *other* parallels remain parallel to the standard parallel and are therefore concentric arcs on the map projection. The meridians are straight lines radiating outward from the apex of the cone.

In its simplest form, the conic projection is derived by perspective from the center of the globe so that the parallels are unevenly spaced, becoming farther apart away from the standard parallel. The ordinary *simple conic projection* has the parallels equally spaced at an arbitrarily

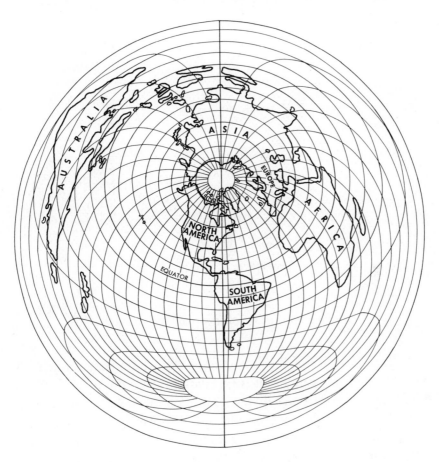

Azimuthal-equidistant oblique projection

chosen interval, and is particularly suited to areas of middle latitudes which extend a greater distance from east to west than from north to south. An improvement in scale can be attained by giving the conic projection *two standard parallels*. The concept here employed can be likened to passing the cone through a portion of the circumference of the globe, making the surface of the cone coincide with the two parallels (diagram below).[1] The overall result is better, since scale errors are reduced, compared to a simple conic.

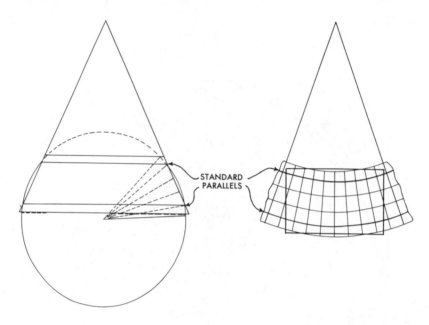

STANDARD PARALLELS

Conic projection with two standard parallels

22. To add either of these desirable properties to conic projections with two standard parallels it is necessary to space the parallels to get quadrilaterals proportionately the same as on the globe, or to space the parallels so that scale along parallel and meridian is the same at their intersections. The former spacing is known as *Alber's Equal-Area* projection and may be recognized by the fact that outside of the standard parallels the spacing of other parallels decreases. The latter is *Lambert's Conformal Conic* projection, and its parallels are increasingly wider apart beyond the standard parallels. Once again, these conic projections are best adapted to areas extending primarily east and west. By careful selection of the standard parallels, either projection will give

[1] Obviously a cylindrical projection also may be constructed secant to the globe, rather than tangent. Such a projection, for example, is Gall's Stereographic in which the parallels of 45° N. and 45° S. become standard parallels, true to scale.

506   *Maps*

a map of the United States, for example, with very little scale error.[1]

23. The simple conic projection may be modified in other ways than the above. *Bonne's projection,* shown on this page, is commonly encountered in atlases for continental areas having the north-south axis longer than the east-west (North America or South America, for example). The equally-spaced concentric arc parallels are retained, but the meridians are curved so that they meet at the pole, rather than extending as straight lines meeting in space at the apex of the cone. The spacing of meridians on the parallels gives quadrilaterals of true proportion to similar ones on the earth, and thus the projection is equal-area. Shapes are good along the straight central meridian only.

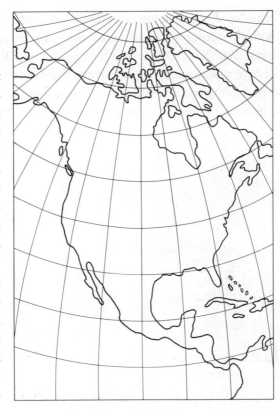

Bonne's projection

24. Another modification of the conic is particularly well known to Americans because it is the projection used for the detailed maps of the United States comprising the "Topographic Atlas," issued in the form of the familiar quadrangle sheets. This is the American polyconic projection in which not one cone but a whole series of cones are

[1] Both of these projections have been calculated for the United States by the United States Coast and Geodetic Survey. Alber's Equal-Area, with standard parallels at 29½° N. and 45½° N., has a maximum scale error at 1¼% in the United States. Lambert's Conformal Conic, with standard parallels at 33° N. and 45° N., is 2½% off at the maximum, within the United States.

considered to rest tangent on the globe, each at a different parallel but
with their apexes in a common line. Each parallel then is an arc of a
circle, but the circles have different centers so that the arcs are not concentric to one another. Meridians drawn through the parallels at their
true scale positions will yield one straight central meridian, and the
remainder curved (diagram below). Since the principle is one of ad-

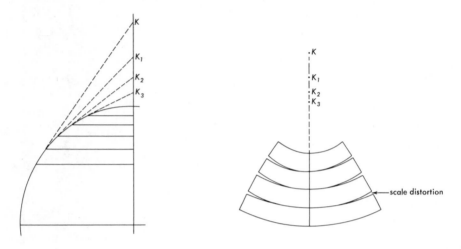

Polyconic projection

justment northward and southward along many parallels representing
many cones, this projection is best suited for areas of great length in
those directions and of limited east-west extent. Although the polyconic projection is neither equal-area nor conformal, its use for quadrangle sheets has been firmly established, probably because of the ease
of construction from published figures.[1] At the publication size and
large scale of the quadrangles, it is not easy to recognize the lack of
equivalence or conformality on an individual sheet. A disadvantage of
the American polyconic is that sheets lying along the same parallels will
not fit together except by distorting the paper, although any number
may be placed in a N.–S. line with perfect coincidence of margins.

25. The International Map of the World at the scale of 1:1,000,000
is divided into sheets 6° in longitude and 4° in latitude. It is on the

[1] United States Coast and Geodetic Survey, Special Publication No. 5.

Lallemand Polyconic projection in which the familiar principle of two standard parallels is employed for each sheet and for each of the many cones. This projection also uses straight-line meridians with two standard meridians on each sheet. This device permits each sheet to be independently adjusted to one of the secant cones, yet to fit against the margins of the adjacent sheets north, south, east, and west. Obviously the Lallemand projection is a compromise and is neither equal-area nor conformal.

26. The catalogue of map projections is by no means exhausted by the projections named above. Some additional manipulations take the following general forms:

a. Projections onto geometrical figures other than cylinder, plane, and cone. The figure may be a cube or other polyhedron. The geographical grid may be arbitrarily spaced within a conventional surface such as a circle.

b. Turning the cylinder or cone so that the developable geometrical figure is "skewed" with relation to the geographical grid. Examples are the *Transverse Mercator* and the *Transverse Polyconic,* in which the "good parts" along the equator of the Mercator and along the central meridian of the polyconic are given other orientations. Bonne's projection becomes *Werner's* when the tangent cone is fitted across the pole instead of along a parallel. *Werner's projection* becomes *Goode's Polar Equal-Area projection* when interrupted (see map, p. 26).

IV. Map Symbols

27. It has previously been stated that maps are selective representations of facts of distribution. This is true even of the topographic map, which shows a small area at large scale, because all the manifold aspects of the earth's surface cannot be depicted. The usual combination of selected features on topographic maps falls into five categories:

a. The surface configuration, including form, elevation, and relief.[1]

b. The drainage pattern, including running water, standing water, and permanent ice.

[1] See definition of relief given on page 101.

c. The material works of man, including settlements, structures he erects, transportation ways he builds, and other facts of his land use.

d. Certain invisible aspects of man's use of the land such as political boundaries and air routes.

e. The conventions of the map such as geographical grid, borders, index numbering, and so forth.

Sometimes a sixth category consists of the vegetation cover.

Obviously the category of invisible facts can be represented on the map only by means of symbols. It is less obvious perhaps, but just as true, that all the other categories also require symbols. How can a railroad track 4' 8½" between rails be drawn to scale, with ties, ballast, and switches? How can a stream be shown that changes its course, its width, and its volume? How would you draw a hill? The use of symbols or conventions that stand for given facts is imperative. The quality and accuracy of a topographic map depends on the selection of data and their symbolization.

The symbols commonly used on the United States topographic maps are depicted on page 511. Those that represent point locations or linear distributions require no explanation, for they are generally a stylized portrayal of a tangible fact as seen from a vertical position,[1] or an arbitrary representation of an intangible. However, surface configuration has a broad two-dimensional aspect that is difficult to symbolize and a third, or vertical, dimension that must be shown and is even more difficult to present on the two-dimensional surface of a map.

28. **Representing the Vertical Dimension.** An oblique (nonvertical) photograph such as that taken out of a window of an airplane shows the vertical dimensions of the land by the principles of perspective, but scale obviously changes away from the camera, and objects are obscured by both distance and intervention of other objects between them and the camera. The cartographer may render a similar "pictorial" impression of relief. He may adjust distance and scale by changing his position with reference to perspective from place to place on the map. However, he must always displace some portion of the landforms from

[1] This fact will be appreciated by noting that the marsh symbol is viewed from a horizontal position.

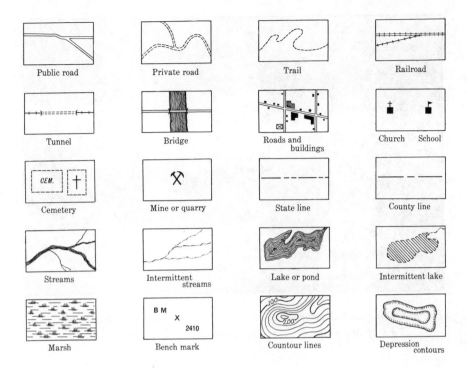

Public road	Private road	Trail	Railroad
Tunnel	Bridge	Roads and buildings	Church School
Cemetery	Mine or quarry	State line	County line
Streams	Intermittent streams	Lake or pond	Intermittent lake
Marsh	Bench mark	Countour lines	Depression contours

Symbols on U. S. topographic maps

their true positions and obscure some areas by that displacement, in order to show height and depth. The high volcanic cone of Fujiyama in the map on page 442, for example, is drawn from an oblique view, whereas the urban areas of Yokohama and Tokyo are seen from a vertical position. The realistic effects of this map by Guy-Harold Smith, or of the "physiographic method" used so effectively by Erwin Raisz (see maps on pages 68, 70, and 76 and many others in this book) may compensate for the errors inherent in an oblique view. The physiographic method is, of course, a symbol system because each type of land surface is represented in a particular way, rather than as an individual unique form.[1] If each mountain were drawn as exactly as possible, which of the numerous oblique views would be representative of it?

[1] Erwin Raisz, "The Physiographic Method of Representing Scenery on Maps," *Geographical Review,* Vol. 21 (1931), 297–304. A considerable degree of realism characterizes the use of these symbols in that the drainage pattern is closely followed, as well as the trends of uplands and changes in slope.

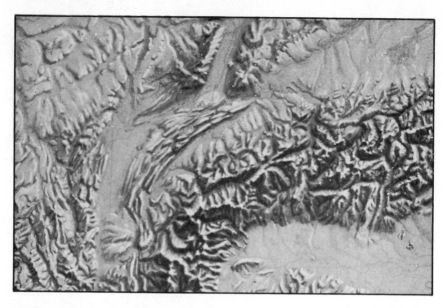

Plastic shading with oblique illumination. (*Switzerland and adjacent areas, from a map of Europe by R. E. Harrison, Ginn and Company, 1958*)

29. The vertical aerial photograph gives some impression of surface forms by the distribution of light and shadow. Unless the contrasts are strong and the relief of the surface is great the nature of the surface may not be readily recognized. This is a common disadvantage of photomaps. Indeed vertical photographs must be used in stereographic pairs [1] in order to measure slope, height, and relief. The cartographer may employ light and shadow more effectively than most photographs to give the appearance of the vertical dimension on a two-dimensional surface because he can select the amount and the angle of illumination. This method is called plastic shading (as in the map above, which should be compared with the map on page 455). It is not susceptible to measurement, unless combined with some other form of relief representation.

30. A more measurable employment of light and shadow is known as the hachure system. Hachures are short lines drawn vertical to the

[1] A pair of photographs which have some part of their area in common but are photographed from different angles so that when placed in a stereoscopic instrument (or properly viewed by the unaided eyes) they produce a three-dimensional image.

steepest slope, thin lines representing gentle slopes and thick lines representing steep slopes. In the Lehman system, slopes of 45° or greater employ hachures so close together that they merge into solid black masses. Hachured maps are difficult to draw and difficult to make measurements from, although the effect of relief is pleasant to the eye, particularly when combined with light and shadow effects (map at right). High and flat areas may be difficult to distinguish from low and flat areas, and absolute altitude must be indicated by figures.

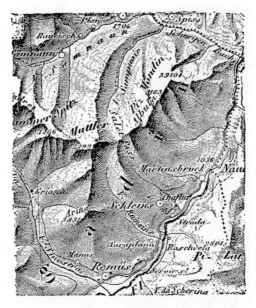

Hachuring with oblique illumination.
(From the Dufour map of Switzerland)

31. While all the above systems have their peculiar merits, cartographers more commonly employ another system, particularly for maps of topographic quality. This is the contour line, which may be defined as an imaginary line on the surface of the ground everywhere at the same elevation above the datum plane for vertical measurements. Successive contour lines above and below each other are separated by an arbitrary contour interval. In reading a map employing contour lines it is mandatory that we know the contour interval as well as the exact elevation of the lines. Since a contour line is everywhere throughout its length parallel to the datum plane, it neither rises nor falls in elevation, and it must, if traced far enough, come back to close with itself to form an endless line. No two contour lines may touch each other, since they are separated by a contour interval, although a vertical or overhanging cliff because of the horizontal position of the lines printed on the map will cause the contours to join or cross each other.

The way in which certain surface features are represented by contour lines is shown on the relief sketch and map on page 514.

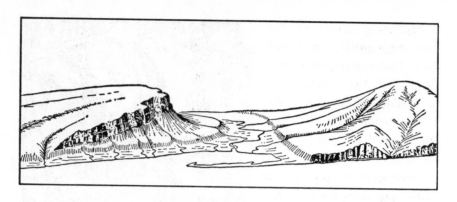

A relief sketch and its contour map representation

Certain basic rules for the interpretation of contour lines are:

a. Contour lines are continuous and do not branch or cross.

b. If a contour line closes upon itself within the area of the map, the land slopes upward from the area outside to the area within the enclosure. Therefore, a group of more or less concentric closed contour lines represents a hill.

c. Contour lines bend when they approach a stream valley so that the bend in the line points in the upstream direction. Relations of valleys to contour lines may be seen in the radial drainage pattern around Mount St. Helens in the map on page 427.

d. Contour lines that enclose depressions which have no outlets at the altitude of the contour lines must be specially marked in order to reveal that the enclosed area is lower (see rule *b* above). This marking usually is in the form of hachures pointing downslope drawn along the contour lines, at right angles to the lines.

e. Some map producers emphasize particular lines (for example every fifth line) by greater width of line in order to guide the eye through the complexities of many adjacent lines.

When properly selected as to contour interval and width of line in relation to the scale of the map and the relief of the area, contours may give a very excellent *visual* impression of the configuration of the surface. Where the contours are bunched together the slopes are great and, if the contour lines are irregular, the surface is rough. Where the contours are closed and concentric the reader sees ridge tops, hilltops, and mountain ranges. Areas of widely spaced contours are low in slope and may represent plains, valleys, or broad upland surfaces according to their relationships to other features. Thus, the qualitative characteristics of the surface may be read almost at a glance and with about as full comprehension as provided by any other symbol system. Quantitatively, it is possible to read altitude within the limits of the contour interval. Spot heights may be used to supplement the value of the lines. It is also possible to determine the vertical relief between two or more points. Horizontal distances being known, the calculation of slope is possible. The contoured topographic map, then, is favored by engineers and others who must have quantitative data. Some geographers and physiographers have transformed contour maps into relative relief and average slope maps.[1]

32. **Quantitative and Non-quantitative Data.** The principle behind the contour line has been applied to the representation of quantitative data on maps. These lines are called *isarithms,* or lines of equal value. Examples of isarithms are furnished in the field of climatology: isotherms (lines of equal temperature, Plate 24); isobars (lines of equal pressure, Plate 25); isohyets (lines of equal precipitation, Plate 27). In

[1] Examples are: C. K. Wentworth, "A Simplified Method of Determining the Average Slope of Land Surfaces," *American Journal of Science,* Series 5, Vol. 20 (1930), pp. 184–194. E. Raisz and J. Henry, "An Average Slope Map of Southern New England," *Geographical Review,* Vol. 27 (1937), pp. 467–472. Guy-Harold Smith, "The Relative Relief of Ohio," *Geographical Review,* Vol. 25 (1935), pp. 272–284.

these examples the data are continuous in their distribution and change only in amount or degree. Some authorities therefore distinguish *iso-pleths,* or lines of equal value drawn through data that are discontinuous, such as the distribution of people on the face of the earth. Very often the interval between isarithms or isopleths is given a color or pattern to focus attention not on the line of equal value but on the value category comprehended between two such lines. This principle is used in the snowfall map of Canada (p. 368), the average rainfall map of the world (Plate 7), and the population maps of the world (Plates 1 through 6).

33. Quantitative data may also be represented by dots placed on the map. These dots may have a uniform value as on the maps of corn production in the United States (p. 331), or their value may differ with the size of the dot as in the map of distribution of population in Pennsylvania (p. 275). In either case the visual impression of distribution may be excellent if the relationships between scale, size, or sizes of dots and values of dots are carefully considered. However, the difficulty of counting many dots, and the impossibility of counting merging dots limits the quantitative use of this symbol system. To obviate this objection, various schemes have been proposed such as arrangement of dots in countable patterns like squares or rectangles; use of open or shaded large circles through which the individual dots of congested areas may be recognized; employment of "spherical dots," in which value equals the volume of the sphere rather than area of the circle or dot; and the erection of square dots or cubes into piles of blocks. The latter is a step toward a graphical system. It is possible to place any of the common figures such as pie graphs, bar graphs, and line graphs on the face of a map.

34. Non-quantitative distributions are represented by a great diversity of symbols indicating points, linear patterns, or areal patterns. Sometimes the symbol selected is purely arbitrary, and sometimes it is a pictorial effect. Consider as an example the map of the rice-land topography on the delta of the Mahanadi (p. 121). Drainage ditches and unpaved roads use symbols employed on many maps, although the ditch symbol also is used for a wall on some maps. Coastal bar and waste land is an arbitrary symbol easily drawn and in good contrast to the mangrove and jungle symbol, which attempts to look like

the vegetation it presents. One must read more closely and accurately to appreciate that the blank areas are rice land, the avowed subject of the map. Because symbols are not always self-explanatory, a well-considered map has a legend or key defining such symbols. It is a good map-reading habit to examine the legend as well as the scale (and contour interval and projection) before attempting the interpretation of a map.

35. Greater legibility on maps often is obtained by the use of colors. Colors may be selected with some relationship to the facts they present, as, for example, on many atlas maps presenting the world distribution of natural vegetation. The number of categories being limited, colors may be selected that suggest the vegetative associations portrayed. The Dry Lands and Grasslands may be assigned grays or yellows whose color density varies in proportion to the floral density. The forest groups may be designated by greens whose shades and densities may be related to temperature concepts. Tundra and icecaps may then be gray or white. Colors thus used are easily remembered. A false impression often is conveyed to the uninitiated by the hypsometric system used to represent altitude of land surfaces, particularly on small-scale maps. Contour lines at large and often irregular intervals separate colors which usually begin with greens at low altitudes and progress through yellows and browns to reds at high altitudes. Because of the infrequency of the contour lines and the wide extent of the color areas, the unfortunate and erroneous impression may be given that elevation changes abruptly at the contact of two colors, and that little change takes place within a given color area.

Legibility of maps is more than a matter of color or of symbol selection. It is related to the function of the map. Topographic maps portraying many of the tangible features of a landscape and some related intangible data require approximately equal emphasis and clarity among cultural symbols, so that all may be distinguishable, and sufficient emphasis on physical symbols (often obtained through color) so that they form a readily intelligible pattern upon which the cultural symbols are distributed. Maps of smaller scale covering larger areas usually place particular emphasis on a limited number of distributions. For example, note the emphasis given to Indian trails in Michigan in the map on page 272 and to the road from Peshawar to Bukhara in the map on page 457. Lack of a striking symbol for the cropland of Alaska in the map on page 386 makes the cropland difficult to locate among the mountains and taiga.

V. Map Sources and Collections

36. **Atlases.** Collections of maps brought together in bound or loose-leaf form are known as atlases. Because of their great utility and handiness compared to individual sheet maps, atlases form a basic reference source comparable to dictionaries and encyclopedias. The subject area of an atlas may be as general as the world, or as detailed as a county or other minor political division. In the United States most atlases are produced commercially, but some countries, such as France, Finland, Poland, Czechoslovakia, the U.S.S.R., and Canada, have provided extremely valuable and significant national atlases.

37. **Sheet Maps.** Unbound sheet maps exist for such a variety of areas and subjects, and in such tremendous quantities, that reference collections are very limited in comparison with the distribution of atlases. In the United States, local and state government offices and libraries often are well supplied with sheet maps of their particular areas. For the nation as a whole and for foreign coverage the major sources available to the student or map user are the Federal Government and the major geographical societies. Inquiries concerning domestic mapping may be directed to Map Information Office, U. S. Geological Survey, Washington 25, D. C. This office has knowledge not only of the topographic quadrangles and other mapping work of the U.S.G.S. but also of the work of the Coast and Geodetic Survey, the U. S. Department of Agriculture, and all other mapping sections of the Federal Government. Foreign map collections of real significance exist in Washington at the Library of Congress, Army Map Service (Department of the Army), Hydrographic Office (Department of the Navy), and Department of State. The most important non-governmental collection is in New York City at the American Geographical Society.

The list of publishers of sheet maps is very extended. However, a limited number of publishers should be known to every map user. For the United States, the topographic quadrangles of the U.S.G.S. (supplementary work by Mississippi River Commission; U.S.C.&G.S., Tennessee Valley Authority; and others) are basic. The largest scale map covering all the United States is supplied by the Coast and Geodetic Survey's 1:500,000 air map. In the field of foreign and world mapping, the International Map of the World occupies an important position. This map is intended to cover the entire world at 1:1,000,000 as a co-operative effort among many nations, following map specifications agreed upon in 1909 and subsequently. Although far from complete, great progress has been made, particularly during World War II. The American Geographical Society has completely mapped the Americas south of the United States. European coverage has been completed by various national groups, and reissued by the British government, which also has prepared large parts of Asia and of Africa. The British group working on this and many other maps in Europe, Africa, and Asia is the Geographical Section of the General Staff (GS,GS). The American counterpart, which worked co-operatively with GS,GS during World War II to fill in the gaps in world maps at various scales, is the Army Map Service (AMS). Through the latter many universities and public libraries in the United States are participants in a map depository program which features the placement of AMS copies of foreign topographic maps in major population centers throughout the country.

Most topographic maps are of such detail that they must be issued in many individual sheets which form parts of the whole map. These sheets make up a set (or series) of maps. A map set commonly has the same characteristics throughout its sheets, which differ from each other primarily in position. The usual method of keeping records of these sheets is to plot them in miniature on a small-scale index map. All the maps mentioned in the paragraph above are grouped into sets.

Sheet maps which do not comprise sets must be regarded as individual items. Their cataloguing and filing raise problems comparable, but not entirely similar, to problems encountered with books and documents. The primary differences between the latter and maps are that area is the map subject of importance, and that a map is physically a thin, and often large, sheet of paper. A number of library systems for maps have been devised, but no general recognition of the merits of a particular one over all others has been forthcoming. However, the most useful systems all depend upon division of the world into arbitrary areas (usually political units). Small-scale maps of large areas are then catalogued with the major divisions of the world, and large-scale maps of small areas with the subdivisions. Maps that present unusual combinations of area are placed in one arbitrary division and cross-referenced as necessary. In large collections, the designation of area is supplemented with a definition of subject matter of the map. With these principles in mind, it will be found that the library system of any of the major collections may be readily used.

REFERENCES

1. DEETZ, C. H., and ADAMS, O. S. *Elements of Map Projection.* United States Coast and Geodetic Survey, Special Publication 68. Washington, D. C., 1921.
2. DEBENHAM, FRANK. *Map Making.* London, 1936.
3. DEETZ, C. H. *Cartography.* United States Coast and Geodetic Survey, Special Publication 205. Washington, D. C., 1936.
4. HINKS, A. R. *Maps and Survey,* Fourth Edition. Cambridge (England), 1942.
5. FISHER, I., and MILLER, O. M. *World Maps and Globes.* New York, 1944.
6. GREENHOOD, DAVID. *Down to Earth.* New York, 1944.
7. CHAMBERLIN, WELLMAN. *The Round Earth on Flat Paper,* National Geographic Society. Washington, D. C., 1947.
8. RAISZ, ERWIN. *General Cartography,* Second Edition. New York, 1948.
9. BROWN, L. A. *Story of Maps.* Boston, 1949.
10. MONKHOUSE, F. J., and WILKINSON, H. R. *Maps and Diagrams, Their Compilation and Construction.* New York, 1952.
11. ROBINSON, A. H. *Elements of Cartography.* New York, 1953.
12. ROBINSON, A. H., and THROWER, N. J. W. "A New Method of Terrain Representation," *Geographical Review,* Vol. 47 (1957), pp. 507–520.

B · THE ATMOSPHERE

I. Some Fundamental Meteorological Principles [1]

1. **Composition of the Atmosphere.** The atmosphere is a mixture of gases. About 78 per cent is nitrogen and about 21 per cent is oxygen; but of the remaining 1 per cent the small proportion of water vapor and carbon dioxide is of the greatest importance in determining the character of the earth's climates. Water vapor is confined almost wholly to the lower layers of the atmosphere, 90 per cent of it lying below twenty-one thousand feet. Its average mass the world over is such that, if it were condensed, it would be the equivalent of a layer of water about one inch deep over the entire surface of the earth.

2. **Insolation.** For all practical purposes the sun is the only source of the heat which maintains the temperature of the earth's surface and the atmosphere. The solar radiation received at the surface of the earth depends upon four things: (1) the solar output of radiation, which fluctuates slightly in cycles of more or less regular recurrence; (2) the distance of the earth from the sun, which varies seasonally during the passage of the earth around the sun; (3) the inclination of the sun's rays to the plane of the horizon, which varies seasonally owing to the

Latitude	0	10	20	30	40	50	60	70	80	90
Summer half-year	160.5	169	173.5	173	169	160.5	149	139	134	133
Winter half-year	160.5	147	129.5	109	84	58.5	33	13	4	0
Annual	321.0	316	303.0	282	253	219.0	182	152	138	133

[1] These greatly condensed statements can offer to the student little more than an outline. The demands of time and space in this general survey do not permit a more penetrating treatment of the fundamental elements of geography; the student who plans to go on professionally must go much more deeply into the basic sciences of meteorology, climatology, geology, and geomorphology.

Some Fundamental Meteorological Principles 521

inclination of the earth's axis to the plane of its orbit and which also varies with latitude and local exposure; and (4) the transmission and absorption of the atmosphere. The preceding table (reference 6, p. 543) gives the total amounts of insolation (in kilogram-calories per square centimeter of level surface) at the top of the atmosphere. From these figures we see that in a year only about 40 per cent as much insolation is received above the poles as above the equator, and also that the rate of insolation falls off most rapidly between latitudes 50° and 60°.

3. **Heating of the Earth's Surface.** The effect of the distribution of insolation over the earth is to produce, in general, the greatest amount of heating near the equator and the least amount at the poles. This simple latitudinal arrangement, however, is complicated by the *differential heating of land and water.* Water heats more slowly than land and retains its heat longer under similar atmospheric conditions. The relatively slow heating of water is the result chiefly of three facts: (1) the specific heat of land is lower than that of water; (2) water is translucent, so that a given amount of insolation which is concentrated on the surface of the land penetrates through a considerable depth of water; and (3) water is mobile, and so can distribute the heat which it absorbs. Radiation from a water body being less rapid than from the land, the former retains for a longer period the heat which it receives.

4. **Heating the Air.** About 37 per cent of the solar radiation which reaches the top of the atmosphere is returned again to space by reflection, chiefly from upper cloud surfaces, but in part also from the earth's surface, especially from ice and snow. Of the 63 per cent not immediately returned to space, only about 10 per cent is absorbed by the atmosphere, and the remainder makes its way directly, or as diffuse sky-light, to the earth's surface.

The atmosphere is warmed chiefly by *conduction,* or contact with the earth, and by *radiation* from the earth. Owing primarily to the water vapor and, to a lesser extent, to the ozone and carbon dioxide, the air is able to absorb about 90 per cent of the long-wave terrestrial radiation, whereas it can absorb only about 10 per cent of the solar radiation. Since radiation absorbed in an air stratum is again radiated equally upward and downward, 45 per cent of the outgoing terrestrial radiation is returned again to the earth, and an equal amount finds its way out to space.

5. Cooling of the Earth.   Eventually as much heat is radiated from the earth as is received from the sun, for if this were not true the earth's average temperature would not remain approximately constant.   The effect of the atmosphere is to let through the incoming solar radiation and to intercept the outgoing terrestrial radiation, so that the surface temperature of the earth is somewhat higher than it would be without the protection of its gaseous envelope.   The effect of this absorption of earth radiation is greater as the amount of water vapor increases.   The cooling of the earth's surface by radiation is therefore most rapid at high altitudes and in dry regions where the amount of water vapor is at a minimum.

6. Vertical Arrangement of Temperature.   Because the atmosphere is heated chiefly from the surface of the earth, the temperature generally decreases with increasing altitude.   Up to an elevation of from six to nine miles this decrease is about 1° F. for each three hundred and thirty feet of increased altitude.   This is the average *vertical temperature gradient* in the free air.   Above six to nine miles (higher over the equator and lower near the poles) the temperature remains fairly constant with increasing elevation.   This upper atmosphere is known as the *stratosphere* (illustrated by the diagram on page 423).   The lower zone, in which the temperature decreases with increasing altitude and in which vertical air movements are common, is known as the *troposphere*.

7. Adiabatic Cooling and Warming of Air.   A mass of rising air is cooled adiabatically; that is, without the removal of any heat from the mass of air involved.   With increase of elevation the pressure decreases (see section 9, p. 524) and the air expands.   As air expands, it cools; in a mass of rising dry air this rate of cooling is about 1.6° F. for every three hundred feet.   This is the dry *adiabatic rate*.   When an air mass descends, this process is reversed, the air being warmed adiabatically at the same rate.

When the cooling of air results in the condensation of water (sect.

14), the dry adiabatic rate no longer prevails. Because of the liberation of latent heat in the process of condensation, the rate of temperature decrease becomes less, and the departure of this *retarded adiabatic rate* from the dry rate is greater as the rate of condensation is greater.

8. **Vertical Air Movements.** When the temperature of a mass of air is higher than that of surrounding air, the colder air settles and forces the warmer air to rise. This action is due to the fact that colder air has a greater density than warmer air. As long as the rising air mass is relatively warmer than the surrounding air at the same level, it will continue to rise. The relationship between the vertical temperature gradient in the surrounding air and the adiabatic rate in the rising air determines, therefore, whether a vertical movement shall continue or quickly cease. For if the rising air is cooled so rapidly that it becomes cooler than the surrounding air, it must settle back. If, on the other hand, the rising air is cooled more slowly, so that the ascending air remains warmer than the surrounding air, the rise is continued. Anything which increases the vertical temperature gradient or decreases the adiabatic rate tends to increase vertical air movements. For instance, if moisture is condensing in the rising air mass, the rate of cooling is retarded (sect. 7); therefore, air in which moisture is condensing tends to be more buoyant than air in which no condensation is taking place. Buoyancy is also increased if a cold layer of air overriding a warmer surface layer increases the vertical temperature gradient.

In general, then, vertical air movements are common in warm, moist air, and if clouds are present they take the *cumulus* (cauliflower-shaped) form. Cold air, on the other hand, is sluggish and does not rise easily; clouds in such air are commonly *stratus* (sheetlike).

9. **Pressure.** Atmospheric pressure is the result only of the weight of the overlying column of air. It is commonly measured in terms of the length of a column of mercury which will balance this weight. Normal pressure at sea level is about 30 inches of mercury (exactly 29.94 in.). With increasing altitude the pressure decreases: at 5000 feet it is about 25 inches; at 10,500 feet, about 20 inches; at 16,000 feet, about 16 inches.

The pressure is not uniform over the earth's surface, however, even at sea level. In general an area which becomes relatively warm compared with a neighboring area becomes also an area of low pressure. This can be explained by a consideration of two neighboring masses of air, one of which is heated and the other cooled. The column of air which is heated expands, while the cooled-air column contracts. This produces a movement at a high level away from the column of heated air and toward the column of cooled air, and as a result the pressure of the one is decreased and of the other is increased.

10. **Convection.** The result of the increase of pressure in one air mass and of the decrease in the other (sect. 9) is a movement of air along the surface of the earth from the cooler area, with its higher pressure, to the warmer area, with its lower pressure. In a closed system a complete circulation would become established: air moving away from the top of the warmed-air column toward the cooled column; air descending over the cooled area; air moving over the surface of the earth from the cooled area to the warmed area; and air rising over the warmed area. Such a circulation is called *convection*.

11. **Deflection Due to the Earth's Rotation.** On the surface of our planet, however, all moving bodies are deflected from their courses as a result of the earth's rotation. In this brief summary the causes of this deflection cannot be presented.[1] The fact is, however, that all moving bodies in the Northern Hemisphere are deflected to the right and that all moving bodies in the Southern Hemisphere are deflected to the left. This deflection is strongest at the poles and reaches zero along the equator.

12. **Winds and Pressures.** As a result of this deflection (sect. 11), the winds which otherwise might blow out from a center of high pressure across the isobars (lines of equal pressure) actually move parallel or nearly parallel to the isobars. In the Northern Hemisphere, with deflection to the right, the winds whirl around a high-pressure center in a clockwise direction; and in the Southern Hemisphere, with a deflection to the left, the air movement around a high is counterclockwise. The movement around a low-pressure center is just the reverse:

[1] See reference 6 (p. 543), p. 176 ff.

Some Fundamental Meteorological Principles 525

counterclockwise in the Northern Hemisphere and clockwise in the Southern Hemisphere. Over the oceans, where friction with the earth's surface is reduced to a minimum, the whirls are best developed and the winds are most nearly parallel to the isobars; but over the land, where friction retards the effect of the earth's rotation, the winds cross the isobars at larger angles (compare Plates 25 and 26).

13. **Humidity.** The amount of water vapor which can be mixed with the air depends on the temperature. At higher temperatures more water vapor can be present, but at lower temperatures much less water can exist in the air as a gas. Most of the time the actual amount of water vapor in the air is not so great as the maximum amount possible. The ratio between the water vapor actually present and the total possible amount at a given temperature is called the *relative humidity;* the ratio of the mass of water vapor to the total mass of air is called *specific humidity.* Relative humidity is measured in percentage: saturated air has a relative humidity of 100 per cent; air with half as much water vapor present as might be there has a relative humidity of 50 per cent.

14. **Condensation of Moisture.** In a mass of rising air the temperature is lowered at the adiabatic rate; and as the temperature decreases, the relative humidity, but not the specific humidity, increases. Eventually a level is reached where the relative humidity is 100 per cent. As cooling continues, the water vapor is now ready to condense into liquid form. Condensation must take place around some nucleus. As a matter of fact, in the earth's atmosphere there is no lack of minute particles, so that condensation can take place at once when the air reaches the saturation point. Condensation and the formation of clouds in nature are produced only by the cooling of moist air.

15. **Evaporation.** The evaporation of water takes place when the relative humidity of the air into which the water is evaporating is less than 100 per cent. It increases in rapidity as the relative humidity becomes lower. Water vapor can therefore be picked up rapidly by masses of descending air, since in them the temperature is constantly rising and the relative humidity falling (although, if evaporation is

going on, the specific humidity is increasing). Evaporation is more rapid from warm-water surfaces than from cold-water surfaces, it is more rapid over fresh water than over salt water, and it is more rapid in windy places than in places where the air is still.

16. **Precipitation.** Precipitation includes three forms: rain, snow, and hail. Rain falls when the drops of condensed moisture become large enough to fall through the ascending air currents. When the drops of water blown upward in the air currents reach temperatures below the freezing point, hail is formed. When the condensation takes place below the freezing point, snow crystals are formed.

The causes of rain are the same as the causes of condensation (sect. 14), although condensation may, of course, proceed only far enough to form clouds from which no precipitation takes place. In nature rain is caused almost exclusively by the cooling of moist air. Furthermore, the cooling of air is most effectively, but not exclusively, accomplished by upward movement (sect. 7). Air may be caused to rise by the convergence of air masses in motion, especially by the rapid convergence upon a center of low pressure; or it may be forced to rise as it moves onto the shore of a continent or over a range of mountains. Unless the air is warm and moist, however, rain will not be produced under either of these conditions; for the condition which would produce a rapid rise in buoyant air would cause only a sluggish rise, if any, in cold, dry air (sect. 8).

Conversely, the lack of rain in a given area is the result either of the prevalence of descending and warming air masses or of remoteness from the sources of moisture, or both.

II. The Physical Bases of Climatic Differences on the Earth

17. **The Controls of Climate.** The controls of climate may be grouped under seven headings: latitude, land and water, pressures and winds, cyclonic storms, ocean currents, mountain barriers, and a group of other minor controls.

18. **Latitude.** Because of the decrease of insolation with increase of

latitude (sect. 2), there is a general decrease of air temperature toward the poles. However, this arrangement of temperature is much modified by other controls, not only seasonally but also in the average annual conditions. Even the annual isotherms (lines of equal temperature) do not cross the continents parallel to the lines of latitude (diagram, p. 181).

19. **Distribution of Land and Water.** The differential heating of land and water is of chief importance in modifying the effect of latitude as a control of climate (sect. 3). An important distinction is recognized between *marine* and *continental* climates. Marine climates are characterized by smaller annual ranges of temperature, retarded maximum and minimum of temperature (that is, the maximum occurs in August or later in the Northern Hemisphere instead of in July), greater cloudiness, and a tendency toward fall or winter maximum of rainfall. Continental climates, on the other hand, have relatively large ranges of temperature (in other words, hotter summers and colder winters at the same latitude), the maxima and minima of temperature are not retarded (that is, they come in July and January, respectively, in the Northern Hemisphere), there is less cloudiness (especially in winter), and the rainfall shows a tendency toward a summer or late-spring maximum.

20. **Areas of High and Low Pressure** (Plate 25). Areas of high or low pressure develop over various portions of the earth's surface and remain there permanently or change with the passage of the seasons. Permanent areas of high pressure develop over those portions of the earth which remain throughout the year relatively much colder than neighboring areas in the same latitude. Such areas are located over the eastern sides of the oceans at about latitude 30° north and south and also over the icecaps of the polar regions (Greenland and Antarctica). The pressures over the continental regions of the middle latitudes change seasonally: equatorward of 40° during the summer months the lands become much hotter than the neighboring oceans and build up low-pressure centers; but during the winters these lows are dissipated, and where broad land masses extend far into the higher middle latitudes (poleward of 50°, as in North America and Eurasia)

they become much colder than neighboring water bodies of the same latitude and develop winter high pressures.

21. **General Circulation of Air** (Plate 26). There are three elements in the general circulation of air on the earth: (1) the *oceanic whirls;* (2) the *monsoons;* and (3) the *polar outbursts.*

The air moves around the permanent oceanic highs in great whirls. Because of the location of these highs about latitude 30° over the oceans, the air in the low latitudes moves generally from the east, and the air in the middle latitudes moves generally from the west. Over the bordering land masses the air over the east coasts in lower middle latitudes is moving poleward, while the air on the western sides is moving equatorward. Traditionally the easterly winds of the low latitudes are known as *trade winds,* and the westerly winds of the middle latitudes are known as *westerlies.* These winds are best developed over the oceans. The zone of high pressure about latitude 30° is known as the *horse latitudes.* The belt of calms along the equator where the two oceanic whirls converge is known as the *doldrum belt.*

The coasts of large land masses in lower middle latitudes and higher low latitudes which face toward the equator develop great seasonal differences between the temperatures and pressures over the land and over the water (sect. 3). Along these coasts, therefore, the oceanic whirls are interrupted by monsoons—winds which blow for six months in one direction and for six months in the opposite direction. These winds are onshore in summer and offshore in winter, deflected to the right or left according to the hemisphere. The greatest monsoon area of the world involves the whole south-facing coast of Asia and the north-facing coast of Australia. A monsoon tendency, subject to occasional interruptions, occurs also along the east coasts of continents in lower middle latitudes, where the oceanic whirl is made stronger in summer and is replaced by offshore winds in winter.

The polar outbursts are generated in areas of cold air accumulation. These are chiefly the permanently ice-covered lands—Greenland and Antarctica—and to a lesser extent the polar ocean, and the snow-covered surfaces of the northern continents in winter. Cold air accumulates under conditions of clear skies and an absence of surface winds. When conditions permit, the cold air is heavy enough to move away from the center of accumulation. It moves in all directions from the center, but chiefly toward the nearest area of low pressure, that is, the nearest warm area. Frequent outbursts therefore take place southeastward from Greenland to the North Atlantic Drift (Plate 23). Over the land these outbursts are known as *Polar Continental* air masses. As each puff of cold air moves southward over the northern continents it is warmed in its lower layers and is gradually pushed eastward in the stream of the westerlies. The cold air masses come farther and farther south as the Northern Hemisphere winter proceeds because they can move over previously snow-covered surfaces and so are to a less extent warmed in their lower layers. The cold waves which reach farthest toward the equator come in late winter and move over largely snow-covered lands. In summer, the cold air masses are quickly warmed and cannot push so far into the stream of the oceanic whirls. Cold air masses, being heavy and lying close to the earth, are to a much greater extent guided by terrain features than are the warm air masses of tropical origin. Also the deflective force of the earth's rotation has less effect on these moving masses of heavy air than on lighter tropical air, and consequently they move nearly at right angles to the isobars. For this reason the high pressures are speedily reduced, and the outbursts are pulsatory rather than continuous.

The actual wind in any one locality may be the result of the interaction between all three of these major systems. Cold air masses, perhaps much modified in their lower layers, penetrate far toward the equator. They push all the way across North America to the Caribbean; and one exceptionally strong polar outburst from Antarctica in 1942 brought temperatures in the 40's to the Amazon across the central lowlands of South America. It is important to note that only the cold air masses while they are still cold and heavy can move for long distances in nearly straight lines. All other air masses must move in curved lines under the action of the earth's deflective force, except within about 10° of the equator. So it is that easterly winds can cross northern South America and bring rain to the eastern slopes of the Andes. In the middle latitudes air masses moving onto the land from warm water areas cannot carry moisture to the continental interiors, which consequently remain dry.

22. **Cyclonic Storms.** It is chiefly the interaction between the air masses which form a part of the oceanic whirls and the air masses originating as polar outbursts which produces cyclonic storms. The term "cyclone" is applied to any whirling storm. In the tropics, on the eastern sides of the continents poleward of 10°, violent whirling storms known as *hurricanes* or *typhoons* sometimes develop and move along in the general stream of the oceanic whirl. Very violent local whirls of air in mid-latitude plains sometimes develop out of thunderstorms. These are *tornadoes*. These are all special kinds of cyclones—and in the popular vocabulary the word "cyclone" usually applies to such very violent storms. But meteorologists use the term "cyclone" also to apply to the much less violent whirling storms which develop normally and frequently along the fronts of advancing cold air masses.

As the cold air masses originating as polar outbursts are projected into the stream of relatively warm light air of the oceanic whirls, they become separated from the source region and proceed as homogeneous bodies of air shaped much like drops of water running on an inclined surface: they are steep in front, rounded on top, and trail out behind. The lighter winds of the westerlies ride up over the backs of these cold air masses, the rising air forming clouds and perhaps bringing rain in the process. But the warm light air forms eddies around the front of the cold air mass, eddies which circulate counterclockwise in the Northern Hemisphere and clockwise in the Southern Hemisphere. As the eddies form on the cold front, the cold air mass moves forward, pushing the eddy itself aloft. The result is strong, shifting winds, much cloudiness, and heavy rains. Along the immediate cold front thunderstorms develop in summer when the air of the oceanic whirl has a high temperature and carries much water vapor. In winter the advance of the cold air mass is marked by the familiar signs of an approaching storm—cirrus clouds, then stratus clouds forming a gray pall over the sky, then dark nimbus rain or snow clouds. The blizzards of the plains of North America are carried along by the front of the cold air through which snow is falling from aloft. Then the clouds are swept away and the weather becomes clear and cold. The alternation of warm, humid air of equatorial origin and clear, cold air of polar origin provides the rapid and extreme weather contrasts which are so characteristic of the

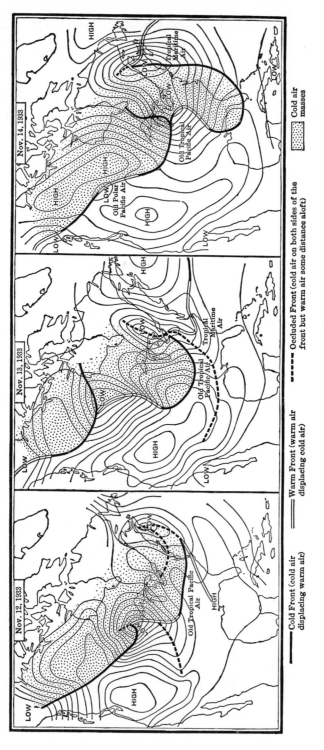

Air mass movements across North America on three successive days. Stippled areas are covered by air of polar-continental origin. These maps illustrate the southeastward advance of a fresh mass of polar air from its place of origin over northern Canada. Temperatures dropped from 20° to 30° in the midwestern states as the old tropical air was displaced. A second surge of cold polar air followed the first one. Rain or snow fell along the fronts where warm moist air was forced to rise and cool. The polar air masses, however, brought clear, cold weather. (After H. C. Willett)

middle-latitude climates. The accompanying maps (p. 532) show the sequence of conditions during the advance of a cold air mass across North America. Since these cyclonic storms produce large-scale updrafts of air, they are major causes of heavy rainfall, especially where the lighter air which they meet is already carrying large quantities of moisture.

23. **Ocean Currents** (Plate 23). The circulation of water in the oceans (see Appendix D, section 3) brings warm water into higher latitudes and cold water into the lower latitudes, and is therefore of great importance in producing the temperature differences which, in turn, maintain the system of pressure and winds. The arrangement of the warm and cold ocean water with reference to latitude and the continental coasts is a major factor, also, in determining the supply of moisture.

Where warm water closely approaches very cold lands there is a frequent and often violent movement of cyclonic storms. The world's stormiest ocean is in the higher middle latitudes of the Southern Hemisphere surrounding the ice-covered Antarctic Continent. Very stormy, also, are the warm waters south and southeast of Greenland, and those which approach the coldest part of Siberia in the North Pacific. These are all regions of maximum cyclonic activity and so of frequent and violent weather changes.

Since cold water yields little moisture to the air (sect. 15) and since the cooled air is sluggish and heavy, the coasts which have cold water to windward of them are commonly dry. Since cold water occurs on the west coasts of the continents from about 15° to 35°, this is also a region of low rainfall—especially the center of the belt between 20° and 30°, where the land is arid. Warm ocean water, on the other hand, is the one major source of moisture in the air, and lands which have warm water to windward are usually wet.

These relationships can be seen clearly by comparing the maps of rainfall, winds, and ocean currents (Plates 23, 26, and 27).[1]

24. **Mountains.** Mountains produce important local differences of climate. Updrafts of air through mountain valleys result in bringing

[1] See reference 9, pp. 599 ff.

more rain to mountainous areas than to neighboring lowlands. However, the effect of mountains in producing rain depends to a large degree on the character of the air which blows against them. Cold air can rise only sluggishly, if at all, and may produce only a low stratus cloud, as along the Peruvian coast. The heaviest rains in the world, however, are received on mountain slopes which lie in the path of warm, buoyant, moisture-laden air (sect. 8).

East-west mountain ranges act as temperature divides as well as rain-producers. If the movement of north or south winds is prohibited, the lowlands on the poleward side of a mountain range are made colder than they would otherwise be, and the lowlands on the equatorward side are made warmer.

25. **Other Lesser Controls of Climate.** Local climates are affected by other lesser controls. Forests moderate the temperature somewhat. The effect of forests on rainfall has been greatly exaggerated: rainfall is produced by forces which can be affected by the vegetation to only a very minor degree. Evaporation is greater over a forest than over bare ground, so that a forest cover permits the moisture from the ocean to penetrate farther inland than would be the case if no forests were present. But agricultural land is probably fully as effective as a forest in providing moisture for evaporation.

Among the many other minor controls affecting temperature and humidity are soils, and even the works of man, such as cities.

III. The Koppen Classification of Climates

26. The Köppen classification of climates is a quantitative system based on monthly and annual means of temperature and rainfall. Unlike many other climatic classifications, the lines which are used to limit the climatic types are given exact definitions and so are subject to checking and revision on the basis of new data. The boundaries, being isarithms (that is, connecting points of equal value), reveal the arrangement of the climatic elements much as contours reveal the shape of a hillside. The direction of greatest climatic difference is always at right angles to the boundary lines. The values which are used in the definitions of these boundaries are based on temperature, on precipita-

tion, or on combinations of these. This is not only because temperature and rainfall are among the most important climatic elements but also because these data are the only ones which are available for a large number of stations throughout the world. The Köppen system has become an international standard, and therefore it is presented in this book without modification.

27. The History of the Classification. Dr. Wladimir Köppen spent more than fifty years of his lifetime in the development of the system of classification which bears his name. His first attempt at a world classification included only temperature distinctions.[1] In 1900 temperature and moisture were both considered.[2] Eighteen years later a revised statement of the climatic classification was published, this time in essentially its present form.[3] With minor variations of definition, the system formed the basis of a book on world climatology, published in 1923.[4] Important revisions were introduced, however, on a wall map published by Köppen and Geiger in 1928. On this map certain changes in definition were made which were later discarded. The wide use of the wall map and the reproduction of its lines and definitions elsewhere have led to considerable confusion. In 1931 a second edition of Köppen's book was published, with still further revisions.[5] This last publication remains the latest pronouncement, and the definitions contained in it are being used in the preparation of a handbook of climatology.[6]

28. Main Outlines of the System. Köppen recognizes five major divisions of the world's climates. These divisions were intended to

[1] W. Köppen, "Die Wärmezonen der Erde, nach der Dauer der heissen, gemässigten und kalten Zeit, und nach der Wirkung der Wärme auf die organische Welt betrachtet," *Meteorologische Zeitschrift,* Vol. 1 (1884), pp. 215–226.

[2] Ibid. "Versuch einer Klassifikation der Klimate, vorzugsweise nach ihren Beziehungen zur Pflanzenwelt," *Geographische Zeitschrift,* Vol. 6 (1900), pp. 593–611.

[3] Ibid. "Klassifikation der Klimate nach Temperatur, Niederschlag, und Jahreslauf," *Petermann's Mitteilungen,* Vol. 64 (1918), pp. 193–203, 243–248.

[4] Ibid. *Die Klimate der Erde,* Berlin, 1923.

[5] Ibid. *Grundriss der Klimakunde,* Berlin, 1931.

[6] W. Köppen and R. Geiger, *Handbuch der Klimatologie* (in five volumes by various authors, still incomplete because of the disruption of German science by World War II).

correspond with A. de Candolle's five principal vegetation groups.[1] The five climatic divisions, identified by capital letters, are: *A*, rainy climates with no winters (no cool or cold season); *B*, dry climates; *C*, rainy climates with mild winters; *D*, rainy climates with severe winters; and *E*, polar climates with no warm season.

These various major categories are then subdivided. The *B*, or dry climates, are separated into semiarid, *BS* (*S* from the word *steppe*, or dry grassland), and arid, *BW* (*W* from the German *Wüste*, meaning "desert"). The polar deserts, or *E* climates, are subdivided into the marginal or tundra type, *ET*, and the climates of continuous frost, *EF*. The rainy climates, *A*, *C*, and *D*, are subdivided on the basis of the distribution of rainfall through the year. Those with no marked dry seasons are identified by the small letter *f* (from the German *feucht*, meaning "moist"), those with winter dry seasons are indicated by the small letter *w*, and those with summer dry seasons are indicated by the small letter *s*.[2]

Still further subdivision is made on the bases of other significant features of temperature and rainfall (sect. 30).

29. **Procedure in Classifying a Climate.** Since all these various letters have quantitative definitions, it is possible to determine from the statistics of temperature and rainfall the proper symbols to describe a climate. Climatic data for numerous stations are given in Appen-

---

[1] A. de Candolle, "Constitution dans le règne végétal des groupes physiologiques applicables à la géographie ancienne et moderne," *Archives des sciences physiques et naturelles*, Geneva, May, 1874.

De Candolle recognized as his five major plant groups: (1) megatherms, plants needing continuously high temperature and abundant moisture; (2) xerophytes, plants which tolerate dryness and need at least a short hot season; (3) mesotherms, plants needing a moderate amount of heat and a moderate supply of moisture; (4) microtherms, plants needing less heat, less moisture, and tolerant of shorter summers and colder winters; (5) hekistotherms, plants of the polar zone beyond the limits of the forest. It is now recognized that this classification of plants is quite inadequate. Any classification of climates, however, would recognize Köppen's basic categories, so that this historical relation to De Candolle is irrelevant.

[2] Note that there is an important distinction between capital and small letters. Capital *W* and capital *S* are used only with the *B* climates; small *w* and small *s* are used throughout the system, in every case to indicate the presence of a dry season. Similarly, *F* is used only with *E* climates and must not be confused with *f*. It is important, in writing the climatic symbols, to distinguish carefully between capital and small letters.

dix E. In classifying each station the following procedure should be used:

1. Is the station *E*? If so, is it *ET* or *EF*? If not—
2. Is the station *B*? If so, is it *BS* or *BW*? If one of these, what small letters must also be used? If not—
3. Is it *A*, *C*, or *D*? If *A*, is it *f*, *m*, or *w*? If one of these, what other small letters must also be used? If *C*, is it *f*, *s*, or *w*, and is it *a*, *b*, or *c*? What other small letters must also be used? If *D*, is it *f*, *s*, or *w*, and is it *a*, *b*, *c*, or *d*? What other small letters must also be used?

30. Definitions of the Symbols. The following definitions are arranged under the five major types and in the order *E*, *B*, *A*, *C*, and *D*. The figures are given in Fahrenheit degrees and inches, with the equivalents in centigrade and centimeters given in parentheses.[1]

E CLIMATES

E: warmest month below 50° (10°). *ET:* warmest month below 50° (10°) and above 32° (0°). *EF:* warmest month below 32° (0°).

B CLIMATES

Several formulae are used to identify the dry climates. This is necessary because the effectiveness of the rainfall in providing moisture in the ground for plants varies with the rate of evaporation, which, in turn, varies with the temperature and with the other elements previously listed (sect. 15). The formulae for the identification of the semiarid and arid climates must therefore take into account the total annual rainfall and the temperature, and they must also show that if the rain comes chiefly in the hot season its effectiveness is decreased, and that if it comes chiefly in the cold season its effectiveness is increased.

The phrase "chiefly in summer" is interpreted as meaning that at least 70 per cent of the total annual rainfall comes in the summer six months (April to September, inclusive, in the Northern Hemisphere). "Chiefly in winter" means that at least 70 per cent comes in the winter six months (October to March, inclusive, in the Northern Hemisphere). If less than 70 per cent is concentrated in either six-month period, then the rainfall is said to be evenly distributed.[2]

---

[1] Definitions from reference 5, pp. 127–136.

[2] Köppen's text is not definite concerning the exact meaning of "chiefly in summer" etc. Many writers use the same definition of summer rain as is used for the identification of *w* with *C* and *D* climates (ten times as much rain in the rainiest summer month as in the driest winter month). The most adequate definition hitherto suggested has been worked out by Russell, who recognizes nine rainfall regimes instead of only three (R. J. Russell, *Dry Climates of the United States, I, Climatic Map,* University of California Publications in Geography, Vol. 5 (1931), pp. 16–22).

There are two sets of formulae. One set gives us the humid limits of the dry climates, BS/H; the other set gives us the limits between arid and semiarid, BW/BS. There are three formulae in each set—one for evenly distributed rain, one for summer rain, and one for winter rain.

In these formulae r is the amount of rain which marks the humid boundary of the B climates, the amount of rain less than which is considered deficient; r' is the amount of rain which marks the limit between arid and semiarid, less than which is considered arid; t is the average annual temperature. The formulae are based on an empirical relationship between the temperature in degrees centigrade and the rainfall as measured in centimeters. They can therefore be used only with centigrade degrees and centimeters.

	BS/H	BW/BS
Rainfall evenly distributed	$r = 2(t + 7)$	$r' = t + 7$
Rainfall chiefly in summer	$r = 2(t + 14)$	$r' = t + 14$
Rainfall chiefly in winter	$r = 2t$	$r' = t$

These formulae were used in the preparation of the numerical tables on pages 540 and 541, which are given in degrees Fahrenheit and inches. Table I gives the BS/H boundary; Table II gives the BW/BS boundary.[1]

The following small letters are also used with the BW and BS climates:

$h:$ average annual temperature over 64.4° (18°).
$k:$ average annual temperature under 64.4° (18°).
$k':$ temperature of the warmest month under 64.4° (18°).
$s:$ indicates that at least 70 per cent of the rain falls in the winter six months.
$w:$ indicates that at least 70 per cent of the rain falls in the summer six months.

(The absence of s or w indicates that the rainfall is evenly distributed.)

Letter Combinations in the B Climates

$BSh, BShs, BShw; BSk, BSks, BSkw; BSk', BSk'w$
$BWh, BWhs, BWhw; BWk, BWks, BWkw; BWk', BWk'w$

(The small letter n is sometimes added to these to indicate the presence of frequent fogs. This letter, however, is not given exact definition and cannot be identified from the climatic data given in this book.)

A CLIMATES

$A:$ temperature of the coldest month above 64.4° (18°).
    $f:$ rainfall of the driest month is at least 2.4 in. (6 cm.).

[1] These tables were prepared by Dr. Henry M. Kendall.

m: short dry season exists, but is compensated by heavy rains during the rest of the year (see *w*).

w: dry season exists which is not compensated by rains during the rest of the year. The dry season comes during the low-sun period of the hemisphere.

w': used if the rainfall maximum comes in autumn of the hemisphere.

w": used if there are two distinct maxima of rainfall, separated by two dry seasons.

s: used when the dry season comes during the high-sun period.

The distinction between *m* and *w* (*w'*, *w"*, and *s*) depends upon the amount of rain in the driest month and the total annual rainfall. As the total annual rainfall increases, smaller and smaller amounts of rain in the driest month can be compensated. If the total annual rainfall is 100 inches (exactly 98.5 in.), one month can be completely dry and still merit the symbol *m*; or if the total annual rainfall is 200 inches, two months can be entirely dry. The distinction between *m* and *w* is given in the table on page 542, in which the amount of rain in the driest month varies inversely with the total annual rainfall. If the rainfall of the driest month is less than the amount shown in the second column, the symbol *w* (*w'*, or *w"*, or *s*) is used; if the rainfall is more, but less than 2.4 (*f*), the symbol *m* is used.[1]

After *f* or *m* the letter *w*, *w'*, *w"*, or *s* is sometimes used to indicate the season of less rain.

i: range of temperature between the coldest and warmest months less than 9° (5°).

g: hottest month comes before the solstice.

Letter Combinations in the A Climates

Afi, Afwi (w', w", s)
Am, Ami, Amwi (w', w", s)
Aw, Awi, Aw', Aw", As (i); Awg, Awgi, etc.

C CLIMATES

C: temperature of the coldest month below 64.4° (18°) but above 26.6° (−3°); temperature of the warmest month over 50° (10°).

f: no dry season; difference between rainiest and driest month less than that required for *s* or *w*; or, in the case of winter rain and summer drought, driest month of summer receives more than 1.2 in. (3 cm.).

s: dry season in summer; rainiest month of winter receives at least three times as much rain as the driest month of summer, and the driest month of summer receives less than 1.2 in. (3 cm.).

---

[1] The table was prepared by Dr. Henry M. Kendall.

TABLE I. FOR THE DETERMINATION OF THE *BS/H* BOUNDARY

AVERAGE ANNUAL TEMPERATURE	AT LEAST 70 PER CENT IN WINTER	EVEN DISTRIBUTION	AT LEAST 70 PER CENT IN SUMMER
32	.00	5.52	11.02
33	.44	5.96	11.46
34	.86	6.38	11.88
35	1.32	6.82	12.34
36	1.74	7.26	12.76
37	2.18	7.70	13.20
38	2.62	8.14	13.64
39	3.06	8.58	14.08
40	3.50	9.02	14.52
41	3.94	9.46	14.96
42	4.38	9.90	15.40
43	4.82	10.34	15.84
44	5.26	10.78	16.28
45	5.68	11.20	16.70
46	6.12	11.64	17.14
47	6.56	12.08	17.58
48	7.00	12.52	18.02
49	7.44	12.96	18.46
50	7.88	13.40	18.90
51	8.32	13.84	19.34
52	8.74	14.26	19.76
53	9.18	14.70	20.20
54	9.62	15.14	20.64
55	10.06	15.58	21.08
56	10.50	16.02	21.52
57	10.94	16.46	21.96
58	11.38	16.90	22.40
59	11.82	17.34	22.84
60	12.26	17.78	23.28
61	12.68	18.20	23.70
62	13.12	18.64	24.14
63	13.56	19.08	24.58
64	14.00	19.52	25.02
65	14.44	19.96	25.46
66	14.88	20.40	25.90
67	15.30	20.82	26.32
68	15.74	21.26	26.76
69	16.18	21.70	27.20
70	16.62	22.14	27.64
71	17.06	22.58	28.08
72	17.50	23.02	28.52
73	17.94	23.46	28.96
74	18.38	23.90	29.40
75	18.82	24.34	29.84
76	19.24	24.76	30.26
77	19.68	25.20	30.70
78	20.12	25.64	31.14
79	20.56	26.08	31.58
80	21.00	26.52	32.02
81	21.44	26.96	32.46
82	21.88	27.40	32.90
83	22.30	27.82	33.32
84	22.74	28.26	33.76
85	23.18	28.70	34.20

TABLE II. FOR THE DETERMINATION OF THE *BW/BS* BOUNDARY

AVERAGE ANNUAL TEMPERATURE	AT LEAST 70 PER CENT IN WINTER	EVEN DISTRIBUTION	AT LEAST 70 PER CENT IN SUMMER
32	.00	2.76	5.51
33	.22	2.98	5.73
34	.43	3.19	5.94
35	.66	3.42	6.17
36	.87	3.63	6.38
37	1.09	3.85	6.60
38	1.31	4.07	6.82
39	1.53	4.29	7.04
40	1.75	4.51	7.26
41	1.97	4.73	7.48
42	2.19	4.95	7.70
43	2.41	5.17	7.92
44	2.63	5.39	8.14
45	2.84	5.60	8.35
46	3.06	5.82	8.57
47	3.28	6.04	8.79
48	3.50	6.26	9.01
49	3.72	6.48	9.23
50	3.94	6.70	9.45
51	4.16	6.92	9.67
52	4.37	7.13	9.88
53	4.59	7.35	10.10
54	4.81	7.57	10.32
55	5.03	7.79	10.54
56	5.25	8.01	10.76
57	5.47	8.23	10.98
58	5.69	8.45	11.20
59	5.91	8.67	11.42
60	6.13	8.89	11.64
61	6.34	9.10	11.85
62	6.56	9.32	12.07
63	6.78	9.54	12.29
64	7.00	9.76	12.51
65	7.22	9.98	12.73
66	7.44	10.20	12.95
67	7.65	10.41	13.16
68	7.87	10.63	13.38
69	8.09	10.85	13.60
70	8.31	11.07	13.82
71	8.53	11.29	14.04
72	8.75	11.51	14.26
73	8.97	11.73	14.48
74	9.19	11.95	14.70
75	9.41	12.17	14.92
76	9.62	12.38	15.13
77	9.84	12.60	15.35
78	10.06	12.82	15.57
79	10.28	13.04	15.79
80	10.50	13.26	16.01
81	10.72	13.48	16.23
82	10.94	13.70	16.45
83	11.15	13.91	16.66
84	11.37	14.13	16.88
85	11.59	14.35	17.10

TABLE III. FOR THE DETERMINATION OF THE *Am/Aw* BOUNDARY

YEARLY RAINFALL IN INCHES	RAINFALL OF DRIEST MONTH IN INCHES	YEARLY RAINFALL IN INCHES	RAINFALL OF DRIEST MONTH IN INCHES	YEARLY RAINFALL IN INCHES	RAINFALL OF DRIEST MONTH IN INCHES
39.5	2.36	59.5	1.56	79.5	.76
40	2.34	60	1.55	80	.74
40.5	2.32	60.5	1.53	80.5	.72
41	2.30	61	1.51	81	.70
41.5	2.29	61.5	1.48	81.5	.68
42	2.26	62	1.47	82	.66
42.5	2.24	62.5	1.45	82.5	.63
43	2.22	63	1.42	83	.61
43.5	2.20	63.5	1.41	83.5	.59
44	2.18	64	1.38	84	.58
44.5	2.16	64.5	1.36	84.5	.56
45	2.14	65	1.34	85	.54
45.5	2.12	65.5	1.33	85.5	.51
46	2.10	66	1.30	86	.50
46.5	2.08	66.5	1.28	86.5	.48
47	2.07	67	1.26	87	.46
47.5	2.04	67.5	1.24	87.5	.44
48	2.02	68	1.22	88	.42
48.5	2.00	68.5	1.20	88.5	.40
49	1.98	69	1.18	89	.37
49.5	1.96	69.5	1.15	89.5	.36
50	1.94	70	1.13	90	.34
50.5	1.92	70.5	1.11	90.5	.32
51	1.90	71	1.10	91	.29
51.5	1.88	71.5	1.08	91.5	.28
52	1.86	72	1.06	92	.26
52.5	1.85	72.5	1.03	92.5	.24
53	1.82	73	1.02	93	.22
53.5	1.80	73.5	1.00	93.5	.20
54	1.78	74	.98	94	.18
54.5	1.77	74.5	.96	94.5	.16
55	1.75	75	.94	95	.14
55.5	1.73	75.5	.92	95.5	.11
56	1.70	76	.90	96	.09
56.5	1.68	76.5	.88	96.5	.07
57	1.66	77	.86	97	.06
57.5	1.64	77.5	.84	97.5	.04
58	1.63	78	.81	98	.02
58.5	1.60	78.5	.80	98.5	.00
59	1.58	79	.78		

w: dry season in winter; rainiest month of summer receives at least ten times as much rain as the driest month of winter.

a: hot summers; temperature of the warmest month over $71.6°$ ($22°$).

b: cool summers; temperature of the warmest month under $71.6°$ ($22°$), but with at least four months above $50°$ ($10°$).

c: cool, short summers; only one to three months above $50°$ ($10°$).

i: range of temperature between the coldest and warmest months less than $9°$ ($5°$).

g: hottest month comes before the summer solstice.

t': hottest month delayed until autumn.

x: maximum rainfall in spring or early summer; late summer dry.

s': maximum rainfall in autumn.

(*n* is used, as elsewhere, to indicate frequent fogs.)

Letter Combinations in the C Climates

Cfa, Cfb, Cfc; Cfbi, Cfci, Cfx
Csa, Csb; Csbt'n, Cs'
Cwa, Cwb; Cwbi, Cwg

D CLIMATES

D: temperature of the coldest month below $26.6°$ ($-3°$), and temperature of the warmest month above $50°$ ($10°$).

f, s, and *w:* defined exactly as in the *C* climates.

a, b, c: defined exactly as in the *C* climates.

d: temperature of the coldest month less than $-36.4°$ ($-38°$).

Letter Combinations in the D Climates

Dfa, Dfb, Dfc, Dfd
Dsb
Dwa, Dwb, Dwc, Dwd

REFERENCES

1. BLODGET, L. *Climatology of the United States and of the Temperate Latitudes of the North American Continent.* Philadelphia, 1857.
2. MAURY, M. F. *Explanations of Sailing Directions to Accompany the Wind and Current Charts,* Eighth Edition. Washington, D. C., 1858–1859.
3. WARD, R. deC. *Climates of the United States.* Boston, 1925.
4. KENDREW, W. G. *Climate.* Oxford, 1930.
5. KÖPPEN, W. *Grundriss der Klimakunde.* Berlin, 1931.
6. National Research Council, Bulletin 79, *Physics of the Earth, III, Meteorology.* Washington, D. C., 1931.
7. NAMIAS, J. *An Introduction to the Study of Air Mass and Isentropic Analysis.* Milton, Massachusetts (Blue Hill Meteorological Observatory), 1940.

8. Landsberg, H. E. *Physical Climatology.* State College, Pennsylvania, 1941.

9. United States Department of Agriculture. *1941 Yearbook of Agriculture. Climate and Man.* Washington, D. C., 1941.

10. Conrad, V. *Fundamentals of Physical Climatology.* Milton, Massachusetts (Blue Hill Meteorological Observatory), 1942.

11. Sverdrup, H. U. *Oceanography for Meteorologists.* New York, 1942.

12. Byers, H. R. *General Meteorology.* New York, 1944.

13. Willett, H. C. *Descriptive Meteorology.* New York, 1944.

14. Landsberg, H. E. "Climatology," in Berry, F. A., Jr., Bollay, E., and Beers, N. R. (editors), *Handbook of Meteorology,* pp. 927–997. New York, 1945.

15. Jacobs, W. C. *Wartime Developments in Applied Climatology,* Meteorological Monographs 1, 1947.

16. Thornthwaite, C. W. "An Approach Toward a Rational Classification of Climate," *Geographical Review,* Vol. 38 (1948), pp. 55–94.

17. Willett, H. C. "Long-Period Fluctuations of the General Circulation of the Atmosphere," *Journal of Meteorology,* Vol. 6 (1949), pp. 34–50.

18. Conrad, V., and Pollak, L. W. *Methods in Climatology,* Second Revised Edition. Cambridge, Massachusetts, 1950.

19. Geiger, R. *The Climate Near the Ground.* Cambridge, Massachusetts, 1950.

20. Brooks, C. E. P. *Climate in Everyday Life.* New York, 1951.

21. Landsberg, H. E., and Jacobs, W. C. "Applied Climatology," in American Meteorological Society, *Compendium of Meteorology,* 1951, pp. 976–992.

22. Kendrew, W. G. *The Climates of the Continents,* Fourth Edition. Oxford, 1953.

23. Shapley, H. (editor). *Climatic Change.* Cambridge, Massachusetts, 1954.

24. Riehl, H. *Tropical Meteorology.* New York, 1954.

25. Trewartha, G. T. *An Introduction to Climate,* Third Edition. New York, 1954.

26. Kimble, G. H. T. *Our American Weather.* New York, 1955.

27. Köppen, W., and Geiger, R. (editors). *Handbuch der Klimatologie.* (In five volumes by various authors, not all of which had been published when the work was interrupted by World War II. Published in Berlin by Borntraeger.)

C · THE LITHOSPHERE

I. Tectonic Forms

1. **The Earth's Crust.** The geologists recognize three major types of rocks which make up the solid crust of the earth. There are the *igneous* rocks, which have cooled and solidified from a previously molten condition. These are crystalline: coarsely crystalline where they have cooled slowly at great depths below the surface; finely crystalline, or even glassy, where they have cooled more rapidly near or at the surface. There are many kinds of igneous rocks, depending on the minerals in them. *Sedimentary* rocks make up the second major type. These are derived from the erosion of earlier rocks and were accumulated as unconsolidated deposits either in the water or on the land. The deposits range from coarse material to fine: gravels, sands, and muds. In the course of time and deep burial under later deposits, the layers of gravel, sand, or mud were gradually consolidated into rock: into conglomerate, sandstone, shale, or limestone. The third major division of rocks includes those which have been altered from either igneous or sedimentary types as a result of pressure or heat, or both. These are known as *metamorphic* rocks. Such a process rearranges the crystal structure of the igneous rocks into more compact forms. Similarly, the individual rock particles of the sedimentary strata are melted and solidified again as tightly fitted crystals. The result in either case is a rock mass more compact and more resistant to the processes of erosion. The coarsely crystalline igneous rocks are changed to gneiss, sandstone to quartzite, shale to slate or schist, and limestone to marble.[1]

From the point of view of the effect of these rock types on the shape of the surface of the earth the most important distinction is between those which are massive and those which are arranged in layers, or strata. Igneous rocks may be either massive or stratified; sedimentary rocks are always stratified; metamorphic rocks may be either.

[1] For a more exact discussion of rock types see any modern textbook in geomorphology, such as references 16, 20, 21, or 25, listed at the end of this appendix.

2. Deformation of the Earth's Crust.

The rock crust of the earth has been subjected to stresses and strains throughout geologic history. Mountain ranges have been raised up only to be worn down again countless times. While certain sections of the lithosphere have remained more stable than others, there is no part which does not bear the record of some deformation. The crust of the earth is raised, lowered, broken, crumpled, or folded by these movements.

Four chief types of *tectonic* forms—that is, forms produced by forces from within the earth—are recognized. On the spheroidal surface of the planet a gentle uplift usually results in the formation of a simple *dome*. This is probably the commonest of the tectonic forms. Some mountain ranges are the result of the erosion of domes (diagram, p. 547); on a large scale the Laurentian Upland of northeastern North America represents a dome structure of continental proportions.

Where the forces which disturb the earth's crust are stronger, the rocks may be crumpled in the process of deformation. A *folded* structure is the result of compression which wrinkles the rock strata. Among the examples of this are strata with simple, open folds with horizontal axes. But there are many examples where the folding has been more intense: where the *anticlines,* or upfolds, have toppled over into the *synclines,* or downfolds, or where the axes of the folds have themselves been warped from the horizontal (upper diagram, p. 421). The Jura Mountains furnish a standard example of simple folding, while the Appalachians are somewhat more complex; and still more complex are the Alps, which are noted for the complicated distortions of the rock layers.

Actual breaking of the earth's crust is known as *faulting*. This is the third chief kind of tectonic deformation. The rock masses may be broken into blocks which are raised or lowered with reference to one another. The result is the formation of *block mountains* or of *rift valleys.* These tectonic forms are repeated in many parts of the world, the middle valley of the Rhine (diagram, p. 548), Death Valley in California, the Dead Sea–Red Sea rift, and the lakes of eastern Africa being a few well-known examples. Earthquakes are produced by the slipping which takes place along fault lines.

These tectonic forms are produced very slowly as measured by human time. The old popular phrase "convulsions of nature" implies

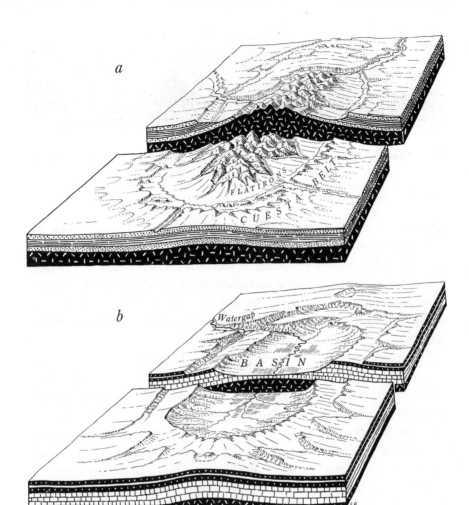

Block diagrams illustrating the landforms characteristically associated with the erosion of a structural dome: (a) where the rocks exposed in the center are relatively resistant; (b) where the rocks exposed in the center are relatively weak

violent movements. In the last century, however, geologists have come gradually to realize that sudden spectacular movements are rare and that most of the deformations take place only very slowly. *Volcanoes,* however, the fourth type of tectonic form, are quite different.

3. **Volcanoes.** There are two chief kinds of volcanoes. Where the molten material which pours out from within the earth emerges

A generalized cross section of the rift valley of the Rhine and the adjoining block mountains of the Vosges and the Black Forest

quietly, a broad dome is piled up around the crater or fissure. One of the finest examples of the *dome volcano* is furnished by the island of Hawaii, which has been built up by successive flows of lava to a height of more than thirty thousand feet above the floor of the Pacific Ocean. Such volcanoes are not explosive, but the lava in them is of a kind which cools slowly and flows great distances after it has reached the surface.

The second type of volcano is explosive. It builds around its crater a cone composed of alternating flows of lava and falls of ash and dust. Of the *cone volcanoes,* Fujiyama in Japan is noted for the perfection of its form. The eruptions of cone volcanoes are violent and destructive. Vesuvius, for example, after lying dormant for many centuries, in the year 79 A.D. suddenly blew its old cone to pieces and built a new one inside the rim of the old one. At this time the neighboring towns of Pompeii and Herculaneum were destroyed, the former being buried under from 25 to 30 feet of ash and dust. Another striking example of the explosion of a long-dormant conical volcano is that of Krakatoa, formerly located on an island in Sunda Strait, between Java and Sumatra. In 1883, with but little warning, it exploded violently, with a concussion which was heard in Australia, 2200 miles distant. About two thirds of the mountain was blown away, and the water under the spot where the central peak had stood was found to be 1000 feet deep after the explosion. Enormous "tidal" waves produced by this cataclysm were very destructive. Dust was blown 20 miles into the air and in the course of a few weeks drifted entirely around the world, giving vivid colors to the sunset skies. Dust from Krakatoa has been identified on the snow surfaces of the polar regions.

II. Destructional Forms

4. The Destructional Forms. As soon as the tectonic forces begin to raise a portion of the earth's crust above the sea, the exposed land is attacked by various processes of destruction. Since these processes result from the contacts with the atmosphere, the particular combination of processes in any one area is largely controlled by the climatic conditions. All these processes, however, in the long run have the effect of reducing the elevations and filling the low places of the lithosphere. Erosion proceeds by *weathering* (rock fracture and decay), *corrasion* (wearing away of exposed surfaces), and *transportation* (movement of loose material). Corrasion and transportation can be accomplished in six different ways, each of which produces a peculiar set of landforms. These six processes are (1) running water, (2) direction action of gravity on slopes, (3) glaciers, (4) wind, (5) solution, and (6) waves and currents. We shall consider in turn the landforms produced by each of these.

5. The Products of Weathering. The first step in the wearing down of the land is the breaking up of solid rock into pieces under the influence of the atmosphere. This is known as weathering. It proceeds by two different methods: the rocks are physically broken, or *disintegrated;* or the rocks are attacked chemically and the minerals are transformed, or *decomposed.* Disintegration is hastened by the expansion and contraction which come from heating and cooling, or by frost action, or, to a lesser extent, by the prying action of tree roots or the burrowing of animals. The physical fracturing of the rocks reaches a maximum in the deserts, where there is a great contrast between the temperatures of day and night, and in the polar regions or high mountains, where frost action is most active. Decomposition requires the presence of water, and since most chemical processes go on more rapidly at higher temperatures this type of weathering is most active in the rainy tropics.

The result of weathering is the production of a mantle of loose material at the surface of the earth. This mantle is more or less thick, depending on the strength of the weathering processes, the resistance of the rock to these processes, the length of time the rock has been exposed to them, and the rate of removal. Such a mantle of loose material is known as *regolith*. The regolith which is chiefly the result of disintegration is generally coarse, whereas the mantle produced by decomposition is generally fine.

6. **Landforms Produced by Running Water.** In most parts of the world the landforms produced by running water are of dominant importance. Where this is the case the surface features may be described under four headings: the valleys, the interfluves, the stream pattern, and the relief. Sections 7 to 19, inclusive, deal with these elements as produced by running water.

7. **V-Shaped Valleys.** When a portion of the earth's crust is raised rapidly enough and far enough above the sea, the streams of water which flow over its surface cut rapidly downward and headward to excavate V-shaped valleys. The slope of the stream channel in such valleys is steep and is usually interrupted by falls and rapids. However, as the stream cuts down in the valley bottom, the sides of the valley are changed both by the movement of regolith on the steep slopes and by the headward cutting of tributaries. The transverse profile of the valley depends on the ratio between the rate of downward cutting of the main stream and the rate of valley-side erosion. Where erosion on the valley side is relatively slight, as in the dry lands, the V is narrow and canyon-like; but where the valley-widening processes are very active, as in the rainy tropics, especially where the forest has been removed, the V becomes broad and open. In all V-shaped valleys the stream occupies the whole bottom (diagram *a,* p. 269 and p. 552).

8. **Baselevel and Grade.** However, streams cannot cut down their valley bottoms indefinitely. No stream can cut below the body of water into which it flows; nor can any stream reduce its valley bottom to the level of the body of water into which it is flowing, except at its mouth, for it must maintain a slope on which to flow. The level below which a stream cannot cut at its mouth is known as *baselevel*. After the stream reaches baselevel at its mouth, little by little it establishes a slope on which it is just able to flow. An equilibrium is reached be-

tween three variable elements: slope, volume of water, and load. A change in any one of these elements necessitates readjustment of the others to maintain this equilibrium. When a stream has developed this balance, it is said to be *graded*.[1]

9. **Floodplain Scroll Valleys.** The valleys remain V-shaped until the streams establish grade. But as soon as downward cutting ceases, the streams must expend their energy in lateral cutting at the base of the valley sides. At each river bend the current swings against the outside bank, and by *sapping,* or undercutting, it pushes back and steepens the valley side. The lateral movement of the river, however, leaves exposed a small piece of flat valley bottom on the inside of each bend. The first bits of valley flat to appear are scroll-shaped in outline (diagram, p. 552, *b* and *c*). As the river swings from one side of its valley to the other, the scrolls appear on alternate sides, each of them isolated by the river and by the steep valley slopes behind them. Since these flats are submerged during flood water, they are included under the general term "floodplain," or that portion of the valley bottom covered by water during flood. Valleys of this kind are called floodplain scroll valleys.

10. **Floodplain Valleys.** All stages of gradation may be seen between the floodplain scroll valley and a third type, the floodplain valley. Little by little the valley sides are pushed back and the floodplain scrolls become more extensive. From the somewhat irregular swings of the river in its earlier stage, more regular meanders are gradually developed, the width of these meanders being proportional to the size of the river. Since the meanders tend to migrate downstream, they not only cut against the valley slopes on the outside of each bend but they also begin to undercut the upstream side of each spur which, in the floodplain scroll valley, extends from the valley slope into the inside of each river bend (diagram *d,* p. 552). When the spurs are eliminated, the flats lose their scroll-shaped outline and become continuous, and the river is able to meander freely across a wide and unobstructed floodplain (diagram *e,* p. 552).

[1] For classical discussions of these concepts see references 1 and 4; for more recent studies which modify many older ideas see references 17 and 23.

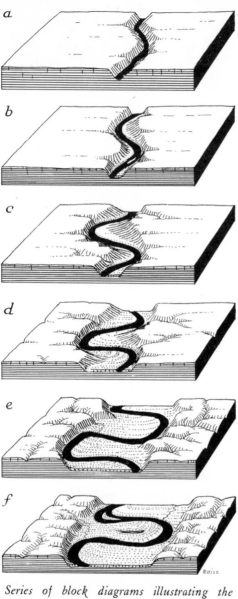

a

b

c

d

e

f

Series of block diagrams illustrating the stages in the evolution of a valley from youth to old age

A number of distinctive features characterize valleys of this type. The floodplain is bordered by sharply defined *valley bluffs,* which are especially steep where the river swings against them (diagram *f* on this page). Since the floodplain is covered at high water, it is built up of the loose silts and sands deposited by the water and known as *alluvium.* During a flood the greatest amount of deposition takes place along the immediate edges of the channel, for here the largest checking of the current is felt. In the course of time the edge of the channel is built up higher than the rest of the plain. These highest parts of the floodplain, the last to be covered by water in time of flood, are called *natural levees.* Back from the channel, near the margins of the floodplain, are the lowest places—the *back marshes,* which may remain wet even during low water (map, p. 270).

All these various features of river floodplains are arranged in crescentic patterns. Rivers seldom flow in straight lines, unless controlled by man; on a floodplain they meander, and not uncommonly whole meanders are cut off during high water, and the river channel is shifted to another position. As a result the typical floodplain is marked by a confused array of abandoned channels, or oxbow lakes, each bordered by natural levees, and all arranged in characteristic crescentic plan (map, p. 271).

11. **Interfluves.** During the development of these various types of valleys the interfluves also pass through a sequence of forms. At first much of the initial surface of the land remains undissected. The land between the main V-shaped valleys is flat-topped, and the divides between neighboring streams are ill-defined or entirely absent. The slopes of the V-shaped valleys begin to retreat away from the rivers. The interfluve then develops four elements. At the divide the initial surface becomes gently convex. This upper surface ends sharply where the free face of the underlying bedrock is exposed, and it is this free face which is most rapidly worn back. At the base of the free face is a debris slope, or *colluvial base.* And between this and the river banks there is a *pediment,* smooth and concave. Eventually the initial surface disappears, and only low, rounded swells separate the drainage basins.[1]

12. **The Cycle of Erosion.** The ideal succession of landforms developed during the wearing down of an upraised surface toward baselevel is called a cycle of erosion. As formulated by William Morris Davis, the landforms pass through stages known as *youth, maturity,* and *old age.*[2] When the streams are flowing vigorously and turbulently in V-shaped valleys, they are said to be youthful. When grade is established along the valley bottoms and the floodplain scroll valley makes its appearance, the valleys are described as mature. When the river occupies a broad floodplain across which it meanders freely, it is said to be old. According to Davis's concept the interfluves would during the same time be gradually worn down to gently sloping convex surfaces. The late stage of old age he called a *peneplain,* an almost featureless plain surmounted by only a few erosion remnants known as *monadnocks.*

Modern geomorphologists recognize that there is also a cycle of interfluve forms, which goes on independently of the valley development. The retreat of hillsides parallel to their initial position results in the

[1] References 17, 23, and 24.   [2] References 4 and 5.

formation of wide concave areas of pediment, surmounted, in the late
stages, by only a few erosion remnants which stand abruptly above the
pediment. The parallel retreat of valley sides, or of scarps produced
by tectonic movements, permits remnants of earlier erosion surfaces to
remain in the landscape even in the stage of old age. The resulting
plain is described as a *pediplain*.[1]

These ideal landform sequences, however, are almost always interrupted. In the first place, for every foot of rock material removed from
an uplifted surface by erosion, the underlying rock column rises some
nine to eleven feet. This is because the earth's crust sinks when weight
is placed on it and rises when weight is removed. The result is a con-
tinuing succession of uplifts that return the valley forms again and
again to the youthful stage. This is called *rejuvenation*. The landforms of a region always carry the record of several cycles.

13. **Associations of Valley and Interfluve Forms.** The simple cycle
is complicated in many cases by variations in the association of valley
and interfluve forms. Valleys, for example, may be youthful while the
interfluves are mature;
or interfluves may re-
main youthful while val-
leys are old. Only rarely
is it possible to find both
valleys and interfluves
that are in the same
stage. Where the uplift
which initiates a cycle of
erosion is slight, so that

*Valley and interfluve profiles: (a) youthful in-
terfluves and mature valleys; (b) mature interfluves and youthful valleys*

baselevel lies only a short distance below the initial surface, the streams
may develop floodplain scrolls and so advance their valleys to maturity
or even old age while the central portions of the interfluves remain undissected and youthful (diagram *a,* above). On the other hand, if
uplift is very great or if it is continuous, the interfluves may develop the
sharp divides of maturity while the streams are still deepening their
youthful V-shaped valleys (diagram *b,* above). All the various stages
between these extremes may be observed in different parts of the world.

[1] Reference 24.

554 The Lithosphere

14. **Some Complex Valley Forms.** As a result of various kinds of earth movement, or from other causes which we cannot discuss here, valleys of greater complexity are developed. Since the cycle of erosion can be interrupted at any stage, valleys may be composite in character. For example, the rejuvenation of an old stream results in the preservation of the meanders of old age in the youthful V-shaped valley which follows; in other words, it results in the development of *intrenched meanders*. Or a wide mature valley, if rejuvenated, may be transformed into a valley with an upper flare and lower **V**. On the other hand, valleys may become *aggraded*: a decrease of slope (by depression of the land instead of uplift), a decrease of the volume of water, or an increase of load may cause a stream to fill up its valley bottom. Aggraded youthful valleys are especially noticeable because of the contrast between the steep valley sides and the flat bottom. This is a valley type which is very common in the desert, where many streams flow only after a rain and most of the time are dry.

15. **Complex Valleys Produced by Rock Structure.** Where valleys are being excavated through stratified rocks of varying degrees of resistance the stronger layers project on the valley sides as cliffs. If the strata lie in a horizontal or nearly horizontal position, the *cliff and platform* type of valley is produced; if the strata are inclined, the valleys between the outcrops of resistant layers become *asymmetrical*.

16. **Interfluve Forms Produced by Rock Structure.** The forms of the interfluves are similarly affected by the rock structure (diagram, p. 556). Horizontal strata produce flat-topped interfluves, or *mesas*. Tilted rock layers produce ridgelike *cuestas*. The erosion of a dome structure produces a series of infacing cuestas (diagrams, p. 547), whereas the erosion of a structural basin produces a series of outfacing cuestas.[1]

17. **Stream Patterns.** The third of the four major headings under which landforms produced by running water can be described (sect.

[1] Some writers prefer to distinguish between steeply sloping ridges, where the rock layers are very steeply inclined and are called *hogbacks,* and ridges where one slope is scarcely distinguishable, so gentle is the dip of the resistant stratum. They reserve the term "cuesta" for this latter type (reference 16).

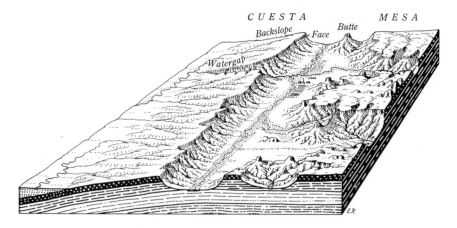

Block diagram illustrating the characteristics of mesas and cuestas

6) is the stream pattern. The arrangement of the valleys and interfluves is a function of the stream pattern. The commonest type of pattern, developed where the rock structure does not interfere with the free development of the streams, is *dendritic;* that is, branching like a tree (map *a,* p. 557). Around a dome the dendritic pattern can be arranged in radial fashion, but elsewhere the main streams may lie roughly parallel to one another. The dendritic pattern is first elaborated and later simplified during the cycle of erosion: in youth the main streams are relatively straight, with few and only short tributaries; in maturity the fullest development of the drainage is reached, with many small tributaries joining the larger main stream and with numerous examples of drainage rearrangement resulting from the capture of one stream by the tributaries of another; in old age only a few master streams have survived the competition, and these are large, with a few large tributaries.

The second type of drainage pattern is formed where rock strata of varying degrees of resistance are inclined at an angle, so that the more resistant beds come to the surface to form cuesta ridges separated by asymmetrical valleys. Because of the relative ease of stream erosion on the weaker beds, the valleys are quickly excavated along the outcrops of these strata between the upstanding cuestas. The main streams may cross the ridges through deep, relatively youthful water gaps. The resulting drainage pattern is one of striking parallelism—of long, straight

556 *The Lithosphere*

valleys, in strict accordance with the arrangement of the rock strata, joined by short right-angled jogs where the rivers cross the resistant beds. This is known as *trellis* drainage (map *b* at right).

Where the cuestas are arranged around the margins of a dome in circular plan, the trellis pattern is curved and is described as *annular*.

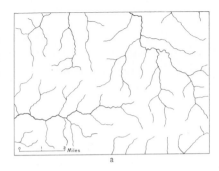

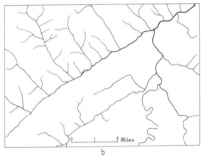

18. **Relief.** These various features developed by running water may be constructed in various degrees of relief. They may occur in miniature in a plain where the relief is slight, or they may be built on a grand scale in a mountain region with very high relief. There is no essential difference in form between the Grand Canyon

Stream patterns: (*a*) *dendritic;* (*b*) *trellis*

of the Colorado and the gully which develops in a plowed field after a heavy rain.

During an uninterrupted cycle of erosion the surface is changed from one of slight initial relief to one of considerable relief, and again to an ultimate surface of slight relief. As soon as the main streams feel the effects of rejuvenation they start the work of downward cutting. During youth, therefore, the local relief is gradually increased. The amount of this increase in the long run depends on the depth of baselevel below the surface; in other words, on the amount of uplift. The maximum relief is reached when the interfluves become mature, when the tributaries have extended headward to dissect the last remnants of the initial surface. After the streams become graded the relief gradually decreases as long as the land remains undisturbed by earth movements.

19. **Landforms Developed in Arid Climates.** Even in dry climates the sculpturing by running water is of dominant importance in pro-

ducing landforms. The rare but violent desert rains give rise to floods which do the work of erosion and deposition quickly. The chief contrast with the work of running water in rainy lands, however, is the absence of a regional baselevel. Since most desert streams do not reach the ocean, they can carry material only from the higher surfaces into the desert basins, or *bolsons*. The waste products are not removed from the region as a whole, but are accumulated not far from their point of origin. The sequence of desert landforms therefore consists of the vigorous erosion of the elevations and in the gradual accumulation of a great sheet of alluvium. At first the mouths of the valleys are marked by *alluvial fans* where they enter the basins. Later these coalesce to form a continuous compound alluvial fan around the piedmont. At this stage the landforms consist of three chief parts (diagram *b*, p. 559): (1) the rapidly crumbling mountains, deeply dissected by youthful streams; (2) the gentle slopes of the alluvial fans, which emerge from the mouths of the valleys and extend toward the center of the bolson in long, sweeping curves; and (3) the *playa*, or the salt-incrusted flat at the center of the bolson, in which water may accumulate temporarily after the heavy rains in the mountains.

As the desert sequence continues, the bolson is gradually buried beneath the advancing fans. In some cases a higher bolson may be dissected by streams leading to neighboring basins at lower levels (diagram *c*, p. 559). In the late stages, however, the bolson is filled with a great sheet of waste material, while the mountains are reduced to rocky pediments thinly mantled with the fans and surmounted here and there by a few island-like *inselberge,* the mountain remnants.[1] These rocky platforms are called *hamadas* (diagram *e*, p. 559). Wind action reaches a maximum in these areas (see section 30).

20. **The Direct Action of Gravity on Slopes.** The direct action of gravity on slopes is the second of the six chief processes of corrasion and transportation. The movement of the regolith on the slopes begins as soon as the streams develop valley sides and the interfluves are dissected by tributaries. The effect of this movement is to change the interfluve profiles from the sharp concavity of running-water excavation to a rounded convexity.

[1] Reference 9.

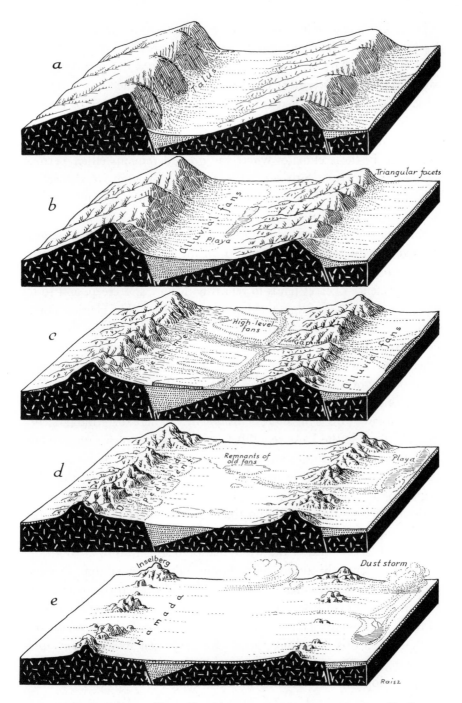

a

b

Triangular facets

c

Playa

alluvial fans

High-level fans

Pediment

Gap

alluvial fans

d

Remnants of old fans

Pediment

Playa

e

Inselberg

Hamada

Dust storm

Raisz

Series of block diagrams illustrating a sequence of landforms in an arid climate

Three kinds of regolith movement can be observed, which we shall describe as *creep, flow,* and *slide.* Earth creep is perhaps the most common of these. Any occurrence which causes the waste mantle to expand produces a movement out at right angles to the slope, and the subsequent contraction then takes place under the influence of gravity directly downward. The result is a gradual downhill movement. Wetting and drying produce rapid earth creep, and earth creep is at a minimum in those climates where the ground remains either permanently dry or permanently wet. Freezing and thawing are also active aids of earth creep. The presence of burrowing animals is another but quite different cause of creep.

Earth flow is a smooth, downward semiliquid movement, generally restricted to the waterlogged regolith of the rainy tropics. The effect of earth flow is to produce concave rather than convex slopes.

The presence of trees tends to retard both flow and creep, and so to maintain steeper slopes than would otherwise form. The gentlest slopes of the old-age interfluves would theoretically be developed in the tropical grasslands, where wetting and drying would be extreme and yet where no retaining network of tree roots would hold back the movement of regolith.

The third type of regolith movement is generally limited to mountainous areas. This is the slide, or *avalanche.* Where the geologic structure is favorable the loose regolith forming on the steep slopes stands perilously balanced until some slight jar gives it a start. Slides are most common in the spring in middle-latitude mountains, when the frost begins to melt and when there is plenty of water to aid the movement. Slides occur more frequently on shady slopes where the ground does not dry out quickly. Starting high up, perhaps with a single boulder, a larger and larger mass of the waste mantle begins to move. With destructive violence the avalanche rushes into the valley bottom, forming there a jumbled accumulation of boulders and broken tree trunks, arranged in a series of low concentric ridges, perhaps blocking the stream to form a temporary lake. The *avalanche scar* on the valley side and the pile of debris below are forms often repeated in mountain areas (drawing, p. 420). Man sometimes creates avalanches through oversteeping slopes in connection with excavating for roads, railroads, and canals.

560   *The Lithosphere*

21. **Glaciers.** During a recent period of geologic history somewhat cooler and stormier climates produced great accumulations of ice in various parts of the world. This period is known as the *Pleistocene*. In order to produce glaciers it is necessary that more snow should fall during the winter than is melted during the summer; heavy snowfall and cool summers, then, are the climatic conditions which lead to glaciation. As the snow piles up to greater and greater depths, ice is gradually formed underneath. As this ice increases in thickness, it tends to spread, either downhill, if it lies on a steeply inclined slope, or out in all directions from a center of accumulation, if it lies on a flattish surface. In this way the great ice sheets came into existence. In the course of long periods of time, as measured by human standards, the ice grew to great thicknesses and extended by further accumulation in the directions of heavier snowfall. Near the margins of the ice sheets, at least, there was considerable outward movement, and the resulting grinding and scraping over the hills and through the valleys of the preglacial surfaces brought about important changes in the character of the landforms.

The distribution of the ice sheets during the Pleistocene is shown on page 372. At present large ice sheets exist only in Greenland and Antarctica; but high mountains, even on the equator, have smaller glaciers.

22. **Forms of Glacial Erosion by Ice Sheets.** In hilly areas the work which the ice accomplished was largely that of erosion. The loose rock material at the surface was scraped off and dumped into the valleys as irregular masses of heterogeneous debris. The bedrock, exposed on the preglacial ridges, was smoothed, rounded, and polished. Passing over a preglacial hill, the scraping action of the ice was concentrated on the side toward which the ice was moving. The contour of the hill was smoothed and rounded; but on the lee side, where the ice, in moving away, plucked from the slopes any loose or broken fragments of rock, steep, jagged cliffs were formed. The characteristic *rock hill* of a glaciated upland therefore has a relatively gentle slope in the direction from which the ice came; a rounded summit, composed in many instances of bare, smooth rock; and a jagged cliff on the lee side. Many of the preglacial valleys, however, were completely filled with the rock

debris scraped from the hills. Except for the rock hills, the ice left such hilly country rougher than before, although, perhaps, with less total relief; and with the melting back of the glacier, the many small depressions, produced both by ice gouging in bedrock and by irregular deposition, were left as lakes and marshes.

23. **Glacial Deposition.** The enormous amount of debris picked up and carried by the ice was deposited on the lowlands, and, especially near the margins of the glaciated area, forms a covering in some places hundreds of feet deep over the preglacial surface. As long as the climatic conditions over the glacier favored snow accumulation, the ice itself, at least near the margins, continued to move outward in great tongues, or lobes. The actual position of the margin of the glacier, however, was dependent on two things: the rate of advance and the rate of melting. If the summers were cool and the melting slow, the ice front would advance; but if the summers were warmer, melting might go on so much faster than the rate of advance that the actual front of the ice would retreat. Cycles of wetter and drier and hotter and cooler years apparently prevailed during the glacial period, as they do now, for the ice advanced and retreated many times, and the rate of advance and retreat was very irregular.[1]

24. **Moraines.** Along the glacier front, where melting was active, the rock debris contained in the ice was dropped in irregular piles. If the rates of advance and melting were balanced and the ice front remained stationary for a period of years, a belt of little hills was built up, following the lobate pattern of the ice margin (map, p. 563). These hilly belts are called *moraines.* In some cases the moraines had extremely rough surfaces, composed of knobby hills and deep depressions—described as *knob and basin moraines.* In other places only *sag and swell moraines* were formed. Moraines are best developed on plains, and near the margins of the glaciated areas where the supply of rock material was large.

25. **Outwash.** Moraines were deposited directly from the ice, but much of the material carried by the melting glaciers was spread out

[1] Reference 22.

by floods of water. Glacial outwash filled in around the moraines and buried the pre-existing landforms under a mantle of water-laid sands and gravels even beyond the limits of the ice.

The water which poured from the melting glacier deposited its load under three different sets of circumstances. Where the valleys sloped away from the front of the ice, as in the case of the Mississippi system, ready-made drainage channels were provided, and the floods were con-

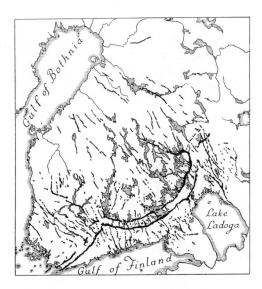

The two large moraines and the chief eskers of Finland. (After J. J. Sederholm)

centrated in them. Hundreds of miles beyond the limits of glaciation the floods of glacial waters filled the valleys. Broad floodplains were developed as the reinforced streams advanced their valleys more rapidly than their smaller tributaries in the cycle of erosion. Such outwash deposits are called *valley trains*. Except for the prematurely old main valleys, this type of outwash leaves the preglacial landforms untouched.

On the other hand, in areas where surfaces without adequate preglacial valleys lay beyond the melting ice, the torrential waters were not concentrated. They spread an apron of sand or gravel in front of the moraine. The resulting plain, sloping gently away from the former position of the ice front, is called an *outwash plain*. Not uncommonly such surfaces are pitted with innumerable small depressions, resulting from the subsequent melting of ice masses buried under the sands. When an outwash plain has been deposited over a country previously mantled with moraines, landforms of the most varied kinds are mixed together in heterogeneous confusion.

26. **Glacial Lakes.** A very different situation was presented when the water found a surface sloping toward the ice instead of away from it.

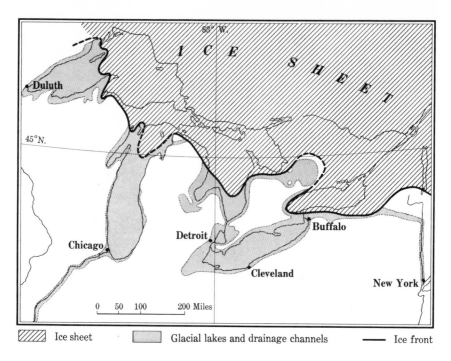

| Ice sheet | Glacial lakes and drainage channels | —— Ice front |

A stage in the retreat of the last ice sheet from the Great Lakes region, showing formation of glacial lakes ponded against the ice front, and the temporary drainage channels by way of the Illinois and Mohawk rivers. (After F. B. Taylor)

In this case a lake was formed, with one side held in by the ice itself and with an outlet over a low place in the divide. The present Great Lakes of North America are bordered by lake plains which were formed in this way when the outlet through the St. Lawrence River was blocked (see map above).[1] The lake waters spread over much of northern Ohio and eastern Michigan, finding outlets at various times through the present site of Chicago to the Illinois River and through the Mohawk Valley to the Hudson. Similarly, when the outlet to Hudson Bay was blocked, the waters of the Red River of the North were ponded in the basin of the present Lake Winnipeg. A glacial lake, referred to as Lake Agassiz, extended southward along the Red River Valley as far as the northern part of South Dakota. The lake

[1] Reference 6.

plains are among the flattest surfaces in existence in the world; and in glaciated regions they provide exceptionally good agricultural lands.

27. **Other Glacial Forms.** In addition to these widespread forms of glacial deposition, there are a number of more unusual forms, which, nevertheless, are of great importance locally. The *drumlins* are rounded, elongated hills which loom conspicuously above their surroundings and are composed of an unstratified mixture of boulders and clay. *Kames* are small, knobby hills of stratified sand and gravel, commonly associated with moraines and not easily distinguished from morainic hills by surface form alone. *Eskers* are long, narrow ridges of irregular height, some of which can be traced for scores of miles across the country (map, p. 563). They are composed of coarse gravels with faint stratification and are believed to mark the courses of subglacial streams.

28. **Glacial Forms in Mountains.** Glacial forms in mountains differ in many ways from those produced by continental ice sheets. Since the glaciers are mostly confined to the valleys, the ice erosion results in a sharpening of the peaks and a steepening of the valley sides. The *glacial trough* is the most striking feature developed by valley glaciers. Here we find that whatever the preglacial form of the valley, the ice gouges it out, scraping away the spurs, steepening the sides, and deepening and widening the bottom. The characteristic profile of a glaciated valley is that of a flattened **U**. The deep excavation of the main valley leaves the former tributaries perched high on the cliffed sides as *hanging valleys* (diagram *d*, p. 566). In the bottom of the trough horseshoe moraines, marking the places where the ice front hesitated during its retreat, act as dams to hold back little valley lakes. Where the glaciers were big enough to reach the piedmont and spread terminal moraines on the neighboring lowlands or gouge out rock basins in the valley bottoms, large *marginal lakes* were formed, extending up-valley for many miles. A number of these lakes appear on the map of the southern Andes (p. 419); they are common in other parts of the world where similar alpine scenery has been developed,—for example, the lakes of the southern Alpine piedmont in Italy (map, p. 566).

The most spectacular alpine scenery, however, is produced at higher

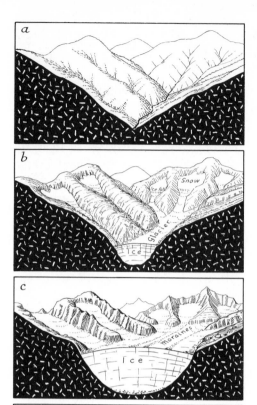

altitudes. The snow field in which the ice of a valley glacier has its origin is commonly located high on the mountain slopes at the valley head. As the ice forms and moves off downgrade it plucks away the rocks loosened by frost. The plucking action, quite similar to that which takes place on the lee side of a rock hill covered by a continental ice sheet (sect. 22), results in the hollowing out of an amphitheater backed by steepened cliffs. Vigorous glaciation produces great semicircular amphitheaters near the mountain crest at the head of each valley. In many cases small remnant glaciers still survive at these high levels; but where the ice has melted entirely away the almost vertical rock walls overlook the exposed floor of the basin, in which is nestled, among the smoothed and polished rocks of the glacier bed, a little lake of crystal-clear, ice-cold water. The lake occupying such an ice-gouged basin is called a *tarn;* the whole amphitheater is known as a *cirque* (diagram *d,* above).

A series of diagrams illustrating the development of glacial landforms in high mountains

The sculpturing of the mountain crests by the headward erosion of the cirques develops a jagged sky line. Glaciers gouging out their amphitheaters on opposite sides of a range push back the head walls until only a knife-edge of crumbling rock separates them. Here the divide is lowered to form a *col*. Knife-edge divides, or *arêtes,* also separate the neighboring cirques on the same side of the range. Meanwhile between the cols, and towering high above the neighboring cirques, stand massive pyramids of frost-fractured rock. These are the *horns* which produce the characteristic "saw-tooth" sky line of alpine scenery.

29. **Postglacial Mountain Forms.** Since the glacial period a deluge of rock fragments from the towering walls of the cirques and horns has partially obscured the glacial forms in some localities. Frost action at high altitudes is very active. Especially in the spring large quantities of broken rock fall from the cliffs and accumulate as *talus cones* at the base. Loosened fragments of rock break off and clatter noisily down into the valley. In some of the cirques the accumulation of waste is so great that huge *rock streams* are formed, descending into the amphitheater bottoms and filling them with a tumbled confusion of rock piled on rock.

30. **Landforms Produced by Wind.** Landforms produced by wind are of much less importance than those developed by the processes already discussed. Wind erosion can be effective only where there is a supply of dry sand or dust to abrade the exposed rock surfaces. In the dry lands, especially in the late stages (sect. 19), wind-sculptured forms are not uncommon, but elsewhere they are rare. Wind sweeping over the fans of the desert bolsons, or over the ergs which succeed them in the dry-land sequence, picks up whatever loose material is available. Some of the material is too heavy to be carried far; this is rolled or skipped into dunes. The very fine particles, however, are lifted high into the air and may even be carried beyond the limits of the deserts. Great accumulations of fine wind-blown material, known as *loess,* are found on the lee sides of the world's great deserts. The removal of the finer particles from the desert fans is known as *deflation.* Little by little the surface comes to be mantled with only the coarser pieces which are too large to be moved by the wind. These fragments are fitted tightly together to form what is known as the *desert pavement.*

Dunes are also formed in rainy lands where a large supply of dry sand is available, as along a sea or lake shore.

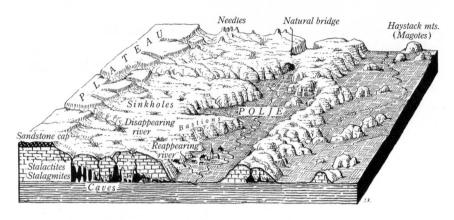

Block diagram illustrating some characteristic karst landforms

31. Karst. Landforms resulting from rock solution are also narrowly limited in their distribution. Only certain kinds of rocks are sufficiently soluble to permit such development. Of the soluble rocks, limestone is the chief kind, although not all limestones are soluble and each limestone layer is of a somewhat different degree of solubility. Where solution can go on rapidly enough, caverns are formed underground; and the collapse of the cave roofs marks the surface of the earth with pitlike depressions, or *sinks* (diagram above). The surface streams find entrance into these underground caverns and disappear, leaving only dry valleys above ground. Such areas may, as a result, be deficient in moisture at the surface. Lands pockmarked in this way with sinks are called *karst* lands after the type locality where such forms are developed on a spectacular scale, on the Karst Plateau, near the head of the Adriatic Sea in Yugoslavia (map, p. 455).[1]

32. Shorelines. The relative changes of level between the land and the sea are most noticeable along the shores. So unstable are the relations of land and sea and so rapid are the processes of shoreline development by waves and currents that these modifications can be observed in historical time. Many are the ancient seaports which now are separated from open water by miles of delta or coastal plain.

In general two major classes of shorelines may be recognized. There are *shorelines of submergence* and *shorelines of emergence*.[2] The

[1] See reference 10.   [2] Reference 7.

568   *The Lithosphere*

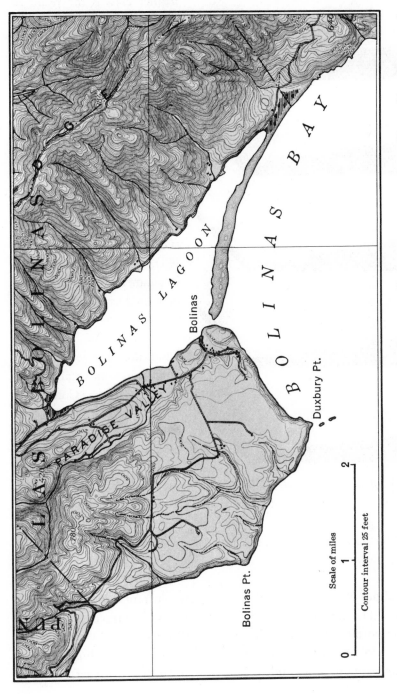

A portion of the coast of California—a shoreline of recent emergence following local subsidence. (From Tamalpais quadrangle, California, United States Geological Survey)

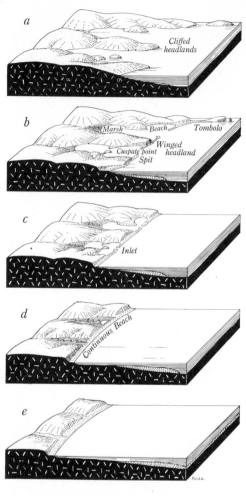

a

Cliffed headlands

b

Marsh *Beach* *Tombolo*
Cuspate point *Winged headland*
Spit

c

Inlet

d

Continuous Beach

e

A series of block diagrams illustrating the development of a shoreline of submergence

former class is the result of either a depression of the land or a rise of the water; it is characterized by a greatly indented shore, with numerous bays, inlets, promontories, and islands. Where pre-existing river-cut valleys are drowned by submergence, leaving the interfluves to extend seaward as promontories or strings of islands, the descriptive term *ria shore* is used (map, p. 146). Where a glacial trough is submerged, the result is described as a *fiord* (map, p. 419). The shorelines of emergence, on the other hand, are relatively straight, with few indentations or promontories. Commonly these are *coastal-plain shores;* but in some places mountainous shores are emergent, in which case the land rises abruptly from the water's edge. Evidences of emergence can be seen in the raised terraces (see section 33) now well above the sea level (map, p. 569).

33. **Shore Modifications.** The waves and currents along shores produce rapid changes on the land. The formation of terraces is one of the most important of these modifications. Actual cutting by the waves is confined to a horizontal zone between the wave crests at high tide and the wave troughs at low tide. This zone of cutting, however, results in

the development, by sapping, of a steep *wave-cut cliff*. Under the water, and not visible unless raised on an emerging shore, is a *wave-cut terrace,* continued on its seaward edge by a *wave-built terrace* composed of the material cut from the land.

Whether shorelines are emergent or submergent, in the long run the waves transform them into shores of very similar appearance. The accompanying diagrams illustrate the sequence of forms of a shoreline of submergence (diagrams, p. 570). First the promontories are cliffed, and then spits and bay-head bars appear across the indentations. Beaches are eventually formed across the mouths of the bays, festooned from headland to headland and enclosing half-moon-shaped marshy lagoons. Later the headlands are farther worn

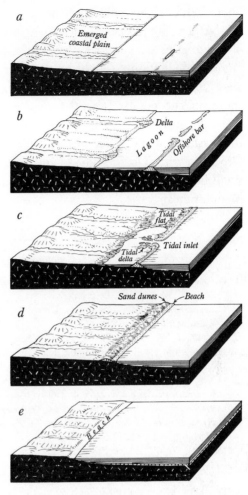

A series of block diagrams illustrating the development of a shoreline of emergence

back and the bays filled until a straight shore is produced. A shoreline of emergence (diagrams above) is quickly protected by an *offshore bar,* behind which a lagoon forms. In the rainy tropics this lagoon, like the smaller lagoons of the indented coast, is filled with mangrove, but in the middle latitudes it is commonly covered with salt-marsh grass. Little by little the bar retreats landward until eventually a straight shore again appears, with no lagoon. All these various stages can be observed on the shores of the lakes or the oceans.

Destructional Forms 571

34. **Deltas.** The building of deltas by streams is dependent on various factors. Submergence and emergence are balanced against the rate of delta growth; and delta growth, in turn, is determined by the amount of alluvium brought by the river, by the nature of the body of water into which the stream is flowing, and by other things. Marked shore currents greatly affect the shape of the growing delta. As a general rule rivers entering seas with strong tides do not build deltas, for the washing of the water in and out of the river mouths keeps them free from silt. On the other hand, deltas form rapidly in seas with small tidal range, such as the Caribbean and the Gulf of Mexico or the Mediterranean.

REFERENCES

Geomorphology

1. GILBERT, G. K. *Geology of the Henry Mountains,* United States Geological Survey Report. Washington, D. C., 1877.
2. GILBERT, G. K. *Lake Bonneville,* United States Geological Survey, Monograph I. Washington, D. C., 1890.
3. POWELL, J. W. *Physiography of the United States,* National Geographic Society Monograph No. 1. Washington, D. C., 1895.
4. DAVIS, W. M. *Geographical Essays.* Boston, 1909.
5. DAVIS, W. M. "Meandering Valleys and Underfit Rivers," *Annals of the Association of American Geographers,* Vol. 3 (1913), pp. 3–28.
6. LEVERETT, F., and TAYLOR, F. B. *The Pleistocene of Indiana and Michigan and the History of the Great Lakes,* United States Geological Survey, Monograph LIII. Washington, D. C., 1915.
7. JOHNSON, D. W. *Shore Processes and Shoreline Development.* New York, 1919.
8. CRESSEY, G. B. *The Indiana Sand Dunes and Shore Lines of the Lake Michigan Basin,* Geographic Society of Chicago, Bulletin No. 8. Chicago, 1928.
9. DAVIS, W. M. "Rock Floors in Arid and in Humid Climates," *Journal of Geology,* Vol. 38 (1930), pp. 1–27, 136–158.
10. DAVIS, W. M. "The Origin of Limestone Caverns," *Bulletin of the Geological Society of America,* Vol. 41 (1930), pp. 475–628.
11. MATTHES, F. E. *Geologic History of the Yosemite Valley,* United States Geological Survey, Professional Paper 160. Washington, D. C., 1930.
12. ASHLEY, G. H. "Studies in Appalachian Mountain Sculpture," *Bulletin of the Geological Society of America,* Vol. 46 (1935), pp. 1395–1436.
13. CRESSEY, G. B. "The Land Forms of Chekiang," *Annals of the Association of American Geographers,* Vol. 28 (1938), pp. 259–276.
14. SHARPE, C. F. S. *Landslides and Related Phenomena: A Study of Mass-Movements of Soil and Rock.* New York, 1938.
15. IRELAND, H. A., SHARPE, C. F. S., and EARGLE, D. H. *Principles of Gully Erosion in the Piedmont of South Carolina,* United States Department of Agriculture, Technical Bulletin No. 633. Washington, D. C., 1939.

16. LOBECK, A. K. *Geomorphology: An Introduction to the Study of Landscapes.* New York, 1939.

17. BRYAN, K. "The Retreat of Slopes," *Annals of the Association of American Geographers,* Vol. 30 (1940), pp. 254–268.

18. THORNTHWAITE, C. W., SHARPE, C. F. S., and DOSCH, E. F. *Climate and Accelerated Erosion in the Arid and Semi-Arid Southwest, with Special Reference to the Polacca Wash Drainage Basin, Arizona,* United States Department of Agriculture, Technical Bulletin No. 808. Washington, D. C., 1942.

19. FLINT, R. F. *Glacial Geology and the Pleistocene Epoch.* New York, 1947.

20. SHEPARD, R. P. *Submarine Geology.* New York, 1948.

21. STRAHLER, A. N. *Physical Geography.* New York, 1951.

22. COTTON, C. A. *Geomorphology,* Sixth Edition. New York, 1952.

23. PENCK, W. *Morphological Analysis of Land Forms.* New York, 1953.

24. KING, L. C. "Canons of Landscape Evolution," *Bulletin of the Geological Society of America,* Vol. 64 (1953), pp. 721–753.

25. THORNBURY, W. D. *Principles of Geomorphology.* New York, 1954.

26. BRETZ, J. H., SMITH, H. T. U., and NEFF, G. E. "Channeled Scabland of Washington: New Data and Interpretations," *Bulletin of the Geological Society of America,* Vol. 67 (1956), pp. 957–1049.

Soils

27. GLINKA, K. D. *The Great Soil Groups of the World and Their Development.* Translated from the German by C. F. Marbut. Ann Arbor, Michigan, 1927.

28. MARBUT, C. F. "Soils of the United States," Part III of the *Atlas of American Agriculture,* United States Department of Agriculture. Washington, D. C., 1935.

29. United States Department of Agriculture, *1938 Yearbook of Agriculture. Soils and Men.* Washington, D. C., 1938.

30. KELLOGG, C. E. *The Soils that Support Us.* New York, 1941.

31. JENNY, H. *Foundations of Soil Science.* New York, 1946.

32. KELLOGG, C. E., CLINE, M. G., and Others. *Soil Science,* Vol. 67 (1949), pp. 77–260.

33. KELLOGG, C. E. *Soil Survey Manual,* United States Department of Agriculture, Miscellaneous Publications 274, Second Edition. Washington, D. C., 1951.

34. United States Department of Agriculture, *1957 Yearbook of Agriculture. Soils.* Washington, D. C., 1957.

D · THE HYDROSPHERE

1. **The Hydrosphere.** Water covers 72 per cent of the earth's surface. It not only fills the major depressions of the earth's crust but also submerges the margins of the continents. The oceans are the reservoirs from which is derived not only the water that appears as a visible feature of the landscape in rivers, lakes, and marshes but also the invisible water vapor that plays such a vital part in determining the world's climates (Appendix B). Among the first recorded observations of mankind was the apparently strange fact that "the rivers flow into the sea, yet the sea is not full." The ancients were observing only the visible part of a cycle which is of fundamental importance among the natural processes of our earth. Water is evaporated from the surface of the ocean. Onshore winds carry the water vapor inland, where, later, it is deposited as rain, hail, or snow. When this water reaches the land, it returns again through the rivers to the sea, either directly or indirectly. Not only is the supply of moisture essential to living organisms on the earth, but also, of the six processes of land sculpture listed in Appendix C, only one, the wind, is neither directly nor indirectly dependent on the presence of water.

Two general facts regarding the hydrosphere should be remembered. The first is the peculiar range of the earth's atmospheric temperatures, which permits water to exist on the face of our planet in the form of a liquid. The second is the contrast between fresh and salt water with regard to freezing point and temperature of greatest density. Fresh water is densest at 39.2° F. If this were not true, lakes and rivers would freeze at the bottom instead of at the surface, and the circulation of water in them would be very different. Salt water with a salinity of 3.5 per cent freezes at 28° and also reaches its greatest density at this same temperature. As a consequence the deepest parts, which descend as much as six and one-half miles below sea level, are very cold.[1]

[1] For the characteristics of the oceans, and for many references to additional sources, see references 11, 12, and 13.

2. **The Nature of Ocean Water.** The water of the ocean is by no means uniform in character. There are great differences from place to place, and these differences are of fundamental importance not only in the geography of the oceans themselves but also in the climatic patterns of the whole earth. There are great differences in temperature—from temperatures well over 80° in the equatorial regions to temperatures below 32° in the polar regions. The highest ocean temperatures are in the Persian Gulf and the Red Sea. Where temperatures are high and evaporation is rapid, the salt content of the water is generally higher than it is in areas of low water temperature. Marine organisms are usually more abundant in cool or cold water than in warm or hot water. And associated with these things are the colors of ocean water, which range from greenish to bluish.

Generally, three major kinds of ocean water can be recognized. (1) In the high latitudes *polar water* is low in temperature, low in salt content, rich in plankton and other marine organisms, and greenish in color. (2) In the low latitudes the *tropical* and *subtropical water* is high in temperature, high in salt content, low in organic forms, and blue in color. (3) In between are the so-called *mixed waters* of the middle latitudes.

3. **Movements of Ocean Water.** As in the case of all phenomena on the face of the earth that are directly or indirectly related to the climatic features, there is a tendency toward symmetry in the pattern of arrangement. Departures from the symmetrical arrangement as regards ocean currents are due to the asymmetrical configuration of the continents and ocean basins. In both hemispheres there are two major lines of convergence where water masses differing in temperature, salt content, life forms, and color are in contact. These are known as the *polar convergence* and the *subtropical convergence* (indicated by black lines on Plate 23). In the Northern Hemisphere low latitudes the easterly winds produce a west-moving current of water, which, under the influence of the earth's rotation, tends constantly to swing to the right, or north. In the Southern Hemisphere the swing is to the left, or south. In the middle latitudes there is an east-moving current of water which, urged on by the prevailing westerly winds, swings to the right, or south, in the Northern Hemisphere, and to the left, or north, in the Southern

The Hydrosphere 575

Hemisphere. These two currents of water in each hemisphere tend to swing toward each other, meeting along the lines of convergence. There is relatively little mixing along this line; rather, the denser water sinks under the lighter water.

The warm, west-moving currents of subtropical water strike the continental east coasts in the low latitudes. In the Pacific Ocean a strong equatorial countercurrent is developed, moving eastward between 5° and 10° north of the equator all the way to the coast of Panama and Colombia. In the Atlantic, on the other hand, the countercurrent which returns to the equatorial part of western Africa is relatively weak. The projecting nose of South America splits the west-moving current, deflecting a considerable part of it northward into the Caribbean and the Gulf of Mexico. This strong current of warm tropical and subtropical water emerges between Cuba and Florida as the Gulf Stream, which bathes the east coast of North America as far as about 40° north. It then swings eastward across the Atlantic as the North Atlantic Drift to the shores of Europe north of 35°. The configuration of Norway permits this relatively warm water to penetrate even into the polar ocean, bringing ice-free waters to the northernmost part of Europe. The similar current in the North Pacific, the Kuro Siwo, is not so strong and does not penetrate so far north. The configuration of Alaska and the Aleutian Islands does not permit it to reach the polar sea. The relative weakness of the Kuro Siwo can be matched against the relatively slight development of the equatorial countercurrent in the Atlantic.

The west coasts of the continents between 35° and 15° are bathed by relatively cold water. Here the equatorward-moving currents in both hemispheres tend to swing offshore. Close to the land, the water is being replaced by up-welling from below, and is especially cold.

Cold polar water moves equatorward along the east coasts of the continents in higher middle latitudes, and meets the east-moving water of the middle latitudes along the line of the polar convergence. The continental east coasts are bathed by cold water as far as 40° of latitude; and off the coast of eastern South America this cold water area is especially wide. These several currents are indicated and named on Plate 23.

The movements of water in the Indian Ocean are complicated by the seasonal shift of the monsoons. In the Northern Hemisphere winter there is a well-developed westerly movement of the subtropical water both north and south of the equator. These currents, striking the east coast of Africa, give rise to a strong equatorial countercurrent. In the Northern Hemisphere summer, on the other hand, the onshore south Asian monsoon reverses the direction of the ocean current north of the equator, and the equatorial countercurrent entirely disappears. The currents in the Bay of Bengal and among the East Indies are similarly reversed by the seasonal shift of the winds.

4. **Ground Water.**[1] Three things can happen to the water that falls on the surface of the land: it can evaporate again, it can run off over the surface, or it can sink into the ground. These processes are sometimes described as fly-off, run-off, and cut-off. The circumstances which increase or decrease evaporation have already been described (Appendix B). As regards the ratio between run-off and cut-off, the cut-off is greater where the regolith is porous than where it is relatively impervious, it is greater on gentle slopes than on steep slopes, it is greater when the rain falls slowly than when it comes in violent showers, and it is greater where the ground is protected by a cover of vegetation than where the ground is bare.

The water which sinks into the ground and is not used near the surface by plants fills the spaces between the rock particles of the regolith and even the cracks in the bedrock below. This store of water is known as *ground water*. The portion of the bedrock and regolith which is saturated with water is known as the *zone of saturation,* and the top of the zone of saturation is termed the *ground-water table.* Above the ground-water table is the *zone of aeration,* through which the cut-off must sink on its way down to the zone of saturation. Water on its way down through the zone of aeration is called *vadose water.* The zone of aeration, however, may be moist even when there is no vadose water actually seeping through it; for just as a blotter may remain damp but not saturated, the upper zone of the regolith may contain considerable *soil moisture,* even during a protracted drought.

The ground-water table lies at varying depths below the surface. In general it follows the contour of the surface but without the smaller

[1] References 1 through 10.

irregularities. The water table rises under the hills and falls under the valleys, but it is farther below the surface under a hill than under a valley. Where the water table reaches the surface of the ground, it forms a marsh; where it rises above the surface, it forms a lake or supports the continued flow of a permanent stream. Even in the dry lands, where the characteristic streams flow only during and for a short time after a rain, ground water is usually to be found not far below the valley floors. Anything which diminishes the cut-off results eventually in a general lowering of the water table: thus the removal of the forest cover of a rainy land may result in the drying up of marshes and the fall of lake levels without any actual decrease in the rainfall.

The ground water in rainy lands seeps through the regolith toward the valleys to come to the surface again in springs. Because of the varied structure of the regolith and of the bedrock, the movement of ground water is not always uniform. The position and force of water in springs are determined by the underlying geologic structure.

5. **Common Wells.** The common well is used to tap the supply of ground water. It consists simply of an excavation deep enough to reach the zone of saturation. The ground water seeps into the well, filling it to the height of the water table.

6. **Artesian Wells.** In some wells water rises independently of the local ground-water table and may even flow out at the surface. These are *artesian wells*. The true artesian system requires the existence of a special set of geologic conditions the essentials of which are illustrated in the accompanying cross section (p. 579). A stratum of porous rock (W)—a sandstone, let us say—is inclined at an angle. Its outcrop is in an area of plentiful ground water (C). This is the intake of the artesian system, where the local ground water not only fills the usual cracks and fissures near the surface but also is absorbed by the porous sandstone. Gradually this layer of rock is saturated, and water seeps underground long distances, even hundreds of miles, from the intake. Overlying the water-bearing stratum is an impervious rock (B),—a shale, for example,—through which the imprisoned water cannot make its escape. Thus when a fissure is found, or when man makes a boring, as at D_1, D_2, or D_3, the water rises under pressure until it reaches the

level of *E*. In some cases the system is so placed that water actually flows out at the surface, making a flowing artesian well (*D₂* and *D₃*); but in others the intake is not high enough for this, and the water rises only part way in the boring and must be pumped the remainder of the distance to the surface (*D₁*). The essential requirements for such a system are tilted layers of rock, among which there is a porous water-bearing stratum under an impervious stratum. Wells may be bored hundreds of miles from the source of water. Obviously, however, the overuse of such a system may remove water faster than it is stored up and may bring about the eventual exhaustion of the supply, as is threatened at D_1.

7. **Hot Springs and Geysers.** In many parts of the world there are natural springs the temperature of which varies from slightly warm to hot or even boiling. These are produced where the cracks and fissures in the bedrock are deep enough to bring the ordinary ground water in contact with heated rocks. Few cracks reach depths greater than five miles, but even at that distance below the surface the rock is very hot. Where pools of molten rock lie near the surface, as in volcanic regions, hot springs are common.

Geysers are less common. A geyser is produced in a fissure from which there is no outlet save at the top. Ground water seeping down into such an opening is heated at the lower end. The temperature at the bottom may rise above the boiling point, but the weight of the overlying water does not permit the formation of steam. Eventually the super-

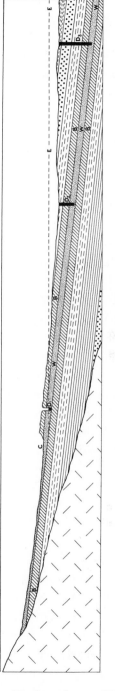

Diagram of an artesian system

heated water below is able to force a passage up through the tube, blowing out at the surface in a tall plume of spray.

8. Hard and Soft Waters. As water sinks through the zone of aeration or seeps through the regolith to emerge again in the rivers, many minerals are picked up in solution. It is the constant addition of mineral matter to the oceans and to the desert lakes which have no surface outlets that gives such bodies of water their high mineral content. Waters which have a considerable amount of mineral matter in solution (chiefly $CaCO_3$, $MgCO_3$, and $FeCO_3$) are said to be *hard*. In general the ground water and the water in rivers is hardest in areas of limestone rock or on plains where movement is slow. The softest waters are found where the rocks are relatively insoluble, as in granitic areas, or in hilly or mountainous country where the run-off is too rapid to permit the dissolving of such mineral matter.

9. Surface Water. Surface water includes rivers, lakes, marshes, and glaciers. The landforms related to these kinds of surface water have been discussed in Appendix C.

The more or less regular rise and fall of streams with the passage of the seasons is known as the *regimen*. Regimens may be described as regular, irregular, or intermittent. The regimen of a stream bears a close resemblance to the rainfall of its drainage basin, but it is also controlled to a certain extent by a number of other factors. De Martonne [1] illustrates the factors in regimen by a simple equation:

$$F = P - (C + E^1 + E^2) + S.$$

In this equation F is the flow of the river. This is determined primarily by the rainfall (P), subtracting, however, the amount of water which is cut off by sinking into the ground (C) and the amount which is evaporated directly (E^1) or indirectly through plants (E^2), and adding the amount of water which emerges again from the ground water through springs (S). Any condition which diminishes the values of C and E increases the flow of rivers. Yet since in the long run C and S are very nearly balanced, it follows that the volume of water in the streams must vary largely with P and E. The regimen of a stream, then, reflects

[1] Martonne, E. de, *Traité de géographie physique*, Paris, 1926.

closely the climatic conditions; it is most irregular in the *w* or *s* climates and most regular in the *f* climates (see Appendix B). In the case of streams draining areas of considerable snowfall, however, the spring melting is commonly the season of high water. Lakes have the effect of regularizing the flow of water, regardless of the regime of rainfall.

10. **Ice.** The following classification of ice forms was suggested by Nordenskjöld.[1]

A. Highland Glaciers
  I. Ice forms and ice motion dependent on the character of the underlying terrain.
    1. Glaciers in distinct catchment basins bordered by dominating ice-free ridges, outlets down-valley (valley glacier). Diagrams, p. 566.
    2. Glacier occupying an isolated catchment basin on the top of a plateau or highland (plateau glacier).
    3. Glacier resulting from the accumulation of several converging valley glaciers at the base of a mountain (piedmont glacier).
  II. Ice forms and ice motion independent or partially independent of the underlying terrain.
    4. Glacier covering most of surface, although the general shape of the underlying terrain is visible in the ice contour (near icecap). Map, p. 419.
    5. Glacier covering the whole surface to such a depth that no sign of the underlying terrain is apparent in the ice contour (inland ice). Map, p. 399.
B. Lowland Glaciers
    6. Accumulation of glacial ice in a band along the base of a mountain; not fed, as is the piedmont glacier, by converging valley glaciers, but formed in place from snow accumulation (ice foot).
    7. Accumulation of glacial ice on the seacoast, extending out into the water so that in some cases its outer margin is floating, and formed in place from snow accumulation (shelf ice). Map, p. 398.

REFERENCES

Water on the Land

1. MEINZER, O. E. *Outline of Ground-Water Hydrology*, United States Geological Survey, Water-Supply Paper 557. Washington, D. C., 1923.
2. JARVIS, C. S., and Others. *Floods in the United States: Magnitude and Frequency*, United States Geological Survey, Water-Supply Paper 771. Washington, D. C., 1936.

[1] Nordenskjöld, O., and Mecking, L. *The Geography of the Polar Regions*, American Geographical Society, Special Publication No. 8 (New York, 1928), p. 25.

3. Barrows, H. H. "A National Plan and Policy for the Control and Use of Water Resources," in Colby, C. C. (editor), *Geographic Aspects of International Relations,* Harris Foundation Lectures, 1937, pp. 99–123. Chicago, 1938.

4. Meinzer, O. E. *Ground Water in the United States,* United States Geological Survey, Water-Supply Paper 836-D. Washington, D. C., 1939.

5. Foster, E. E. *Rainfall and Runoff.* New York, 1948.

6. The President's Water Resources Policy Commission. *A Water Policy for the American People* (Vol. 1); *Ten Rivers in America's Future* (Vol. 2); *Water Resources Law* (Vol. 3). Washington, D. C., 1950.

7. McGuinness, C. L. *The Water Situation in the United States with Special Reference to Ground Water,* United States Geological Survey, Circular 114. Washington, D. C., 1951.

8. Thomas, H. E. *The Conservation of Ground Water.* New York, 1951.

9. Meigs, P. "Water Problems in the United States," *Geographical Review,* Vol. 42 (1952), pp. 346–366.

10. United States Department of Agriculture, *1955 Yearbook of Agriculture. Water.* Washington, D. C., 1955.

Water in the Oceans

11. Schott, G. *Geographie des Indischen und Stillen Ozeans.* Hamburg, 1935.

12. James, P. E. "The Geography of the Oceans: A Review of the Work of Gerhard Schott," *Geographical Review,* Vol. 26 (1936), pp. 664–669.

13. Sverdrup, H. U., Johnson, M. V., and Fleming, R. H. *The Oceans: Their Physics, Chemistry, and General Biology.* New York, 1942.

14. Schott, G. *Geographie des Atlantischen Ozeans,* Fourth Edition. Hamburg, 1944.

15. Russell, R. J. "Instability of Sea Level," *American Scientist,* Vol. 45 (1957), pp. 414–430.

E · STATISTICS

Table I. Metropolitan Areas of More than a Million Population (Arranged by Culture Areas)
(Based on A. M. Lambert, "Millionaire Cities," *Economic Geography*, Vol. 32, 1956, pp. 283–293)

City	Country	1935	ADDED BY 1955	FORECAST FOR 1960
EUROPEAN				
London	United Kingdom	×		
Manchester		×		
Birmingham		×		
Glasgow		×		
Leeds-Bradford		×		
Liverpool-Merseyside		×		
Newcastle-Tyneside				×
Berlin	Germany	×		
The Ruhr		×		
Hamburg-Altona		×		
Paris	France	×		
Rome	Italy	×		
Milan		×		
Naples		×		
Madrid	Spain	×		
Barcelona		×		
Vienna	Austria	×		
Athens-Piraeus	Greece		×	
Copenhagen	Denmark			×
Stockholm	Sweden			×
Brussels	Belgium			×
AMERICAN–ANGLO-AMERICAN				
New York	United States	×		
Chicago		×		
Los Angeles		×		
Philadelphia		×		
Detroit		×		
Boston		×		
San Francisco-Oakland		×		
Pittsburgh-Youngstown			×	
St. Louis		×		
Washington			×	
Cleveland		×		
Baltimore		×		
Minneapolis-St. Paul				×
Buffalo				×
Montreal	Canada	×		
Toronto		×		
AMERICAN–LATIN AMERICAN				
Habana	Cuba		×	
Mexico City	Mexico	×		
Rio de Janeiro	Brazil	×		
São Paulo		×		
Buenos Aires	Argentina	×		
Santiago	Chile		×	
Caracas	Venezuela		×	
Lima	Peru			×

(TABLE I CONTINUED)

Region / Country	City	1935	Added by 1955	Forecast for 1960
NORTH AFRICAN–SOUTHWEST ASIAN				
Egypt	Cairo	X		
	Alexandria			X
Turkey	Istanbul		X	
Pakistan	Karachi		X	
	Lahore			X
ORIENTAL				
India	Bombay	X		
	Calcutta	X		
	Madras		X	
	Delhi		X	
	Hyderabad		X	
China	Shanghai	X		
	Peking	X		
	Tientsin	X		
	Canton	X		
	Hankow	X		
	Nanking	X		
	Mukden (Shenyang)			
	Chungking			X
	Tsingtao			X
Japan	Tokyo	X		
	Osaka	X		
	Kyoto	X		
	Nagoya			
	Yokohama		X	
	Kobe			X
Korea	Seoul			X

Region / Country	City	1935	Added by 1955	Forecast for 1960
Viet Nam	Saigon		X	
Thailand	Bangkok		X	
Philippines	Manila		X	
Indonesia	Jakarta		X	
Hong Kong	Hong Kong-Kowloon			X
Singapore	Singapore			X
SOVIET				
U.S.S.R.	Moscow	X		
	Leningrad	X		
Hungary	Budapest	X		
Romania	Bucharest			
Czechoslovakia	Prague		X	
Poland	Warsaw			
AFRICAN				
Union of S. Africa	Johannesburg-Rand		X	
PACIFIC				
Australia	Sydney	X		
	Melbourne	X		

TABLE II. PERCENTAGE OF LAND AREA IN THE EIGHT GROUPS

	NORTH AMERICA	SOUTH AMERICA	AFRICA	EUROPE	ASIA	AUSTRALIA NEW ZEALAND PHILIPPINES EAST INDIES	ANTARCTICA	WORLD
I	10	8	34	(T)[1]	25	27	—	18
II	4	45	14	—	13	27	—	15
III	(T)	(T)	1	6	(T)	5	—	1
IV	14	2	(T)	38	7	7	—	7
V	12	30	46	19	10	27	—	21
VI	21	—	—	22	18	—	—	10
VII	23	—	—	4	6	—	100	16
VIII	16	15	5	11	21	7	—	12

TABLE III. POPULATION (IN HUNDREDS OF THOUSANDS) BY CONTINENTS AND GROUPS. POPULATION STATISTICS FROM VARIOUS SOURCES, ESTIMATED AS OF 1938. PERCENTAGES ARE GIVEN IN ITALICS

	NORTH AMERICA	SOUTH AMERICA	AFRICA	EUROPE	ASIA	AUSTRALIA NEW ZEALAND PHILIPPINES EAST INDIES	WORLD
I	5,900	3,800	27,100	100	44,100	100	81,100
	3	*4*	*17*	*(T)*	*4*	*(T)*	*4*
II	19,900	35,800	32,500	—	442,700	77,100	608,000
	11	*· 39*	*20*		*40*	*81*	*28*
III	3,800	3,100	9,300	48,300	12,500	1,300	78,300
	2	*3*	*6*	*9*	*1*	*2*	*4*
IV	106,700	2,300	1,800	327,600	395,400	6,900	840,700
	58	*3*	*1*	*62*	*36*	*7*	*39*
V	22,000	26,700	68,400	87,300	55,600	400	260,000
	12	*29*	*42*	*17*	*5*	*(T)*	*12*
VI	2,100	—	—	20,100	12,800	—	35,000
	1			*4*	*1*		*1*
VII	(T)	—	—	700	300	—	1,000
				(T)	*(T)*		*(T)*
VIII	23,100	19,700	22,100	43,300	140,900	9,800	258,900
	13	*22*	*14*	*8*	*13*	*10*	*12*

[1]T indicates less than one half of one per cent.

585

TABLE IV. CLIMATIC DATA FOR SELECTED STATIONS

T. = temperature in degrees Fahrenheit; Rf. = rainfall in inches

	Jan.	Feb.	Mar.	April	May	June	July	Aug.	Sept.	Oct.	Nov.	Dec.	Year
1. T.	27.9	28.8	35.6	46.4	57.1	66.5	71.7	69.9	63.2	53.6	42.0	32.5	49.6
Rf.	3.6	3.4	3.6	3.3	3.2	2.9	3.5	3.6	3.1	3.1	3.3	3.4	40.0
2. T.	25.6	27.0	36.6	47.4	58.4	68.1	74.0	72.9	66.3	54.8	41.5	30.3	50.2
Rf.	2.0	2.1	2.6	2.8	3.6	3.3	3.4	3.0	3.1	2.6	2.4	2.1	33.0
3. T.	−23.1	−11.3	3.8	29.1	46.4	56.7	59.3	54.3	42.4	25.1	0.7	−13.1	22.5
Rf.	0.8	0.8	0.5	0.7	0.9	1.3	1.6	1.6	1.7	1.3	1.3	1.1	13.6
4. T.	29.9	31.6	38.9	47.4	56.7	67.2	72.2	70.9	62.4	50.5	39.2	31.6	49.9
Rf.	0.4	0.5	1.0	2.1	2.4	1.3	1.6	1.4	1.0	1.0	0.6	0.7	14.0
5. T.	5.5	10.5	23.4	40.5	51.0	57.2	61.1	59.2	50.2	41.1	24.7	14.3	36.5
Rf.	0.9	0.6	0.7	0.8	1.8	3.2	3.4	2.4	1.4	0.7	0.7	0.8	17.4
6. T.	18.5	18.7	23.5	30.9	40.1	46.6	49.8	47.3	41.0	33.8	26.4	20.7	33.1
Rf.	3.3	2.7	3.4	2.4	3.6	3.0	3.3	3.8	6.0	5.9	4.4	3.1	44.9
7. T.	57.0	60.1	64.9	70.7	73.9	72.3	69.8	69.6	67.8	64.9	61.2	56.8	65.7
Rf.	0.4	0.3	0.7	0.2	1.2	4.5	6.1	5.2	4.5	1.4	0.5	0.4	25.4
8. T.	57.9	61.7	67.8	73.0	79.0	81.9	82.2	82.6	78.1	71.4	63.5	57.4	71.4
Rf.	0.5	0.5	0.7	1.1	1.2	2.3	2.1	2.0	4.4	2.4	1.3	1.0	19.5
9. T.	13.0	14.7	25.4	41.1	55.1	64.7	69.3	67.0	58.7	46.7	32.7	19.1	42.3
Rf.	3.7	3.2	3.7	2.4	3.1	3.4	3.7	3.3	3.5	3.3	3.4	3.7	40.4
10. T.	54.2	57.3	62.8	68.8	75.4	80.6	82.4	82.2	79.2	71.0	61.6	55.6	69.2
Rf.	4.3	4.2	4.7	5.2	4.6	5.9	6.4	5.8	5.0	3.3	3.1	4.8	57.3
11. T.	30.6	30.5	38.0	48.5	59.4	68.5	73.5	72.1	66.4	55.8	44.1	34.3	51.8
Rf.	3.2	3.3	3.4	3.3	3.5	3.5	4.1	4.3	3.4	3.4	3.4	3.3	42.1
12. T.	50.4	54.4	60.2	66.9	74.6	84.2	89.6	88.0	81.7	70.0	58.6	51.6	69.2
Rf.	1.0	0.7	0.6	0.4	0.1	0.1	1.3	1.0	0.7	0.5	0.8	0.7	7.9
13. T.	16.0	18.6	31.5	46.8	58.0	68.5	75.3	72.8	63.8	49.8	33.6	21.8	46.4
Rf.	0.5	0.5	0.9	1.8	2.5	3.0	2.7	2.1	1.1	0.8	0.5	0.5	16.9
14. T.	−19.9	−13.0	−13.1	−1.7	21.7	35.3	40.9	38.5	32.1	16.3	0.3	−15.4	10.2
Rf.	0.1	0.4	0.2	0.3	0.3	0.3	0.9	0.9	0.5	0.7	0.3	0.4	5.3
15. T.	38.9	41.5	46.3	51.2	56.6	61.4	66.6	66.4	60.9	53.6	45.9	41.0	52.5
Rf.	6.5	5.5	4.8	3.0	2.3	1.6	0.6	0.6	1.9	3.2	6.5	6.9	43.5
16. T.	45.8	50.1	54.3	58.1	63.3	69.4	73.2	72.9	69.3	62.9	53.6	46.2	59.9
Rf.	3.7	3.0	2.6	1.5	0.8	0.1	0	0	0.4	0.9	1.9	3.0	17.9
17. T.	22.5	22.3	25.7	31.3	35.8	39.0	39.9	40.1	38.8	34.3	30.9	26.2	32.2
18. T.	31.6	33.7	44.2	55.8	66.2	75.0	79.2	77.3	70.1	58.3	45.4	35.6	56.0
Rf.	2.3	2.6	3.5	3.8	4.5	4.6	3.6	3.5	3.2	2.8	2.9	2.5	39.8
19. T.	12.1	15.2	29.0	45.6	58.6	67.4	72.3	69.4	60.6	48.1	32.1	19.8	44.2
Rf.	0.9	0.9	1.5	2.3	3.5	4.3	3.5	3.3	3.1	2.3	1.3	1.0	27.9
20. T.	54.0	54.9	56.5	58.3	60.5	63.5	66.8	68.4	66.9	63.2	59.1	55.6	60.6
Rf.	1.8	1.9	1.5	0.6	0.3	0.1	0.1	0.1	0.1	0.4	0.9	1.8	9.6
21. T.	49.4	51.4	52.8	54.3	55.5	57.2	57.3	57.8	59.9	58.9	55.5	50.6	55.0
Rf.	4.8	3.6	3.1	1.6	0.7	0.1	0	0	0.3	0.9	2.4	4.5	22.0
22. T.	31.7	34.1	36.5	41.3	46.6	51.3	54.8	55.5	51.7	45.8	38.2	35.4	43.6
Rf.	7.6	6.5	5.6	5.5	4.1	3.4	4.2	7.1	10.1	12.2	9.5	9.0	84.8
23. T.	71.0	72.1	71.0	68.5	65.3	63.1	62.2	64.4	68.1	70.3	70.3	70.1	68.0
Rf.	13.2	7.2	7.7	2.9	0.6	0.4	0.2	0.6	0.9	4.4	8.8	11.6	58.5
24. T.	73.6	72.5	68.7	61.3	55.0	49.6	48.9	51.1	55.0	59.9	65.8	70.9	61.0
Rf.	3.1	2.7	4.4	3.5	2.9	2.5	2.2	2.5	3.0	3.5	3.1	3.9	37.3

	JAN.	FEB.	MAR.	APRIL	MAY	JUNE	JULY	AUG.	SEPT.	OCT.	NOV.	DEC.	YEAR
25. T.	73.8	72.5	68.5	62.1	55.8	49.6	50.4	51.6	58.6	63.3	68.4	72.3	62.2
Rf.	4.2	4.2	3.5	1.8	1.0	0.3	0.3	0.5	0.9	2.4	4.0	4.6	27.7
26. T.	81.0	80.8	80.7	80.2	77.5	75.4	75.9	78.3	82.0	81.7	82.0	81.3	79.8
Rf.	9.8	8.3	8.3	4.0	2.0	0.3	0.2	1.1	2.2	4.5	5.9	8.1	54.7
27. T.	69.4	69.4	67.6	64.8	62.6	61.2	60.4	60.3	61.2	63.0	65.3	67.5	64.4
Rf.	0	0	0	0	0	0	0	0	0.1	0	0	0	0.1
28. T.	46.6	46.8	46.0	44.2	41.9	39.9	39.0	39.4	40.1	41.7	42.6	44.8	42.7
Rf.	12.1	9.7	11.7	11.2	9.0	9.4	9.5	8.4	9.0	9.4	9.8	10.2	119.4
29. T.	72.7	74.3	73.6	70.2	66.0	62.6	61.2	61.0	61.3	63.0	65.7	70.0	66.8
Rf.	0	0	0	0	0.1	0.2	0.3	0.4	0.4	0.2	0.1	0	1.7
30. T.	79.9	80.1	79.7	79.9	80.1	80.1	80.6	81.7	82.8	82.8	82.2	80.6	80.9
Rf.	9.2	9.0	9.6	8.5	7.0	3.6	2.2	1.4	2.0	4.1	5.5	7.7	69.8
31. T.	75.2	75.4	76.3	77.8	79.1	78.1	77.9	77.8	78.3	78.2	77.5	76.3	77.3
Rf.	2.7	1.5	1.8	1.8	3.6	7.9	8.8	9.6	7.4	6.6	7.0	4.7	63.4
32. T.	54.6	54.5	54.5	54.5	54.6	54.6	54.5	54.6	54.8	54.6	54.5	54.6	54.6
Rf.	4.1	4.2	5.1	7.4	5.0	1.5	0.8	1.4	2.9	3.6	3.7	3.8	43.5
33. T.	58.8	57.6	54.5	47.9	41.2	35.4	35.1	38.3	43.5	48.8	53.1	56.3	47.5
Rf.	0.6	0.4	0.3	0.6	0.6	0.5	0.7	0.4	0.2	0.4	0.5	0.9	6.1
34. T.	67.3	66.0	61.9	56.1	50.5	46.0	46.0	48.2	52.2	56.1	61.0	65.7	56.4
Rf.	0	0.1	0.2	0.6	2.6	3.3	3.1	2.2	1.3	0.5	0.2	0.2	14.3
35. T.	61.9	60.4	57.9	53.1	49.6	45.5	45.7	46.4	48.0	52.0	55.0	59.0	52.9
Rf.	2.4	3.0	5.5	9.4	15.2	17.0	16.1	13.2	8.7	5.2	5.0	4.1	104.8
36. T.	8.1	9.7	17.4	30.0	41.5	52.7	59.5	55.2	45.7	33.8	21.4	12.2	32.3
Rf.	0.9	0.7	1.1	0.7	1.2	1.8	2.5	2.4	2.1	1.6	1.2	0.9	17.1
37. T.	19.2	22.8	32.7	47.8	63.5	72.5	76.1	73.8	62.6	49.5	36.0	26.6	48.6
Rf.	0.5	0.4	0.4	0.7	0.7	0.8	0.5	0.5	0.5	0.5	0.5	0.6	6.6
38. T.	24.1	23.8	24.0	27.6	33.0	39.7	41.1	40.4	38.0	31.4	28.9	25.2	31.4
Rf.	18.7	15.1	17.0	10.2	8.3	7.8	11.3	14.0	16.9	14.8	16.0	21.2	171.3
39. T.	26.2	30.6	41.0	52.2	62.2	68.9	72.9	72.0	63.5	52.9	39.7	30.9	51.1
Rf.	1.3	1.1	1.6	1.7	2.4	3.5	2.7	2.0	1.5	1.7	1.9	1.6	23.0
40. T.	50.5	52.2	54.3	57.6	60.3	66.7	70.0	71.1	68.4	62.2	56.5	51.6	60.1
Rf.	3.6	3.5	3.4	2.5	1.9	0.7	0.1	0.2	1.4	3.2	4.3	4.0	28.8
41. T.	12.6	15.6	24.3	38.1	53.2	60.1	64.4	60.4	49.8	38.6	27.0	17.6	38.5
Rf.	1.3	1.2	1.4	1.3	1.8	2.6	3.2	3.1	2.2	2.1	1.7	1.6	23.5
42. T.	34.9	39.4	43.2	49.3	56.1	61.7	64.6	63.9	58.5	50.0	42.4	38.1	50.2
Rf.	1.5	1.4	1.6	1.7	1.9	2.1	2.2	2.1	1.9	2.3	1.9	2.0	22.6
43. T.	29.8	29.8	31.1	36.3	42.8	48.6	51.6	50.5	45.5	39.2	33.8	30.0	39.1
Rf.	3.8	3.3	2.7	2.4	1.9	1.9	1.9	2.0	3.5	3.4	3.7	3.5	34.0
44. T.	44.6	46.8	50.9	56.7	64.4	70.9	76.1	75.6	69.6	61.7	52.7	46.4	59.7
Rf.	3.2	2.7	2.9	2.6	2.2	1.5	0.7	1.0	2.5	5.0	4.4	3.8	32.5
45. T.	30.6	32.9	39.7	49.3	60.4	68.0	72.1	71.1	63.9	55.0	43.7	35.8	51.9
Rf.	1.0	0.8	1.1	1.1	1.2	1.9	1.4	1.3	1.4	1.5	1.5	1.1	15.3
46. T.	24.4	23.4	27.9	37.8	48.7	57.4	61.9	58.5	50.4	41.4	32.2	25.5	40.8
Rf.	1.2	1.1	1.1	1.2	1.7	2.0	2.7	2.8	2.0	2.1	2.7	1.6	22.2
47. T.	44.7	44.8	45.1	48.1	52.4	55.6	58.9	59.2	56.4	51.7	47.5	45.4	50.8
Rf.	5.9	5.1	4.4	3.7	3.2	3.5	3.9	4.8	4.5	5.8	5.4	6.5	56.7
48. T.	61.3	65.6	76.8	87.3	93.1	92.6	86.4	84.4	84.3	79.3	69.4	61.7	78.5
Rf.	0.7	0.5	0.4	0.1	0.3	4.7	12.0	11.0	6.3	2.3	0.3	0.2	38.8

	JAN.	FEB.	MAR.	APRIL	MAY	JUNE	JULY	AUG.	SEPT.	OCT.	NOV.	DEC.	YEAR
49. T.	−0.6	2.3	14.9	33.6	52.3	63.7	68.0	63.0	51.8	35.8	16.9	5.0	33.9
Rf.	0.7	0.5	0.5	0.6	1.3	1.6	2.0	1.8	1.1	1.2	1.0	0.9	13.2
50. T.	77.9	77.9	78.1	79.5	79.7	79.2	78.6	79.0	79.7	79.9	79.3	78.4	78.9
Rf.	13.0	12.8	7.8	5.1	4.0	3.7	2.6	1.7	2.9	4.5	5.5	8.5	72.1
51. T.	56.5	57.7	61.2	66.0	71.8	77.7	82.0	83.1	80.8	76.1	67.3	60.6	70.1
Rf.	7.3	5.7	3.9	2.2	0.8	0.1	0	0	0.3	2.1	5.3	7.5	35.2
52. T.	75.5	75.7	79.5	83.1	85.8	84.0	81.4	80.8	80.9	82.4	80.6	77.4	80.6
Rf.	0.1	0.1	0	0	0.7	19.9	24.2	14.5	10.6	1.9	0.4	0	72.4
53. T.	57.9	59.0	65.5	74.1	82.4	86.1	89.6	90.2	86.5	79.5	70.1	61.5	75.2
Rf.	2.7	1.9	0.9	0.5	0	0	0	0	0	0.1	1.4	2.9	10.4
54. T.	66.6	71.2	80.2	85.6	86.1	85.1	83.7	83.2	83.2	79.3	73.5	66.5	78.7
Rf.	0.4	1.0	1.4	2.2	5.6	11.9	12.7	13.4	10.0	4.9	0.6	0.2	64.3
55. T.	53.2	54.9	60.9	63.7	66.3	68.1	68.6	68.6	68.9	66.1	61.0	54.7	62.9
Rf.	0.7	2.3	10.6	31.3	50.8	103.6	107.4	81.5	49.4	16.8	2.3	0.3	457.0
56. T.	80.5	82.0	84.2	85.0	83.6	80.0	79.0	79.2	79.9	80.4	81.1	80.7	81.3
Rf.	0.8	0.8	1.7	3.7	11.4	27.8	25.3	12.5	9.2	12.9	6.7	1.9	114.7
57. T.	79.5	80.4	81.8	82.7	82.8	81.6	81.2	81.2	81.2	80.5	80.0	79.5	81.0
Rf.	3.2	1.9	4.3	9.7	10.9	7.3	4.4	3.2	4.8	13.4	11.8	5.1	80.0
58. T.	40.1	42.6	50.4	61.9	71.4	79.7	85.5	85.5	76.6	66.6	55.2	44.6	63.3
Rf.	1.8	1.9	3.8	6.0	6.5	9.5	7.1	3.8	2.8	3.2	1.9	1.1	49.4
59. T.	60.0	58.7	63.0	70.4	76.8	80.9	82.0	81.5	80.5	76.3	69.3	62.7	71.8
Rf.	1.3	1.6	2.7	5.3	11.6	15.9	13.8	14.1	9.8	4.9	1.8	1.1	83.9
60. T.	61.3	64.7	75.0	85.0	91.8	92.4	86.2	83.6	83.6	79.7	70.3	62.9	78.0
Rf.	0.4	0.3	0.3	0.2	0.6	2.6	8.3	7.3	3.2	0.3	0.1	0.3	23.9
61. T.	65.3	68.4	75.0	80.6	84.7	86.8	84.3	82.4	82.0	80.0	74.0	67.4	77.6
Rf.	0.6	0.4	0.3	0.1	0.1	0.6	2.8	1.7	0.6	0	0.1	0.2	7.5
62. T.	76.2	77.7	81.1	85.3	89.8	90.0	87.6	86.0	85.2	82.3	78.9	76.7	83.1
Rf.	1.1	0.3	0.3	0.6	1.8	2.0	3.8	4.5	4.8	11.1	13.6	5.3	49.2
63. T.	30.9	31.5	36.7	46.8	54.1	60.8	67.8	71.6	65.1	54.7	45.0	36.0	50.1
Rf.	2.7	2.6	3.5	3.8	4.7	5.0	5.3	7.0	8.5	6.6	3.2	2.4	55.3
64. T.	8.1	14.0	29.7	46.9	60.1	70.5	76.5	74.5	61.3	48.4	29.1	14.0	44.4
Rf.	0.2	0.3	0.7	1.1	2.2	3.4	5.8	5.3	3.3	1.5	0.9	0.2	24.9
65. T.	22.8	23.3	31.6	37.2	43.9	50.0	57.6	62.6	58.8	50.4	39.4	29.3	42.1
Rf.	1.3	1.0	2.2	2.9	3.7	3.7	3.8	4.3	5.5	3.8	3.3	2.3	37.8
66. T.	57.3	57.4	58.9	60.4	61.7	60.9	58.8	59.3	59.3	59.5	59.1	57.8	59.2
Rf.	5.6	2.1	3.4	5.6	6.8	12.8	11.9	7.8	8.1	11.0	9.0	8.7	92.8
67. T.	79.0	81.0	83.7	85.8	84.2	82.2	81.5	81.7	81.7	81.1	80.2	78.8	81.7
Rf.	0.9	0.1	0.3	1.7	8.3	12.6	11.1	11.0	13.3	11.1	3.7	3.1	77.2
68. T.	79.8	80.1	81.1	82.3	82.6	81.7	81.8	81.8	81.7	81.5	80.8	80.1	81.3
Rf.	18.4	9.6	8.0	4.1	5.9	7.3	6.5	8.1	9.4	10.0	14.7	17.7	119.7
69. T.	37.4	38.8	44.4	54.5	61.9	68.9	75.6	77.7	71.4	60.4	50.5	41.4	56.9
Rf.	2.2	2.8	4.4	4.9	5.7	6.5	5.3	5.7	8.7	7.4	4.2	2.1	59.9
70. T.	−2.9	2.1	12.9	30.2	46.6	59.0	64.0	59.2	48.4	31.8	12.7	1.6	30.5
Rf.	1.1	0.8	0.8	0.7	1.5	2.7	3.0	2.3	1.4	2.4	1.4	1.9	20.0
71. T.	−58.2	−48.1	−23.8	9.5	36.3	56.1	59.9	51.6	36.1	5.7	−34.1	−51.3	3.3
Rf.	0.2	0.1	0.1	0.2	0.9	0.9	1.1	1.0	0.5	0.3	0.3	0.2	5.2
72. T.	−45.9	−33.2	−9.2	16.7	41.4	59.5	66.4	58.8	42.6	16.7	−20.0	−40.4	12.8
Rf.	0.2	0.2	0.1	0.2	0.5	1.1	1.3	1.7	0.9	0.5	0.4	0.3	7.4

CLIMATIC DATA FOR SELECTED STATIONS (*continued*)

	JAN.	FEB.	MAR.	APRIL	MAY	JUNE	JULY	AUG.	SEPT.	OCT.	NOV.	DEC.	YEAR
73. T.	37.8	39.4	46.0	56.1	65.5	73.4	80.4	80.2	73.0	63.5	52.0	42.1	59.1
Rf.	2.0	2.3	3.5	3.7	3.5	7.2	6.0	5.7	4.4	3.2	2.1	1.4	45.0
74. T.	49.3	50.4	52.5	55.8	61.0	67.9	73.4	74.7	70.3	63.7	56.8	51.8	60.6
Rf.	4.0	2.6	3.3	2.0	1.7	0.7	0.1	0.1	1.1	3.4	4.1	3.9	27.0
75. T.	71.5	70.2	68.9	66.0	61.2	57.4	57.2	61.2	67.6	72.4	72.5	71.8	66.5
Rf.	5.9	4.0	3.1	0.6	0.3	0	0	0	0.1	0.9	3.3	5.2	23.4
76. T.	54.1	56.8	62.4	70.2	76.8	81.9	83.5	82.6	78.1	71.4	65.1	57.9	70.1
Rf.	0.3	0.2	0.2	0.1	0	0	0	0	0	0	0.2	0.2	1.2
77. T.	69.9	70.3	68.1	63.2	58.9	55.7	54.7	55.6	57.9	61.2	64.4	67.9	62.3
Rf.	0.7	0.6	0.9	1.9	3.8	4.5	3.6	3.4	2.3	1.6	1.1	0.8	25.2
78. T.	71.1	71.1	71.3	70.3	69.8	69.4	68.6	68.6	69.4	70.1	70.1	70.2	70.0
Rf.	2.6	3.6	5.8	9.7	8.5	5.1	2.9	3.1	3.1	3.5	5.0	5.1	58.0
79. T.	81.3	82.3	82.4	82.4	81.5	80.3	78.6	77.9	79.1	80.1	81.2	81.4	80.7
Rf.	0.4	0.3	1.2	4.1	11.5	20.0	35.6	36.6	28.5	12.6	5.1	1.4	157.3
80. T.	66.5	65.4	63.3	59.8	54.4	50.7	50.5	54.3	59.4	62.7	63.5	65.1	59.6
Rf.	6.2	5.2	4.4	1.7	0.8	0.1	0.3	0.5	1.0	2.6	5.0	5.4	33.2
81. T.	72.5	75.2	81.0	81.0	92.5	93.4	89.6	87.8	89.2	88.9	82.0	74.7	84.0
Rf.	0	0	0	0	0.1	0.3	1.8	2.6	0.7	0.2	0	0	5.7
82. T.	75.6	73.9	69.5	62.9	54.7	48.9	49.3	54.1	61.3	66.9	70.7	75.0	63.6
Rf.	2.8	3.1	3.0	1.3	0.9	0.3	0.4	0.4	0.7	1.0	1.7	2.4	18.0
83. T.	80.9	82.2	83.3	82.5	81.8	79.3	78.0	77.7	78.4	79.5	81.4	81.5	80.5
Rf.	1.1	2.1	3.7	5.7	10.5	18.6	10.7	2.8	5.3	7.8	2.6	0.8	71.7
84. T.	72.1	73.3	71.1	66.0	58.5	53.0	53.4	54.0	58.2	62.9	65.8	70.2	63.2
Rf.	0.2	0.3	0.4	0.6	1.0	1.1	0.8	0.9	0.6	0.4	0.2	0.2	6.7
85. T.	69.4	69.7	68.0	65.1	61.6	59.3	57.9	58.4	59.8	61.8	64.5	67.6	63.6
Rf.	1.2	1.3	1.8	2.0	2.4	1.7	1.9	2.1	2.2	2.1	2.1	1.7	22.5
86. T.	73.6	73.9	73.6	72.3	72.1	70.9	70.2	70.7	71.1	70.7	72.3	73.0	72.0
Rf.	1.6	2.7	5.9	9.1	8.1	4.5	2.6	3.3	7.6	8.9	5.9	2.0	62.2
87. T.	73.9	74.1	69.8	63.9	57.9	53.5	51.7	54.0	57.1	61.9	66.9	71.1	63.0
Rf.	0.7	0.6	1.0	1.7	2.8	3.1	2.6	2.5	2.0	1.7	1.2	1.0	20.9
88. T.	77.2	76.5	74.3	70.3	64.5	60.2	58.5	60.4	65.4	69.8	73.6	76.4	68.9
Rf.	6.3	6.2	5.6	3.6	2.8	2.6	2.3	2.1	2.0	2.6	3.7	4.8	44.6
89. T.	83.8	83.4	84.0	84.1	81.8	78.9	77.4	79.4	82.6	85.3	85.8	85.1	82.6
Rf.	15.9	12.9	10.1	4.1	0.7	0.1	0.1	0.1	0.5	2.2	4.8	10.3	61.8
90. T.	70.3	70.9	69.2	65.8	60.6	55.8	54.3	56.1	59.2	62.6	65.8	68.7	59.9
Rf.	0.7	0.5	0.9	1.3	1.2	1.1	0.9	0.8	0.8	0.7	0.7	0.4	10.0
91. T.	67.5	67.6	64.6	59.4	54.1	50.4	48.7	51.1	54.1	57.7	61.3	64.9	58.4
Rf.	1.8	1.8	2.1	2.2	2.1	2.0	1.8	1.7	2.4	2.6	2.2	2.2	24.9
92. T.	83.3	82.0	76.6	68.1	59.7	54.4	52.6	58.2	65.5	73.3	79.0	82.3	68.6
Rf.	1.8	1.7	1.2	0.7	0.7	0.6	0.4	0.4	0.4	0.7	1.0	1.6	11.2
93. T.	71.7	71.3	69.3	64.7	58.8	54.6	52.7	55.0	59.2	63.5	67.1	70.1	63.1
Rf.	3.7	4.2	4.8	5.6	5.1	4.8	4.8	3.0	2.9	3.2	2.8	2.9	47.8
94. T.	21.7	9.3	−7.4	−24.0	−27.0	−29.4	−33.7	−34.2	−29.4	−14.1	8.6	23.7	−11.3

589

SOURCES OF CLIMATIC DATA

1. CLAYTON, H. H. *World Weather Records,* Smithsonian Miscellaneous Collections, Vol. 79. Washington, D. C., 1927.
2. United States Weather Bureau. "Normals of Daily Temperature for the United States," *Monthly Weather Review,* Supplement No. 25 (Washington, D. C., 1925), and idem. "The Daily, Monthly, and Annual Normals of Precipitation in the United States, . . . ," *Monthly Weather Review,* Supplement No. 34. Washington, D. C., 1930.
3. NORDENSKJÖLD, O., and MECKING, L. *The Geography of the Polar Regions,* American Geographical Society, Special Publication No. 8. New York, 1928.
4. Minas Geraes (Brazil), Commissão Geographica e Geologica. *Boletim de Normaes de Temperatura, Chuva, e Insolação.* Belo Horizonte, 1923.
5. KÖPPEN, W., and GEIGER, R. *Handbuch der Klimatologie* (in five volumes). Berlin.
6. KENDREW, W. G. *The Climates of the Continents.* Oxford, 1922.
7. VOZNESENSKII, A. V. *Karta klimatov U.S.S.R., Trudy po Selsko-khoz.* Meteorologii, No. 21. Leningrad, 1930 (quoted by L. I. Prasolov, "The Climate and Soils of Northern Eurasia as Conditions of Colonization," in *Pioneer Settlement,* American Geographical Society, Special Publication No. 14. New York, 1932).
8. Chinese official statistics, quoted by G. B. Cressey, *China's Geographic Foundations.* New York, 1934.
9. HANN, J. *Handbuch der Klimatologie,* pp. 82–83. Hamburg, 1908.

CLIMATIC STATIONS FOR WHICH DATA ARE GIVEN ON PAGES 586–589

The number in parentheses refers to the source of the data; the letter symbols are those of the Köppen classification (see definitions in Appendix B, sect. 30).

North America

1. Boston, U.S.A. . . . . (2) *Cfa*
2. Chicago, U.S.A. . . . . (1) *Dfa*
3. Dawson, Canada . . . (1) *Dfc*
4. Denver, U.S.A. . . . . (1) *BSkw*
5. Edmonton, Canada . . (1) *Dfb*
6. Ivigtut, Greenland . . (1) *ET*
7. León, Mexico . . . . . (1) *BShw*
8. Monterrey, Mexico . . (1) *BSh*
9. Montreal, Canada . . . (1) *Dfb*
10. New Orleans, U.S.A. . (2) *Cfa*
11. New York, U.S.A. . . . (1) *Cfa*
12. Phoenix, U.S.A. . . . (1) *BWh*
13. Pierre, U.S.A. . . . . (2) *BSkw*
14. Point Barrow, Alaska . (2) *ET*
15. Portland (Oregon), U.S.A. . . . . (1) *Csb*
16. Sacramento, U.S.A. . . (2) *Csa*
17. Sagdlit, Greenland . . (3) *ET*

18. St. Louis, U.S.A. . . . (1) *Cfa*
19. St. Paul, U.S.A. . . . (1) *Dfa*
20. San Diego, U.S.A. . . (1) *BSksn*
21. San Francisco, U.S.A. . (1) *Csbt'n*
22. Sitka, Alaska . . . . . (1) *Cfbs'*

South America

23. Belo Horizonte, Brazil . (4) *Cwa*
24. Buenos Aires, Argentina (1) *Cfa*
25. Córdoba, Argentina . . (1) *Cwa*
26. Cuiabá, Brazil . . . . (1) *Awi*
27. Iquique, Chile . . . . (1) *BWh (k)*
28. Islote de los Evangelistas, Chile . . . . . (1) *ET*
29. Lima, Peru . . . . . . (5) *BWhsn*
30. Manaus, Brazil . . . . (5) *Ami*
31. Port-of-Spain, Trinidad (1) *Amwi*
32. Quito, Ecuador . . . . (5) *Cfbi*
33. Santa Cruz, Argentina . (1) *BWk'*

34. Santiago, Chile . . . . (1) *Csb*
35. Valdivia, Chile . . . . (5) *Cfbs*

Europe

36. Arkhangelsk, U.S.S.R. . (1) *Dfc*
37. Astrakhan, U.S.S.R. . . (1) *BSk*
38. Ben Nevis, Great Britain (6) *ET*
39. Bucureşti, Romania . (1) *Dfa*
40. Lisboa, Portugal . . . (1) *Csb*
41. Moskva, U.S.S.R. . . . (1) *Dfb*
42. Paris, France . . . . . (1) *Cfb*
43. Reykjavik, Iceland . . (5) *Cfc*
44. Roma, Italy . . . . . (1) *Cs'a*
45. Sulina, Romania . . . (1) *Cfa*
46. Uppsala, Sweden . . . (1) *Dfb*
47. Valentia, Ireland . . . (1) *Cfb*

Asia

48. Allahabad, India . . . (1) *Cwg*
49. Barnaul, U.S.S.R. . . . (7) *Dfb*
50. Batavia (Jakarta), Java (1) *Amwi*
51. Beirut, Syria . . . . . (1) *Csa*
52. Bombay, India . . . . (1) *Awg*
53. Bushire, Iran . . . . . (1) *BShs*
54. Calcutta, India . . . . (1) *Awg*
55. Cherrapunji, India . . (1) *Cwb*
56. Cochin, India . . . . (1) *Amgi*
57. Colombo, Ceylon . . . (1) *Amw''i*
58. Hankow, China . . . (8) *Cfa*
59. Hong Kong, China . . (1) *Cwa*
60. Jaipur, India . . . . . (1) *BShw*
61. Karachi, Pakistan . . (6–1) *BWhw*
62. Madras, India . . . . (1) *Aw'*
63. Miyako, Japan . . . . (1) *Cfb (a)*
64. Mukden, Manchuria . (1) *Dwa*
65. Nemuro, Japan . . . . (1) *Dfb*
66. Nuwara Eliya, Ceylon . (1) *Cfbgi*
67. Saïgon, Viet Nam . . . (1) *Awgi*

68. Sandakan, British North
    Borneo . . . . . . (1) *Afsi*
69. Tokyo, Japan . . . . . (1) *Cfa*
70. Tomsk, U.S.S.R. . . (1–6) *Dfc*
71. Verkhoyansk, U.S.S.R. . (7) *Dwd*
72. Yakutsk, U.S.S.R. . . . (7) *Dwd*
73. Zi-ka-wei (Shanghai),
    China . . . . (1) *Cfa*

Africa

74. Algiers, Algeria . . . . (1) *Csa*
75. Bulawayo, Rhodesia . . (1) *BShw*
76. Cairo, Egypt . . . . . (9) *BWhs*
77. Capetown, South
    Africa . . . . (1) *Csb*
78. Entebbe, Uganda . . . (1) *Amw''i*
79. Freetown, Sierra Leone (1) *Amgi*
80. Johannesburg, South
    Africa . . . . . . (1) *Cwb*
81. Khartoum, Sudan . . . (1) *BWhw*
82. Kimberley, South Africa (1) *BSkw*
83. Lagos, Nigeria . . . . (1) *Aw''gi*
84. O'Okiep, South Africa . (1) *BWks*
85. Port Elizabeth, South
    Africa . . . . . . (1) *Cfb*
86. Yaunde, Cameroon . . (6) *Amw''i*

Australia

87. Adelaide . . . . . . (1) *Csa*
88. Brisbane . . . . . . (1) *Cfa*
89. Darwin . . . . (1) *Awgi*
90. Eucla . . . . (5) *BSk*
91. Melbourne . . . . . (5) *Cfb*
92. Stuart . . . . (1) *BWhw*
93. Sydney . . . . (1) *Cfa*

Antarctica

94. Framheim, Little Amer-
    ica . . . . (3) *EF*

F · REFERENCES

As a guide to students who wish to become familiar with geographic writings the following suggestions and lists of references are offered. In the first place the student should become familiar with the chief geographical bibliographies. The most important of these is the *Bibliographie géographique internationale,* published annually since 1891 by Armand Colin in Paris. Many geographical societies in many countries collaborate in preparing this bibliography. In the United States the American Geographical Society of New York maintains a current list of writings. Since 1938 this Society has published monthly (except July and August) its *Current Geographical Publications: Additions to the Research Catalogue of the American Geographical Society.* These and many other geographical bibliographies are listed and described in J. K. Wright and E. T. Platt, *Aids to Geographic Research,* American Geographical Society Research Series, No. 22, Second Edition, New York, 1947.

For lengthy lists of geographic writings arranged by topics or branches of geography, the student is directed to P. E. James and C. F. Jones (editors), *American Geography, Inventory and Prospect,* Syracuse, New York, 1954.

The following references provide a selected list of readings in geography. For references dealing with maps, see the list at the end of Appendix A; for those dealing with climatology, see the end of Appendix B; for those dealing with landforms and soils, see the end of Appendix C; and for those dealing with hydrography and oceanography, see the end of Appendix D.

A. HISTORY OF GEOGRAPHIC THOUGHT

BUNBURY, E. H. *A History of Ancient Geography.* London, 1883.
MILL, H. R. *The Realm of Nature.* London, 1892.
HERBERTSON, A. J. "The Major Natural Regions: An Essay in Systematic Geography," *Geographical Journal,* Vol. 25 (1905), pp. 300–312.

DAVIS, W. M. "An Inductive Study of the Content of Geography," *Bulletin of the American Geographical Society,* Vol. 38 (1906), pp. 67–84.

VIDAL DE LA BLACHE, P. *Principes de géographie humaine.* Paris, 1922.

SAUER, C. O. "The Morphology of Landscape," *University of California Publications in Geography,* Vol. 2 (1925), pp. 19–53.

HETTNER, A. *Die Geographie—Ihre Geschichte, ihr Wesen, und ihre Methoden.* Breslau, 1927.

VALLAUX, C. *Les Sciences géographiques.* Paris, 1929.

DICKINSON, R. E., and HOWARTH, O. J. R. *The Making of Geography.* Oxford, 1933.

KIMBLE, G. H. T. *Geography in the Middle Ages.* London, 1938.

HARTSHORNE, R. *The Nature of Geography: A Critical Survey of Current Thought in the Light of the Past.* Lancaster, Pennsylvania, 1939. Available in Central Office, Association of American Geographers, Library of Congress, Washington, D. C.

STAMP, L. D., and WOOLDRIDGE, S. W. (editors). *London Essays in Geography.* London, 1951.

JAMES, P. E., and JONES, C. F. (editors). *American Geography, Inventory and Prospect.* Syracuse, New York, 1954. Available in Central Office, Association of American Geographers, Library of Congress, Washington, D. C.

B. THE WORLD AS A WHOLE OR LARGER PARTS

MARSH, G. P. *The Earth as Modified by Human Action.* New York, 1874.

WHITTLESEY, D. S. *The Earth and the State.* New York, 1939.

MACKINDER, H. J. *Democratic Ideals and Reality.* New York, 1942.

BROWN, R. H. *Mirror for Americans, Likeness of the Eastern Seaboard, 1810.* New York, 1943.

SORRE, M. *Les Fondements biologiques de la géographie humaine.* Paris, 1943.

HUNTINGTON, E. *Mainsprings of Civilization.* New York, 1945.

BROWN, R. H. *Historical Geography of the United States.* New York, 1948.

GEORGE, P. *Introduction a l'étude géographique de la population du monde.* Paris, 1951.

RUSSELL, R. J., and KNIFFEN, F. B. *Culture Worlds.* New York, 1951.

SAUER, C. O. *Agricultural Origins and Dispersals.* New York, 1952.

GOUROU, P. *The Tropical World.* London, 1953.

STAMP, L. D. *Africa: A Study in Tropical Development.* New York, 1953.

JONES, C. F., and DARKENWALD, G. G. *Economic Geography,* Revised Edition. New York, 1954.

SPENCER, J. E. *Asia, East by South; A Cultural Geography.* New York, 1954.

CRESSEY, G. B. *Land of the 500 Million; A Geography of China.* New York, 1955.

THOMAS, W. L., JR., and Others (editors). *Man's Role in Changing the Face of the Earth.* Chicago, 1956.

EAST, W. G., and MOODIE, A. E. (editors). *The Changing World, Studies in Political Geography.* London and New York, 1956.

WEIGERT, H. W., BRODIE, H., DOHERTY, E. W., FERNSTROM, J. R., FISCHER, E., and KIRK, D. *Principles of Political Geography.* New York, 1957.

JAMES, P. E. *Latin America,* Revised Edition. New York, 1959.

VIDAL DE LA BLACHE, P., and GALLOIS, L. (editors). *Géographie universelle* (15 volumes by various authors). Paris.

References 593

C. AREAL STUDIES

Group I

BARTH, H. *Travels and Discoveries in North and Central Africa.* New York, 1857.

HUNTINGTON, E. *The Pulse of Asia.* Boston, 1907.

GAUTIER, E. F. *Le Sahara.* Paris, 1923.

BOWMAN, I. *Desert Trails of Atacama,* American Geographical Society, Special Publication No. 5. New York, 1924.

WALTHER, J. *Das Gesetz der Wüstenbildung.* Leipzig, 1924.

GAUTIER, E. F. "The Ahaggar, Heart of the Sahara," *Geographical Review,* Vol. 16 (1926), pp. 378–394.

RUSSELL, R. J. "The Land Forms of Surprise Valley, Northwestern Great Basin," *University of California Publications in Geography,* Vol. 2 (1927), pp. 323–358.

HEWES, L. "Huepac: An Agricultural Village of Sonora, Mexico," *Economic Geography,* Vol. 11 (1935), pp. 284–292.

HOOVER, J. W. "Navajo Land Problems," *Economic Geography,* Vol. 13 (1937), pp. 281–300.

LATTIMORE, O. *Inner Asian Frontiers of China,* American Geographical Society, Research Series, No. 21. New York, 1940.

TWITCHELL, K. S. "Water Resources of Saudi Arabia," *Geographical Review,* Vol. 34 (1944), pp. 365–386.

MOOLMAN, J. H. "The Orange River, South Africa," *Geographical Review,* Vol. 36 (1946), pp. 653–674.

GLENDINNING, R. M. "Desert Contrasts Illustrated by the Coachella," *Geographical Review,* Vol. 39 (1949), pp. 221–228.

FISHER, W. B. *The Middle East: A Physical, Social, and Regional Geography.* London, 1950.

CRARY, D. D. "Recent Agricultural Developments in Saudi Arabia," *Geographical Review,* Vol. 41 (1951), pp. 366–383.

CRESSEY, G. B. "Qanats, Karez, and Foggaras," *Geographical Review,* Vol. 48 (1958), pp. 27–44.

Group II

WALLACE, A. R. *A Narrative of Travels on the Amazon and Rio Negro.* London, 1853.

WOOD, W. H. A. "Rivers and Man in the Indus-Ganges Alluvial Plain," *Scottish Geographical Magazine,* Vol. 40 (1924), pp. 1–16.

VLIELAND, C. A. "The Population of the Malay Peninsula: A Study in Human Migration," *Geographical Review,* Vol. 24 (1934), pp. 61–78.

JAMES, P. E. "The Changing Patterns of Population in São Paulo State, Brazil," *Geographical Review,* Vol. 28 (1938), pp. 353–362.

PRICE, A. G. *White Settlers in the Tropics,* American Geographical Society, Special Publication No. 23. New York, 1939.

DOBBY, E. H. G. "Settlement Patterns in Malaya," *Geographical Review,* Vol. 32 (1942), pp. 211–232.

GEDDES, A. "The Population of India . . . ," *Geographical Review,* Vol. 32 (1942), pp. 562–573.

RUSSELL, J. A. "Fordlandia and Belterra, Rubber Plantations on the Tapajos River, Brazil," *Economic Geography,* Vol. 18 (1942), pp. 125–145.

Davis, C. M. "Coconuts in the Russell Islands," *Geographical Review,* Vol. 37 (1947), pp. 400–413.

Spate, O. H. K. "The Partition of India and the Prospects of Pakistan," *Geographical Review,* Vol. 38 (1948), pp. 5–29.

Pendleton, R. L. "The Belgian Congo: Impressions of a Changing Region," *Geographical Review,* Vol. 39 (1949), pp. 371–400.

Monbeig, P. *Pionniers et Planteurs de São Paulo.* Paris, 1952.

James, P. E. "Trends in Brazilian Agricultural Development," *Geographical Review,* Vol. 43 (1953), pp. 301–328.

Jarrett, H. R. "Some Aspects of the Urban Geography of Freetown, Sierra Leone," *Geographical Review,* Vol. 46 (1956), pp. 334–354.

Group III

Ahlmann, H. W. "The Geographical Study of Settlements . . . ," *Geographical Review,* Vol. 18 (1928), pp. 93–128.

Almagià, R. "The Repopulation of the Roman Campagna," *Geographical Review,* Vol. 19 (1929), pp. 529–555.

Semple, E. C. *The Geography of the Mediterranean Region: Its Relation to Ancient History.* New York, 1931.

Broek, J. O. M. *The Santa Clara Valley, California: A Study in Landscape Changes.* Utrecht, 1932.

Torbert, E. N. "The Specialized Commercial Agriculture of the Northern Santa Clara Valley," *Geographical Review,* Vol. 26 (1936), pp. 247–263.

Meigs, P. "Water Planning in the Great Central Valley, California," *Geographical Review,* Vol. 29 (1939), pp. 252–273.

Bowman, R. G. "Prospects of Land Settlement in Western Australia," *Geographical Review,* Vol. 32 (1942), pp. 598–621.

Unger, L. "Rural Settlement in the Campania," *Geographical Review,* Vol. 43 (1953), pp. 506–524.

Dickinson, R. E. *The Population Problem of Southern Italy, An Essay in Social Geography.* Syracuse, New York, 1955.

Melamid, A. "The Geographical Distribution of Communities in Cyprus," *Geographical Review,* Vol. 46 (1956), pp. 355–374.

Group IV

Gallois, L. *Régions naturelles et noms de pays, étude sur la région parisienne.* Paris, 1908.

Sauer, C. O. *The Geography of the Ozark Highland of Missouri,* Geographical Society of Chicago, Bulletin No. 7. Chicago, 1920.

Demangeon, A. *La Picardie . . .* Paris, 1925.

Ogilvie, A. G. (editor). *Great Britain, Essays in Regional Geography.* Cambridge (England), 1928.

James, P. E. "The Blackstone Valley: A Study in Chorography in Southern New England," *Annals of the Association of American Geographers,* Vol. 19 (1929), pp. 67–109.

East, G. *An Historical Geography of Europe.* London, 1935.

Torbert, E. N. "The Evolution of Land Utilization in Lebanon, New Hampshire," *Geographical Review,* Vol. 25 (1935), pp. 209–230.

Kendall, H. M. "A Survey of Population Changes in Belgium," *Annals of the Association of American Geographers,* Vol. 28 (1938), pp. 145–164.

Friis, H. R. "A Series of Population Maps of the Colonies and the United States, 1625–1790," *Geographical Review,* Vol. 30 (1940), pp. 463–470.

Cumberland, K. B. "A Century's Change: Natural to Cultural Vegetation in New Zealand," *Geographical Review,* Vol. 31 (1941), pp. 529–554.

Trewartha, G. T. *Japan: A Physical, Cultural, and Regional Geography.* Madison, Wisconsin, 1945.

Trewartha, G. T. "Types of Rural Settlement in Colonial America," *Geographical Review,* Vol. 36 (1946), pp. 568–596.

Stamp, L. D. *The Land of Britain: Its Use and Misuse.* London, 1950.

Prunty, M., Jr. "Land Occupance in the Southeast: Landmarks and Forecast," *Geographical Review,* Vol. 42 (1952), pp. 439–461.

Brush, J. E. "The Hierarchy of Central Places in Southwestern Wisconsin," *Geographical Review,* Vol. 43 (1953), pp. 380–402.

Dickinson, R. E. *Germany, A General and Regional Geography.* London, 1953.

Veatch, J. O. *Soils and Land of Michigan.* East Lansing, Michigan, 1953.

Klimm, L. E. "The Empty Areas of the Northeastern United States," *Geographical Review,* Vol. 44 (1954), pp. 325–345.

Garland, J. H. (editor). *The North American Midwest: A Regional Geography.* New York, 1955.

Pounds, N. J. G. "Lorraine and the Ruhr," *Economic Geography,* Vol. 33 (1957), pp. 149–162.

Group V

Bowman, I. "Jordan Country," *Geographical Review,* Vol. 21 (1931), pp. 22–55.

Brown, R. H. "Belle Fourche Valleys and Uplands," *Annals of the Association of American Geographers,* Vol. 23 (1933), pp. 127–156.

Mackintosh, W. A. *Prairie Settlement, The Geographic Setting,* Vol. 1 of *Canadian Frontiers of Settlement.* Toronto, 1934.

Malin, J. C. "Grassland, 'Treeless,' and 'Subhumid' . . . ," *Geographical Review,* Vol. 37 (1947), pp. 241–250.

Buchanan, K. "The Northern Region of Nigeria, The Geographical Background of its Political Duality," *Geographical Review,* Vol. 43 (1953), pp. 451–473.

Davis, C. M. "Merino Sheep on the Australian Riverina," *Geographical Review,* Vol. 44 (1954), pp. 475–494.

Wellington, J. H. *Southern Africa: A Geographical Study* (2 vols.). Cambridge (England), 1955.

Hewes, L., and Schmieding, A. C. "Risk in the Central Great Plains . . . ," *Geographical Review,* Vol. 46 (1956), pp. 375–387.

Group VI

Albright, W. D. "Gardens of the Mackenzie," *Geographical Review,* Vol. 23 (1933), pp. 1–22.

Leppard, H. M. "The Settlement of the Peace River Country," *Geographical Review,* Vol. 25 (1935), pp. 62–78.

Lloyd, T. "The Mackenzie Waterway: A Northern Supply Route," *Geographical Review,* Vol. 33 (1943), pp. 415–434.

Hare, F. K. "Climate and Zonal Divisions of the Boreal Forest Formation in Eastern Canada," *Geographical Review,* Vol. 40 (1950), pp. 615–635.

Platt, R. R. *Finland and its Geography.* New York, 1955.

Jackson, W. A. D. "The Virgin and Idle Lands of Western Siberia and Northern Kazakhstan: A Geographical Appraisal," *Geographical Review,* Vol. 46 (1956), pp. 1–19.

Group VII

Nordenskjöld, O., and Mecking, L. *The Geography of the Polar Regions,* American Geographical Society, Special Publication No. 8. New York, 1928.

Friis, H. R. "Greenland: A Productive Arctic Colony," *Economic Geography,* Vol. 13 (1937), pp. 75–92.

Kimble, G. H. T., and Good, D. (editors). *Geography of the Northlands.* New York, 1955.

Gould, L. M. "Antarctic Prospect," *Geographical Review,* Vol. 47 (1957), pp. 1–28.

Group VIII

Bowman, I. *The Andes of Southern Peru.* New York, 1916.

Unstead, J. F. "The Lötschental: A Regional Study," *Geographical Journal,* Vol. 79 (1932), pp. 298–317.

Garnett, A. "Insolation, Topography, and Settlement in the Alps," *Geographical Review,* Vol. 25 (1935), pp. 601–617.

James, P. E. "Regional Planning in the Jackson Hole Country," *Geographical Review,* Vol. 26 (1936), pp. 439–453.

Peattie, R. *Mountain Geography.* Cambridge, Massachusetts, 1936.

Parsons, J. J. *Antioqueño Colonization in Western Colombia,* Ibero-Americana, No. 32. Berkeley, California, 1949.

Lewis, N. N. "Lebanon—The Mountain and Its Terraces," *Geographical Review,* Vol. 43 (1953), pp. 1–14.

Gajdusek, D. C. "The Sierra Tarahumara," *Geographical Review,* Vol. 43 (1953), pp. 15–38.

D. THE INDUSTRIAL SOCIETY

Fawcett, C. B. *A Political Geography of the British Empire.* Boston, 1933.

Mumford, L. *The Culture of Cities.* New York, 1938.

Voskuil, W. H. "Coal and Political Power in Europe," *Economic Geography,* Vol. 18 (1942), pp. 247–258.

Harris, C. D. "A Functional Classification of Cities in the United States," *Geographical Review,* Vol. 33 (1943), pp. 86–99.

Lovering, T. S. *Minerals in World Affairs.* New York, 1943.

Davis, K. (editor). "World Population in Transition," *Annals of the American Academy of Political and Social Science,* Vol. 237 (1945), pp. 1–203.

Harris, C. D. "The Cities of the Soviet Union," *Geographical Review,* Vol. 35 (1945), pp. 107–121.

Bertram, G. C. L. "Population Trends and the World's Resources," *Geographical Journal,* Vol. 107 (1946), pp. 191–210.

DICKINSON, R. E. *City, Region, and Regionalism: A Geographical Contribution to Human Ecology.* London, 1947.

PRATT, W. E., and GOOD, D. (editors). *World Geography of Petroleum.* New York, 1950.

WHITAKER, J. R., and ACKERMAN, E. A. *American Resources, Their Management and Conservation.* New York, 1951.

ZIMMERMANN, E. W. *World Resources and Industries,* Second Edition. New York, 1951.

KLOVE, R. C. "The Definition of Standard Metropolitan Areas," *Economic Geography,* Vol. 28 (1952), pp. 95–104.

ALEXANDER, J. W. "The Basic-Nonbasic Concept of Urban Economic Functions," *Economic Geography,* Vol. 30 (1954), pp. 246–261.

HARRIS, C. D. "The Market as a Factor in the Localization of Industry in the United States," *Annals of the Association of American Geographers,* Vol. 44 (1954), pp. 315–348.

MURPHY, R. E., and VANCE, J. E., JR. "Delimiting the CBD," *Economic Geography,* Vol. 30 (1954), pp. 189–222.

THOMPSON, J. H. "A New Method for Measuring Manufacturing," *Annals of the Association of American Geographers,* Vol. 45 (1955), pp. 416–436.

HOFFMAN, G. W. "The Role of Nuclear Power in Europe's Future Energy Balance," *Annals of the Association of American Geographers,* Vol. 47 (1957), pp. 15–40.

GINSBURG, N. "Natural Resources and Economic Development," *Annals of the Association of American Geographers,* Vol. 47 (1957), pp. 197–212.

REFERENCE MAPS

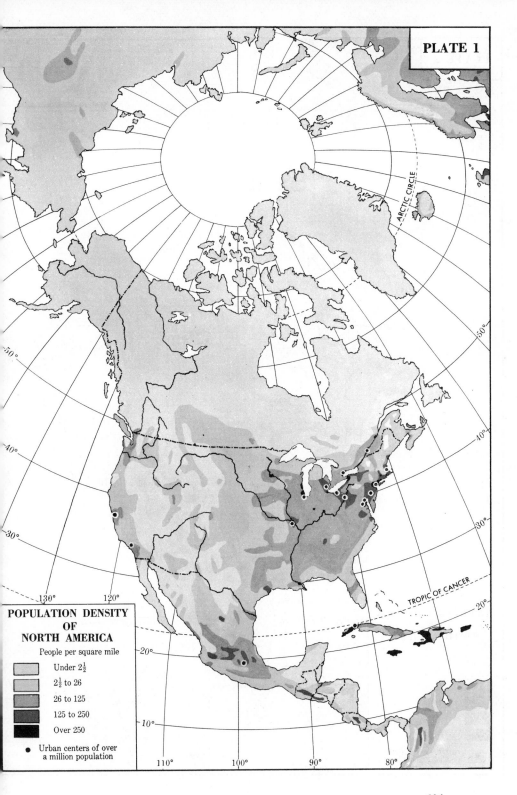

PLATE 1

ARCTIC CIRCLE

50°

40°

50°

40°

30°

30°

TROPIC OF CANCER

20°

20°

POPULATION DENSITY
OF
NORTH AMERICA

People per square mile

Under 2½

2½ to 26

26 to 125

125 to 250

Over 250

● Urban centers of over
a million population

10°

130° 120° 110° 100° 90° 80°

601

PLATE 2

70° 60° 50° 40° 30°

TROPIC OF CANCER

10°

EQUATOR

0°

10°

TROPIC OF CAPRICORN

20°

30°

POPULATION DENSITY
OF
SOUTH AMERICA

People per square mile

Under 2½

2½ to 26

26 to 125

125 to 250

Over 250

• Urban centers of over
  a million population

40°

50°

100° 90° 80° 70° 60° 50° 40° 30° 20° 10°

602

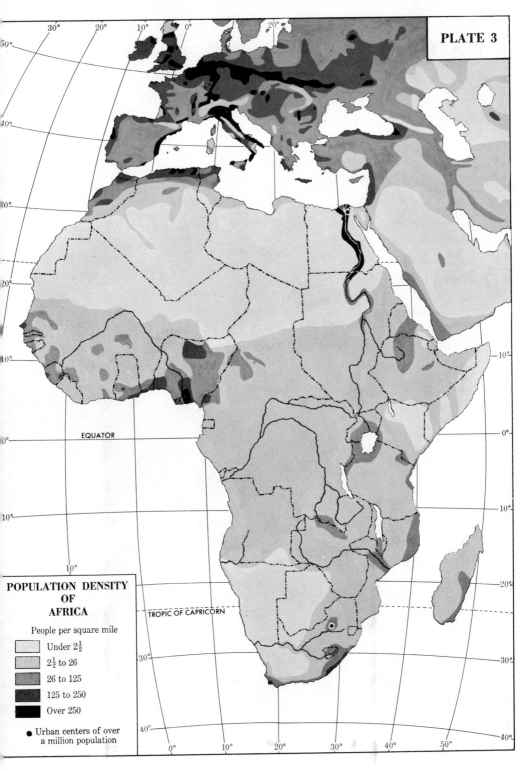

PLATE 3

POPULATION DENSITY
OF
AFRICA

People per square mile

Under 2½

2½ to 26

26 to 125

125 to 250

Over 250

● Urban centers of over
a million population

30° 20° 10° 0° 20°

50°

40°

30°

20°

10°

EQUATOR

10°

10°

TROPIC OF CAPRICORN

30°

40°

0° 10° 20° 30° 40° 50°

10°

0°

10°

20°

30°

40°

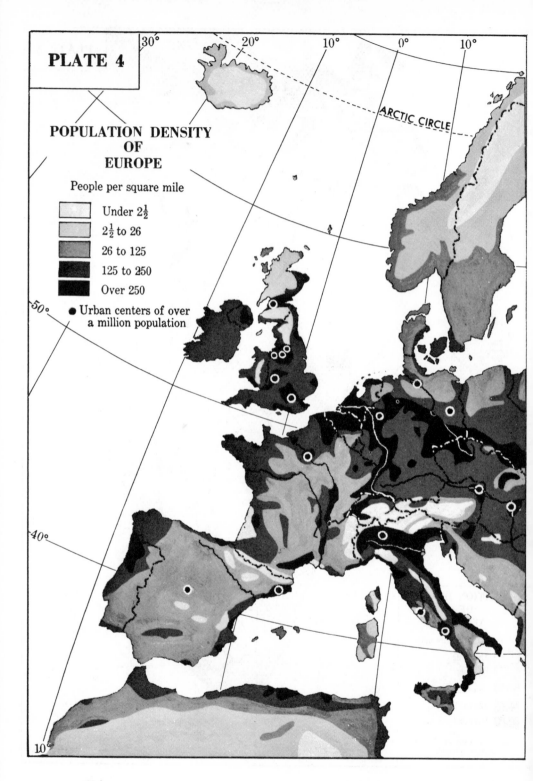

PLATE 4

POPULATION DENSITY
OF
EUROPE

People per square mile

Under 2½
2½ to 26
26 to 125
125 to 250
Over 250

● Urban centers of over
a million population

ARCTIC CIRCLE

604

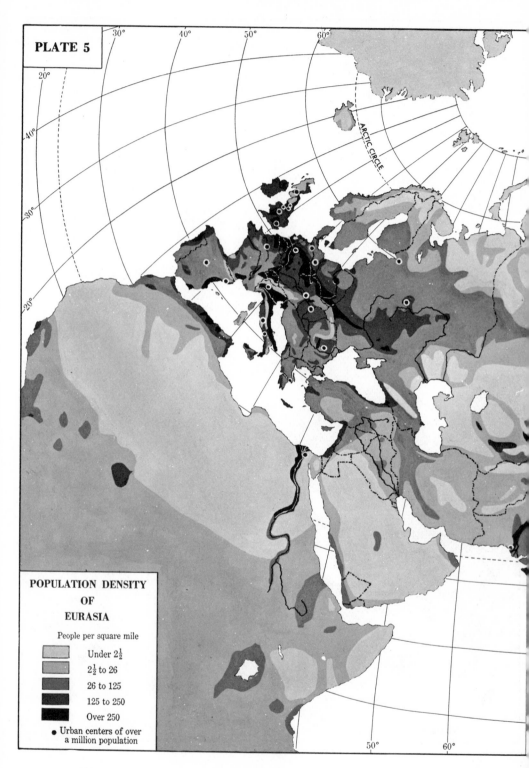

PLATE 5

POPULATION DENSITY
OF
EURASIA

People per square mile

Under 2½
2½ to 26
26 to 125
125 to 250
Over 250
• Urban centers of over
a million population

TROPIC OF CANCER

EQUATOR

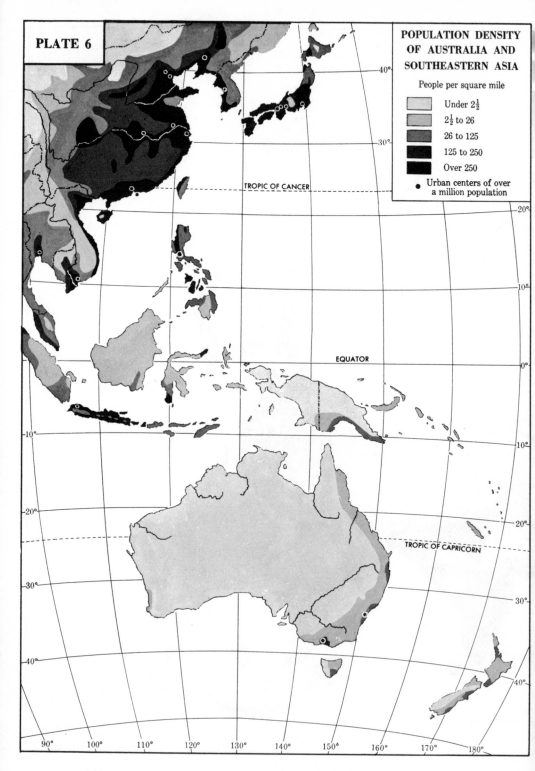

PLATE 6

POPULATION DENSITY
OF AUSTRALIA AND
SOUTHEASTERN ASIA

People per square mile

Under 2½

2½ to 26

26 to 125

125 to 250

Over 250

• Urban centers of over
a million population

TROPIC OF CANCER

EQUATOR

TROPIC OF CAPRICORN

PLATE 7

AVERAGE ANNUAL RAINFALL

Under 10 inches
10 – 20 inches
20 – 40 inches
40 – 80 inches
Over 80 inches

"after Gerhard Schott"

ARCTIC CIRCLE
EQUATOR
TROPIC OF CANCER
TROPIC OF CAPRICORN

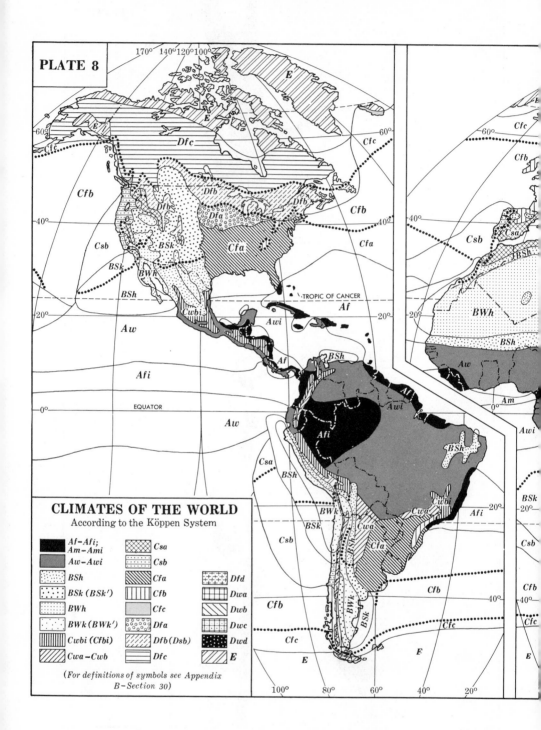

PLATE 8

170° 140° 120° 100°

E

E

60°

E

Cfc

60°

Cfc

60°

Dfc

Cfc

Cfb

Cfb

40°

Dfb

Dfb

Dfb

Cfb

Cfb

40°

Cfb

Csb

Csa

Dfb

Dfa

Cfa

Csb

Csb

Csa

BSk

Cfa

BSh

Csb

Cfa

BSk

BWh

BSh

TROPIC OF CANCER

Af

BWh

Cwbi

Af

Awi

Aw

BSh

BSh

Afi

Af

BSh

Aw

Af

Aw

Am

Afi

Awi

Awi

EQUATOR

Aw

Afi

BSh

Csa

Afi

BSh

BWk

Cwa

BSk

Cwbi

Csb

BWk

Cwa

Csb

BSk

Cfa

BSk

CLIMATES OF THE WORLD
According to the Köppen System

■ Af–Afi; Am–Ami	Csa	
Aw–Awi	Csb	
BSh	Cfa	Dfd
BSk (BSk')	Cfb	Dwa
BWh	Cfc	Dwb
BWk (BWk')	Dfa	Dwc
Cwbi (Cfbi)	Dfb (Dsb)	Dwd
Cwa–Cwb	Dfc	E

(For definitions of symbols see Appendix
B – Section 30)

BWk

BSk

Cfb

Cfb

40°

Cfc

Cfc

Cfc

E

E

E

100°   80°   60°   40°   20°

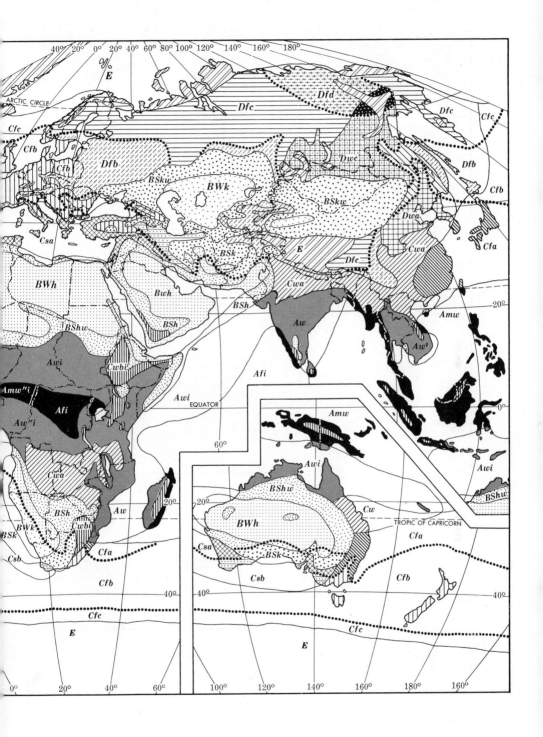

611

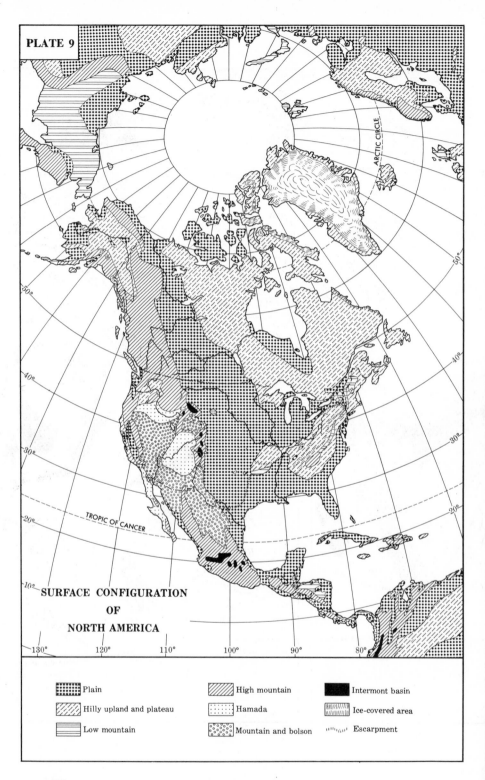

PLATE 9

ARCTIC CIRCLE

TROPIC OF CANCER

SURFACE CONFIGURATION

OF

NORTH AMERICA

▦ Plain		▨ High mountain		■ Intermont basin	
▨ Hilly upland and plateau		⋮ Hamada		▥ Ice-covered area	
▤ Low mountain		⊙ Mountain and bolson		◠ Escarpment	

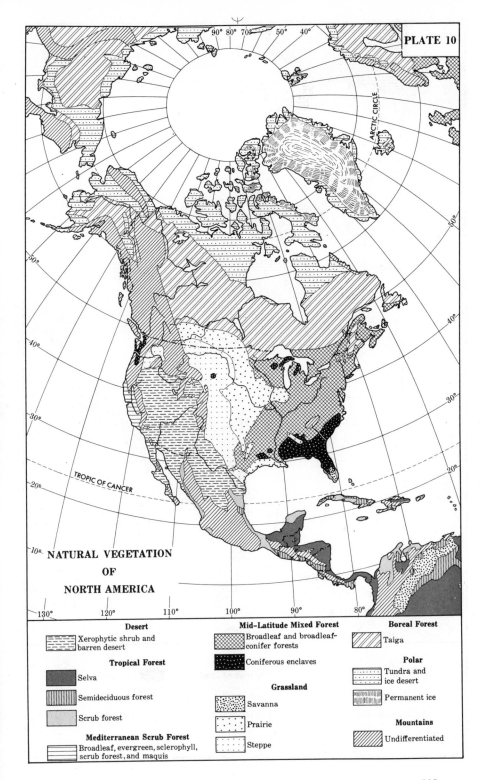

PLATE 10

NATURAL VEGETATION
OF
NORTH AMERICA

Desert
Xerophytic shrub and barren desert

Tropical Forest
Selva

Semideciduous forest

Scrub forest

Mediterranean Scrub Forest
Broadleaf, evergreen, sclerophyll, scrub forest, and maquis

Mid-Latitude Mixed Forest
Broadleaf and broadleaf-conifer forests

Coniferous enclaves

Grassland
Savanna

Prairie

Steppe

Boreal Forest
Taiga

Polar
Tundra and ice desert

Permanent ice

Mountains
Undifferentiated

613

PLATE 11

TROPIC OF CANCER

EQUATOR

TROPIC OF CAPRICORN

SURFACE CONFIGURATION

OF

SOUTH AMERICA

Plain		High mountain		Intermont basin	
Hilly upland and plateau		Hamada		Ice-covered area	
Low mountain		Mountain and bolson		Escarpment	

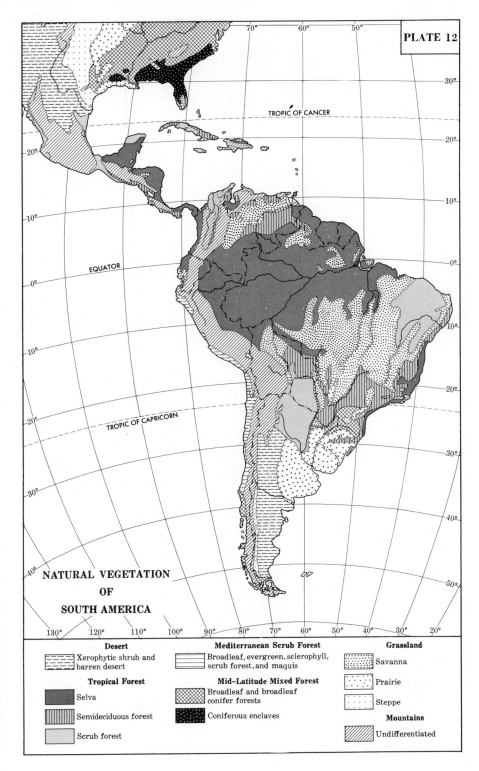

PLATE 12

TROPIC OF CANCER

EQUATOR

TROPIC OF CAPRICORN

NATURAL VEGETATION

OF

SOUTH AMERICA

Desert	Mediterranean Scrub Forest	Grassland
Xerophytic shrub and barren desert	Broadleaf, evergreen, sclerophyll, scrub forest, and maquis	Savanna
Tropical Forest	**Mid-Latitude Mixed Forest**	Prairie
Selva	Broadleaf and broadleaf conifer forests	Steppe
Semideciduous forest	Coniferous enclaves	**Mountains**
Scrub forest		Undifferentiated

615

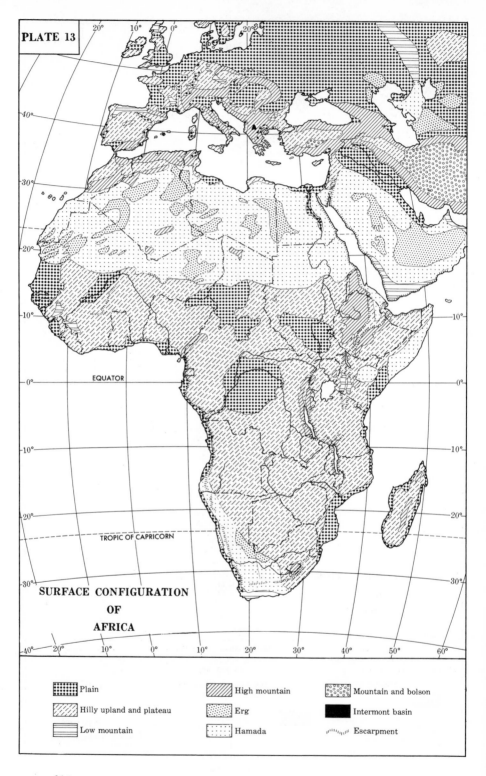

PLATE 13

20° 10° 0° 20°

40°

30°

20°

10°

EQUATOR

0°

10°

20°

TROPIC OF CAPRICORN

30°

SURFACE CONFIGURATION

OF

AFRICA

40° 20° 10° 0° 10° 20° 30° 40° 50° 60°

10°

0°

10°

20°

30°

▓▓ Plain	▨ High mountain	◦◦ Mountain and bolson
◪ Hilly upland and plateau	⋮ Erg	■ Intermont basin
☰ Low mountain	⋯ Hamada	⌇ Escarpment

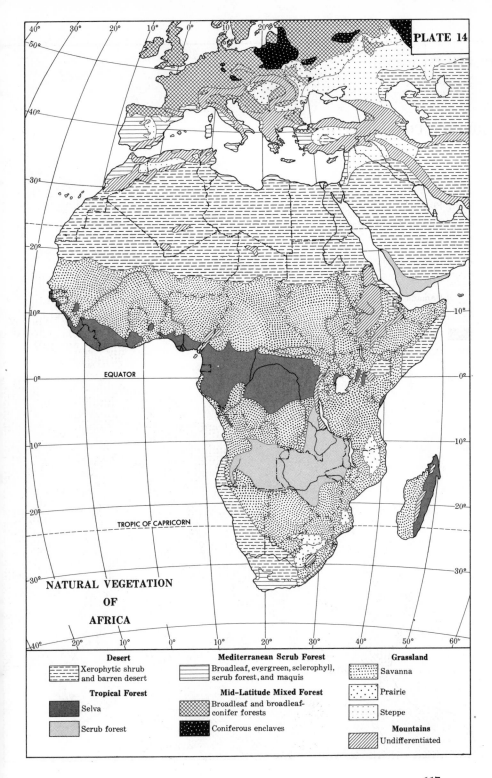

PLATE 14

40° 30° 20° 10° 0° 20°
50°
40°
30°
20°
10°
EQUATOR 0°
10°
20°
TROPIC OF CAPRICORN
30°

NATURAL VEGETATION
OF
AFRICA

40° 20° 10° 0° 10° 20° 30° 40° 50° 60°
10°
0°
10°
20°
30°

Desert	**Mediterranean Scrub Forest**	**Grassland**
Xerophytic shrub and barren desert	Broadleaf, evergreen, sclerophyll, scrub forest, and maquis	Savanna
Tropical Forest	**Mid-Latitude Mixed Forest**	Prairie
Selva	Broadleaf and broadleaf-conifer forests	Steppe
Scrub forest	Coniferous enclaves	**Mountains**
		Undifferentiated

617

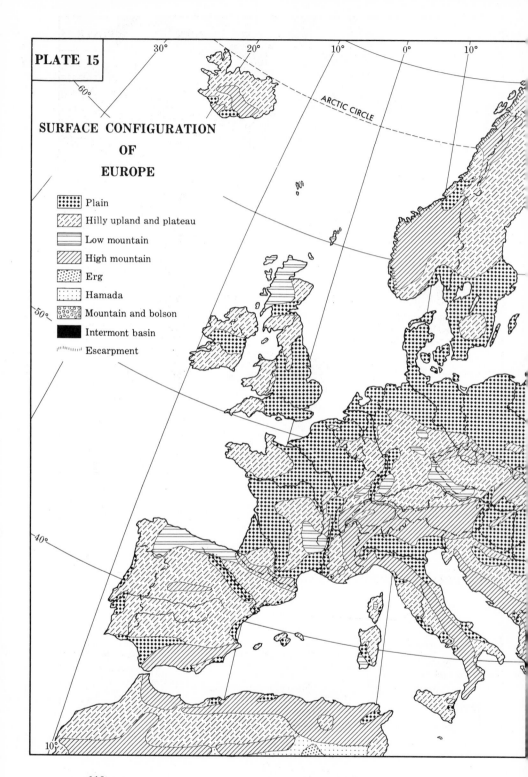

PLATE 15

SURFACE CONFIGURATION

OF

EUROPE

Plain	
Hilly upland and plateau	
Low mountain	
High mountain	
Erg	
Hamada	
Mountain and bolson	
Intermont basin	
Escarpment	

ARCTIC CIRCLE

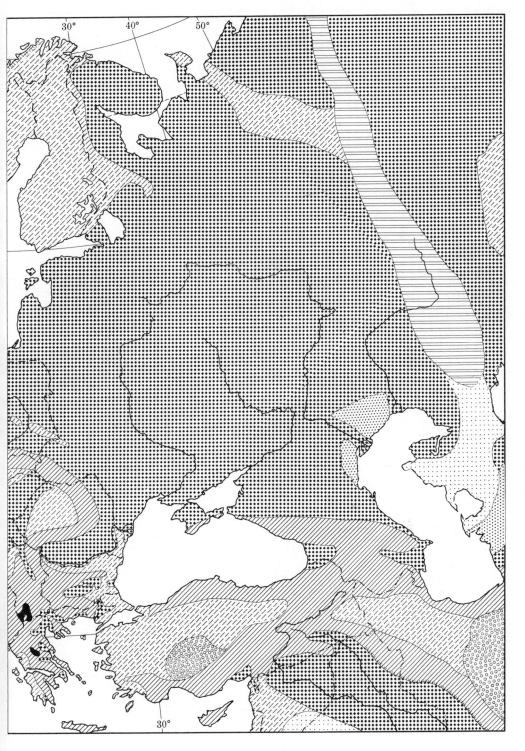

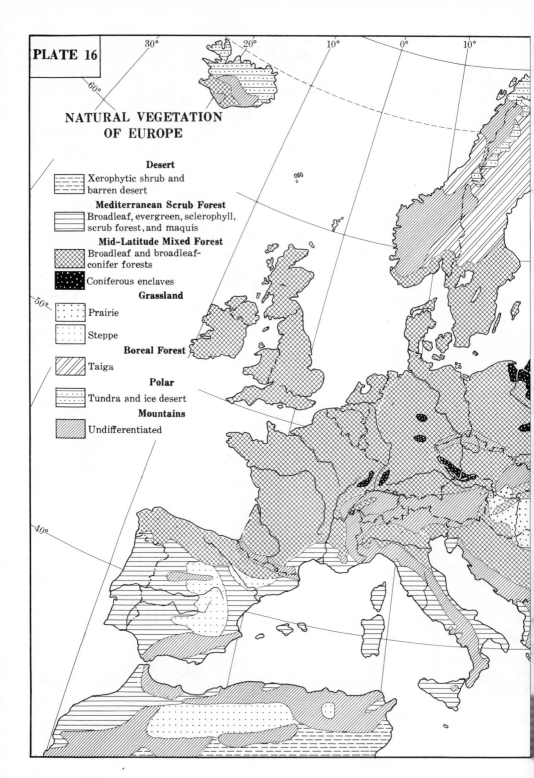

PLATE 16

NATURAL VEGETATION
OF EUROPE

Desert
Xerophytic shrub and
barren desert

Mediterranean Scrub Forest
Broadleaf, evergreen, sclerophyll,
scrub forest, and maquis

Mid-Latitude Mixed Forest
Broadleaf and broadleaf-
conifer forests

Coniferous enclaves

Grassland
Prairie

Steppe

Boreal Forest
Taiga

Polar
Tundra and ice desert

Mountains
Undifferentiated

620

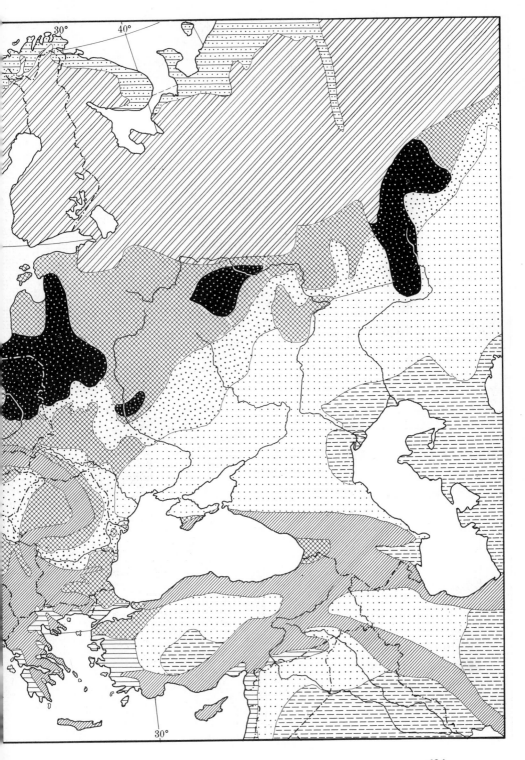

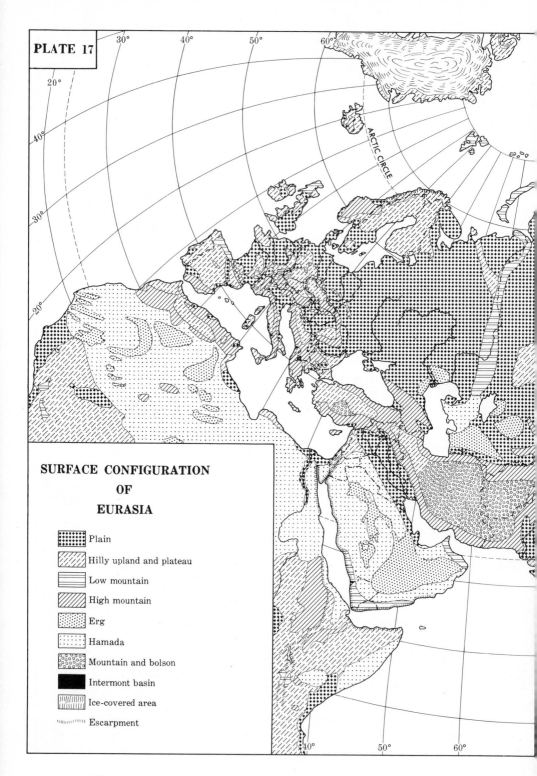

PLATE 17

ARCTIC CIRCLE

20° 30° 40° 50° 60°
40°
30°
20°

40° 50° 60°

SURFACE CONFIGURATION
OF
EURASIA

Plain

Hilly upland and plateau

Low mountain

High mountain

Erg

Hamada

Mountain and bolson

Intermont basin

Ice-covered area

Escarpment

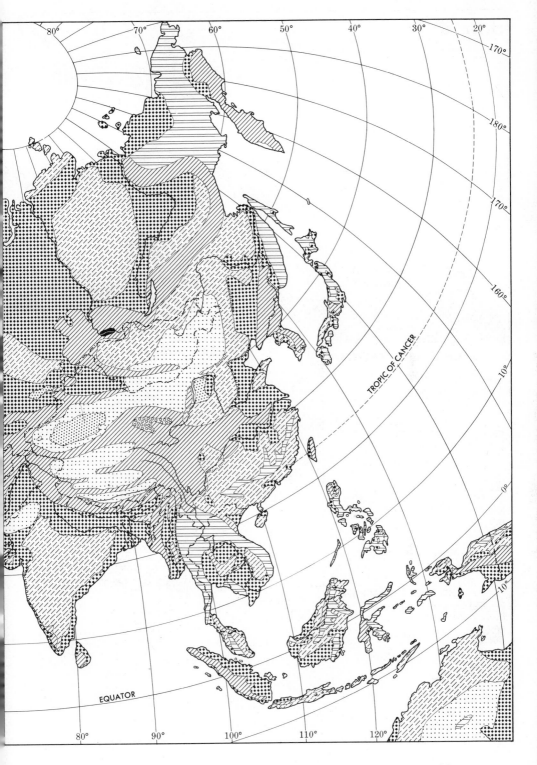

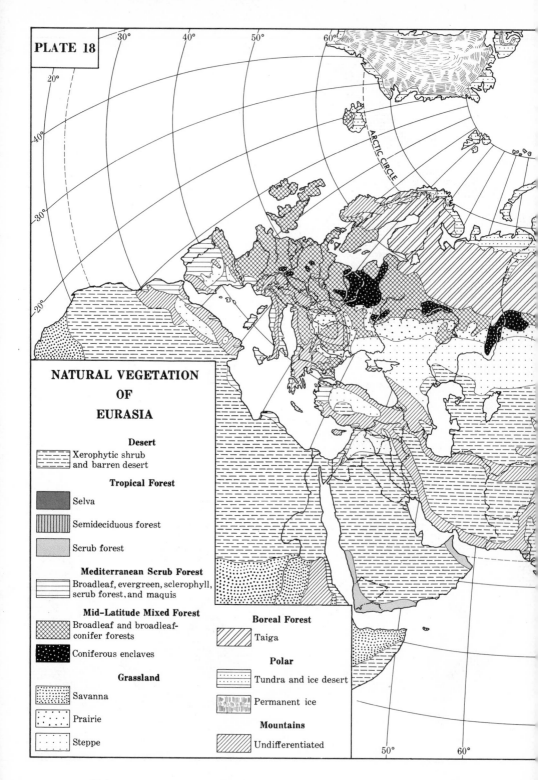

PLATE 18

30° 40° 50° 60°

20°

40°

30°

20°

ARCTIC CIRCLE

NATURAL VEGETATION
OF
EURASIA

Desert

Xerophytic shrub
and barren desert

Tropical Forest

Selva

Semideciduous forest

Scrub forest

Mediterranean Scrub Forest

Broadleaf, evergreen, sclerophyll,
scrub forest, and maquis

Mid–Latitude Mixed Forest

Broadleaf and broadleaf-
conifer forests

Coniferous enclaves

Grassland

Savanna

Prairie

Steppe

Boreal Forest

Taiga

Polar

Tundra and ice desert

Permanent ice

Mountains

Undifferentiated

50° 60°

624

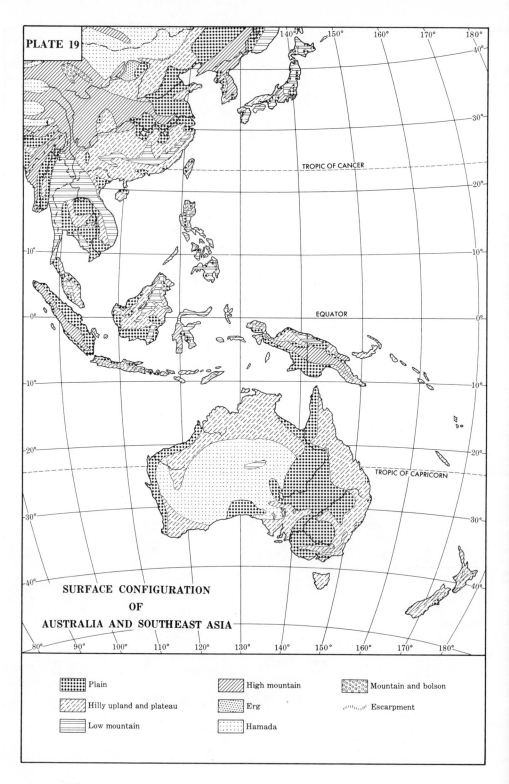

PLATE 19

140° 150° 160° 170° 180°
40°

30°

TROPIC OF CANCER

20°

10° 10°

EQUATOR

0° 0°

10° 10°

20° 20°

TROPIC OF CAPRICORN

30° 30°

40° 40°

SURFACE CONFIGURATION
OF
AUSTRALIA AND SOUTHEAST ASIA

80° 90° 100° 110° 120° 130° 140° 150° 160° 170° 180°

Plain   High mountain   Mountain and bolson

Hilly upland and plateau   Erg   Escarpment

Low mountain   Hamada

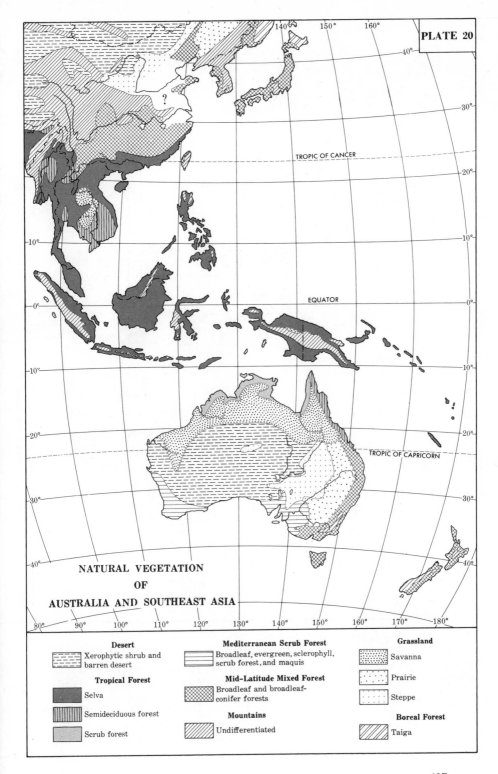

PLATE 20

140° 150° 160°

40°

30°

TROPIC OF CANCER

20°

10°

EQUATOR

0°

10°

20°

TROPIC OF CAPRICORN

30°

40°

NATURAL VEGETATION

OF

AUSTRALIA AND SOUTHEAST ASIA

80° 90° 100° 110° 120° 130° 140° 150° 160° 170° 180°

Desert	**Mediterranean Scrub Forest**	**Grassland**
Xerophytic shrub and barren desert	Broadleaf, evergreen, sclerophyll, scrub forest, and maquis	Savanna
Tropical Forest	**Mid-Latitude Mixed Forest**	Prairie
Selva	Broadleaf and broadleaf-conifer forests	Steppe
Semideciduous forest	**Mountains**	**Boreal Forest**
Scrub forest	Undifferentiated	Taiga

627

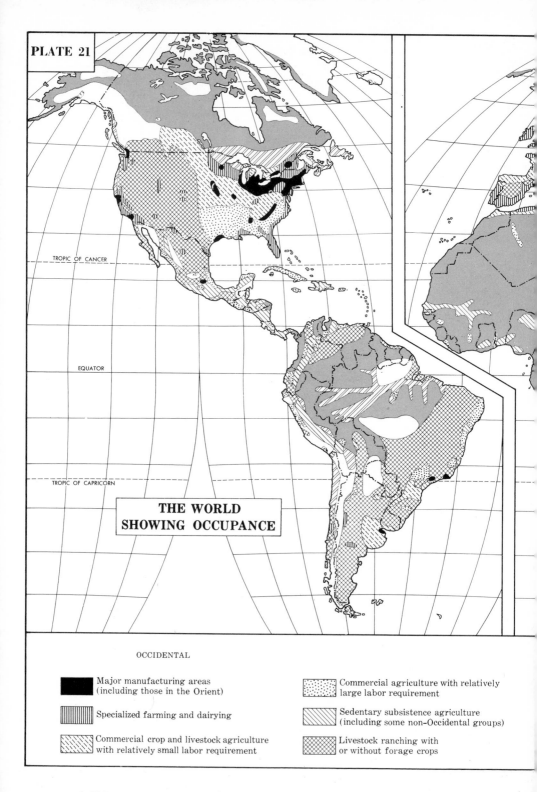

PLATE 21

TROPIC OF CANCER

EQUATOR

TROPIC OF CAPRICORN

**THE WORLD
SHOWING OCCUPANCE**

OCCIDENTAL

■ Major manufacturing areas
(including those in the Orient)

▦ Specialized farming and dairying

▨ Commercial crop and livestock agriculture
with relatively small labor requirement

▦ Commercial agriculture with relatively
large labor requirement

▧ Sedentary subsistence agriculture
(including some non-Occidental groups)

▩ Livestock ranching with
or without forage crops

628

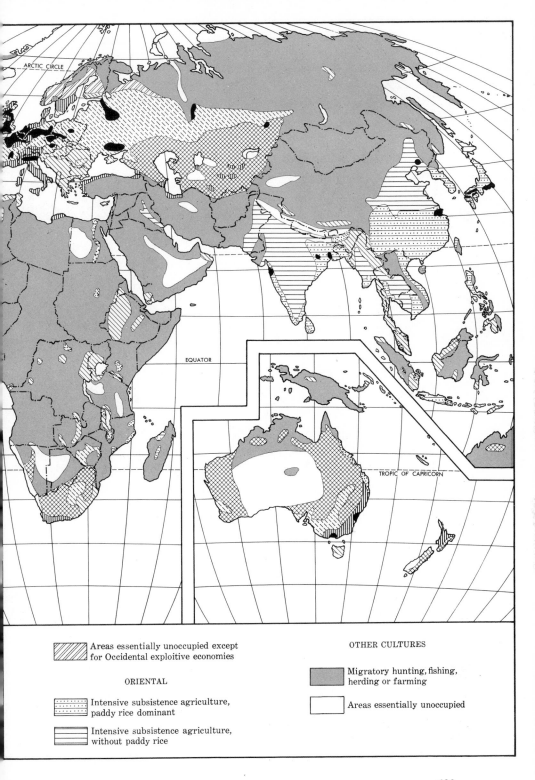

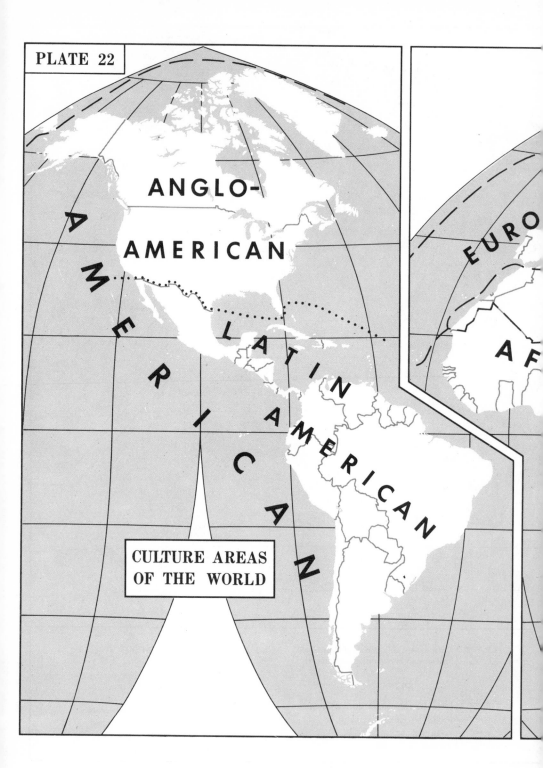

PLATE 22

ANGLO-
AMERICAN

LATIN
AMERICAN

AMERICAN

EURO

AF

CULTURE AREAS
OF THE WORLD

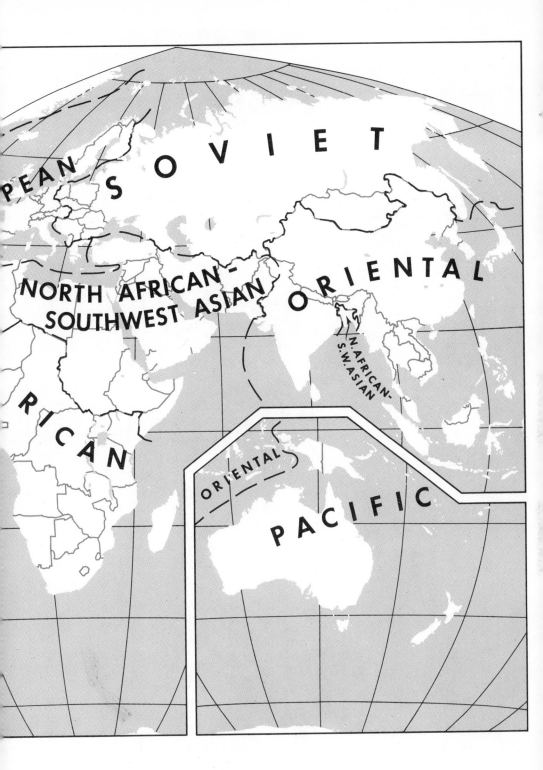

PEAN

S O V I E T

NORTH AFRICAN – SOUTHWEST ASIAN

O R I E N T A L

N. AFRICAN – S.W. ASIAN

RICAN

ORIENTAL

P A C I F I C

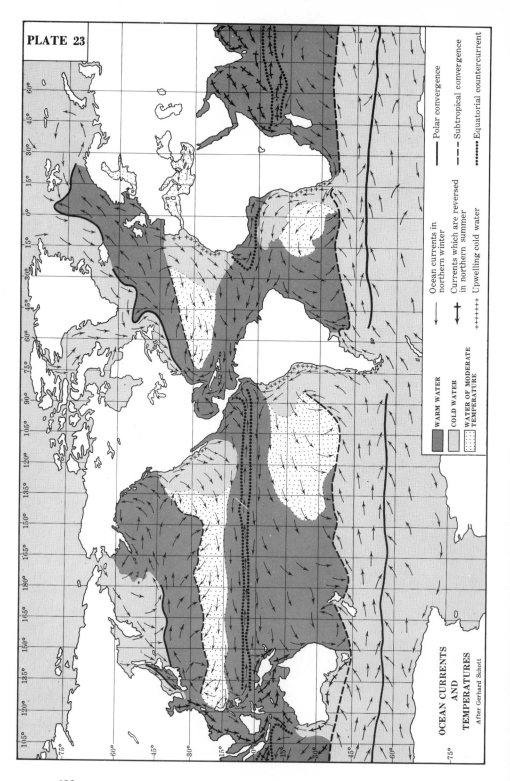

PLATE 23

OCEAN CURRENTS
AND
TEMPERATURES

After Gerhard Schott

WARM WATER

COLD WATER

WATER OF MODERATE
TEMPERATURE

→ Ocean currents in
northern winter

⟹ Currents which are reversed
in northern summer

++++++ Upwelling cold water

—— Polar convergence

– – – Subtropical convergence

••••• Equatorial countercurrent

PLATE 24

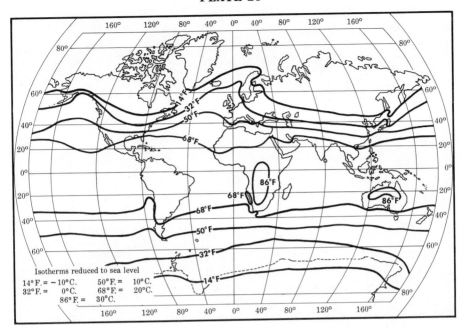

(a) Average temperatures in January. (After Gerhard Schott)

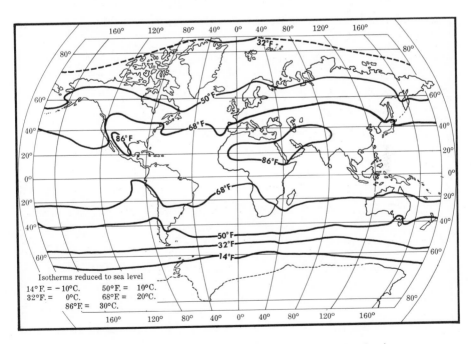

(b) Average temperatures in July. (After Gerhard Schott)

PLATE 25

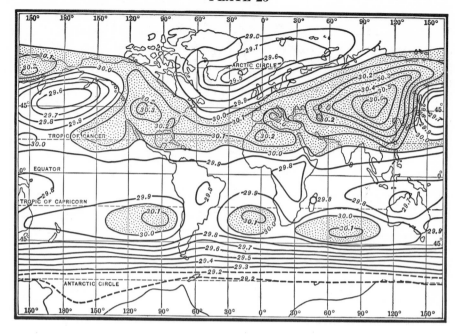

(a) Mean pressure for January. (After Kendrew)

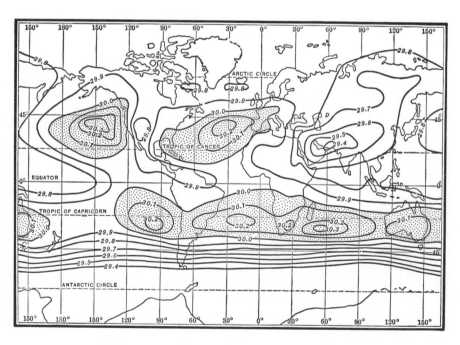

(b) Mean pressure for July. (After Kendrew)

PLATE 26

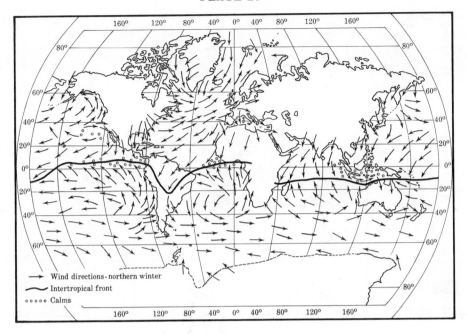

(a) *Average wind direction in January.* (*After Gerhard Schott*)

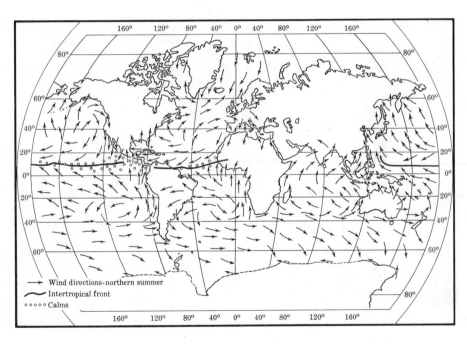

(b) *Average wind direction in July.* (*After Gerhard Schott*)

PLATE 27

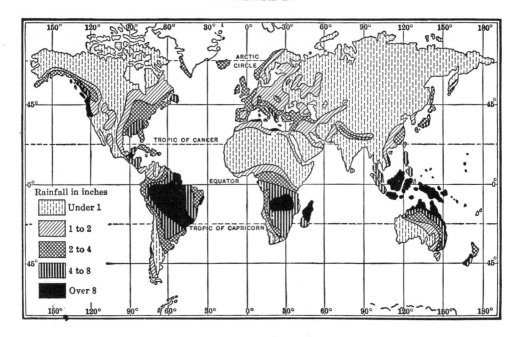

(a) Mean rainfall for January. (After Kendrew)

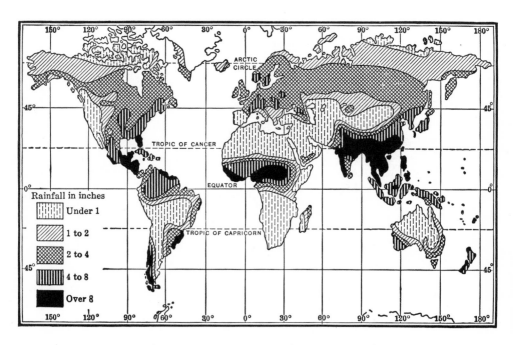

(b) Mean rainfall for July. (After Kendrew)

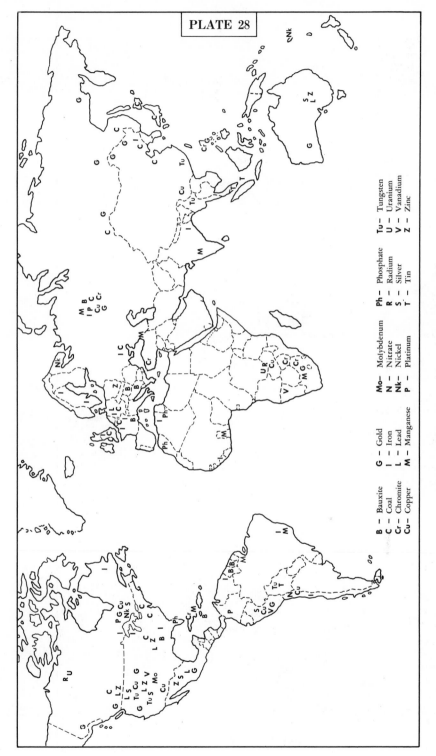

PLATE 28

B – Bauxite   G – Gold   Mo– Molybdenum   Ph – Phosphate   Tu – Tungsten
C – Coal   I – Iron   N – Nitrate   R – Radium   U – Uranium
Cr – Chromite   L – Lead   Nk– Nickel   S – Silver   V – Vanadium
Cu– Copper   M – Manganese   P – Platinum   T – Tin   Z – Zinc

Major world sources of certain raw materials

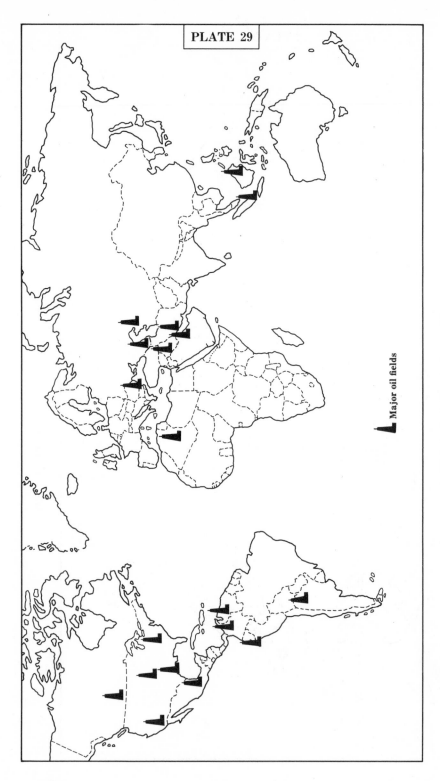

PLATE 29

Major oil fields

Major oil fields of the world

PLATE 30

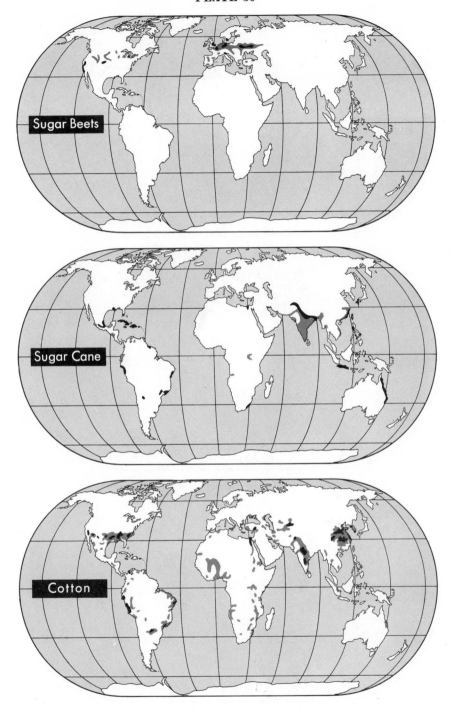

World distribution of sugar beets, sugar cane, and cotton

PLATE 31

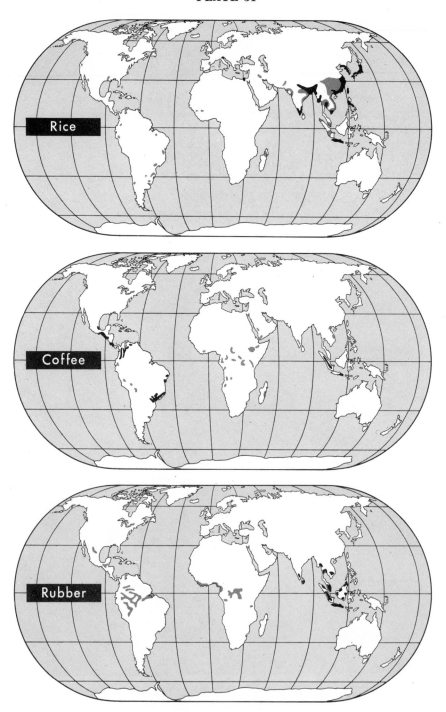

World distribution of rice, coffee, and rubber

PLATE 32

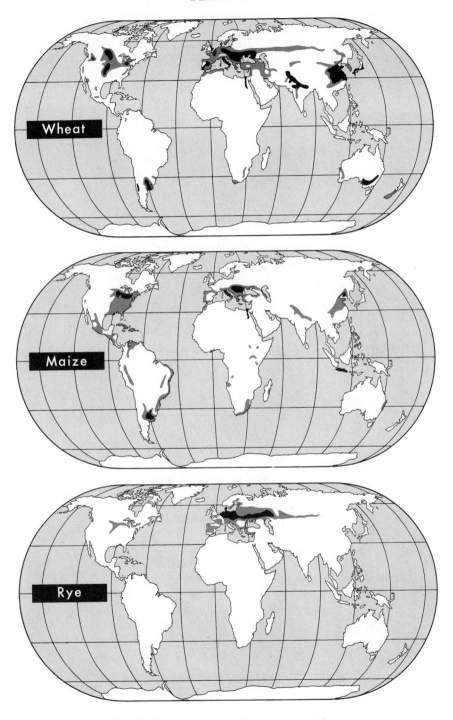

World distribution of wheat, maize, and rye

PLATE 33

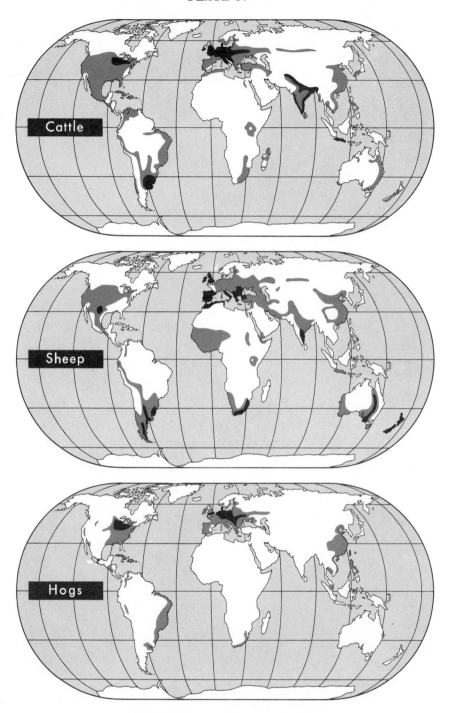

World distribution of cattle, sheep, and hogs

INDEX

Andorra, 444–445, **445**

animals, domestic: in nomadic cultures, 315–316, 317–318; origin of, 9, 10. *See also under* group names and specific animals

animals, native, *see under* group names

annular drainage, 557

Antarctica, 396, 397, **398**, 399, 401; climatic data for Little America, 591

antecedent rivers, 422

anticline, 546

Apennines, **160**, 161

Appalachian Highlands, *191,* 192, **261**

Arabia, 46, 54

Arabs, 59

Aral Sea, 55, **67**, 68, 69

arête, 424, **566**, 567

Argentina, see Humid Pampa. *See also under* regional and group names

Arkhangelsk, 384; climatic data, 591

arroyo, *see* wadi

artesian wells, 53–54, 578–579, **579**

Asia: origin of concept, 136; population, 484; population and area in the eight groups, 585. *See also under* Eurasia *and* group or regional names

Aswan Dam, **62**, 64

Atacama Desert, 42, 46, 69–72, **70**

Athens, **146**, 152, 583

Atlas Mountains, 53, **57**, 58, 60, 318

atmosphere: composition, 27–28, 521; general circulation, 29–32, 182–186, 521–544; vertical divisions, **423**. *See also under* climate

Australia: agricultural settlement, 126, 129–130, 169; deserts, 46, 69; forests, 97, 142, 145; surface features and climates of southeast and southwest, 147, **170**, 194. *See also* Australia-Southeastern Asia

Australia-Southeastern Asia: population, **Plate 6;** surface features, **Plate 19;** vegetation, **Plate 20**

avalanche, 420, **420,** 560

azimuth, 490

azimuthal projections, 495, 501, **504, 505**

Azizia, 43, **57**

Baltimore, **261,** 285, 583

bananas, 9, 109, 436

Barcelona, 583

Barcelonnette, hours of sunlight, 429, **430**

barley: in mediterranean agriculture, 10, 12, *144,* 154, 156; at polar limit of agriculture, 388

Barnaul, **346;** climatic data, 591

barriers, significance in Europe, 238–239

baselevel, 550–551

basin irrigation, 63

bauxite, 476, **Plate 28**

Beirut, climatic data, 590

Belém, 94–95, **103**

Ben Nevis, climatic data, 591

Benguela Current, 46, **Plate 23**

Berbers, 59

Berlin, **224,** 252, 583

Birmingham, 468, 583

black prairie soil, 313; profile, **312**

block mountain, 546, **548**

Boers, 74, 469

bolson, 48, 558. *See also* mountain and bolson deserts

Bombay, **118,** 119, 120–121, **120,** 584; climatic data, 591

Bonne's projection, 507

Bonneville, Lake, **76,** 81

bora, 140

Boreal Forest Lands, 361–388; agriculture, 384–388; animals, 364, 387; characteristics, 361; climate, 364–369; distribution, 180, **360,** 366; mining and lumbering, 381–383; position on generalized continent, **177;** settlement, 378–381; soils, 377–378; surface features and drainage, 369–377

Borneo, 104, **112**

Boston, **261,** 281, 583; climatic data, 590

braided channel, 54

Brazil: clearing of semideciduous forest, 1700–1950, **128;** process of settlement, 126–129; vegetation, *102, 127. See also under* regional and group names

Brenner Pass, 454–456, **455**

Brisbane, 130, 194; climatic data, 591

brown forest soil, 198; profile, **197**

Brussels, **224,** 583

Bucharest (Bucuresti), **224,** 584; climatic data, 591

Budapest, **224,** 584

Buenos Aires, 15, 16, *321,* 343, **344,** 345, 347, 583; climatic data, 590

Bukhara, **67,** 68, **457,** 458

caatinga, 91, 97, *102*

Cairo, **62,** 64, 584; climatic data, 591

Calama, 70, **70,** 72

Calcutta, 15, **118,** 119, 120–121, **120,** 584; climatic data, 591

California: citrus orchards, *166;* crop localization, 79, *80,* 167–168; Salinas Valley, 147, *165,* 168; sequent occupance, 165–169; surface features and climate, 137, **138,** 147, **569;** vegetation, 144, *144,* 145

camels, 10, *50,* 59, 60, 69, 83

Canada: agriculture and settlement, **385,** in Group IV, 288, in Group V, 342–343, in Group VI, 384–385; cities, 288–289, *289;* forests, *365, 376;* glaciation, 373; industries, 288–289; Laurentian Upland, 369, 546; mining, 382–383; snowfall, **368;** temperatures, 364, 365; trading posts and routes, **380**

Canal Zone, *see* Panama Canal

Canton, **199,** 210, 584

Capetown, **73,** 145, 169; climatic data, 591

cattle: domestication, 9; in United States, 1860–1954, **333;** world distribution, **Plate 33**

Caucasoid, 7–8

central business district, *see* commercial core

Ceylon, 97, **120**

Chaco, *see* Gran Chaco

Chao Phraya, 97, 104, **112**

chaparral, 143–144

chernozem, 313; profile, **312**

Cherrapunji, 99; climatic data, 591

chestnut-brown soil, 313; profile, **312**

Chicago, **261,** 262, 324, 564, 583; climatic data, 590

Chile: Middle, 70, 145, 147, **148,** 169, 194; Northern, 69–72, **70;** South, 187, 190, 417, **419**

China: agriculture and settlement, 201–211; communist, 211–214; culture hearth, 11, 75, 208; population, 203–205, **204,** 213–214; rice, 114, 207–208, **207;** surface features, 192, **199;** wheat, 207–208, **207.** *See also* Manchuria

chorography, defined, 121

chromite, 476

circulation, defined, 230

cirque, *418, 424,* **566;** defined, 566

cities: great, 15, 243, 583–584; location, in eastern North America, 280–288, in Western Europe, 239–243; primate, 243, 285; service area, 239; urban functions, 241–242, **279;** urban structure, 239–240, 242, 276, 278, **278**

citrus fruit, 12, *52,* 154, *166,* 167

civilizations, early, 10–12

Cleveland, **261,** 283, 583

climate: classification, 32–33, 135–136, 534–543; climatic data, 586–591; comparison of Charleston and Shanghai, 187–188; continental and marine, 29, 180; controls, 28–32, 175, 180–182, 527–534; definition, 33, 94; fluctuations of arid and semiarid borders in United States, 301–303, 302, 303; general arrangement of summer and winter temperatures, 181; physical bases, 527–534; references, 534–544; systematic arrangement, 28; tropical, 94–96; tropical high-altitude, 423–424. *See also* atmosphere *and under* group names

climatic regions (Köppen), 32, 33, **Plate 8**

climatic zones, origin of concept, 135

coal: in China, 212; in Europe, 244–246, 245, 253–255; in Manchuria, 356; in Ruhr district, 253; in United States, 283–284, 284; world production, 476, **Plate 28**

coffee, 124; altitude limits, **434**; world distribution, **Plate 31**

col, **566**, 567

cold front, 140–141, 184–185, *184,* 531, **532**

colluvial base, 553

Colombo, **120**; climatic data, 591

Colorado Plateau, 46, 55

Colorado River, 54, 55, 77

Columbia Plateau, 46

commercial core, 242, *283*

Commonwealth of Nations, analysis of geographic structure, 466–472, **467**

compass bearing, 490

Concepción, 145, **148**, 169

condensation, 526, 527

conduction, 522

Congo Basin, 93, 97, 102, 103, **104**

conic projection, 504–509

contour lines, 513–515, **514**

conurbation, *see* metropolitan area

convection, 525

copper, *71,* 476, **Plate 28**

Córdoba, **344**; climatic data, 590

cork oak, *143*

corn, *see* maize

Corn Belt, 279, 327–336, **328,** *329;* development, 1839–1879, **330**, 1899–1954, **331**; forest and prairie sections, **324, 325**

corrasion, 549

cotton: in India, **118,** 119; long-staple in dry lands, 64, 79; in Soviet Union, 68; in United States, 77, 266, 280, **328,** *335;* world distribution, **Plate 30**

cuesta, 49, 555, **556**

culture: defined, 7; culture areas, defined, 471, of world, 462–465, **Plate 22**; hearth, defined, 260

cycle of erosion, 553–554, 557

cyclone, 140–141, 531; cyclonic storms, 31, 531–533

cylindrical projections, 495–497

Dairen (Talien), **353, 355**

Darwin, 352, climatic data, 591

date palm, 59, 60, 78–79, *80*

Dawson, 365; climatic data, 590

Dead Sea-Red Sea rift, 100, 162, 546

Death Valley, *42,* 43, 100, 101, **138,** 546

Deccan Plateau, 97, 119, **120**

deciduous forest, defined, 89

deflation, 567

delta, 572

Democratic Revolution, 16–17, 252, 461

demography, 35

Denoyer projection, 499

Denver, 45; climatic data, 590

desert pavement, 567

Detroit, **261**, 262, 271, *283,* 583

differential heating of land and water, 28–29, 522

doldrums, 98, 99, 183, 529
dome, 546; diagram illustrating erosion, **547**
drainage patterns, *see* stream patterns
Drakensbergen, 72, **73,** 194
drumlins, 565
dry farming, 156, 341
Dry Lands, 41–83; agriculture, 77–79; animals, 83; characteristics, 41; climate, 41–47; distribution, **40,** 45–46; nomadism, 83; oasis towns, 79–81; population, 55, 81; surface features, 47–51, 54–55; vegetation, *42,* 43–44; water, 51–54
Durban, 72, **73,** 194, 292
dust storm, 342, *343*

earthquakes and earthquake regions, **416,** 546
edaphic factors, 45
Edmonton, 343, **380, 385;** climatic data, 590
Egypt, **62,** 63–65, 469, 472. *See also* Nile Valley
elliptical projections, 498–501
El Paso, 45
eluviation, 106, 309
erg, 49, *50,* 51, 53
erosional processes, *340,* 549
eskers, 565; in Finland, **563**
Eskimo culture, 401–406, **402**
Etesian Winds, 139
Eucalyptus forest, 142
Eurasia: population, **Plate 5;** surface configuration, **Plate 17;** vegetation, **Plate 18**
Euratom, 258
Europe: agricultural regions, **250;** center of land hemisphere, 236; coal and coke production, 244–246, **245,** 253–255; ethnic distribution, **226;** medieval towns, *239, 240,* 240–241; origin of concept, 136; political units,

246; population, 484, **Plate 4;** population and area in the eight groups, 585; settlement, 223–225; surface configuration, 191, **224,** 227–229, **Plate 15;** vegetation, **Plate 16**
European Coal and Steel Community, 258
European Economic Community, 258–259
evaporation, 29, 526–527
evergreen forest, defined, 89
exotic stream, 54, 55
extensive economy, defined, 77

Falkland Current, 46, **Plate 23**
fault, 546
Fayum Basin, **62,** 64
Finland, 369, 373, 383, **563**
fiord, 400, *438, 439;* in South Chile, 417, **419**
floodplain, 105, 268, **269, 270, 271,** 551–553
floods, *195,* 196, 308, 309, 376–377
Florence, 153, *155,* **160;** topographic detail, **153**
forests, effect on rainfall, 149, 534. *See also* vegetation
Formosa, **199,** 211, 214, 218. *See also* Taiwan
France, **224,** 238, 247–251
Fresno, **138,** 167
functional area, 242

galeria forest, 92, 190, 301
General Land Office plan, 271, **326,** 327
generalized continent, 176–182, **177, 181**
geography, defined, iii, 121
Germany, 224, 251–258, **255;** post-war division, 257–258
geysers, 579–580
giraffes, *307*

glacial drainage patterns, 375–376, **377**
glacial lakes, 373–374, 563–565, **564;** stages in filling, 374–375, **375**
glacial landforms, 371–377, 561–567; in high mountains, 417–420, *418, 424,* **427,** 565–567, **566**
glaciation, extent in Pleistocene, **372,** 373
glaciers, categories, 581
globe, gores for, **500**
gnomonic polar projection, 501, 502–503, **503**
Gobi, 46, 69
gold, 381–382; dredge, *381;* world distribution, **Plate 28**
Goode's homolosine projection, 499–500, **500**
grade, 550–551
Gran Chaco, 91, 94, 97
grasslands, 297–358; characteristics, 297; climate, 298–303; distribution, **296;** nomadism, 315–318; occupance, in Argentina, 343–347, in Canada, 342–343, in Manchuria, 352–357, in Russian steppes, 347–350, in savannas, 350–352, in United States, 323–342; simple cultures, 314–315; soils, 311–313, **312;** surface features and drainage, 307–309; vegetation, 297–307
Great Basin, 46, 75–77, **76**
great circle, 498
great cities, 15, 243; list, by culture areas, 583–584
Great Lakes, glacial origin, 373, 564, **564**
Great Plains, 299, *320,* 340, 341–342, *343*
great powers, 465–481
Great Salt Lake, 48, 75, **76**
Great Sandy Desert, 46
Great Victoria Desert, 46
Greece, 12, **146,** 147
Greenland, 30, 184, 373, 394, **399,** 409

Grosseto, **158,** 159
ground water, 52, 577–581
groups: distribution on continents, **Plates 10, 12, 14, 16, 18, 20;** general distribution, **177;** list, 36; percentage of land area and population in the eight groups, by continents, 585
Gulf Stream, 185, 576, **Plate 23**

hachuring, 512–513, **513**
hamada, 49–50, 53, 54, 61, 558, **559**
hanging valley, 565, **566**
Hankow, **199,** 584; climatic data, 591
Harbin (Pinkiang), **353,** 355
Hawaiian Islands, 447, 465, 472, 548
heat equator, 95
high mountains: definition, 413; distribution, **26, 412**
highways, 230–231, 234, *235*
hilly upland, 101, *102, 191, 193, 263*
Hindu Kush Mountains, *449,* 457, **457**
hippopotamuses, *306*
hogs: United States, **332;** world, **Plate 33**
Homestead Act, 321, 341
Hong Kong, **199,** *209,* 210, 584; climatic data, 591
horn, **566,** 567
horse latitudes, 529
Hudson Bay, **261,** 369, 373, 380, 564
Hudson's Bay Company, 380
Humid Pampa, 343–347, **344**
humidity, 526
humus accumulation, 106, 310
hurricane, 531
Hwang Ho and valley, 11, 175, 192, **199**
hydrosphere, 27, 574–581; ground water, 52, 577–581; ice, 581; ocean water, 574–577; references, 581–582

Iguaçu River, 194
India, 104, 113, 115, 116–122, **118, 120**

matic regions, 186–188; culture hearths of eastern North America, 260–265; distribution, **174**, 180, 188, 190; early settlement, Europe, 223–227, North America, 265–267; New Zealand, 293; occupance, by Occidental cultures, 221–293, by Oriental cultures, 198–221; population, 175–176, *202,* 203–205, **204, 206,** 217, 220, 225, 256–257, 267, **275;** soils, 196–198; South Africa, 292; South Brazil, 292; South Chile, 290, 292; surface features, Asia, 192–193, Australia, 194, Brazil, 194, Europe, 191–192, 223, **224,** North America, 192, 193–194, South Africa, 194, South Chile, 194; vegetation, 176, 180, 188–190; western North America, 289–290

Middle Colonies, culture hearth, 264–265

Middle East, conflicts in, 66, 481

minerals: table of mineral production, 476; world distribution, selected minerals, **Plate 28.** *See also under* specific minerals

Minneapolis, **261,** 324, 583

Mississippi River and Valley, floodplain, 192, 268, **270, 271;** headwaters, **377**

mistral, 140

Mojave Desert, 46, **138**

Mollweide projection, 498, **499,** 500

molybdenum, 476, **Plate 28**

monadnock, 553

Mongoloid, 7–8

monsoon, 31, 99–100, 185–186, 577

Montreal, **261,** 288, *289,* 583; climatic data, 590

moraines, 562–563; in Finland, **563;** in Michigan, 272 .

Moscow, **224,** 584; climatic data, 591

Moslem world, 65–66, **65**

mountain and bolson deserts, 48, 52–53, 54. *See also* bolson

Mountain Lands, 413–458; as barriers, 448–458; characteristics, 413–414; climate, 422–431; distribution, **26, 412;** pass routes, 448–458; spotty distribution, 428–431, 444–447; surface features, 415–422; transhumance, 440; vertical differentiation, 422–428, 432–444

Mukden (Shenyang), **353,** 356, 584; climatic data, 591

Nagoya, 217, **353,** 584

Nanking, **199,** 208, 584

Naples, 154, **160,** 583

natural levee, *195,* **270,** 552

Negroid, 7–8

Neolithic period, 9

New England: agriculture, 278–279; culture hearth, 262–264; industries, 276, 280–282; settlement, 276, **277**

New Orleans, **261,** 262; climatic data, 590

New York City, 15, 183, 192, **261,** 285–288, **286,** *287,* 583; climatic data, 590

New Zealand, 194, 293

nickel, 289, 476, **Plate 28**

Niger River, 54, **57,** 58, **304**

Nile River and Valley, 11, 54, 56, 61–65, **62**

nitrate, **70,** 71, 72, **Plate 28**

nomadism, 83, 315–318, 440–441

North America: agricultural regions, **328;** air masses, 531–533, **532;** cities and industries, 280–290; population, **Plate 1;** population and area in the eight groups, 585; surface features, **Plate 9;** vegetation, **Plate 10.** *See also under* regional and group names

North Atlantic Drift, 185, 366, 530, 576, **Plate 23**

potassium, 476

prairie, 301; relation to climate, 301–304

precipitation, 527. *See also* rainfall

pre-industrial society, 12–13

pressure: areas of, 528–529; atmospheric, 524–525; in mountains, 427–428; winds and, 525–526; world distribution in January and July, **Plate 25**

Pretoria, **73,** 352

primate city, law of, 243

Princeton, Illinois, 276, **278**

principal hemisphere, 236, **237**

Queensland, 126, 130

Quito, 425; climatic data, 590

race and culture, defined, 7

radiation, 522

railroads, world distribution, 231–234, **232–233**

rain shadow, 430

rainfall: causes, 29, 527; distribution, **Plates 7 and 27;** in low latitudes, 98–99; in mountains, 427, 530, 534; in Switzerland, **431;** world's heaviest, 99–100

rainfall effectiveness, 44, 45

raubwirtschaft, 111, 125

Red Sea, 61, **62,** 96, 546, 575

regolith, 47–49, 309–310, 415, 550, 558–560

reindeer, 315, 379, 387, 394, 407

relative humidity, 526

relief, 25, 101, 557

Reno, 75, **76**

representative fraction, 491

Rhine River and Valley, 191, **224,** *256,* 546, **548**

Rhodesia, 126, *126,* 129

rhumb line, 497–498

rice: in Brazil, *109,* 128; in China, *114,* 207–208, **207;** in Indian peninsula, 115, 117–119, **118;** in Japan, 200, *200, 216;* in Java, 115, *116;* origin of crop, 9; requirements of, 111–112; rice land topography, **121;** in Southeast Asia, 111–115; world distribution, **Plate 31**

rift valley, 100, 546

Río Bío Bío, 147, **148**

Rio de Janeiro, 126, 583

rock field, 400

Rome, 12, 152, **160,** 583; climatic data, 591

rubber, 125; world distribution, **Plate 31**

Ruhr district, 246, 252–255, **253,** *254,* 583

Russian steppes, 322, 347–350; detail of settlement, **349**

rye, 10, 12; world distribution, **Plate 32**

Sacramento, **138,** 168, 169; climatic data, 590

Sahara, 46, *50, 53,* 54, 56–61, **57**

Saigon, **112,** 584; climatic data, 591

St. Lawrence River, 192, 260, **261,** 262, 284, 288, *289,* 564

St. Louis, **261,** 262, 324, 583; climatic data, 590

St. Paul, **261,** 324, 583; climatic data, 590

Salt Lake City, 75, **76,** *82*

Samarkand, **67,** 68

San Diego, **138;** climatic data, 590

San Francisco, **138,** 161, 165, *168,* 169, 583; climatic data, 590

Sanson-Flamsteed projection, 498, **499**

Santiago (Chile), 16, 147, **148,** 169, 583; climatic data, 591

São Paulo, city, 16, 583; state, 127

Saône-Rhône Valley, 191, 223

savannas, 304–307, *308, 316;* central Sudan, **304;** Occidental settlement, 350–352

scale, map, 490–491

Scandinavian Upland, 369

sclerophyll, 143

seasonal seminomadism, 440–441

selva, 88–89, 97. *See also* tropical rain forest

sequent occupance, defined, 61

settlement patterns, *see under* Occidental culture

Shanghai, 187–188, **199,** *202,* 584; climatic data, 591

Shari River, 54, **304,** 309

sheep, 10, 159; world distribution, **Plate 33**

shipping, 234–236

shorelines, emergent and submergent, 150–152, 568–571, **569, 570, 571**

Siberia, *see* Boreal Forest Lands *and* Union of Soviet Socialist Republics

Sierra Leone, *89, 123*

Singapore, **112,** 472, 584

sink, 150, 568, **568**

sirocco, 141

Sitka, 183; climatic data, 590

skerry, 400, *403*

snowfall, 368; in Canada, **368**

soils: horizon, defined, 310; processes, 105–106, 196–198, 309–311; of western U.S.S.R., **346.** *See also under* group and regional names

Somaliland, 46, 47

Sonora, 46

South Africa, 72–75, **73,** 147, 169, 292, 351–352

South America: population, 484, **Plate 2;** population and area in the eight groups, 585; surface features, **Plate 11;** vegetation, **Plate 12.** *See also under* regional and group names

Southern Colonies, culture hearth, 264

soviet society, 18, 479

standard parallel, 504, 505–506, **506**

steel industry: in Germany, 252–256; in Great Britain, 471; in India, 121–122; in North America, 282–285, *282,* 480; in Soviet Union, 480

steppes, 298–301, *299, 317*

stereographic projection, 501, **502**

strand flat, 400

stratosphere, **423,** 523

stream patterns, 555–557, **557**

Sudan, 59, **304,** 305, *307*

Sudbury, 382–383

Suez Canal, 65, 66, 162, 236, 472

sugar beets, 77, 79, 349, *350;* world distribution, **Plate 30**

sugar cane, 79, 124, 125, 130; world distribution, **Plate 30**

sulfur, 476

Sumatra, 104, **112,** 125

sunshine: in high latitudes, 366, **367;** in mountains, 428–429; in valley of Barcelonnette, 429, *430*

surface features: asymmetrical arrangement, **26,** 27; definitions of major categories, in dry lands, 47–50, in rainy lands, 100–102; major lineaments, 25–27; world distribution, **Plates 9, 11, 13, 15, 17, 19**

Switzerland: population density, 444; rainfall, **431;** surface features, **455**

Sydney, 194, 584; climatic data, 591

syncline, 546

Syr Darya, 55, **67,** 68

taiga, 362–364, *363, 365, 370, 374, 376, 392*

Taiwan, **199,** 210, 211, 218, 221. *See also* Formosa

talus cone, **566,** 567

tanezrouft, 53, 58

Tarim Basin, 46, 68–69, **68,** 77

tarn, 566

Tashkent, **67,** 68

Tel Aviv, **163,** 164

temperate zone, origin of concept, 135

temperature: greatest annual range, 365; greatest diurnal range, 43; in mountains, 423–425; vertical arrangement, **423;** world distribution, **Plate 24;** world's highest, 43; world's lowest, 365

Thailand, **112,** 131

Thar, 46, 54, 91, **120**

thorn forest, *see* caatinga

Tientsin, **199,** 210, 584

tierra caliente, **434,** 436, 437

tierra fria, **434,** 436

tierra templada, **434,** 436

Tigris-Euphrates, river and valley, 11, 55, 78–79

tin, 476, **Plate 28**

Tokyo, 15, 217, **353,** 584; climatic data, 591

Tomsk, 346, 383, 384; climatic data, 591

topography: defined, 121; U. S. Geological Survey symbols, 510, **511**

tornado, 140, 531

trade winds, 98, 529

transhumance, 440–441

transportation, 549. *See also* circulation

traverse, 492

triangulation, 492–493

Tropical Forest Lands, 87–132; agriculture, migratory, 109–111, Occidental, 124–130, Oriental, 111–122, on plantations, 124–125; animals, 93–94; characteristics, 87; climate, 94–96; distribution, **86,** 96–97; soils, 105–106; surface features, 100–105; vegetation, 87–93

tropical rain forest, 87, 88, *89,* 92–93

tropical scrub forest, 91, *92,* 93, *102, 126*

tropical semideciduous forest, 88, 89–90, *109,* 126, **128**

tropical weather, 95

troposphere, 523

tundra, 393–394, *395, 406;* distribution, **397**

tungsten, 212, 476

Turkestan, 46, 66–67, **67**

typhoon, 531

ubac, 428, *429,* 447

Uganda, *92, 110*

unearned increment, 20, 325–327

Union of Soviet Socialist Republics: agriculture and settlement, in Boreal Forest Lands, 384–387, **384,** in grasslands, 347–350, **349;** as great power, 477–481, **478;** soils, 346

United States, as great power, 472–477, **473**

uranium, 129, 383, **Plate 28**

urban functions, *see under* cities

urban structure, *see under* cities

Uspallata Pass, *424*

uvala, *see* sink

V-shaped valleys, 417, 550, 553, **554**

Val d'Anniviers, 441

valley bluff, 268, 552

valley train, 563

Valparaiso, **148,** 151, 169

vanadium, 476, **Plate 28**

vegetation: generalized pattern, **177;** major categories, 34–35; world distribution, **Plates 10, 12, 14, 16, 18, 20.** *See also under* group names and types of vegetation

Verkhoyansk, 365, 369, **384;** climatic data, 591

vertical temperature gradient, 523, 524

vertical zones, *see* altitude limits

Vienna, **224**, 583

vines and vineyards, 154, 156, 157–158, *157*, 167

volcanoes, *291*, **416**, 547–548

wadi, 51, *51*, 53, 58

Wasatch Mountains, 75, *82*

waterbuck, *92*

weather, defined, 94

weathering, 549–550

Wei Ho, 11, 199, **199**

westerlies, 183, 529

whaling, 408

wheat: altitude limits, **434**, 436; in Argentina, **344**, 345; in China, 207–208, **207**; climatic requirements, 387–388; in Mediterranean agriculture, 12, 154, 156; northern limit, 387; origin of crop, 10; in Soviet Union, 349–350, 387; in United States, 336–342, *339*, distribution, 1839–1889, **336**, 1899–1954, **337**; winter and spring, 338,

387; world distribution, **Plate 32;** yields in selected countries, 338

winds and wind systems: general circulation, 529–530, **Plate 26;** of low latitudes, 98; and pressures, 525–526; prevailing, 29–32. *See also* names of winds

Winnipeg, Lake, 373, 564

Wisconsin, 277, **279**

xerophytic plants, *42*, 44, 143

Yangtze River and valley, 175, 192, 199, **206**, 422

Yarkand, **68**, 69

yellow forest soil, 196–198; profile, **197**

Yellow River, 11, *114*. *See also* Hwang Ho

Yemen, 91

Yokohama, 217, **353**, 584

Yugoslavia, 140, *150*, 422, 462, 568

zinc, 476, **Plate 28**

CONVERSION SCALES

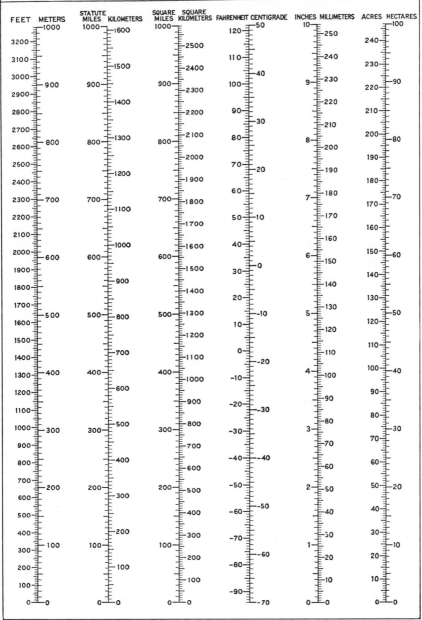

PRINTED IN THE UNITED STATES OF AMERICA